INTRODUCTION TO CHEMICAL THERMODYNAMICS

M. H. EVERDELL,
B.Sc., Ph.D.
Warden of Gracie Hall, and
Senior Lecturer in Physical Chemistry,
The University of Aston in Birmingham (designate)
(The College of Advanced Technology, Birmingham)

THE ENGLISH UNIVERSITIES PRESS LTD
SAINT PAUL'S HOUSE · WARWICK LANE
LONDON E.C.4

First printed 1965

Copyright © 1965
M. H. EVERDELL

Printed in Great Britain for the English Universities Press Ltd.,
by Richard Clay (The Chaucer Press), Ltd., Bungay, Suffolk

INTRODUCTION TO CHEMICAL THERMODYNAMICS

CALCULATIONS IN PHYSICAL CHEMISTRY

B. W. V. HAWES, B.Sc., Ph.D., F.R.I.C.
Formerly Head of the Science Department, Slough College

N. H. DAVIES, B.Sc., Ph.D., F.R.I.C.
Senior Lecturer Responsible for Chemistry,
Newport and Monmouthshire College of Technology;
Formerly Lecturer in Physical Chemistry, College of
Advanced Technology, Birmingham

LABORATORY MANUAL OF PHYSICAL CHEMISTRY

W. J. POPIEL, B.Sc., Ph.D.,
Chemistry Department, Brighton College of Technology

PHYSICAL METHODS IN ORGANIC CHEMISTRY

A. R. PINDER, D.Sc. Ph.D., D.Phil.
Senior Lecturer in Chemistry, University College, Cardiff

PROBLEMS IN INORGANIC CHEMISTRY

B. C. SMITH, M.A., Ph.D.
Lecturer in Chemistry, Birkbeck College, University of London

B. J. AYLETT, M.A., Ph.D.
Lecturer in Chemistry, Westfield College, University of London; formerly Lecturer in
Chemistry, University of Aberdeen

PREFACE

A great many books have been written on Chemical Thermodynamics in recent years. The fact remains that the majority of students find the subject difficult, and, what is more to the point, in more cases than not fail to understand why they are made to study it, or to appreciate its elegance and power. This is probably because the best books on the subject tend to be authoritative rather than explanatory, and although read with delight by those familiar with the subject, fail to appeal to the student in the early stages of his training. The present volume is written for the undergraduate. It attempts to present the principles of classical and statistical thermodynamics and to show how these principles may be applied.

The book is divided into four parts. Part I establishes the language of thermodynamics and attempts to describe the scope of the subject. Part II is concerned with the four laws of thermodynamics and shows how they may be developed using the methods of classical thermodynamics, while Part III is concerned with the statistical approach. Part IV shows how the principles established form the foundation from which stem most of the laws governing physical and chemical change. The treatment of all four parts is open to criticism. Some would consider that in Part I, which serves merely as an introduction to the subject, too great an emphasis is placed on its application to the determination of the feasibility of a reaction, and that too small an emphasis is placed on its application to other problems. There are two reasons why the present treatment was chosen; the first is that this particular application is the most dramatic and is the most likely to demonstrate to the student the power of the subject, and the second is that it explains why so much time is devoted in some chapters in Part II to the determination of quantities which at first sight are neither of great interest nor of great significance. Thus it should be clear from Part I that the free energy change brought about by a chemical reaction is of great importance, but it is explained that this quantity cannot normally be measured directly, but is calculated from other quantities, one of which is the enthalpy change. This gives point to the great deal of time which is spent in Part II in explaining how the change in enthalpy (not a very interesting quantity in its own right) is obtained.

The Second Law is stated in terms of the irreversibility of all natural spontaneous processes, because it is thought that this statement shows its relationship to chemistry more clearly than any other. The derivation of the entropy principle from this statement follows classical lines, but in Chapter 9 the principle is restated in terms of the quantity ds_{irrev} (introduced originally by de Donder), because it is thought that this quantity leads more clearly than most to an appreciation of the significance of free energy. A feature of the book is the great emphasis which is placed on chemical potentials. These quantities are treated analytically in Chapter 11, where their most important characteristics are demonstrated. In order to emphasise the power and economy which obtains from use of these quantities, their four most important characteristics are summarised in four statements which are called the *First, Second, Third and Fourth Statements of Chemical Potentials*. The first, which states that the chemical potential of a particular component present in more than one phase in an equilibrium system is the same in each phase, is one of the most powerful statements known to science: much of the fourth part of the book proves to be an essay in its application. In order to facilitate the introduction of chemical potentials use has been made of the de Donder affinity, and this concept has been developed towards the end of Part II to show how it gives information on the driving force of the reaction at any point in its course.

The chapters on statistical thermodynamics were rewritten many times. Although it is shown that the principles concerned are applicable to systems of all sorts, the analytical treatment is limited to systems of independent particles. The partition function of the *particle* is used rather than that of the *system as a whole* because it is simpler to handle. In order to emphasise that statistical calculations result in values of thermodynamic properties relative to those at absolute zero, a distinction is made between the *absolute* partition function and its *rational* analogue. Some time is spent in discussing rather difficult subjects such as the significance of the distinguishability or indistinguishability of like particles, and the reasons why the absolute value of the entropy of a system is unobtainable.

Part IV of the book is concerned with the application of thermodynamics to special systems, Chapter 15 with phase relations and solutions of non-electrolytes, and Chapter 16 with solutions of electrolytes. Chapter 17 is concerned with the thermodynamics of electro-chemical cells and their use in the determination of thermodynamic quantities. Considerable attention has been given to the methods available for the determination of the free energies of formation, enthalpies of formation and entropies of electrolytes in solution, and to the conventions used to partition these quantities between the separate ion species. Although fugacity and activity coefficients have been used where necessary throughout the book, the methods available for their determination have been reserved to the last chapter.

The author wishes to thank Professor W. H. Latimer and the publishers for permission to reproduce Figure 12,6 and the contents of Tables 12,III and 12,IV from Latimer's *Oxidation Potentials* (Prentice-Hall, 1952), and the Society for Industrial and Engineering Chemistry for permission to reproduce Figures 18,2, 18,3 and 18,4 from R. H. Newton's paper (*Ind. Eng. Chem.*, *27*, 302 (1935)). It is a pleasure to acknowledge the great help given to the author by some of his colleagues in discussing the treatment given in various parts of the book. He is particularly grateful to Dr. A. V. Golton, Mr. A. R. Cooper and Mr. P. D. Groves. He must thank Professor J. S. Rowlinson of the Imperial College of Science and Technology, who was kind enough to read the script of the first three parts and to suggest some amendments. He must also thank Mrs. M. Picken who typed and retyped a most difficult manuscript with great skill and patience.

M. H. EVERDELL

Birmingham

CONTENTS

PART IV

APPLICATION OF THERMODYNAMICS
TO SPECIAL SYSTEMS

APPENDICES

MATHEMATICAL THEOREMS
USED IN THIS BOOK

1. If A is a function of three or more variables $B, C, D \ldots$ of the form $A = B + CD \ldots$, and B, C and D are allowed to change simultaneously, the change in A is given by the expression

$$dA = dB + CdD + DdC \ldots$$

2. If A is any function of $B, C, D \ldots$

$$dA = \left(\frac{\partial A}{\partial B}\right)_{C, D \ldots} dB + \left(\frac{\partial A}{\partial C}\right)_{B, D \ldots} dC + \left(\frac{\partial A}{\partial D}\right)_{B, C \ldots} dD \ldots$$

3. If A is any function of B and C

$$\left(\frac{\partial A}{\partial B}\right)_C \left(\frac{\partial B}{\partial C}\right)_A \left(\frac{\partial C}{\partial A}\right)_B = -1$$

4. The *order* in which successive differentiations are undertaken is immaterial. The most important application of this theorem as far as we are concerned is shown below:

If five quantities A, B, C, D and E are so connected that

$$dA = BdC + DdE$$

$$\left(\frac{\partial A}{\partial C}\right)_E = B \quad \text{and} \quad \left(\frac{\partial A}{\partial E}\right)_C = D$$

so that

$$\left(\frac{\partial \left(\frac{\partial A}{\partial C}\right)_E}{\partial E}\right)_C = \left(\frac{\partial B}{\partial E}\right)_C$$

and

$$\left(\frac{\partial \left(\frac{\partial A}{\partial E}\right)_C}{\partial C}\right)_E = \left(\frac{\partial D}{\partial C}\right)_E$$

Since it follows from theorem 4 that the left-hand sides of these equations are equal, it follows that

$$\left(\frac{\partial B}{\partial E}\right)_C = \left(\frac{\partial D}{\partial C}\right)_E$$

5. $\int \dfrac{dx}{x} = \log_e x + C$

6. $\int x^n dx = \dfrac{x^{n+1}}{n+1} + C'$

7. $\displaystyle\int_{n=0}^{n=\infty} e^{-an^2}\,dn = \dfrac{1}{2}\Big(\dfrac{\pi}{a}\Big)^{\frac{1}{2}}$

8. $\displaystyle\int_{J=0}^{J=\infty} Je^{-aJ^2}\,dJ = \dfrac{1}{2a}$

These are two special integrals which are used in Statistical Thermodynamics.

Combination Theorems

9. The number of permutations of N distinguishable objects is $N!$

10. The number of ways assigning N *distinguishable* objects to r *distinguishable* containers so that there are $N_1, N_2, N_3 \ldots N_i \ldots N_r$ objects in each is

$$\frac{N!}{N_1!\,N_2!\,N_3!\ldots N_i!\ldots N_r!} = \frac{N!}{\displaystyle\prod_{i=1}^{i=r} N_i!}$$

11. The number of ways of assigning N *indistinguishable* objects to g *distinguishable* containers when each container can hold only one object at a time is

$$\frac{g!}{N!\,(g-N)!}$$

12. The number of ways of assigning N *indistinguishable* objects to g *distinguishable* containers when there is no restriction as to the number of objects in any one container is

$$\frac{(g+N-1)!}{(g-1)!\,N!}$$

13. The number of ways of putting N *distinguishable* objects into g *distinguishable* boxes is g^N as long as there is no restriction on the number of objects which can be placed in any box.

14. *Stirling's Approximation.* For large values of N

$$\log_e N! \simeq N \log_e N - N$$

UNITS AND DIMENSIONS

It is convenient to express such mathematical quantities as velocity, acceleration, force, etc., as functions of three fundamental concepts mass m, length L and time t.

$$\text{Velocity} = \frac{L}{t}$$

$$\text{Acceleration} = \frac{L}{t^2}$$

$$\text{Force} = \text{Mass} \times \text{Acceleration} = \frac{mL}{t^2}$$

$$\text{Pressure} = \text{Force per unit area} = \frac{m}{Lt^2}$$

$$\text{Work} = \text{Force} \times \text{Distance} = \frac{mL^2}{t^2}.$$

Since work is a form of energy in transit any other form of energy must also have dimensions $\frac{mL^2}{t^2}$.

Units

1. Velocities are usually expressed in cm sec^{-1}.

2. Accelerations are expressed in cm sec^{-2}.

3. Force is expressed in dynes (1 dyne is that force required to give a mass of 1 gramme an acceleration of 1 cm sec^{-2}).

4. Pressure is expressed in dynes-cm^{-2}, centimetres of mercury or atmospheres. The pressure of 1 centimetre of mercury implies the weight of 1 cm^3 of mercury on a horizontal surface of 1 cm^2. Since 1 cm^3 of mercury has mass 13·6 gm, a pressure of 1 cm of mercury equals 13·6 × 981 dynes-cm^{-2}. 1 atmosphere is the pressure of 76 centimetres of mercury and is defined as 1·013246 × 10^6 dynes-cm^{-2}.

5. Energy is expressed in ergs, joules, calories or litre-atmospheres

1 erg	= 1 dyne-cm
1 joule	= 10^7 ergs
1 calorie	= 4·1840 × 10^7 ergs
1 litre-atmosphere	= 101·32 joules = 24·23 calories

6. Universal Gas Constant

$$R = 8 \cdot 314 \times 10^7 \text{ ergs deg}^{-1} \text{ mole}^{-1}$$
$$= 1 \cdot 987 \text{ calories deg}^{-1} \text{ mole}^{-1}$$
$$= 0 \cdot 08206 \text{ litre-atmosphere deg}^{-1} \text{ mole}^{-1}$$

7. Avogadro's Number

$$N = 6 \cdot 0228 \times 10^{23} \text{ molecules per mole}$$

8. Boltzmann's Constant

$$k = 1 \cdot 3805 \times 10^{-16} \text{ ergs deg}^{-1}$$

9. Planck's Constant

$$h = 6 \cdot 624 \times 10^{-27} \text{ erg seconds}$$

10. The Faraday

$$F = 96,487 \text{ absolute coulombs per gramme equivalent}$$

LIST OF SYMBOLS

		Equation in which the symbol is first used
a	van der Waals constant, stoichiometric coefficient, area, etc.	
a	activity	
a_x	the activity of a component measured in terms of mole fractions	(11,56)
a_c	the activity of a component measured in terms of molar concentrations	(11,58)
a_m	the activity of a component measured in terms of molal concentrations	(11,59)
$a_{\pm}$	mean ionic activity of an electrolyte	(16,9)
$\mathring{a}$	distance of closest approach of ions (Debye–Hückel equation)	(16,22)
$\mathbf{A}$	Affinity of Reaction	(11,2)
A	Helmholtz Available Work Function	(9,9)
b (suffix)	boiling, e.g. T_b, boiling point	
b	van der Waals constant, stoichiometric coefficient, etc.	
B	parameter used in Debye–Hückel equation	
c	velocity of light in vacuo	
c_p	specific heat at constant pressure	
c_v	specific heat at constant volume	
c (suffix)	critical, e.g. T_c critical temperature	
C	number of distinct chemical species (Phase Rule)	
C	molar concentration	
C	degrees on Celsius scale	

xix

		Equation in which the symbol is first used
C_p	molar thermal capacity at constant pressure	(4,14)
C_v	molar thermal capacity at constant volume	(4,13)
C, C_x, C_y, C_z	velocity of a particle, and the component of a velocity along directions X, Y and Z	
d	differential coefficient	
∂	partial differential coefficient (usually used in brackets, e.g. $\left(\dfrac{\partial G}{\partial T}\right)_p$ meaning the partial differential of G with respect to T at constant p)	
D	Nernst Distribution Constant	(15,47)
e	electronic charge	
$\bar{e}$	electron	
$\bar{e}(e)$	electron located on an electrode	
e	base of natural logarithms	
e (suffix)	evaporation	
$\mathbf{E}$	potential difference, electromotive force	
$\mathbf{E_0}$	standard electrode potential or standard electromotive force	(17,13)
E	total energy of a system moving relative to the surroundings	(4,22)
E_k	kinetic energy of system relative to the surroundings	(4,22)
E_p	gravitational potential energy of system	(4,22)
$E_{\circ}^{0}$	the molar energy of a pure substance at absolute zero	
f, f', f'', etc.	a function of the variables that follow: e.g. the equation $$U = f(T,V)$$ means that the internal energy of a system is a function of its temperature and volume	

		Equation in which the symbol is first used
f_{abs}	the absolute partition function of a particle	(13,29)
f, $f_{rational}$	the rational partition function of a particle	(14,3)
f_{trans}, f_{rot}, f_{vib}, f_{elec}	the translational, rotational vibrational and electronic rational partition functions of a molecule	
f (suffix)	fusion, e.g. L_f molar latent heat of fusion	
F	Faraday	
F	Number of degrees of freedom, or variance of system (Phase Rule)	(15,22)
g	degeneracy	
G	Gibbs Free Energy	(9,11)
h	Planck's constant	
h	height above base line	
h_i	partial molar enthalpy of component i	
	$\left(\equiv\left(\dfrac{\partial H}{\partial n_i}\right)_{p,\,T,\,n_1,\,\ldots\,n_{i-1},\,n_{i+1},\,\ldots}\right)$	(11,31)
H	Enthalpy	(4,16)
i	van't Hoff factor	(15,43)
i	symbol for any one component in a mixture (usually used as suffix)	
I	moment of inertia	
I	Ionic strength of a solution	(16,21)
I, I', I^*	integration constants	
j	symbol of a component in a mixture other than i	
j	$\equiv\dfrac{RT}{p}-\bar{V}$	(18,3)
J	rotational quantum number	(14,23)
k	Boltzmann's constant $\left(\equiv\dfrac{R}{N}\right)$	(13,5)
k_1, k_2	velocity constants, general proportionality constants	

		Equation in which the symbol is first used
K	degrees on Kelvin or Thermo-dynamic scale of temperature	
K	equilibrium constant	
K_a, K_c, K_m, K_p $K_p{}^*$, K_x, K_y	equilibrium constant in terms of activities, molar concentrations, molalities, partial pressures, partial fugacities, mole fractions	
K_b	molal boiling point constant	
K_f	molal freezing point constant	
K_s	solubility product of an electrolyte	(16,17)
K_w	ionic product of water	(16,6)
L	distance	
L	molar latent heat (usually followed by a suffix, e.g. L_s molar latent heat of sublimation)	
m	mass of an electron	
m	molality	
m	mass of a molecule	
M	molecular weight	
n	number of moles of component present	
n	population number of an energy level	(13,6)
N	Avogadro Number	
N	total number of particles in system	
p	the pressure of a system	
p (as suffix)	denotes the condition of constant pressure	
p_i	the partial pressure of a component i	
p_i^0	the vapour pressure that a component of a mixture would exert as a pure substance	
p^*	fugacity	(11,39)
$p_i{}^*$	the partial fugacity of a component i	
p_H	$\equiv -\log_{10} a_{H+}$	
P	number of phases in system (Phase Rule)	

		Equation in which the symbol is first used
q	quantity of heat absorbed by a system	
q'	sometimes used to denote quantity of heat rejected by a system	
Q	quantity of electricity	
Q	rational partition function of the system	
R	universal gas constant	
R	number of independent reactions (Phase Rule)	
R (suffix)	reduced, e.g. T_R reduced temperature $$T_R \equiv \frac{T}{T_c}$$	
$\bar{s}_i$	partial molar entropy of component i $$\left(\equiv \left(\frac{\partial S}{\partial n_i} \right)_{p,\,T,\,n_1,\,\ldots\,n_{i-1},\,n_{i+1},\,\ldots} \right)$$	(11,29)
S	Entropy	(7,11)
t	time, temperature (arbitrary scale)	
$t_+,\ t_-$	transport numbers of cation and anion	
T	the absolute temperature of a system	
U	Internal energy of a system	
$\mathbf{V}$	velocity of reaction	(11,1)
v (suffix)	signifies condition of constant volume	
v	vibrational quantum number	(14,31)
$\bar{v}_i$	partial molar volume of component i $$\left(\equiv \left(\frac{\partial V}{\partial n_i} \right)_{p,\,T,\,n_1,\,\ldots\,n_{1-1},\,n_{i+1},\,\ldots} \right)$$	(11,35)
$\bar{V}$	sometimes used to denote molar volume of a pure substance	
V	volume of system	
ϑ	speed of system relative to the surroundings	

		Equation in which the symbol is first used
w	work performed by the system on the surroundings	
W	number of micro-states accessible to the system ($\equiv$ Thermodynamic Probability)	
W_{elec}	number of micro-states accessible to the system due to different electronic configurations	
W_{trans}	number of micro-states accessible to the system due to different translational configurations	
W^{temp}	the number of micro-states accessible to the system due to factors which result from the acquisition of energy from absolute zero to the state under consideration	
W^0	the number of micro-states which are independent of temperature and of the energy acquired when the system changes from absolute zero to the state under consideration	
x	mole fraction of a component (usually used to denote the mole fraction of a component in a liquid or solid phase)	
x (suffix)	to denote that the quantity has been calculated with reference to the mole fraction of the component, e.g. a_x the activity of the component expressed in terms of mole fractions	
X	general symbol used for a thermodynamic property, Cartesian co-ordinate, etc.	
y	sometimes used to denote the mole fraction of a component in the gas phase	

		Equation in which the symbol is first used
Y	Cartesian co-ordinate	
z^+, z^-	ionic charge	
Z	Cartesian co-ordinate	
α	frequently used as a parameter, or to denote a particular phase	
α	volume coefficient of thermal expansion $$\left(\equiv \frac{1}{V}\left(\frac{\partial V}{\partial T}\right)_p\right)$$	
β	frequently used as a parameter, or to denote a particular phase	
β	isothermal compressibility coefficient $$\left(\equiv -\frac{1}{V}\left(\frac{\partial V}{\partial p}\right)_T\right)$$	
β	$$\left(\equiv \frac{1}{kT}\right)$$	(13,28)
γ	ratio of principal specific heats or principal molar thermal capacities	(5,11)
γ	activity coefficient or fugacity coefficient	(11,56)
γ_+, γ_-	activity coefficient of cation and anion	
$\gamma_\pm$	mean ionic activity coefficient of an electrolyte	(16,10)
δ	very small quantity	
Δ	finite difference in the value of a thermodynamic property resulting from a change of state	
ε	energy level of a single particle	
ξ	extent of reaction	
η	thermal efficiency of a cycle	(7,2)
λ	wavelength	
μ_i	chemical potential of component i	
μ_{oi}	standard chemical potential of component i	

Equation in
which the
symbol is
first used

$\mu_\pm$	mean ionic chemical potential of an electrolyte	(16,7)
ν_+, ν_-	number of cations, anions formed by the dissociation of an electrolyte	
π	ratio of circumference to diameter of circle	
$\prod$	osmotic pressure	
$\prod_i$	product of all terms following for all values of i	
ρ	special restriction (Phase Rule)	
σ	polytropic index	(5,20)
σ	symmetry factor	
σ	compressibility factor $\left(\equiv \dfrac{pV}{RT}\right)$	
$\sum_i$	sum of all terms following for all values of i	
$\oint$	summation of all terms over a complete cycle of operations	
τ	surface tension	
ϕ	tension	
ϕ	osmotic coefficient	
ω	reciprocal wavelength	
ω	chance	

ABBREVIATIONS USED AS SUBSCRIPTS

I, II	used to denote path I, path II
1, 2	used to denote state 1, state 2
b, e, f, s	boiling, evaporation, fusion, sublimation
c	critical, e.g. T_c, p_c
R	reduced, e.g. $T_R \equiv \dfrac{T}{T_c}$, $p_R \equiv \dfrac{p}{p_c}$
eq	equilibrium, e.g. $p_{i_{eq}}$ the equilibrium partial pressure of component i
g, liq, s	gas, liquid, solid
sat	denotes that the solution is saturated with respect to the component indicated
p, S, T, V	indicates constancy of pressure, entropy, temperature and volume
$n_1 \ldots n_{i-1}$, $n_{i+1} \ldots$	indicates that the quantities of all components present remain constant except the ith

MATHEMATICAL SYMBOLS

$=$	equal to
$\simeq$	approximately equal to
$\neq$	not equal to
$\equiv$	identical with
$\propto$	proportional to
$>$	greater than
$<$	less than
$\gg$	very much greater than
$\ll$	very much less than
$n!$	factorial n, i.e. $\displaystyle\prod_{i=1}^{i=n} n_i$
$\int y\,dx$	indefinite integral of y with respect to x
$\displaystyle\int_a^b y\,dx$	integral of y with respect to x from $x = a$ to $x = b$
$\oint$	integration around a complete cycle of operations
$\displaystyle\prod_i$	product of all terms following for all values of i
$\displaystyle\sum_i$	sum of all terms following for all values of i
$\oint\!\!\!\sum$	summation of all terms around a complete cycle of operations

PART I

INTRODUCTION

CHAPTER 1

THE LANGUAGE OF THERMODYNAMICS: SYSTEMS, STATES AND PROPERTIES: ENERGY, HEAT AND WORK

Chemical thermodynamics is that branch of science which is primarily concerned with the quantities of *energy* and *entropy* associated with a physical and chemical process, and with the information that these quantities give on the process concerned. The word energy is one which is widely used in everyday life and probably requires no amplification. The word entropy is less familiar, and it is not easy to explain its meaning precisely and economically at this stage. It is probably best regarded as a measure of the degree of disorder in the system concerned, or as a measure of its "mixed-up-ness", so that, for example, the entropy of a mixture of gases is greater than the sum of the entropies of the gases before mixing.

The rules which govern the quantities of energy and entropy associated with any process are contained in three of the four postulates which are called the four laws of thermodynamics. The nature of these postulates will be discussed in the next chapter and an attempt will be made there to give an idea of their power and use, but in order to do so we must use some commonplace words which, in thermodynamics, are given a *precise* meaning which differs somewhat from that implied in their everyday use. In this chapter we shall discuss the thermodynamic meaning of some of these words, and so lay the foundation of the language we shall use in the rest of the book.

The first two words are HEAT and WORK. In thermodynamics these words are used to describe the two forms in which energy can be transferred from one body to another. If we analyse any instance in which one body transmits energy to another, we find one of two things: either that the energy transfer has been occasioned by a difference in temperature between the bodies concerned, or that some *movement* against a *resistance* has been involved. That form of energy which passes from one body to another as the result of a temperature difference between them is called HEAT, and that which passes as the result of some movement against a

3

resistance is called WORK. Thus the words heat and work are used only to denote forms of energy *in transit*, and are never used to denote energy possessed by a body. When we require to discuss the energy possessed by a body we shall use the word energy and none other, and sometimes qualify it by such adjectives as translational, rotational and so on to denote the part played by the particular quantity of energy we are considering at the time. These matters will be discussed in greater detail later in the chapter.

The remaining commonplace words that we must discuss are *system*, *surroundings*, *state*, *path* and *property*.

By the word SYSTEM we mean that particular mass of material in which we happen to be interested at the time. It may be a quantity of gas contained in a cylinder, or a mixture of two or three reactants contained in a reaction chamber. We shall suppose that the system is surrounded by a boundary wall through which matter cannot pass, so that the total mass of material in the system remains the same, even though its physical nature or chemical composition may change as the result of such processes as the evaporation of a liquid, the condensation of a gas or a chemical reaction taking place between two or more components. We may be interested in a quantity of gas contained in a cylinder fitted with a movable piston: in such a case the boundary wall is the inner surface of the cylinder and piston; in another case we may be interested in a quantity of gas enclosed in a balloon, in this case the boundary wall is the inner surface of the balloon. The boundary wall is merely that which separates the system from the remainder of the universe which we call the SURROUNDINGS.

Boundary walls can be of various types. In some instances we shall make use of a boundary wall through which the passage of energy in any form is impossible: under these circumstances the system is said to be *isolated*. In other instances we shall suppose that the boundary wall is impermeable to heat, but permits passage to or from the system of that form of energy in transit called work. Such a wall is called *adiabatic*, and any process which takes place in a system surrounded by an adiabatic wall is called an adiabatic process. An example of an adiabatic process is a reaction which takes place in a vessel which has been efficiently lagged, but which is not necessarily of fixed volume; so that although no energy in the form of heat can pass between the system and the surroundings, the system may possibly expand against the surroundings and so perform work against it. If on the other hand we choose to allow the reaction to proceed in a vessel which is both lagged and of fixed volume, so that no expansion is possible, no energy either as heat or work can pass between the system and the surroundings, and it is evident that the system is isolated. Clearly all processes which take place in isolated systems are adiabatic, but all adiabatic processes do not necessarily take place in isolation. Only when the system is isolated will any change therein leave the surroundings unchanged; under all other circumstances any change in the system is necessarily accompanied by a change in the surroundings.

If a system is suddenly subjected to a change in its environment, such as an increase in pressure or being placed in contact with a body at different temperature, fluctuations of the temperature, pressure and volume of the system result, but after a time the system settles down to a particular EQUILIBRIUM STATE, depending on the circumstances to which it is subjected. When the equilibrium state is reached the pressure and temperature will be the same throughout, and the volume of the system will remain constant. We shall require to identify any state in which a system exists by such measurements as pressure, temperature and volume, and since it is evident that such measurements as pressure and temperature will only have meaning if they refer to the system as a whole, it follows that any state which we choose to identify by them must necessarily be in equilibrium throughout. When we refer therefore to a definite state in which a system is found and we identify it by physical measurements, we imply that the state is an equilibrium state whether we use the word equilibrium or not.

Let us consider a system such as a given quantity of hydrogen slowly changing from one state to another. We may, for example, imagine it changing at constant temperature from an initial pressure of 10 atmospheres and an initial volume of 1 litre to a final pressure of 2 atmospheres and a final volume of 5 litres. If the process is made to take place very slowly so that the system passes through a series of equilibrium states, it becomes possible to measure the pressure of the gas and the volume it occupies at various stages during the expansion. The process may then be illustrated by a diagram such as that shown in Figure 1,1. The line drawn between the initial, intermediary and final

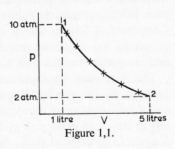

Figure 1,1.

equilibrium states of the system shows the course or PATH that the change has taken.

We point out that a system may change from one state to another in different ways, by following different paths. We may, for example, consider a system changing from one state in which its temperature is T_1 and its pressure p_1 to a state in which its temperature is T_2 and its pressure p_2.

B

Two paths which the system might follow are shown in Figure 1,2. Path I consists of two steps: during the first the system is heated at its initial pressure from T_1 to T_2, and during the second the system is compressed at constant temperature to p_2. Path II also consists of two steps: during the first the system is compressed at its initial temperature to p_2, and during the second it is heated at p_2 to the final temperature. These are only two of the infinite number of different paths which might be chosen to pass from one state to another, just as there are an infinite number of different routes which a traveller might take from Birmingham to London.

In the previous paragraphs we described a particular state of a system by its temperature pressure and volume. These are three of the so-called PROPERTIES of a system, the word PROPERTY being used to denote any

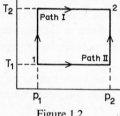

Figure 1,2.

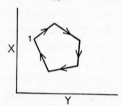

Figure 1,3. A cyclic series of operations.

quantity which helps to describe the state in which the system is found. Consider a given quantity of a single substance existing as a gas; the particular state in which it exists is described by the volume it occupies, the pressure it exerts, its temperature and its density. When these quantities have definite numerical values the state of the system is unambiguous. Conversely, it follows that if a system is in a particular state each of its properties has a definite numerical value determined solely by the state and independent of the past history of the system.

This fact may be expressed mathematically. We may denote any property by the symbol X, an infinitesimal change in its value by dX, and a finite change by the symbol ΔX. We now permit the system originally in state 1 to undergo a cyclic series of changes, at the end of which it is again in its original state. We illustrate this in Figure 1,3 by graphing the value of X against some other function Y. During each operation the value of X may change, but because the final state of the system is the same as its initial state, the final value of X must be the same as the initial value, so that the algebraic sum of the changes in X which have occurred throughout the cycle must equal zero. We represent the overall change in X by the expression

$$\oint dX = 0 \qquad \ldots \ldots \ldots \quad (1,1)$$

where the circle drawn through the integral sign denotes that the summation has been made over a complete cycle of operations.

We now consider a process in which the system changes from state 1, at which the value of the property X is X_1, to state 2, at which the value of X is X_2. Since the numerical values X_1 and X_2 are determined solely by the initial and final states of the system *the change in X is independent of the path taken by the system during the process*, and is described completely by the expression

$$\Delta X = X_2 - X_1 = \int_{\text{State 1}}^{\text{State 2}} dX \qquad . \quad . \quad . \quad . \quad (1,2)$$

These expressions may be used to determine whether a particular quantity is related to a thermodynamic property of a system or not. Thus, if we find that when a change of state occurs a particular quantity changes by a definite amount which is independent of the path by which the change proceeds, we may conclude that that change in quantity represents a change in some—perhaps hitherto unrecognised—property of the system.

The properties we have so far mentioned—temperature, pressure, volume and density can all be observed directly and measured against any conventional scale, but by making use of the principles explained above we shall find that there are other properties of a system, the existence of which may be deduced, but which cannot be directly observed. The most important are the INTERNAL ENERGY and ENTHALPY of the system, the existence of which follows from the First Law of Thermodynamics, the ENTROPY, the existence of which follows from the Second Law, and two others, the GIBBS FREE ENERGY and the HELMHOLTZ AVAILABLE WORK FUNCTION, which are convenient functions of the other three.

The student might well inquire why it is so important to know whether a particular quantity is a thermodynamic property or not. We will now try to make this clear.

We know from experience that certain properties are inter-related and connected by what is called an *equation of state*. Thus we know that if a gas approaches ideal behaviour we may write

$$p = \frac{kT}{V}$$

where the value of the constant k depends merely on the quantity of gas involved. For a so-called van der Waals gas we may write

$$p = \frac{kT}{V - b} - \frac{a}{V^2}$$

where a and b are constants, the values of which are characteristic of the particular gas and the quantity concerned, and the constant k has the same significance as before. Similar equations of state exist for liquids and solids: we may not know what the equation is, that is not necessarily important; what is important is that we recognise that such an equation exists and can be determined, if we require it, by taking sufficient readings of pressure, volume and temperature of a given substance and fitting an equation to the results.

Since, when a given quantity of any substance is in a particular state each property has a definite value, it follows that similar equations of state must exist whereby any property can be expressed as a function of others. Thus, just as we can write

$$p = f(V, T)$$

which says that we know that the pressure of a system is a function of its volume and temperature (although we may not know what the function is), we can write similar expressions for the internal energy of the system (for which we use the symbol U)

$$U = f'(V, T)$$

or for the entropy (for which we use the symbol S)

$$S = f''(p, T)$$

or, that any number of properties $X, Y, Z \ldots$ are connected by some expression

$$X = f'''(Y, Z \ldots)$$

The importance of being able to do this is that we then have at our disposal the whole arsenal of the calculus with which we may treat the expression. We may, for example, require to know the variation in the value of property X if the state of the system is changed by some simultaneous variation in Y and Z. The calculus states that if X is some function of Y and Z, an increase in Y and Z will result in an increase in X given by the equation

$$dX = \left(\frac{\partial X}{\partial Y}\right)_Z dY + \left(\frac{\partial X}{\partial Z}\right)_Y dZ$$

where the quantities in brackets are the partial derivatives which can often be evaluated experimentally with ease.

We might also make use of Theorem 3 on page xv, and write

$$\left(\frac{\partial X}{\partial Y}\right)_Z \left(\frac{\partial Y}{\partial Z}\right)_X \left(\frac{\partial Z}{\partial X}\right)_Y = -1$$

This is of use when it is required to know the value of the quantity in one bracket but impossible to determine it directly. We may, for example, require to know the variation in the temperature of a solid with respect to pressure under such conditions that the volume is kept constant. This quantity is impossible to determine directly. Since, however,

$$p = f(V, T)$$

$$\left(\frac{\partial p}{\partial T}\right)_V \left(\frac{\partial T}{\partial V}\right)_p \left(\frac{\partial V}{\partial p}\right)_T = -1$$

and the quantity we require is given by the equation

$$\left(\frac{\partial T}{\partial p}\right)_V = -\frac{\left(\frac{\partial V}{\partial p}\right)_T}{\left(\frac{\partial V}{\partial T}\right)_p}$$

Both quantities on the right-hand side can be determined with ease, so that the quantity we require can be obtained indirectly.

Intensive and Extensive Properties

If we consider the three properties with which we are familiar, temperature, pressure and volume, we see that the first two differ in type from the last. The first type are INTENSIVE properties; they are independent of the quantity of material involved. Volume is, however, an EXTENSIVE property: it is proportional to the quantity of material present. The other properties we have already mentioned, the Internal Energy, the Enthalpy, the Entropy, the Gibbs Free Energy and the Helmholtz Available Work Function are also extensive.

While extensive analogues of temperature and pressure do not exist, intensive analogues of extensive properties are much used. The intensive analogue of volume is the SPECIFIC VOLUME, or the volume per gramme (it is, of course, the inverse of density), that of the internal energy the SPECIFIC INTERNAL ENERGY which is the internal energy per gramme of material. In fact, in thermodynamics we normally express the quantity of material with which we are concerned in terms of MOLES, one mole of a pure substance being its formal molecular mass expressed in grammes, one mole of CO_2 being 44 grammes and one mole of H_2O being 18 grammes. The intensive analogues of extensive properties are usually expressed in terms of this quantity, and are called the MOLAR VOLUME, the MOLAR INTERNAL ENERGY and so on: they represent the volume per mole and the internal energy per mole.

When we eventually consider complicated systems in which one or more components react to form a third, we shall find it convenient to use a slightly different type of intensive property, of which THE PARTIAL MOLAR FREE ENERGY (or the so-called CHEMICAL POTENTIAL) is the most important example. What is meant by this term will not, however, be discussed at this stage. In this connection, too, we find it convenient sometimes to denote the composition of the system in terms of the number of moles of each component, and sometimes in terms of the MOLE FRACTION of each component. The mole fraction of a component is defined as the number of moles of that component divided by the total number of moles of all components in the system. The mole fraction of a component in a solid or liquid phase is usually denoted by the symbol x, and that of a component in a gas phase by the symbol y, so that in a particular phase containing n_1 moles of component 1, n_2 moles of component 2, . . ., the mole fraction of component 1 is given by the equation

$$x_1 \text{ or } y_1 = \frac{n_1}{n_1 + n_2 \ldots}$$

It will be noted that the mole fraction is an intensive molar quantity, and that since $\Sigma x_1 = 1$, the composition of a mixture is determined if the mole fractions of all the components except one are known.

We introduced the word property by saying that it denotes any quantity which helps to describe the state in which the system is found. It is therefore of interest to discuss what is the *least* number of properties the values of which must be known in order that a particular state be completely defined. It is obvious that we do not require to know the values of *all* the properties of a system in order to know all about the particular state it is in, because many properties are connected by simple equations of such a type that if the values of two or three are known, the values of the others can be deduced. In fact, a system is usually completely defined if the values of a very small number of properties are known, but the exact number depends on the nature and complexity of the system itself and on the particular properties chosen.

If, for example, we consider a system which consists of a single pure substance in a single phase, knowledge of any two intensive properties determines the rest (thus a particular gas at a particular temperature and pressure must be at a particular density and have a particular specific volume), but no matter how many intensive properties are known, calculation of the extensive properties is possible only if we know the quantity of material present, or the value of one extensive property from which the quantity of material present can be determined.

If we consider a homogeneous system which is a mixture of several components which do not react together, we require to know the values of the mole fractions of all the components except one, in addition to any two other intensive properties in order to determine the rest; but as before, the mass or number of moles of one component, or the total mass or total number of moles, or the value of one extensive property must be known in order to determine the system completely.

The most complicated system is that which contains several components present in several phases. This type of system will not be discussed at this stage, the problem is answered later in the book by the PHASE RULE.

ENERGY, HEAT AND WORK

The introduction of a quantity called *Energy* is necessary to explain the fact that the same change in the properties of a system may be brought about by various processes which appear to have little or nothing in common.

Thus, the temperature of a quantity of water may be raised by placing it in contact with a hot body, by focusing upon it the rays of the sun or by stirring it with a paddle-wheel. We say that in all three cases the water has received energy; in the first two cases energy in the form of heat, and in the third case that energy has been transferred to it from the paddle-wheel in the form of work.

It must therefore be supposed that energy can be contained by a system, and can be transferred from one system to another in various ways.

We have already stated that if we analyse any instance in which one body transmits energy to another we find one of two things: either that the energy transfer has been occasioned by a difference in temperature between the bodies concerned, or, that some *movement* against a *resistance* has been involved, and we have stated that the energy in transit is in the first case called HEAT and in the second case WORK.

While the only condition for a flow of heat from one system to another is that a temperature difference should exist between them, the circumstances under which work may be performed by one system on another differ. In all cases work implies the operation of a "force" through a "distance", but the nature of the "force" and the "distance" through which it operates is not always the same.

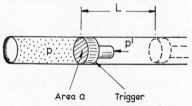

Figure 1,4. Expansion against a constant pressure.

To the chemist the most important form of work is that performed when a system expands against an opposing pressure. Consider a gas contained in a cylinder fitted with a frictionless piston of cross-sectional area a which is kept in position by a trigger; the pressure exerted by the gas being p, and that of the atmosphere p'. If p is greater than p', then when the trigger is released the piston will be moved a distance L. The work done by the gas will equal the product of the force overcome and the distance L, i.e.

$$p' \times a \times L.$$

The product $a \times L$ is, however, the amount by which the gas expands, its increase in volume ΔV. We see therefore that the work performed equals $p'\Delta V$.

It will be noted that the actual pressure of the gas performing the work is not found in the expression for the work performed. We shall return to this point in Chapter 4 when we shall show as a consequence of the First Law, that the work performed by a system when it changes its state depends not only on the initial and final states of the system but also on the path along which the change proceeds, and that a particular (artificial but theoretically important) path "exists", known as the *reversible* path, along which the maximum possible quantity of work is performed. The expression for the maximum possible quantity of work performed when a system expands from V_1 to V_2 is

$$\int_{V_1}^{V_2} p\,dV$$

and is a function only of the properties of the system undergoing the expansion.

The units in which expansion work is expressed depends on those used to express pressure and volume. If the pressure is expressed in dynes-cm^{-2} and the increase in volume in cm^3, the product of the two expresses the energy in ergs. If the pressure is expressed in atmospheres (i.e. $1 \cdot 013246 \times 10^6$ dynes-cm^{-2}) and the increase in volume in litres, the product of the two gives the energy unit known as the litre-atmosphere. If the pressure is expressed in cm of mercury and the increase in volume in cm^3, we must multiply the pressure by $13 \cdot 6$ (the density of mercury) and 981 (g in cm sec^{-2}) to obtain the pressure in dynes-cm^{-2}, and so obtain the work performed in ergs. The various energy units are connected by the equations

1 litre-atmosphere $= 101 \cdot 32$ joules $= 101 \cdot 32 \times 10^7$ ergs $= 24 \cdot 23$ calories.

The second most important form of work is that performed when a quantity of electricity is transferred from a point of one electrical potential to another. If ΔQ is the quantity of electricity transferred expressed in coulombs, and $\mathbf{E}$ the potential difference expressed in volts, the work done $\mathbf{E}\Delta Q$ is expressed in joules.

Work is also performed when a surface film expands. The work performed is the product of the surface tension and the increase in surface area concerned. The product $\tau \Delta a$ gives the work performed in ergs if the surface tension τ is expressed in dynes-cm^{-1}, and the increase in area Δa in cm^2.

Similarly, the work performed by fibre when it is stretched is given by the expression $-\phi \Delta L$, and if the tension ϕ is given in dynes and the extension ΔL in cm, the product gives the work performed directly in ergs. (The negative sign is included because work has to be done *on* the fibre in order to elongate it.)

It is extremely important in thermodynamics to distinguish between the work which is actually performed by a system during a particular change of state and the work that *can* be performed. The two are by no means the same. When a mass m gm falls freely under gravity through the air from a height h cm it may perform no work at all. It certainly loses mgh ergs of potential energy, but this may be dissipated in various ways such as raising the temperature of the ground and the weight when they come into collision, and raising the temperature of the air through which the weight passes. The falling weight could, however, cause work to be performed. It could, for example, in falling strike successively the vanes of a number of paddle-wheels which are geared to a device whereby a weight might be lifted. In fact, if all the mechanical devices used functioned perfectly, a quantity of work equal to mgh ergs would be performed.

The change of state which occurs in a chemical cell is another example. In a Daniell Cell the chemical reaction which results in the liberation of energy is

$$Zn + Cu^{++} \longrightarrow Zn^{++} + Cu.$$

If the reaction is allowed to proceed by shorting the terminals of the cell no work is performed, and the energy liberated is manifested as heat. If, however, the cell is allowed to function by passing current through an electric motor, the energy liberated in the reaction is transformed into electrical energy which may be used to lift a weight and so perform mechanical work. In Chapter 4 we shall recognise the conditions under which the maximum possible quantity of work may be performed in such a reaction.

Energy Contained by a System

Energy may be contained by a system in various forms. The most familiar form is what we call the KINETIC ENERGY of a system moving as a whole relative to its surroundings. If a system mass m gm moves with speed ϑ cm sec^{-1} we say that it possesses kinetic energy equal to $\frac{1}{2}m\vartheta^2$ ergs, because this is the quantity of energy we have to remove from it in order to bring it to rest. Conversely, if we start off with a body at rest, we can cause it to reach speed ϑ by giving it this amount of energy. Another familiar form is the GRAVITATIONAL POTENTIAL ENERGY of a system suspended above the earth's surface. We are not in Chemical Thermodynamics particularly concerned with these two forms of energy, mainly because we shall mostly consider *static* systems such as a quantity of material contained in a beaker, or a quantity of gas enclosed in a cylinder, and during the changes that we shall study, these containers and their contents will not change their positions relative to their surroundings, so that there will be no *change* in the kinetic or gravitational potential energies possessed by them. (The chemical engineer may have to take changes in these quantities into account, because he is so often concerned with the *flow* of reactants through a reaction chamber. The additional terms which he will have to include in his equations to account for them will be discussed in due course.)

Classical thermodynamics does not find it necessary to inquire into the nature of the energy of a *static* system, neither does it require the calculation of its absolute value, nor provide any information on how this quantity might be obtained. It is concerned only with the *change* in energy of the system which results from the particular event upon which attention happens to be focused at the time; and such changes are usually measured in terms of the heat absorbed by the system and the work performed by it during the event. In fact, in Chapter 4 we shall show that if a system undergoes some change of state which involves the acquisition from the surroundings of a quantity of energy q in the form of heat, and the loss of a quantity of energy w in the form of work, the change in internal energy of the system ΔU is given by the equation

$$\Delta U = q - w.$$

Since, when a system is in a particular state all its properties have definite values, we must suppose that before the change of state occurred the internal energy of the system was some definite value U_1, and that after the event it becomes another definite value U_2, so that the quantity ΔU equals $U_2 - U_1$; but the fact remains that we make no attempt to determine U_1 or U_2 *separately*, because there is no use to which we could put the result if we got it. All that is ever required in thermodynamics is the *change* in energy relating to the change of state in which we are interested, and this quantity can usually be obtained with ease.

Classical thermodynamics finds it unnecessary to inquire into the nature of the energy possessed by a system because it is not concerned with the *fine structure* of the system itself. We shall, however, inquire into this matter in the third part of this book when we consider that part of the subject known as Statistical Thermodynamics. There we shall inquire into the nature of the system itself, and evaluate the energy of the system in terms of that possessed by each individual molecule therein. We shall be particularly interested in those forms of energy which decide the physical state and temperature of the system (what can be called the *thermal energy* of the system), and we shall find that of the total thermal energy of a molecule, some is translational (the translational energy of a particle is the energy associated with the velocity with which it moves through the rest of the system), that some is associated with molecular rotation, some with the mode of molecular vibrations and that some is electronic. This enables us to evaluate the change in energy of a system when it is heated from absolute zero to the particular temperature in which we are interested, but we make no attempt to evaluate or even to list those forms of energy which are not temperature dependent, and which are present at absolute zero; firstly, because we should find it impossible, and secondly, because there is no use to which we could put the result.

EXERCISES 1

1,1. It will be shown later in the book that if any infinitesimal process takes place in a system in which no work other than expansion work is possible and in which no change in composition takes place, changes in the properties of the system denoted by the symbols U, H, S, A, G, T, p and V are connected by the following equations

$$dU = TdS - pdV$$
$$dH = TdS + Vdp$$
$$dA = -SdT - pdV$$
$$dG = -SdT + Vdp$$

Use theorem 4, page xv, to show that

$$\left(\frac{\partial T}{\partial V}\right)_S = -\left(\frac{\partial p}{\partial S}\right)_V$$

$$\left(\frac{\partial T}{\partial p}\right)_S = \left(\frac{\partial V}{\partial S}\right)_p$$

$$\left(\frac{\partial p}{\partial T}\right)_V = \left(\frac{\partial S}{\partial V}\right)_T$$

$$\left(\frac{\partial V}{\partial T}\right)_p = -\left(\frac{\partial S}{\partial p}\right)_T$$

1,2. The property entropy is expressed in cal deg^{-1}, so that the dimensions of entropy in terms of mass, length, time and temperature are $mL^2t^{-2}T^{-1}$.

Show that the four partial differential equations quoted in Exercise 1,1 are dimensionally correct.

CHAPTER 2

THE NATURE OF THERMODYNAMICS

It has already been said that thermodynamics is primarily concerned with the quantities of energy and entropy associated with a physical or chemical process, and with the information that these quantities give on the process concerned. Modern thermodynamic theory depends on two disciplines, which are called *classical thermodynamics* and *statistical thermodynamics* respectively.

Classical thermodynamics is based on four postulates which are called the Zeroth,[1] First, Second and Third Laws. These provide the rules governing the quantities of energy and entropy associated with any process, and show how they may be expressed in terms of other quantities which may be directly measured. Statistical thermodynamics traces the origin of the thermodynamic laws to the atomic and molecular theories of matter and provides alternative means of calculating the quantities of energy and entropy concerned. The principles of classical thermodynamics are developed in Chapters 3 to 12, and those of statistical thermodynamics in Chapters 13 and 14.

The Zeroth Law states that if two systems are each found to be in thermal equilibrium with a third, they would, if placed in contact, be found to be in thermal equilibrium with each other. The significance of this statement will be discussed in Chapter 3. Its importance lies in the fact that it leads to the recognition of temperature as a property of a system.

The First Law states that energy can neither be created nor destroyed. Two alternative statements follow. The first is that whatsoever change takes place in an *isolated* system, its energy must remain the same, and the second is that if instead of considering an isolated system, we permit it and its surroundings to interact so that energy passes from one to the other,

[1] The *substance* of the Zeroth Law was known and used in science many years before the development of thermodynamic theory. Unfortunately, the fact that the principle concerned is of the same nature and just as important as the principles concerned in the other three laws was not recognised until long after the others had become widely known as the First, Second and Third Laws. It would have been illogical to have called it the Fourth Law because its substance is necessary to the development of the other three; it was therefore given the name Zeroth.

the quantity of energy lost by one must equal that gained by the second. The First Law establishes the fact that the energy content of a system is a thermodynamic property. We are usually interested only in systems which are static relative to their surroundings, and we call the energy content of such a static system its INTERNAL ENERGY, and denote it by the symbol U. We also find that the First Law leads to the recognition of a second property, one that is called the ENTHALPY of the system, denoted by H. The characteristics of these properties are discussed in Chapter 4.

The Second Law states that the effect of no natural spontaneous event can ever be completely erased, that the clock can never be put back. In Chapter 7 we show that this postulate identifies the thermodynamic property entropy and leads to two further statements. The first is that any spontaneous change which takes place in an isolated system leads to an increase in its entropy, and the second that if changes are allowed to occur in systems which are not isolated, but which are permitted to exchange energy with the surroundings, although nothing can be said about the change in entropy of the system and surroundings taken individually, the *sum* of the entropies of both must increase.

In other words, any spontaneous process is governed by the conservancy of energy (the First Law), and the production of entropy (the Second).

No information on the *nature* of entropy is provided by classical thermodynamics. This branch of the subject shows how *changes* in entropy are related to other quantities and how they may be calculated, but that is all. In other words, it treats entropy as a mathematical function the behaviour of which can be described by mathematical expressions, but that is as far as it goes. The identification of the entropy of a system as a measure of its degree of disorder, or as a measure of its "mixed-up-ness" stems from the statistical branch.

The Third Law of Thermodynamics states that it is impossible by any means to reduce the temperature of a system to absolute zero in a finite number of steps. Its importance in chemistry lies in the fact that it leads to the prediction that as absolute zero is approached the entropy change due to any reaction between crystalline solids approaches zero. The use of this prediction is explained in Chapter 12.

It must be evident to the student that the four so-called laws of thermodynamics differ in nature from most of the scientific laws with which we are familiar. Boyle's Law, for example, is a statement of fact concerned with the change in volume of a given mass of gas when the pressure changes at constant temperature: it can be verified *directly* by a simple experiment. So can most of the others. The four laws of thermodynamics cannot be proved directly—they are *postulates* which we accept because they permit us to make predictions which agree with experiment. We do not, for example, attempt to prove the First Law, but among the many predictions which follow from it is the prediction that the heat exchanged by the system and surroundings when a chemical reaction takes place at constant temperature and pressure is the same whether it proceeds in one stage or in many. This prediction is confirmed by experiment, and therefore serves as support for our acceptance of the First Law from which it derives. The direct proof of the Second Law would also prove impossible, but it can be shown to predict a relationship concerning the variation of the melting point of a solid with respect to pressure. This relationship

$$\frac{dT}{dp} = \frac{T(V_{liq} - V_s)}{L_f}$$

where T is the absolute temperature, L_f the latent heat of fusion and V_s and V_{liq} the molar volumes of solid and liquid, contains only terms which can be determined experimentally. Substitution of known values into the right-hand side of the equation predicts a value of $\frac{dT}{dp}$ which is confirmed precisely by experiment. The equation (it is incidentally called the Clausius–Clapeyron equation) can be derived only from the Second Law. The fact that it proves to be correct is support for our acceptance of the Second Law itself.

The two branches of science to which thermodynamics has contributed most are engineering and chemistry. An idea of its contribution to engineering is simply given. Paramount among the problems of the engineer is the production of power. He has available a quantity of fuel from which, as the result of a chemical or nuclear reaction, energy is available only as heat. His job is to convert as much of this energy as is possible into mechanical work. To do this he feeds the energy into a device called a *heat engine*, which may consist merely of a quantity of air or water contained in a cylinder and closed by a piston. On absorbing the heat the air or water expands, moves the piston against some external resistance and so performs work. The efficiency of the engine is the ratio of the work performed to the heat supplied, and thermodynamics shows how the efficiency of the engine depends on the circumstances under which the engine operates, and indicates the conditions under which maximum efficiency may be attained.

It is more difficult to give a short description of the contribution of thermodynamics to chemistry, simply because it pervades the whole subject so completely. We shall see later how simply it interprets the physical behaviour of solutions and multiphase systems, and how elegantly it establishes a theoretical foundation to many of the laws of physical chemistry discovered empirically in the 19th century. Its application to such matters is the subject of Chapter 15. We shall see how it explains the somewhat anomalous behaviour of solutions of electrolytes and the use it makes of measurements made on electro-chemical cells. These subjects are studied in Chapters 16 and 17. These topics will not be discussed further at this stage. In this chapter we shall describe only what is probably its most important, and certainly its most dramatic contribution.

If the chemist wishes to study any reaction, there are three questions of paramount importance:

(i) the direction in which it is possible for the reaction to proceed under the conditions he wishes to apply;

(ii) the extent to which it will go; and

(iii) the speed with which it will take place.

Thermodynamics provides the answers to the first two questions. The third question is one which at present is the province of another branch of chemistry, that known as Chemical Kinetics. It presents problems which cannot at present be answered by thermodynamics.

We repeat the first two questions rather more formally. The chemist is interested in substances A and B which are capable of interacting according to the equation

$$A \rightleftharpoons B.$$

If presented with a mixture of A and B under particular conditions, he wishes to know whether some of substance A will react to form B, i.e. whether the reaction

$$A \longrightarrow B$$

will proceed, or whether some of substance B will react to form A, so that the reaction will proceed in the direction

$$B \longrightarrow A.$$

The answer to this question is given by the Second Law. It is that the reaction will proceed in that direction which leads to an increase in entropy. If we were content only to study chemical reactions which take place in *isolated* systems, the application of this answer would not be difficult. Let us see what it would mean.

We imagine that we start with reactants A and B in an isolated reaction vessel under specified conditions V, p_1 and T_1. We calculate that the change of a certain quantity of A into B would result in a change in pressure from p_1 to p_2, and in temperature from T_1 to T_2 (since the reaction is isolated there will be no change in V). We then require either to calculate or measure the entropy of the system at V, p_1 and T_1, and that of the system at V, p_2 and T_2, and subtract one from the other; or to determine the change in entropy of the system by some more direct method.[1] We represent the change in entropy by the symbol ΔS. If, as the result of our calculations, we find that

$$\Delta S = S_{V, p_2, T_2} - S_{V, p_1, T_1} > 0 \quad . \quad . \quad . \quad (2,1)$$

the Second Law states that there is no thermodynamic reason why the reaction should not take place in the direction

$$A \longrightarrow B.$$

Unfortunately, in practice we are very rarely interested in carrying out reactions in *isolated* systems. We normally like to conduct reactions under such conditions that the reacting system can exchange energy with the surroundings, so that if necessary we can supply it with heat or keep it cool. We also find it convenient in most cases to carry out the reaction under conditions of constant pressure, and under these conditions the system may expand against the surroundings, so performing work against it, or contract.

Under these circumstances, the Second Law has nothing to say about the change in entropy of the system alone. It states that the reaction is possible if

$$\Delta S_{\text{system}} + \Delta S_{\text{surroundings}} > 0 \quad . \quad . \quad . \quad (2,2)$$

and whereas the calculation of the first quantity on the left-hand side is possible, that of the second, the change in entropy of the surroundings, is extremely difficult if possible at all. Clearly the problem would be much simpler if we were concerned with quantities relating to the system *alone*, so that we could neglect all changes which take place in the surroundings.

For this reason we rarely apply the Second Law direct, but show that by combining the First and Second Laws, other properties exist, which *under particular conditions* show whether or not a reaction can take place. The most important of these other properties is one called the GIBBS FREE ENERGY or just the FREE ENERGY of the system. It is denoted by the symbol G. We shall show in Chapter 9 that any natural spontaneous change *at constant temperature and pressure* leads to a decrease in the free energy of the system, and that no reference to the surroundings need be made. So that instead of the general criterion

$$\Delta S_{\text{system}} + \Delta S_{\text{surroundings}} > 0 \quad . \quad . \quad . \quad (2,2)$$

---

[1] The Third Law of Thermodynamics is required for the actual calculation whichever procedure is chosen.

we prefer to use the particular criterion

$$\Delta G_{T,\,p} < 0 \quad . \quad . \quad . \quad . \quad . \quad . \quad (2,3)$$

where we include the suffixes T, p as a reminder that the criterion applies to systems only under conditions of constant temperature and constant pressure. Because of this restriction criterion (2,3) is of course very much less powerful than criterion (2,2) which is applicable *under all circumstances*, but in practice this restriction is not of great importance, simply because conditions of constant temperature and pressure are precisely those under which, in almost all instances, we wish to study the reaction.

We now come to the important question of how the change in free energy resulting from a chemical reaction may be determined. We shall show that for all changes at constant temperature the change in free energy of the system is related to the absolute temperature, the change in entropy of the system and the change in enthalpy, by the equation

$$\Delta G = \Delta H - T\Delta S \quad . \quad . \quad . \quad . \quad . \quad (2,4)$$

It will be remembered that enthalpy is one of the two properties of a system, the existence of which follows from the First Law. Changes in the enthalpy of a system resulting from a chemical reaction can be calculated from measurements of heats of reaction, the connection between the two being explained in Chapters 4 and 6. The determination of the change in entropy is less simple, and requires both the Second and Third Laws for its appreciation. The method involves the measurement of such quantities as the molar thermal capacities and latent heats of fusion and evaporation of the reactants and reaction products.

We have now answered the first question posed. We can predict the direction which a projected chemical reaction will choose at constant temperature and pressure by calculating from thermal measurements the change in free energy which would result. If our calculations show that the free energy of the system will decrease if the reaction takes place in a particular direction, we can confidently say that there is no thermodynamic reason why it should not take place. If the calculations show that the free energy will increase we can say that, under the particular conditions applied, the reaction will not take place.

We now turn to the second problem posed: how completely will the reaction proceed? Under the conditions applied, will, for example, all of reactant A turn into B, or only a fraction of the material available? If the latter, can we predict what that fraction is likely to be?

It is an experimental fact that whatever conditions are applied no chemical reaction proceeds to completion. Some reactions proceed so far in one direction that for all practical purposes the reaction may be considered complete. The formation of silver chloride when excess hydrochloric acid is added to silver nitrate is an example, so "almost completely" does this reaction occur that it may be used to determine the quantity of silver present in a given solution, but the degree of completeness of the majority of chemical reactions is much less. For example, when nitrogen and hydrogen are heated together to the appropriate temperature to enable the reaction to proceed at an appreciable rate, some ammonia is formed, but the yield is perhaps only 20%; some 80% of the nitrogen and hydrogen remains uncombined no matter how long the reaction is allowed to proceed. We describe this fact by saying that after the reactants have remained in contact for the appropriate time a *state of chemical equilibrium* is established, thereafter the concentrations of the reactants and reaction products remain the same. The actual values of these equilibrium concentrations are determined by the LAW OF MASS ACTION, which for the reaction

$$N_2 + 3H_2 \rightleftharpoons 2NH_3$$

may be written in the form of an equation

$$K = \frac{p^2_{NH_{3eq}}}{p_{N_{2eq}} p^3_{H_{2eq}}}$$

where the symbols $p_{NH_{3eq}}$, $p_{N_{2eq}}$ and $p_{H_{2eq}}$ represent the partial pressures of the three components when equilibrium is reached, and K is called the EQUILIBRIUM CONSTANT.

If the reaction occurs in solution, the equation representing the equilibrium constant contains concentration terms instead of partial pressures. The equilibrium between ethyl alcohol, acetic acid, ethyl acetate and water is an example:

$$C_2H_5OH + CH_3COOH \rightleftharpoons CH_3COO\,C_2H_5 + H_2O$$

$$K = \frac{[CH_3COO\,C_2H_5]_{eq}[H_2O]_{eq}}{[C_2H_5OH]_{eq}[CH_3COOH]_{eq}}$$

where we use the square brackets to indicate the concentration of the reactants.

Similar equations[1] can be written for all homogeneous reactions (that is to say, for all reactions which take place in a single phase), and for all

---

[1] Later we shall see that for complete accuracy we must in fact replace partial pressures by fugacities and concentration terms by activities. The terms fugacities and activities need not, however, be defined at this stage; they may be regarded as partial pressures or molar concentrations "corrected" for non-ideal behaviour.

heterogeneous reactions (those in which the reactants are in different phases), although in the latter case the selection of the terms involved in the equation may not at first sight appear straightforward. *It will be noted that the equilibrium constant is in fact a measure of the completeness with which the reaction will take place: the bigger the value of K, the further will the reaction proceed from left to right.*

In some cases the value of the equilibrium constant for a reaction under particular conditions can be determined directly, sometimes by allowing the reactants to reach equilibrium and by direct analysis of the individual equilibrium concentrations,[1] and sometimes by determining the velocity constants of forward and reverse reactions, but usually such direct measurements are difficult to obtain, particularly over the whole range of temperature and pressure for which the information is required. Usually it is necessary to determine the equilibrium constant of a reaction, and so the degree with which it proceeds, by thermodynamic methods. For reactions at constant temperature and pressure the solution again concerns the free energy change. The decrease in free energy $-\Delta G$ occasioned by the conversion of one mole of reactant A at concentration[2] C_A into reaction product B at concentration C_B at temperature T is given by the equation

$$-\Delta G = RT \log_e K - RT \log_e \frac{C_B}{C_A} \qquad . \quad . \quad . \quad (2,5)$$

where R is the universal gas constant. This particular equation was first derived by van't Hoff and is called the REACTION ISOTHERM. From what has gone before it is clear that it permits the evaluation of the equilibrium constant of a reaction from purely thermal measurements carried out on the substances concerned.

The value of the equilibrium constant for a chemical reaction always depends on the temperature, and sometimes on other factors such as the pressure. Thermodynamics not only permits the calculation of the equilibrium constant under particular conditions but also shows how, when this value is known, the value under any other circumstances can be calculated with ease. This means that it is possible to determine the conditions under which the value of the equilibrium constant is the highest possible; these conditions are of course, those under which the maximum yield may be obtained.[3]

---

[1] See, for example, Taylor and Crist, *J. Am. Chem. Soc.*, 1941, **63**, 1377, in the case of the reaction

$$H_1 + I_2 \rightleftharpoons 2HI.$$

[2] See footnote, page 23.

[3] The student will often find that a particular reaction is carried out in industry under conditions which are *not* those under which the maximum yield is obtained. This is because factors other than thermodynamic may come into play. For example, the

In the preliminary survey given above we have been concerned mainly with such thermodynamic properties as enthalpy, entropy and free energy. It would be wrong, however, in this discussion to omit mention of an intensive property known as the CHEMICAL POTENTIAL. This quantity is of particular use when discussing the physical and chemical behaviour of systems which contain more than one chemical species, or systems which consist of more than one phase. It is a quantity which refers not to the system as a whole but to its individual components, so that we refer not to the chemical potential of the system but to the chemical potential of a component thereof. It is related to the internal energy, enthalpy and free energy of the system as a whole, but the equations connecting it with these quantities will not be given at this stage.

In Chapter 11, when this quantity is first formally introduced, four principles which we shall call the *First, Second, Third* and *Fourth Statements of Chemical Potentials* will be established. The first states that THE CHEMICAL POTENTIAL OF A PARTICULAR COMPONENT PRESENT IN MORE THAN ONE PHASE IN AN EQUILIBRIUM SYSTEM IS THE SAME IN EACH PHASE. The second refers to the diffusion of a component from one part of the system to another and states that DIFFUSION OCCURS FROM THAT PORTION OF THE SYSTEM IN WHICH THE COMPONENT CONCERNED HAS THE HIGHER CHEMICAL POTENTIAL TO THAT IN WHICH IT HAS THE LOWER. The third relates to a spontaneous chemical reaction, and states that A CHEMICAL REACTION WILL PROCEED ONLY IF THE SUM OF THE CHEMICAL POTENTIALS OF THE REACTING SPECIES IS GREATER THAN THE SUM OF THE CHEMICAL POTENTIALS OF THE SPECIES PRODUCED. The fourth is concerned with chemical equilibrium and states that AT EQUILIBRIUM THE SUMS OF THE CHEMICAL POTENTIALS OF THE REACTING SPECIES ON BOTH SIDES OF THE CHEMICAL EQUATION ARE EQUAL.

These statements prove to be the origin from which stem most of the laws governing physical and chemical change. For example, the Law of Mass Action derives from the Fourth Statement, and the Reaction Isotherm from the Third, and Chapter 15 which describes the physical behaviour of solutions and multi-phase systems might be called an essay on the application of the First.

We have now introduced the four laws of thermodynamics, and have indicated how they may be applied to answer some of the questions that

---

reaction between nitrogen and hydrogen to form ammonia is usually carried out in industry at about 450° C, whereas thermodynamics shows that the equilibrium constant would be much greater at temperatures *lower* than this. The point is that at lower temperatures, the *rate* of reaction is so small that equilibrium would take too long to establish. The temperature actually chosen is a compromise between the requirements of thermodynamics which favour a low temperature, and those of chemical kinetics which favour a high one.

the chemist may ask. Much of this book is spent in showing in detail how the results we have discussed have been achieved.

In the ground that we have covered we have implied that quantities such as the change in free energy of a system resulting from a chemical reaction are calculated from thermal measurements such as heats of reaction, thermal capacities and latent heats. In fact, they are very often today determined not from thermal measurements but by statistical means. The branch of the subject which is concerned with such methods is known as Statistical Thermodynamics; it is studied in Chapters 13 and 14. The two branches of the main subject, classical and statistical thermodynamics differ completely in their approach. Classical thermodynamics identifies any particular equilibrium state of that portion of matter called the system by large-scale measurements such as temperature, pressure and volume; measurements which are made either on the system as a whole, or on some more convenient amount of the substances concerned. Neither the measurement of these quantities nor the thermodynamic theory to which they are applied is concerned with the *nature* of the substances involved. In fact, no reference in the development of classical thermodynamics to the atomic or molecular theories of matter need be made.

Statistical thermodynamics is quite different. It accepts the atomic and molecular theories of matter, and bases its calculations on them. Whereas classical thermodynamics utilises large-scale measurements, statistical thermodynamics studies and makes measurements on the individual particles comprising the system, and calculates from their behaviour the properties of the system as a whole. We illustrate this approach in the following way:

Let us consider a quantity of gas existing in some equilibrium state. The individual molecules continually exchange energy as the result of intermolecular collisions, and the energy of each individual molecule changes from time to time. If, however, the gas approaches ideal behaviour so that intermolecular attractions are negligible, the energy of the system as a whole can be considered simply as the sum of the energies of the individual molecules at any instant. Some molecules will be associated with large quantities of energy and some with small, but however the total energy is distributed among the individual particles we can say that at any instant some molecules possess energy ε_0, some ε_1, some ε_2 and so on. In fact, if we know the different quantities of energy that it is possible for any one molecule to possess, we can say that at some particular instant

n_0 molecules possess energy ε_0

n_1 molecules possess energy ε_1

n_2 molecules possess energy ε_2

$\cdot$ $\qquad\qquad$ $\cdot$

$\cdot$ $\qquad\qquad$ $\cdot$

$\cdot$ $\qquad\qquad$ $\cdot$

n_i molecules possess energy ε_i

$\cdot$ $\qquad\qquad$ $\cdot$

$\cdot$ $\qquad\qquad$ $\cdot$

The internal energy of the system as a whole will be given by the equation

$$U = n_0\varepsilon_0 + n_1\varepsilon_1 + \dots n_i\varepsilon_i \dots \quad \dots \quad \dots \quad (2,6)$$

or more concisely by the equation

$$U = \sum_i n_i\varepsilon_i \quad \dots \quad \dots \quad (2,7)$$

The various energy levels accessible to a molecule (or rather, the differences between the various accessible levels) are predicted by Quantum Theory or determined by spectrographic measurements, and the various values $n_0, n_1, \dots n_i \dots$, the so-called population numbers of each energy level can be calculated without difficulty. It follows that the internal energy of the system can be calculated.[1]

We have already said that statistical thermodynamics identifies the entropy of a system with its degree of disorder, its "mixed-up-ness". We must now attempt to show how this is done. Let us suppose that we maintain for a long period some system such as a quantity of gas under such conditions that its pressure, temperature, density, internal energy, entropy and so on remain the same, and suppose that we are able to take at intervals a series of photo-micrographs from which the behaviour of each molecule in the system may be assessed. We should find that although the thermodynamic properties of the system remain the same, the molecular patterns revealed by the photographs are all quite different because the molecules will have moved from one position to another, and the distribution of energy between them will have changed. In other words, to each thermodynamic state identified by "large-scale" properties such as temperature, pressure, internal energy and entropy there corresponds a number of different *micro-states* identifiable only by subjecting the system to microscopic examination. The *number of micro-states* in which a system in a particular thermodynamic state may be found proves to be the most important quantity in statistical thermodynamics. It is given the symbol W, and is called the thermodynamic probability. We shall show in Chapter 13 that when an isolated system changes spontaneously from one equilibrium state to another its W value increases.

---

[1] In fact, the value of the internal energy so calculated is not an *absolute* one, it is the difference between the absolute value and the value of the internal energy at absolute zero, a quantity we shall denote by the expression

$$U - E_0^0.$$

We have, however, already said that a spontaneous change in an isolated system leads to an increase in its entropy, so that it would appear reasonable to suppose that the two quantities entropy and thermodynamic probability are closely related. We shall, in fact, show that they are related by the equation

$$S = k \log_e W$$

where k is a constant.

If the W value of a system is small, so that its constituent particles are able to assume relatively few spacial configurations, the *degree of order* within the system is relatively high. If, on the other hand, the W value is high, so that the particles are able to assume many spacial configurations, the degree of order is small. Since increase in entropy is equivalent to an increase in W value we can identify an increase in entropy with an increase in internal disorder of the system concerned.

We have attempted in this chapter to explain the nature of thermodynamics, and to indicate some of its many applications to chemistry. We summarise the most important points that have been made:

1. Thermodynamics is primarily concerned with the quantities of energy and entropy associated with any physical or chemical process, and is founded on two disciplines called respectively classical and statistical thermodynamics.
2. Classical thermodynamics derives from four postulates which are called the Four Laws of Thermodynamics. They are accepted because they permit predictions to be made which are verified by experiment.
3. The first three laws identify certain properties of a system, the Zeroth Law temperature, the First Law internal energy and enthalpy, the Second Law entropy. The nature of another property, the free energy, is identified by combining the First and Second Laws. These properties refer to the system as a whole. For the study of systems containing more than one chemical species or of systems consisting of more than one phase, use is made of a quantity called the Chemical Potential. This quantity is one which refers not to the system as a whole but to the individual chemical species comprising it.
4. The changes in energy and entropy involved in a chemical reaction can be calculated either by classical or statistical methods. The former make use of thermal measurements such as heats of reaction, molar thermal capacities and latent heats, and the latter require the determination of the various energy levels accessible to the molecules concerned, and these can be predicted by Quantum Theory or determined by spectrographic means.

PART II
CLASSICAL THERMODYNAMICS

CHAPTER 3

THE ZEROTH LAW OF THERMODYNAMICS: TEMPERATURE, AND THE ESTABLISHMENT OF A TEMPERATURE SCALE

It is an everyday experience that if we touch two bodies, one may feel hotter than the other. If two such bodies are placed in contact this difference gradually becomes less perceptible, and eventually no difference can be detected by any means. We describe this final state by saying that the two bodies are in *thermal equilibrium.*

Further, it is an experimental fact that if two bodies are found to be in thermal equilibrium with a third, they will be found to be in thermal equilibrium with each other. There is no *a priori* reason why this should be so, but the fact remains, and the principle proves to be so important that in recent years it has become the custom to call it THE ZEROTH LAW OF THERMODYNAMICS.

The reason for the importance of the Zeroth Law is that it leads to the establishment of temperature as a property of the system.

Two or more bodies in thermal equilibrium may be said to possess some property in common. This property we call TEMPERATURE. So we define temperature as that property of a system which determines whether or not it is in thermal equilibrium with another with which it is in contact, when two such bodies are in thermal equilibrium their temperatures must be the same, and when two such bodies are not in thermal equilibrium their temperatures must be different.

Having established the meaning of temperature we must proceed to devise a scale by which temperature may be denoted. This simply requires a convention whereby one temperature is represented by a number, a second temperature by a different number and so on.

When the energy content of a body increases as the result of heat being absorbed by the body or work being done on it the random motion of the constituent particles increases. As a result there takes place either a change in physical state such as fusion or evaporation or the change of condition which we call rise in temperature, or both. If we were able to measure the velocity of the individual particles we should find that although

31

the temperature of the body may remain constant the rate of movement of any one particle changes continuously as the result of collisions with others, and that at any one time the rate of movement differs from particle to particle. Any attempted correlation therefore between the temperature of the body as a whole and the random movement of any individual particle is impossible, and it follows that the concept of the temperature of an individual particle is meaningless. What we are pleased to call temperature is a property of the body as a whole, or a part of it which though it may be quite small is still large enough to contain many particles.

Although the temperature of a system is indeed dependent on the thermal energy of the particles comprising it, the latter cannot be directly measured and so used to provide some method whereby the temperature of two or more bodies may be compared. Some other properties of a system are, however, dependent on the random movement of the particles composing it. The volume of a system confined at constant pressure increases when the random movement of the particles increases; so does the pressure of a system confined at constant volume. The electrical resistance of a solid conductor changes, so does the vapour pressure of a liquid. These properties can be observed and changes in them directly measured, so that we may devise methods whereby changes in temperature may be indirectly measured as a result of observable changes in other properties.

The establishment of a temperature scale is merely a matter of convenience whereby we assign a particular number to the temperature of a body in one particular state and a different number to the temperature of the body in a different state. Since temperature is the property of a system which determines whether or not it is in thermal equilibrium with other systems placed in contact with it, the number assigned to the temperature of a body in a particular state can be assigned also to the temperature of all other bodies in thermal equilibrium with it.

We may therefore select some system such as a quantity of liquid, the volume of which will increase on rise in temperature, devise some formula by which we relate the volume of the liquid to the numbers assigned to different temperatures (i.e. devise a temperature scale) and we have a thermometer. The temperature of a second body is then measured by placing it in contact with our thermometer and waiting until thermal equilibrium has been established, the volume that the liquid assumes is then observed and the temperature is read from the scale devised.

The earliest thermometers which were of much practical use were of this type. We have now to show in detail how such a device may be used to establish a temperature scale.

A quantity of a suitable liquid such as mercury or alcohol is enclosed in a glass bulb from which issues a capillary tube of regular bore sealed at the top. Sufficient liquid is used to ensure that at the lowest temperature in which we are interested, the bulb is full and some liquid is contained in the capillary tube. As the temperature of the liquid increases it expands and the length of the column of liquid in the capillary increases. The variation in the length of the column of liquid in the capillary is used to establish a temperature scale.

In order to do this we must choose a formula by which we connect the length of liquid column measured with the series of numerical values denoting the temperatures of a system in different states. There is no reason why any one formula should be preferred to another, so we choose a simple linear equation of the form

$$t = aL + b$$

where t is the number by which we represent the temperature at which the length of liquid column is L and a and b are constants. We must now choose two standard fixed temperatures, assign arbitrary numbers to them, determine the value of L in both instances and so calculate the values of a and b. We shall then have an equation from which we can calculate the temperature corresponding to any observed value of L.

The two standard fixed temperatures which in the past were selected for this purpose are the ice-point and the steam-point. The ICE-POINT is the temperature at which ice is in equilibrium with water at one atmosphere pressure. On the Celsius scale the figure 0 is assigned to this temperature. If at this temperature the length of liquid column is L_0, we may write

$$0 = aL_0 + b$$

The STEAM-POINT is the temperature at which steam is in equilibrium with pure water at one atmosphere pressure. On the Celsius scale this temperature is denoted by the figure 100. If at this temperature the length of the liquid column is L_{100}, we may write

$$100 = aL_{100} + b$$

Solving the two equations we obtain

$$a = \frac{100}{L_{100} - L_0}$$

and

$$b = -\frac{100L_0}{L_{100} - L_0}$$

We may substitute these values into our general equation to obtain

$$t = \frac{100(L - L_0)}{L_{100} - L_0} \qquad \cdots \cdots \cdots \quad (3,1)$$

If in a particular thermometer $L_0 = 10$ cm and $L_{100} = 100$ cm, the temperature on our scale at which the length of liquid column is 55 cm. will be 50°.

One point must be emphasised. It would be wrong to say that the scale described by equation (3,1) is based on the fact that the liquid selected expands uniformly with rise in temperature, i.e. is based on the fact that $\Delta L/\Delta t$ is a constant. This fact is true, but it is so only because we decided by choosing originally the equation

$$t = aL + b$$

to design a scale on which equal increments of length of liquid column represent equal differences in temperature. Had we chosen some other equation, for example,

$$t = a \log_e L + b$$

and assigned the values 0 and 100 to the ice- and steam-points, we should have produced a different scale, and one in principle no better or no worse than the one actually chosen, but one in which equal increments of length of liquid column would not represent equal differences in temperature.

The scale based on equation (3,1) describing the change in temperature in terms of the change in volume of a quantity of mercury contained in a glass bulb is called the MERCURY-IN-GLASS scale. It serves adequately between the melting point of mercury and the temperature at which excessive vaporisation introduces obvious errors. Using the mercury-in-glass scale we cannot of course assign values to any temperature below or above this range.

There are other properties of a system which may be used just as conveniently to establish a scale of temperature. The most important are described below.

The Constant Volume Gas Thermometric Scale

If a gas is confined at constant volume the pressure it exerts increases with rise in temperature. A temperature scale can therefore be constructed based on this increase in pressure.

Proceeding as before, a linear equation is chosen to describe temperature in terms of pressure, i.e.

$$t = ap + b$$

The same values are assigned to the ice- and steam-points, and so a general equation is obtained in terms of centigrade degrees

$$t = \frac{100(p - p_0)}{p_{100} - p_0} \qquad \cdots \qquad \cdots \qquad (3,2)$$

In choosing this method we establish our scale by saying that equal increments of pressure will represent equal increases in temperature.

The Constant Pressure Gas Thermometric Scale

The scale of temperature established by this method depends on the fact that if the pressure under which a gas is confined be kept constant the volume occupied increases with rise in temperature. We therefore define temperature in terms of volume by the equation

$$t = aV + b$$

proceed as before and obtain the general equation

$$t = \frac{100(V - V_0)}{V_{100} - V_0} \quad . \quad . \quad . \quad . \quad . \quad . \quad (3,3)$$

The Platinum Resistance Thermometric Scale

The electrical resistance of a strip of metal held under tension varies with temperature, so this property also may be used to establish a temperature scale. Platinum is particularly suitable for this purpose because of its high melting point and resistance to corrosion. The general equation in terms of centigrade degrees is

$$t = \frac{100(R - R_0)}{R_{100} - R_0} \quad . \quad . \quad . \quad . \quad . \quad (3,4)$$

In choosing scales making use of this property and defining temperature in terms of electrical resistance by the equation $t = aR + b$ we define equal increments in temperature in terms of equal increments in electrical resistance.

The Selection of an Absolute Scale

In the preceding paragraphs we have derived four equations whereby different observations can be used to establish a scale of temperature. In them all, equal increments of temperature are defined by equal increments in the property selected as our thermometric measure, i.e. in them all, temperature is defined by the linear equation

$$t = a\phi + b$$

where ϕ represents some property changing from one temperature to another.

The four scales so established coincide at the ice- and steam-points because we chose to make them do so, but we have no reason to suppose that they will coincide at any other temperature. That is to say, we may find that a system is at 80° on the mercury-in-glass scale and that a second system is at 80° on the platinum-resistance scale, but if the two systems be placed in thermal contact it may well be found that they are not in thermal equilibrium, that is, that they are not at the same temperature. It so happens that over a large temperature range the divergence between the various scales is relatively small; for example, there is less than 1% divergence in the worst case between the ice- and steam-points. This is admirable evidence for the dependence of these properties on the random movement of the system concerned, and shows how closely such apparently diverse quantities as changes in electrical resistance and changes in volume with temperature are related. The fact remains, however, that the various scales differ, if only slightly, and it is obviously desirable to establish one scale which we have reason to believe to be absolute.

This decision might be thought to be of little practical importance because of the relatively close agreement found between the scales discussed, but the fact that a very real problem exists is brought sharply into focus in the following instance.

The vapour pressure of a liquid varies with temperature, and in view of the considerations advanced above we should be perfectly justified in using this property as the basis for a thermometric scale. Selecting as before a linear relationship $t = ap + b$ we obtain the general equation

$$t = \frac{100(p - p_0)}{p_{100} - p_0} \qquad \qquad (3,5)$$

In the second column of the table given below we show the values of the vapour pressure of water in atmospheres at the ice- and steam-points, and at four intermediate temperatures A to D. The third column shows the values of temperatures A to D calculated from the general equation given above, and the fourth column the values of these temperatures on the constant volume gas scale.

TABLE 3,I

Temperatures in degrees centigrade	Vapour pressure of water in atmospheres	Temperatures calculated on the vapour pressure scale	Temperatures measured on the constant volume gas scale
0	0·00604	0	0
A	0·0231	1·7	20
B	0·0728	7·7	40
C	0·1967	19·2	60
D	0·4680	46·8	80
100	1·0000	100	100

The difference between the figures in the third and fourth columns require no comment. It is clear that we must seek for some justification to choose one property rather than another on which to establish a basic standard of temperature.

Historically, the choice was made because of the following considerations. On the one hand, the various liquid-in-bulb scales based on the variation of volume with temperature show considerable discrepancies when one liquid rather than another is concerned. Also such scales can only operate over a relatively small temperature range, between the temperature at which the liquid melts and that at which excessive vaporisation leads to obvious inaccuracies. The various resistance thermometers, too, show marked disagreement when one metal rather than another is

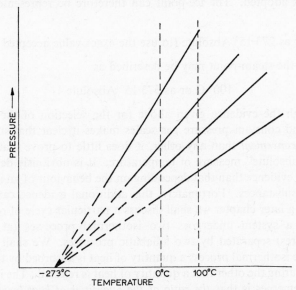

Figure 3,1. The determination of the Absolute Zero.

used; but on the other hand, the so-called "permanent" gases, hydrogen, oxygen, nitrogen, carbon dioxide and methane when used both in constant volume and in constant pressure thermometers establish temperature scales which are almost identical over a large temperature range. Furthermore, the lower the pressure of gas in the thermometer the closer are the identities of the scales established when different gases are used. The constant volume and constant pressure gas scales were therefore adopted. A most useful consequence of these gas thermometric scales is that they lead directlyt o the idea of an absolute zero of temperature. If the pressures exerted by different quantities of various gases at constant volume are measured over a large temperature range, the temperatures being measured on the constant volume gas scale, the readings when plotted

C

naturally fall along straight lines as shown by the full lines in Figure 3,1. If these lines are extrapolated to zero pressure they are found to converge striking the zero pressure axis at about −273° C. The temperature at which a gas exerts no pressure is considered to be the absolute zero of temperature. At this temperature a gas is supposed to have no translational energy. In the same way, if the volumes occupied by various gases at constant pressure are measured at a series of temperatures measured on a constant pressure gas thermometer, the volume–temperature lines cut the zero-volume axis at precisely the same value.

Following this, a temperature scale called the ABSOLUTE CENTIGRADE SCALE was adopted. The ice-point can therefore be represented in two ways, as:

0° C or as 273·15° Absolute (to use the exact value accepted today).

Similarly, the steam-point may be described as

100° C or as 373·15° Absolute

Although the evidence given above for the selection of the constant volume and constant pressure gas scales makes it clear that such scales are more *convenient* than any other, it does little to prove that we have here an "absolute" measure of temperature. It is obviously desirable to seek other evidence than that depending on the behaviour of an individual group of substances. Fortunately, this additional evidence can be provided. In a later chapter we shall discuss a particular cycle of operations in which a system undergoes two isothermal processes (at different temperatures) separated by two adiabatic processes. We shall find that during one isothermal process a quantity of heat is absorbed by the system and that during the other that a quantity of heat is rejected. The important fact that emerges is that *the ratio of the quantities of heat involved is independent of the nature of the system concerned and depends solely on the ratio of the two temperatures at which the isothermal processes take place.* By making use of this cycle we are able to establish a scale of temperature independent of the individual characteristics of any group of substances: we can confidently accept, therefore, that it offers an absolute measure of temperature. It is called THE THERMODYNAMIC SCALE OF TEMPERATURE. Temperatures recorded on the Thermodynamic Scale are usually called KELVIN temperatures and denoted by the term ° K if based on the centigrade system employing 100 degrees between the ice- and steam-points. It so happens that the scale is identical with the so-called Absolute Scale based on the ideal gas constant volume or constant pressure thermometers.

The Absolute Zero of Temperature: the Giauque Convention

The acceptance of the ice-point as $0°$ C is universal, but the determination of the absolute zero relative to this temperature is a matter of experiment, and up to 1939 various experimental results ranging from $-273 \cdot 14°$ C to $-273 \cdot 19°$ C had been recorded in the literature. It was pointed out by Giauque[1] that any inaccuracy, although relatively unimportant at $0°$ C becomes considerable at temperatures very close to absolute zero. If, for example, a particular phenomena is observed precisely $273°$ below the ice-point, the temperature on the thermodynamic scale may be taken as $0 \cdot 14°$ K, $0 \cdot 19°$ K or any intermediate value. The resultant ambiguity is sufficiently important to prevent accurate correlation between the temperature and any other quantities measured.

He therefore suggested that the problem be solved by arbitrarily defining the ice-point as $273 \cdot 15°$ K relative to the absolute zero. Whether or not this produces a degree which is slightly different from that defined by a difference of 100 degrees between ice- and steam-points is of little account, because we are gaining accuracy at the lower end of the scale where extreme accuracy is required, at the cost only of slight possible inaccuracy at higher temperatures where they are of relatively little importance.

It is customary to consider $25°$ C as a particular *standard* temperature at which to calculate and record values of the thermodynamic properties of pure substances. On the Giauque convention $25°$ C is $298 \cdot 15°$ K.

[1] Giauque, *Nature*, 1939, **143**, 623.

CHAPTER 4

THE FIRST LAW OF THERMODYNAMICS

The First Law of Thermodynamics states that ENERGY CAN NEITHER BE CREATED NOR DESTROYED. It implies that during a physical or chemical process in which energy is changed from one form into another within the system, or in which energy is exchanged between the system and the surroundings it must always be possible to *account* for all the energy concerned.

The mathematical formulation of the First Law depends on the circumstances under which it is applied. It so happens that in chemistry we are rarely interested in the changes which take place in the kinetic or gravitational potential energy of a system, we shall therefore consider first, changes which take place in the energy content of *static* systems, and only at a later stage consider systems in which changes in kinetic and gravitational potential energy need to be taken into account.

The first system to be considered is an isolated system in which material may change from one form into another, that is to say, a chemical reaction may take place, but the total quantity of material present remains constant, and which neither absorbs energy (either as heat or work) from the surroundings, nor transfers energy to them.

An example of such a system is the contents of a bomb calorimeter which has been completely lagged. Whatever be the reaction occurring within the calorimeter, the system can do no work on the surroundings, because no expansion is possible, neither can it pass heat to them. Since these are the only two ways in which energy can be given out by a system or absorbed by it, whatever be the result of the reaction within the system the total energy of the system must remain the same.

The second type of system to be considered is of wider application, and is of particular use to the chemist because it typifies the conditions under which chemical reactions are usually carried out. The system is a closed static one, but one which is free to do work on the surroundings and to absorb heat from or transfer heat to them. Such a system may be represented by an assembly of chemicals contained in a beaker. During any reaction which may occur, the system may expand against the atmosphere (so doing work on it) or absorb heat from it.

We will imagine that during some such change the system changes from an initial state which we designate state 1 to some final state designated state 2, and that during this change the system absorbs a quantity of heat equal to q and performs a quantity of work on the surroundings equal to w.

We define a quantity ΔU by the equation

$$\Delta U = q - w \quad . \quad . \quad . \quad . \quad . \quad . \quad (4,1)$$

and describe this quantity as the *increase in internal energy of the system*.

The conventions used in this definition should be carefully noted: the symbol q is always used in thermodynamics to denote the heat absorbed *by* the system, the symbol w is used to denote work performed *by* the system on the surroundings and the symbol ΔU to denote the *increase* in internal energy. All three symbols can have positive or negative values.

We note, too, that there is nothing in the definition of ΔU which implies that it represents some change in some thermodynamic property of the system: the fact that it does is the subject of the next section.

The Proof that Internal Energy is a Property of a System

In Chapter 1 the word *property* was described as any quantity which helps to define the state in which the system is found. The most important characteristic of a property is that when a system is in a particular state each property shall have a particular value dependent purely on the state and independent of the past history of the system. It is now necessary to show that internal energy is such a quantity.

Consider a system in a particular state represented by point A on the diagram in Figure 4,1. The changes we are about to describe could be represented on a diagram of which the ordinates are any two properties chosen. We have chosen the pressure and volume merely because of their familiarity.

We now suppose that the system is taken through a series of operations 1, 2, 3, 4, 5, eventually arriving back at the original state A. We place no restriction whatsoever on the processes involved. During each operation we will suppose a quantity of heat, q_1, q_2, q_3, . . ., to be absorbed by the system, and a quantity of work, w_1, w_2, w_3, . . ., performed by it.

We apply equation (4,1) to each operation in turn

$$(\Delta U)_1 = q_1 - w_1$$
$$(\Delta U)_2 = q_2 - w_2$$
$$(\Delta U)_3 = q_3 - w_3$$

. . .

. . .

. . .

and describe the complete cycle of operations by the equation

$$\Delta U = \Sigma q_1 - \Sigma w_1 \qquad \ldots \ldots \ldots \quad (4,2)$$

where
$$\Delta U = (\Delta U)_1 + (\Delta U)_2 + (\Delta U)_3 \ldots$$

and
$$\Sigma q_1 = q_1 + q_2 + q_3 \ldots$$

and
$$\Sigma w_1 = w_1 + w_2 + w_3 \ldots$$

The right-hand side of equation (4,2) must have a value which is less than, equal to, or greater than zero. Let us consider first whether its value

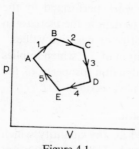

Figure 4,1.

can be less than zero: in this case, since energy can neither be created nor destroyed, the system must possess less energy after the cycle of operations is complete than it did before. Since there is no reason why we should not repeat the cycle of operations an infinite number of times, it is clear that we must eventually reach the position where the energy of the system in state A is zero and after that less than zero. Since this is impossible, $\Sigma q_1 - \Sigma w_1$ cannot be less than zero.

If $\Sigma q_1 - \Sigma w_1$ is greater than zero the system must increase its energy after each cycle of operations. After the cycle of operations has been repeated an infinite number of times the system at state A must possess an infinite quantity of energy. Since this is obviously absurd $\Sigma q_1 - \Sigma w_1$ cannot be greater than zero. It follows that $\Sigma q_1 - \Sigma w_1$ must equal zero, and hence from equation (4,2), $\Delta U = 0$.

It is clear therefore that after any complete cycle of operations the internal energy of a system remains the same: in other words the internal energy of a system has a definite value corresponding to any particular state; and is therefore a property of the system.

A consequence of the above argument is that when a system changes from state 1 to state 2 the change in internal energy ΔU, i.e. $U_2 - U_1$ must be independent of the path taken and dependent only on the two states 1 and 2 concerned.

The internal energy of a system is plainly an *extensive* property. We shall use the same symbol U to denote the internal energy of the system as a whole, and to denote the internal energy of one mole of any pure substance under investigation. The context in which the system is described will ensure that no confusion results. We note that for a finite change the equation

$$\Delta U = q - w \qquad \ldots \ldots \ldots \quad (4,1)$$

can be written

$$U_2 - U_1 = q - w \quad . \quad . \quad . \quad . \quad . \quad . \quad (4,3)$$

We shall find it convenient often to consider infinitesimal changes; for such, the appropriate equation is

$$q = dU + w \quad . \quad . \quad . \quad . \quad . \quad . \quad (4,4)$$

The reason why we do not designate an infinitesimal quantity of heat absorbed by the symbol dq and an infinitesimal quantity of work performed by the symbol dw is explained in the next section.

Finally, we point out that since in an *isolated* process q and w are necessarily zero, a change in an isolated system is described by the equations

or
$$\left. \begin{array}{c} \Delta U = 0 \\ dU = 0 \end{array} \right\} \quad . \quad . \quad . \quad . \quad . \quad . \quad (4,5)$$

Irreversible and Reversible Changes

Consider a system changing from state 1 to state 2. The change may take place along many different paths (an example of this was discussed in Chapter 1). We select any two paths, designate them Path I and Path II, and utilising the usual notation write

$$\Delta U = U_2 - U_1 = q_\mathrm{I} - w_\mathrm{I}$$
$$\Delta U = U_2 - U_1 = q_\mathrm{II} - w_\mathrm{II}$$

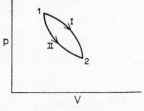

Figure 4,2.

Since U_1 and U_2 have definite values determined by the initial and final states of the system, these equations demand a particular value of $q - w$, but do not require a particular value of q or w individually. That is to say, q_I may differ from q_II, and w_I from w_II, all that is required is that $q_\mathrm{I} - w_\mathrm{I} = q_\mathrm{II} - w_\mathrm{II}$.

This implies that theoretically there is no limit to the number of paths that a system may take during a change of state, and that along each of these paths the system may absorb a different quantity of heat and perform a different quantity of work. This is true even though some restriction may be placed on the paths chosen. We might for example impose some special condition such that the temperature of the system remains constant, but we should still find that different quantities of heat could be absorbed and different quantities of work performed.[1]

[1] It is for this reason that although in an infinitesimal process we denote the change in internal energy by the symbol dU, we do not describe the infinitesimal quantities of heat absorbed and work performed by the symbols dq and dw.
The expression dX is the accepted mathematical symbol for a complete differential.

Since during a particular change of state, the quantity of work performed depends on the path chosen, it is obviously of interest to inquire into the nature of that particular path along which more work is performed by the system than along any other (the importance of this to Chemical Thermodynamics is not at present obvious; it is, however, plainly of fundamental importance to the engineer, because one of his most important problems is so to arrange natural processes that they perform as great a quantity of work as possible).

We can do this best by considering a simple expansion process. Consider a system consisting of a quantity of a gas of ideal behaviour occupying an initial volume $V_1 = 2$ litres at a pressure $p_1 = 10$ atmospheres in a cylinder fitted with a frictionless piston of cross-sectional area a; the surroundings being at a pressure $p' = 1$ atmosphere. We will imagine, for simplicity, that the system and surroundings are initially at the same temperature, and that the temperature of both remains constant throughout the subsequent operations.

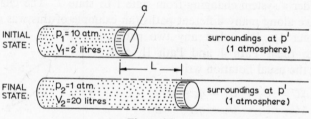

Figure 4,3.

When the piston is allowed to move, the gas will expand until its pressure falls from $p_1 = 10$ atmospheres to $p_2 = 1$ atmosphere, the final volume being $V_2 = 20$ litres.

The work performed by the gas against the surroundings equals the force overcome ($p' \times a$) multiplied by the distance L through which the piston has moved, i.e.

$$w = p' \times a \times L.$$

But $$a \times L = V_2 - V_1$$

It implies that the quantity $\int_1^2 dX$ has a definite value equal to $X_2 - X_1$. The expressions $\int_1^2 dq$ and $\int_1^2 dw$ would imply that a definite quantity of work is performed when the system changes from state 1 to state 2 *by any* path. We have just seen that this is by no means the case. We therefore prefer to use the symbols q and w to denote the quantities of heat absorbed and work performed irrespective of whether the change is infinitesimal or finite.

and inserting the numerical values given we see that the work performed equals 18 litre-atmospheres.

Before going farther we will attempt to reverse the process, that is to compress the gas from a state

$$p_2 = 1 \text{ atmosphere, } V_2 = 20 \text{ litres}$$

to a state $p_1 = 10 \text{ atmospheres, } V_1 = 2 \text{ litres.}$

To do this we require to perform on the gas a quantity of work: in Chapter 5 we shall show how this quantity of work may be calculated: it is in fact equal to $p_1 V_1 \log_e \dfrac{V_2}{V_1}$ litre-atmospheres. Inserting our numerical values we find it to be 46·06 litre-atmospheres.

During the expansion process we obtained from the gas a quantity of work equal to 18 litre-atmospheres; to reverse the process we require 46 litre-atmospheres. In order to do this we need therefore to supply some 28 litre-atmospheres of work from some outside source. The supply of this quantity of work by an outside agency will leave the surroundings changed; they will have lost a quantity of energy available for work.

We describe the type of change such as that of the original expansion process as an IRREVERSIBLE process, the word irreversible meaning in thermodynamics, *not that the process cannot be reversed, but that it cannot be reversed without leaving the surroundings permanently changed.*

We now inquire how it is possible to carry out the original expansion process in such a way that more work can be got from it than that which we actually obtained. Since the work performed by the expanding gas equals the force overcome multiplied by the distance travelled by the piston, it is obvious that we can obtain more work by increasing the force overcome. It is, in fact, clear that the *maximum* work will be obtained from the expansion process if the opposing pressure p' is, at all stages in the expansion, only infinitesimally less than the pressure exerted by the expanding gas.

If we select some moment during the expansion process in which the pressure exerted by the gas equals p, the maximum external force which can be overcome equals $(p - dp) \times a$, and if during this moment the piston moves a distance dL, the work performed equals

$$(p - dp) \times a \times dL$$

i.e. $(p - dp)dV$, or pdV, since the product $dpdV$ may be neglected.

The maximum work obtainable during the complete expansion from $p_1 V_1$ to $p_2 V_2$ is therefore

$$\int_{V_1}^{V_2} pdV$$

In the example cited above, the evaluation of this integral (see Chapter 5) comes to precisely 46·06 litre-atmospheres.

We have now succeeded in carrying out the expansion process in such a way that we have obtained much more work than we did previously, in fact, *just that quantity of work required to reverse the process*. The expansion process carried out in such a way that the maximum quantity of work is obtained is therefore called a REVERSIBLE PROCESS, because it can be reversed without leaving a permanent change in the surroundings.

We have so far examined only an expansion process. The principle of reversibility and irreversibility applies to other types of change. If the chemicals zinc, zinc sulphate, copper sulphate (both in solution) and copper are arranged in the form of a Daniell Cell

$$Zn \mid ZnSO_{4(aq)} \mid\mid CuSO_{4(aq)} \mid Cu$$

and the zinc and copper electrodes are joined by a conductor, two changes occur: one, the chemical reaction

$$Zn + CuSO_4 \longrightarrow ZnSO_4 + Cu$$

and the second, the establishment of a potential difference between the two electrodes (this potential difference is normally called the electromotive force of the cell) and the transfer of a quantity of electricity from one electrode to the other. The system is capable of performing work on the surroundings if it can be made to transfer a quantity of electricity up a potential gradient in some external circuit. The electrical work performed equals the product of the quantity of electricity transferred dQ and the potential difference $\mathbf{E}'$ across which the transference takes place. Clearly the quantity of work which is performed as the result of the transfer of a definite quantity of electricity depends on the potential $\mathbf{E}'$ in the external circuit, and represents the maximum possible quantity of work when the potential difference concerned is only infinitesimally smaller than the electromotive force of the cell.

We have so far established that an expansion process takes place reversibly when no finite difference exists between the pressure of the system and the pressure of the surroundings, and that a process involving the movement of a quantity of electricity takes place reversibly when no finite difference exists between the e.m.f. of the cell and the potential difference through which the charge is transferred. It is logical to extend the argument to a process involving the flow of heat from one system to another and to describe the flow as reversible if the temperature difference between them is infinitesimal, and irreversible if the temperature difference between them is finite.

It will have been observed that in the examples we have considered, a process takes place reversibly *only if the system concerned and the surroundings are in equilibrium and remain so throughout the process.*

We now accept the premise that what we have shown to be true in the particular examples discussed is true for reversible processes of all kinds, and postulate:

That in a reversible process—

1. All parts of the system itself are in complete thermodynamic equilibrium: that is to say, all parts of the system are in thermal equilibrium (i.e. at the same temperature), that all parts are in mechanical equilibrium (i.e. at the same pressure), and that all parts of the system are in chemical equilibrium, and remain so throughout.

2. That if the system and surroundings are free to exchange energy in any form, they must remain in complete equilibrium with each other throughout the process. Thus, if the system and surroundings are free to exchange energy in the form of heat, that they remain in thermal equilibrium, that if free to exchange energy in the form of mechanical work, that the pressure exerted by the system must equal that of the surroundings throughout the process, and that analogous conditions apply when energy is transferred as electrical or as any other form of work.

Under certain circumstances, some of the conditions we have postulated become redundant. If, for example, a system is prevented from exchanging energy with the surroundings in the form of heat, so that any process within the system is adiabatic, the system and surroundings will NOT be in thermal equilibrium, and if a reversible process takes place in a system enclosed in a rigid container, so that it is prevented from performing work on the surroundings, the system and surroundings will NOT be in mechanical equilibrium. Also, the reference to chemical equilibrium is necessary only if a chemical reaction can take place to an appreciable extent in the period under which the system is under observation. We might, for example, be interested in a physical process involving a mixture of water vapour and carbon monoxide at 110° C. The system is not in a state of chemical equilibrium, because this state is reached only after some water vapour and carbon monoxide have reacted to form carbon dioxide and hydrogen, but the reaction is so slow at the temperature concerned that no change in chemical composition would be detected over quite a long period. The system is therefore in a state of *quasi* rather than *true* chemical equilibrium.

A chemical reaction taking place under normal conditions is thermodynamically irreversible. As a result of the reaction, work may or may not be performed on the surroundings. If our previous arguments are sound, it should be possible to devise conditions under which a chemical reaction proceeds in a reversible manner so that the reacting system performs the maximum possible quantity of work. From what we have postulated previously it would appear that such a reacting system must remain in a state of chemical equilibrium throughout. We consider how this might be achieved in a particular case.

When hydrogen and bromine both in the gaseous state react naturally and spontaneously at constant temperature to give hydrogen bromide, no work is performed against the surroundings. This follows from the fact that there is no change in volume, as can be seen from the equation

$$\tfrac{1}{2}H_{2(g)} + \tfrac{1}{2}Br_{2(g)} \longrightarrow HBr_{(g)}$$

We now devise a method whereby this reaction takes place under equilibrium conditions.

When a mixture of hydrogen, bromine and hydrogen bromide reaches equilibrium, the partial pressures of the three reactants are connected with the equilibrium constant by the equation

$$K = \frac{p_{HBr}}{p_{H_2}^{\frac{1}{2}} \times p_{Br_2}^{\frac{1}{2}}}$$

and at $1381°$ K the value of K is 276.

This corresponds to a mixture containing hydrogen bromide at a partial pressure of 1 atmosphere, hydrogen at 3.64×10^{-3} atmospheres, and bromine vapour at 3.64×10^{-3} atmospheres.

We will now calculate the work obtainable when $\tfrac{1}{2}$ mole of hydrogen and $\tfrac{1}{2}$ mole of bromine vapour, both initially at 1 atmosphere pressure, and at $1381°$ K react under equilibrium conditions to give 1 mole of hydrogen bromide at 1 atmosphere pressure and at the same temperature.

If we were to attempt to carry out the reaction under equilibrium conditions we should require a cylinder of hydrogen and one of bromine both at 1 atmosphere pressure and at $1381°$ K, a cylinder in which to receive the hydrogen bromide formed, and a reaction chamber arranged as shown in Figure 4,4.

We now permit the hydrogen and bromine each to expand reversibly and isothermally from a pressure of 1 atmosphere to one of 3.64×10^{-3} atmospheres. At this pressure we permit them to enter the reaction chamber until sufficient hydrogen bromide has been formed to give a partial pressure of 1 atmosphere. Equilibrium conditions have now been established.

We now permit a further $\tfrac{1}{2}$ mole of hydrogen and $\tfrac{1}{2}$ mole of bromine to expand from the cylinders to a partial pressure of $3 \cdot 64 \times 10^{-3}$ atmospheres, regulating the rate of flow so that it corresponds to that of the formation of hydrogen bromide. As the hydrogen bromide is formed it flows into the receiving cylinder at 1 atmosphere pressure. Equilibrium

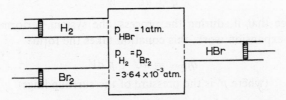

Figure 4,4. The reaction between hydrogen and bromine under equilibrium conditions.

conditions have been maintained throughout. When the reaction proceeds under such conditions, work is performed as the result of the reversible expansion of hydrogen and bromine from 1 atmosphere to $3 \cdot 64 \times 10^{-3}$. The quantity of work performed is given by the expression

$$\int_{p=1\,\text{atm.}}^{p=3\cdot64\,\times\,10^{-3}\,\text{atm.}} p\,dV \qquad + \qquad \int_{p=1\,\text{atm.}}^{p=3\cdot64\,\times\,10^{-3}\,\text{atm.}} p\,dV$$

(Hydrogen)   (Bromine)

In the next chapter we shall find that we can evaluate these integrals, they reduce in both cases to

$$\tfrac{1}{2}RT \log_e \frac{1}{3\cdot64 \times 10^{-3}}$$

and on insertion of the numerical values of R and T provide the answer 15,400 calories.

We see, therefore, that although the direct reaction at 1 atmosphere pressure results in no work being performed, work is performed when the reaction proceeds under equilibrium conditions. The quantity calculated is, in fact, the maximum work obtainable from the reaction at that temperature.

In the above calculation we used the value of the equilibrium constant to calculate the maximum work obtainable from the reaction. The reverse procedure could have been adopted. *Had we found it possible to determine in some other way the value of the maximum work, we could have used it to determine the value of the equilibrium constant.* This is, in fact, one of the most important uses of Chemical Thermodynamics. In later chapters we shall see how quantities relating to a chemical reaction can be calculated from thermal data which permit the calculation of the maximum work related to it, and hence the value of the equilibrium constant.

Further Mathematical Expressions for the First Law

Earlier in this chapter we showed that for an infinitesimal process the First Law can be expressed by the equation

$$q = dU + w \qquad \cdots \qquad (4,4)$$

We now see that if, during the process, the system performs no work other than expansion work, this equation takes the form

$$q_{\text{irrev}} = dU + p'dV \qquad \cdots \qquad (4,5)$$

(where p' is the pressure of the surroundings)

if the process takes place irreversibly,

or the form
$$q_{\text{rev}} = dU + pdV \qquad \cdots \qquad (4,6)$$

(where p is the pressure of the system itself)

for a reversible change.

It follows that a finite reversible process is described by the equation

$$q_{\text{rev}} = \Delta U + \int_{V_1}^{V_2} pdV \qquad \cdots \qquad (4,7)$$

The evaluation of the last term depends on the particular conditions to which the system is subjected. If the pressure exerted by the system changes throughout the process, some equation expressing p in terms of V must be found (this is particularly simple when the system is gaseous, and will be investigated in the next chapter). If, however, the process takes place at constant pressure, we can clearly write

$$q_{\text{rev}} = \Delta U + p(V_2 - V_1) \qquad \cdots \qquad (4,8)$$

If the system undergoes a process in which work other than expansion work is carried out, the First Law equation assumes other forms. The most important case is that in which a reaction takes place in a chemical cell at constant pressure, so that both expansion work and electrical work is performed. If the process takes place reversibly to an infinitesimal degree, the work performed by the system is described by the equation

$$w = pdV + \mathbf{E}dQ \qquad \cdots \qquad (4,9)$$

where $\mathbf{E}$ is the e.m.f. of the cell and dQ is the charge transferred. In this case the First Law equation takes the form

$$q_{\text{rev}} = dU + pdV + \mathbf{E}dQ \qquad \cdots \qquad (4,10)$$

We shall consider such equations only when we come to consider the special systems to which they apply.

The Relationship between the Change in Internal Energy of a Chemical System and the Heat of Reaction at Constant Volume

If a chemical reaction

$$a\mathrm{A} + b\mathrm{B} \longrightarrow c\mathrm{C} + d\mathrm{D}$$

takes place at constant volume, so that a moles of A and b moles of B at temperature T form c moles of C and d moles of D at the same temperature, the heat absorbed[1] is called THE HEAT OF REACTION AT CONSTANT VOLUME. Under the conditions described no expansion work is done, so that for those processes in which no work other than expansion work is possible, the First Law equation reduces to the form

$$q_v = \Delta U \quad . \quad . \quad . \quad . \quad . \quad . \quad (4,11)$$

It is evident therefore that ΔU the increase in internal energy of the system equals the heat of reaction at constant volume.

The Relationship between the Molar Internal Energy of a Pure Substance and its Molar Thermal Capacity at Constant Volume

The molar thermal capacity of a pure substance is defined by the equation

$$C = \frac{q}{dT} \quad . \quad . \quad . \quad . \quad . \quad . \quad (4,12)$$

where q is the infinitesimal quantity of heat required to raise the temperature of one mole of the substance by an amount dT. The quantities q and C depend on the conditions under which the rise in temperature is achieved. If the volume is kept constant no work is done on the surroundings, but if the substance is free to expand some energy will be required to perform work against the surroundings, so that the quantity of heat required to achieve a particular rise in temperature will be so much the greater. The definition of the molar thermal capacity C given in (4,12) is therefore inexact, because the conditions under which it is meant to apply have not been stated. We therefore choose two quantities which are precise and meaningful, the first, the molar thermal capacity of a pure substance at constant volume, defined by the equation

$$C_v = \frac{q_v}{dT} \quad . \quad . \quad . \quad . \quad . \quad . \quad (4,13)$$

and the second, the molar thermal capacity at constant pressure defined by the equation

$$C_p = \frac{q_p}{dT} \quad . \quad . \quad . \quad . \quad . \quad . \quad (4,14)$$

---

[1] The convention adopted is discussed in Chapter 6.

The absorption of a quantity of heat q_v at constant volume by one mole of substance results in an increase in molar internal energy given by the equation

$$q_v = dU$$

It follows that

$$C_v = \left(\frac{\partial U}{\partial T}\right)_v \quad . \quad . \quad . \quad . \quad . \quad . \quad (4,15)$$

Enthalpy and its Relationship to Heats of Reaction and Molar Thermal Capacities at Constant Pressure

The simplicity of the relationships between internal energy, heats of reaction at constant volume and molar thermal capacities at constant volume, prompts us to search for another thermodynamic quantity which will bear the same relationship to heats of reaction and molar thermal capacities at constant pressure. The usefulness of such a quantity is immediately apparent, because it is precisely under the conditions of constant pressure that the majority of chemical reactions take place. Such a quantity is called the ENTHALPY[1] of the system, and is defined by the equation

$$H = U + pV \quad . \quad . \quad . \quad . \quad . \quad . \quad (4,16)$$

Implicit in this definition is of course the condition that the product pV must be expressed in the same units as U.[2]

Since the internal energy, pressure and volume are properties of a system, and are represented by definite values dependent solely upon the state in which the system is found, the enthalpy, being merely an arithmetic combination of them, must also have a definite value, and is therefore a thermodynamic property of the system.

Differentiating equation (4,16) we obtain

$$dH = dU + pdV + Vdp.$$

We now find it convenient to express the work term in the First Law equation

$$q = dU + w \quad . \quad . \quad . \quad . \quad . \quad . \quad (4,4)$$

as the sum of two terms, the pdV work and a term w' comprising all forms of work performed by the system other than pdV work, i.e.

$$q = dU + pdV + w'$$

---

[1] This quantity is referred to in some texts as the HEAT CONTENT or TOTAL HEAT. The use of the word Heat in this context is contrary to the convention used in this book (see Chapter 1), and such terms will therefore not be used.

[2] 1 litre-atmosphere = $101 \cdot 32$ joules = $24 \cdot 23$ calories.

Substituting for $dU + pdV$ in the expression for dH we obtain

$$dH = q - w' + Vdp \quad . \quad . \quad . \quad . \quad . \quad (4,17)$$

This is a perfectly general relationship which applies to *all* infinitesimal processes. It may, in fact, be regarded as a mathematical formulation of the First Law analogous to equation (4,4).

If we now consider processes in which *no work other than pdV work is performed*, so that the w' term vanishes, and if we further restrict our conditions by considering only processes at *constant pressure*, we may write

$$dH = q_p \quad . \quad . \quad . \quad . \quad . \quad . \quad . \quad (4,18)$$

or for a finite change of state

$$\Delta H = q_p \quad . \quad . \quad . \quad . \quad . \quad . \quad (4,19)$$

If a chemical reaction

$$a\text{A} + b\text{B} \longrightarrow c\text{C} + d\text{D}$$

takes place at constant pressure, so that a moles of A and b moles of B at temperature T form c moles of C and d moles of D at the same temperature, the heat absorbed is called THE HEAT OF REACTION AT CONSTANT PRESSURE.

From equation (4,19) it is evident that the increase in enthalpy during such a reaction equals this heat of reaction. During an exothermic reaction at constant temperature the enthalpy decreases; during an endothermic reaction it increases.

We have already defined the molar thermal capacity at constant pressure of a pure substance by the equation

$$C_p = \frac{q_p}{dT} \quad . \quad . \quad . \quad . \quad . \quad . \quad (4,14)$$

where q_p is the infinitesimal quantity of heat required to raise the temperature of one mole of the substance by an amount dT. It follows from equation (4,18) that

$$C_p = \left(\frac{\partial H}{\partial T}\right)_p \quad . \quad . \quad . \quad . \quad . \quad (4,20)$$

where H is the molar enthalpy of the substance.

The Difference in Molar Thermal Capacities of a Pure Substance

From equations (4,15) and (4,20) we obtain

$$C_p - C_v = \left(\frac{\partial H}{\partial T}\right)_p - \left(\frac{\partial U}{\partial T}\right)_v$$

but

$$H = U + pV,$$

therefore
$$\left(\frac{\partial H}{\partial T}\right)_p = \left(\frac{\partial U}{\partial T}\right)_p + p\left(\frac{\partial V}{\partial T}\right)_p.$$

So that
$$C_p - C_v = \left(\frac{\partial U}{\partial T}\right)_p + p\left(\frac{\partial V}{\partial T}\right)_p - \left(\frac{\partial U}{\partial T}\right)_v.$$

Since the molar internal energy is a property of the system it may be expressed as a function of any two other properties. We may therefore write
$$U = f(V, T)$$

where V is its molar volume,

so that
$$dU = \left(\frac{\partial U}{\partial V}\right)_T dV + \left(\frac{\partial U}{\partial T}\right)_v dT$$

and
$$\left(\frac{\partial U}{\partial T}\right)_p = \left(\frac{\partial U}{\partial V}\right)_T\left(\frac{\partial V}{\partial T}\right)_p + \left(\frac{\partial U}{\partial T}\right)_v$$

Hence
$$C_p - C_v = \left\{p + \left(\frac{\partial U}{\partial V}\right)_T\right\}\left(\frac{\partial V}{\partial T}\right)_p \quad . \quad . \quad . \quad . \quad (4,21)$$

Alternative forms of this equation will be derived in due course.

The Mathematical Formulation of the First Law Applicable to Flow Systems

So far we have considered only static systems, the kinetic and gravitational energies of which do not change during the operations to which the system is subjected. The total energy of a *moving* system is composed of the kinetic energy, the gravitational potential energy and the internal energy
$$E = E_k + E_p + U \quad . \quad . \quad . \quad . \quad . \quad (4,22)$$

In the cases so far discussed, changes in E_k and E_p have been zero, and we have considered only changes in U. Such treatment is obviously satisfactory when considering a physical or chemical change in a beaker or sealed reaction vessel. Large-scale industrial processes involve, however, the *flow* of reactants through a reaction chamber. In such cases it may be necessary to take into account changes in E_k and E_p as well as in U. The work term in the First Law will also be complicated by this change because we must now include the work done in transporting the system through the reaction chamber.

The First Law equation (as applied to static systems)
$$q = \Delta U + w$$

will no longer describe such a change. We must substitute for it the equation
$$q = \Delta E + \Sigma w \quad . \quad . \quad . \quad . \quad . \quad (4,23)$$

where ΔE includes changes in E_k, E_p and U, and Σw is the sum of all types of work performed.

We will consider only the simplest case, in which a single liquid or gas flows steadily through some reaction chamber in which changes occur in E_k, E_p, U, molar volume and velocity of movement, and in which heat can be absorbed and work performed by the system on some form of piston or paddle-wheel. Figure 4,5 shows a reaction chamber through which fluid is passing at a steady rate.

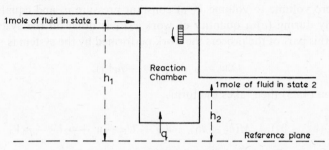

Figure 4,5.

We will consider the changes that occur during the period of time taken for one mole of material of molecular weight M to pass through the reaction chamber, and allow during that time a quantity of heat q to be absorbed and a quantity of shaft work w to be performed. We will assume that when flowing through the inlet pipe the fluid has the following properties and characteristics:

Internal energy, U_1;
Enthalpy, H_1;
Pressure, p_1;
Molar volume, V_1;
Velocity, ϑ_1; and
Location, h_1, above some static reference plane.

In the reaction chamber these properties change and on entry into the outlet pipe assume values U_2, H_2, p_2, V_2, ϑ_2 and location h_2 above the reference plane.

The change[1] in kinetic energy is given by the equation

$$\Delta E_k = \frac{M}{2}(\vartheta_2^2 - \vartheta_1^2)$$

[1] Implicit in these equations is the condition that all energy terms are expressed in the same units as U.

the change in gravitational potential energy by the equation

$$\Delta E_p = M(h_2 - h_1)$$

while
$$\Delta U = U_2 - U_1.$$

Σw includes (a) the shaft work w (expressed in calories), (b) the work done by the system in ejecting fluid occupying volume V_2 at pressure p_2 and (c) the work done on the fluid in forcing into the system material occupying volume V_1 at pressure p_1. Work (b) is equivalent to the expansion of fluid from zero volume to volume V_2 at constant pressure p_2 and equals p_2V_2. Similarly during (c) a quantity of work p_1V_1 is done on the system, so during this part of the process the work performed by the system is $-p_1V_1$.

Hence
$$\Sigma w = w + (p_2V_2 - p_1V_1)$$

Equation (4,23) then takes the form:

$$q = \frac{M}{2}(\vartheta_2^2 - \vartheta_1^2) + M(h_2 - h_1) + U_2 - U_1 + w + p_2V_2 - p_1V_1 \quad (4,24)$$

but since
$$U_2 + p_2V_2 = H_2$$
and
$$U_1 + p_1V_1 = H_1$$

we obtain a final equation

$$q = \frac{M}{2}(\vartheta_2^2 - \vartheta_1^2) + M(h_2 - h_1) + \Delta H + w \quad . \quad . \quad (4,25)$$

Equation (4,25) represents the energy balance sheet for a flow process, and can be applied to any flow process irrespective of its nature. It represents, for example, the energy balance sheet for the flow of steam or gas through a turbine expansion chamber. In such a case, $q = 0$ (the expansion is almost perfectly adiabatic) and the gravitational potential energy term is either zero or negligible. In most cases the kinetic energy term is very small compared to the remaining ones, and neglecting it we arrive at the equation

$$w = -\Delta H = H_1 - H_2$$

so that we see that the shaft work performed by the turbine equals the decrease in enthalpy of the material flowing through it.

Where the reaction chamber is literally a chamber in which a chemical reaction is taking place, no shaft work will be performed. Here the kinetic and gravitational potential energy terms are probably negligible and the equation reduces to

$$q = \Delta H$$

A process of significance to the chemical engineer is that of THROTTLING. This process is illustrated in Figure 4,6.

Figure 4,6 represents a uniform cylinder fitted with two pistons and a plug containing a small orifice. Initially, a quantity of fluid is confined at pressure p_1 and volume V_1 to the left-hand side of the plug. We will imagine that the cylinder is thermally isolated and that the left-hand piston

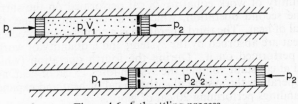

Figure 4,6. A throttling process.

is driven in so that the pressure p_1 is maintained in the left-hand compartment. The fluid is forced through the orifice, so moving the second piston to the right against a pressure p_2. The final state is represented by the lower diagram. In this particular case $q = 0$ since the cylinder is thermally isolated, there is no shaft work, and the kinetic and potential energy terms are zero or negligible.

Equation (4,25) reduces to the statement therefore that

$$\Delta H = 0$$

i.e. $$H_1 = H_2$$

A throttling process is therefore one in which the initial enthalpy of the fluid equals the final enthalpy.[1]

A throttling process is of particular interest when applied to gases. An ideal gas experiences no fall in temperature when passed through a throttling valve; but in the case of a real gas either a rise or fall in temperature is achieved. This fact is known as the *Joule–Thomson* or *Joule–Kelvin Effect*. It is of importance when applied to the liquefaction of gases.

EXERCISES 4

4,1. A system capable of performing no work other than expansion work undergoes a chemical change adiabatically

(a) at constant volume;
(b) at constant pressure.

---

[1] Note: Throttling is *not* a process at constant enthalpy. A throttling process is necessarily irreversible and the system passes through a succession of non-equilibrium states in which our knowledge of the system is inexact. The only knowledge of which we can be certain is that which applies to the system in its initial state and that which applies to the system in its final state.

What can be said about the changes in internal energy and enthalpy in each case?

4,2. It is reported that a particular pure substance incapable of undergoing chemical change and of performing work other than that of expansion is taken through a series of five operations, finally arriving at the same pressure, temperature and volume that it possessed initially. During the first operation a quantity of heat equal to 20 cal is absorbed and a quantity of work equal to 28 cal performed on the surroundings. During the second operation, which is at constant volume, the system loses 10 cal of heat. The third operation is a compression process in which 5 cal of heat are absorbed by the system, and a quantity of work equal to 10 cal is performed on it. During the fourth operation (which is one performed at constant volume) the system loses 15 cal of heat, and during the final operation the system absorbs 26 cal of heat and expands against the surroundings performing 20 cal of work.

Can you say whether this report is possible or not?

What effect would it have on your answer if you were told that at one stage of the cycle the substance is capable of undergoing a chemical reaction of the type $2A \longrightarrow A_2$?

4,3. Calculate the work done on the surroundings when 5 gm of water are evaporated at 100° C and 1 atmosphere pressure. The density of water vapour is $5 \cdot 98 \times 10^{-4}$ gm cm^{-3} under these conditions. The latent heat of evaporation of water at constant pressure is 540 cal gm^{-1}. What is the change in internal energy of the system?

CHAPTER 5

THE APPLICATION OF THE FIRST LAW TO GASES

The relationships derived in the last chapter apply to all substances, but the ease with which some of the quantities concerned may be evaluated depends on the complexity of the system. The evaluation of some of these quantities is usually very much simpler when the system concerned is gaseous rather than liquid, solid or heterogeneous, for two reasons. The first is that a gaseous system can always be represented by an equation of state in which one property such as temperature, pressure or volume is expressed very *simply* in terms of others. As long as the gas is studied at moderately low pressures and at temperatures well above its critical temperature, it approaches ideal behaviour and its pressure, volume and temperature are connected by the equation

$$pV = nRT \qquad \ldots \qquad \ldots \qquad (5,1)$$

Even if it is not ideal it can generally be represented fairly accurately by the van der Waals equation

$$\left(p + \frac{an^2}{V^2}\right)(V - nb) = nRT \qquad \ldots \qquad (5,2)$$

or by an equation such as that due to Berthelot or Dieterici.

These simple relationships mean that some expressions derived in the last chapter; for example, the expression for the work done by a system when permitted to expand reversibly, can be easily evaluated when applied to a gaseous process.

The second reason why thermodynamic equations are often simplified when applied to gases is due to the fact that the internal energy and enthalpy of a gas approaching ideal behaviour are independent of the volume occupied or the pressure to which it is subjected, and are dependent only on its temperature, i.e.

$$\left.\begin{array}{ll} \left(\dfrac{\partial U}{\partial V}\right)_T = 0 & \qquad \left(\dfrac{\partial H}{\partial V}\right)_T = 0 \\[2mm] \left(\dfrac{\partial U}{\partial p}\right)_T = 0 & \qquad \left(\dfrac{\partial H}{\partial p}\right)_T = 0 \end{array}\right\} \qquad \ldots \qquad (5,3)$$

The physical basis of these equations was established by Joule, who showed that if a gas is allowed to expand into a vacuum in a thermally isolated vessel no change in temperature results.

Since in this process both q and w are zero, the change in internal energy must also be zero. Now U can be expressed as a function of T and V, so that

$$dU = \left(\frac{\partial U}{\partial T}\right)_v dT + \left(\frac{\partial U}{\partial V}\right)_T dV \quad . \quad . \quad . \quad . \quad (5,4)$$

Since in the above experiment $dU = 0$, $dT = 0$, but $dV \neq 0$, it must follow that

$$\left(\frac{\partial U}{\partial V}\right)_T = 0.$$

By considering U as a function of T and p, the relationship

$\left(\dfrac{\partial U}{\partial p}\right)_T = 0$ can be established in the same way.

Since in the case of an ideal gas, $pV = nRT$, the expression

$$H = U + pV$$

can be written

$$H = U + nRT \quad . \quad . \quad . \quad . \quad . \quad (5,5)$$

It follows that H is a function only of U and T, so that

$$\left(\frac{\partial H}{\partial V}\right)_T = 0 \quad \text{and} \quad \left(\frac{\partial H}{\partial p}\right)_T = 0.$$

The establishment of equations (5,3) does not, however, depend solely on Joule's experimental evidence. They can be derived theoretically from the Second Law, and this treatment will be given in a later chapter. We shall find then, that if a substance can be described by the equation

$$pV = nRT$$

equations (5,3) follow. *They are, in fact, equivalent criteria for an ideal gas.*

In the following treatment we shall obtain thermodynamic equations for gases of ideal behaviour, and where necessary show how these equations must be complicated in order to cover gases under conditions in which their behaviour is far from ideal.

The Relationship between the Molar Thermal Capacities of an Ideal Gas

Equations (4,15) and (4,20) apply to all substances

$$C_v = \left(\frac{\partial U}{\partial T}\right)_v \qquad \ldots \ldots \ldots \quad (4,15)$$

$$C_p = \left(\frac{\partial H}{\partial T}\right)_p \qquad \ldots \ldots \ldots \quad (4,20)$$

In the special case of the ideal gas, U and H are functions of T only, and the partial derivative with respect to T is the same as the total derivative. We may therefore write

$$C_v = \frac{dU}{dT} \qquad \ldots \ldots \ldots \quad (5,6)$$

and

$$C_p = \frac{dH}{dT} \qquad \ldots \ldots \ldots \quad (5,7)$$

Since for one mole of ideal gas, $pV = RT$, $\frac{d(pV)}{dT} = R$, and since H is defined by the equation

$$H = U + pV, \frac{dH}{dT} = \frac{dU}{dT} + \frac{d(pV)}{dT}$$

so that

$$C_p = C_v + R \qquad \ldots \ldots \ldots \quad (5,8)$$

This result can also be obtained directly from the general equation (4,21)

$$C_p - C_v = \left\{p + \left(\frac{\partial U}{\partial V}\right)_T\right\}\left(\frac{\partial V}{\partial T}\right)_p \quad \ldots \quad (4,21)$$

since

$$\left(\frac{\partial U}{\partial V}\right)_T = 0 \quad \text{and} \quad \left(\frac{\partial V}{\partial T}\right)_p = \frac{R}{p}.$$

We have seen that for an infinitesimal process in which the only work done is expansion work

$$q = dU + pdV$$

and

$$q = dH - Vdp.$$

It follows that such a process applied to one mole of ideal gas can be described by the equations

$$q = C_v dT + pdV \qquad \ldots \ldots \ldots \quad (5,9)$$

and

$$q = C_p dT - Vdp \qquad \ldots \ldots \ldots \quad (5,10)$$

The Ratio of Molar Thermal Capacities

The molar thermal capacities of a substance of molecular weight M and its specific heats are connected by the equations

$$C_v = Mc_v$$

and $$C_p = Mc_p.$$

The quantity γ may therefore be defined either by the equation

$$\gamma = \frac{C_p}{C_v} \quad \cdot \quad \cdot \quad \cdot \quad \cdot \quad \cdot \quad \cdot \quad \cdot \quad (5,11)$$

or $$\gamma = \frac{c_p}{c_v} \quad \cdot \quad \cdot \quad \cdot \quad \cdot \quad \cdot \quad \cdot \quad (5,12)$$

The values of the principal molar thermal capacities and γ depend on the *atomicity* of the gas, that is the number of atoms in the molecule. Although classical thermodynamics succeeds in deriving relationships between such quantities as C_v, C_p and γ and other observable properties, it does not succeed in calculating their actual values. This is because classical thermodynamics is neither concerned with nor dependent on the *nature* of matter, and its findings are independent of the Atomic Theory or of such concepts as molecules.

As we shall see in Chapter 14, Statistical Thermodynamics permits the calculation of the actual values of these quantities. In a monatomic gas the vibrational energy is zero, rotational energies do not come into play (the reason for which will be demonstrated in Chapter 14), and therefore (except at such high temperatures at which electronic excitation becomes appreciable) the only form of energy which is temperature dependent is its translational energy, which for one mole of gas of molecular weight M equals $\frac{1}{2}M\bar{C}^2$, where $\bar{C}$ is the root mean square velocity of the atoms. We may therefore write

$$U = \tfrac{1}{2}M\bar{C}^2 + E_0^0$$

where E_0^0 represents any remaining forms of energy which contribute to the internal energy but which are not temperature dependent.

The Kinetic Theory of Gases shows that for one mole of ideal gas

$$pV = \tfrac{1}{3}M\bar{C}^2,$$

but since $pV = RT$, we may write

$$U = \tfrac{3}{2}RT + E_0^0.$$

Hence $$C_v = \frac{dU}{dT} = \tfrac{3}{2}R = 2\cdot98 \text{ cal deg}^{-1} \text{ mole}^{-1}$$

$$C_p = C_v + R = \tfrac{5}{2}R = 4\cdot97 \text{ cal deg}^{-1} \text{ mole}^{-1}$$

and $$\gamma = \frac{C_p}{C_v} = 1\cdot667.$$

The experimental values of C_v, C_p and γ for monatomic gases at room temperature correspond closely to these values. The values of C_v, C_p and γ for diatomic and polyatomic gases can only be calculated by statistical thermodynamics because rotational and vibrational energies must be taken into account in addition to translational energy. Such calculations will not be done at this stage. It is sufficient to say that, in general, the values of C_v and C_p increase with atomicity, but that the value of γ decreases. The values of C_v, C_p and γ for a diatomic gas are theoretically 4·97, 6·96 and 1·40 respectively. For a triatomic gas γ is close to 1·31.

Theoretically, there would appear no reason why the values of C_v, C_p and γ for a monatomic gas should be temperature dependent (except for non-ideality of behaviour) until such temperatures are reached at which electronic excitation becomes appreciable, and in fact this is borne out by experiment. In the case of diatomic or polyatomic molecules, variation of these quantities with temperature would be expected. However complicated be the actual behaviour, the molar thermal capacities can be expressed by empirical equations of form

$$C = a + bT + cT^2 \dots$$

Adiabatic Changes of State

Consider n moles of ideal gas expanding adiabatically and reversibly from state 1 described by the properties p_1, V_1, T_1, to state 2 described by the properties p_2, V_2, T_2. For any infinitesimal reversible change

$$q = nC_v dT + pdV$$

and $$q = nC_p dT - Vdp.$$

In the case of an adiabatic change, $q = 0$,

so that $$nC_v dT = -pdV$$

and $$nC_p dT = Vdp.$$

It follows that

$$\gamma = \frac{C_p dT}{C_v dT} = -\frac{V dp}{p dV} = -\frac{\dfrac{dp}{p}}{\dfrac{dV}{V}}$$

and

$$\gamma \frac{dV}{V} = -\frac{dp}{p}.$$

The change from $p_1 V_1$ to $p_2 V_2$ is therefore described by the integral

$$\int_{V_1}^{V_2} \gamma \frac{dV}{V} = -\int_{p_1}^{p_2} \frac{dp}{p}$$

so that

$$-\log_e \frac{p_2}{p_1} = \gamma \log_e \frac{V_2}{V_1} = \log_e \left(\frac{V_2}{V_1}\right)^\gamma$$

if γ is assumed to be independent of temperature. We may therefore write

$$p_1 V_1^\gamma = p_2 V_2^\gamma. \qquad \qquad \cdots \quad (5,13)$$

Since $p_1 = \dfrac{nRT_1}{V_1}$ and $p_2 = \dfrac{nRT_2}{V_2}$

the following equations result

$$T_1 V_1^{\gamma-1} = T_2 V_2^{\gamma-1} \qquad \cdots \quad (5,14)$$

and

$$\frac{T_1^\gamma}{p_1^{\gamma-1}} = \frac{T_2^\gamma}{p_2^{\gamma-1}}. \qquad \cdots \quad (5,15)$$

Since γ is necessarily greater than one, equation (5,14) predicts that the reversible adiabatic expansion of a gas results in a fall in temperature. These equations do not of course hold for an expansion which is not carried out reversibly, i.e. for one which is not completely resisted. For an adiabatic expansion into a vacuum we know from Joule's experiment that the temperature remains constant. For a change which is partially but not completely resisted, expansion will result in a temperature drop which is less than that predicted by equation (5,14). The reason for this can be seen from the First Law equation

$$q = \Delta U + w.$$

Since

$$q = 0$$

$$w = -\Delta U = nC_v(T_1 - T_2),$$

the more completely resisted is the expansion the greater will be the work done and the greater the fall in temperature.

The Maximum Work done by a Gas during Expansion

In Chapter 4 we saw that the maximum work which can be performed by a fluid in expanding reversibly from state 1 to state 2 is given by the integral $\int_{V_1}^{V_2} p\,dV$. Since the pressure of a gas can always be expressed as a simple function of its volume the integral can be evaluated easily.

An Isothermal Change

For n moles of ideal gas

$$p = \frac{nRT}{V},$$

hence
$$w = \int_{V_1}^{V_2} \frac{nRT}{V} dV = nRT \log_e \frac{V_2}{V_1}. \quad . \quad . \quad . \quad . \quad (5,16)$$

If we consider one mole of a gas which obeys the van der Waals equation

$$p = \frac{RT}{V-b} - \frac{a}{V^2}.$$

Hence
$$w = \int_{V_1}^{V_2} \left(\frac{RT}{V-b} - \frac{a}{V^2} \right) dV$$

$$= RT \log_e \left\{ \frac{V_2 - b}{V_1 - b} \right\} - a \left\{ \frac{V_2 - V_1}{V_1 V_2} \right\}. \quad . \quad (5,17)$$

An Adiabatic Change

Since T does not remain constant the method used above cannot be used. We proceed as follows:

Since for an ideal gas $\quad p_1 V_1{}^\gamma = p_2 V_2{}^\gamma = k,$

$$p = \frac{k}{V^\gamma},$$

Hence
$$w = k \int_{V_1}^{V_2} V^{-\gamma} dV = k \left\{ \frac{V_2{}^{1-\gamma} - V_1{}^{1-\gamma}}{1 - \gamma} \right\}.$$

Substituting p_1V_1 or p_2V_2 for k as convenient, we arrive at a series of equations:

$$w = \frac{p_1V_1 - p_2V_2}{\gamma - 1}$$

$$= \frac{p_1V_1}{\gamma - 1}\left\{1 - \left(\frac{V_1}{V_2}\right)^{\gamma-1}\right\}$$

$$= \frac{p_1V_1}{\gamma - 1}\left\{1 - \left(\frac{p_2}{p_1}\right)^{\frac{\gamma-1}{\gamma}}\right\} \quad \ldots \ldots \quad (5,18)$$

$$= \frac{p_2V_2}{\gamma - 1}\left\{\left(\frac{V_2}{V_1}\right)^{\gamma-1} - 1\right\}$$

$$= \frac{p_2V_2}{\gamma - 1}\left\{\left(\frac{p_1}{p_2}\right)^{\frac{\gamma-1}{\gamma}} - 1\right\}.$$

Since $\qquad\qquad p_1V_1 = nRT_1 \quad \text{and} \quad p_2V_2 = nRT_2$

we may derive from the first of these equations the expression

$$w = \frac{nR(T_1 - T_2)}{\gamma - 1},$$

and since $R = C_p - C_v$ and $\gamma = \dfrac{C_p}{C_v}$, we finally obtain the equation

$$w = nC_v(T_1 - T_2), \quad \ldots \ldots \quad (5,19)$$

in which the work done is expressed in terms of the fall in temperature.

A Polytropic Change

Reversible isothermal and adiabatic changes although of great theoretical importance are not very easy to achieve in practice, and an expanding gas very often absorbs some heat from the surroundings, but not enough to keep its temperature constant. Such an expansion is very frequently governed by the equation

$$p_1V_1^{\sigma} = p_2V_2^{\sigma}, \quad \ldots \ldots \quad (5,20)$$

where σ acquires a value intermediate between 1 and γ, and is called a *polytropic* change. The work done during such a process carried out reversibly is given by a group of equations identical with (5,18) except that σ is substituted for γ. Equation (5,19) does not of course apply; the equation which must be used instead is

$$w = \frac{nR(T_1 - T_2)}{\sigma - 1}. \quad \ldots \ldots \quad (5,21)$$

The Heat absorbed by a Gas during Expansion
An Isothermal Change

For an ideal gas $\left(\dfrac{\partial U}{\partial V}\right)_T = 0$

and since $\qquad\qquad q = \Delta U + w \quad$ and $\quad \Delta U = 0$

$$q = w$$

Hence $\qquad\qquad q = nRT \log_e \dfrac{V_2}{V_1}.$ . . . . . . (5,22)

If the gas is not ideal $\left(\dfrac{\partial U}{\partial V}\right)_T$ is not zero, but we can evaluate q as follows:

For any substance

$$dU = \left(\frac{\partial U}{\partial V}\right)_T dV + \left(\frac{\partial U}{\partial T}\right)_v dT.$$

For an isothermal change

$$dT = 0$$

so that $\qquad\qquad dU = \left(\dfrac{\partial U}{\partial V}\right)_T dV.$

With the aid of an equation which forms one of MAXWELL'S RELATIONS which result from the Second Law and which will be discussed in a later chapter, we can deduce the following general relationship:

$$\left(\frac{\partial U}{\partial V}\right)_T = T\left(\frac{\partial p}{\partial T}\right)_v - p.$$

For one mole of a van der Waals gas

$$p = \frac{RT}{V - b} - \frac{a}{V^2}$$

and $\qquad\qquad \left(\dfrac{\partial p}{\partial T}\right)_v = \dfrac{R}{V - b}.$

Therefore $\qquad \left(\dfrac{\partial U}{\partial V}\right)_T = \dfrac{RT}{V - b} - p$

$$= \frac{RT}{V - b} - \frac{RT}{V - b} + \frac{a}{V^2}.$$

Hence for an isothermal expansion of one mole of a van der Waals gas from V_1 to V_2

$$\Delta U = \int_{V_1}^{V_2} \frac{a}{V^2} dV = a\left\{\frac{V_2 - V_1}{V_1 V_2}\right\}.$$

Substituting in the general equation

$$q = \Delta U + w$$

and applying equation (5,17) we obtain

$$q = RT \log_e \left\{ \frac{V_2 - b}{V_1 - b} \right\}. \quad \ldots \ldots \quad (5,23)$$

Comparison of (5,23) with (5,17) shows that the heat absorbed in the isothermal expansion of a van der Waals gas is greater than the work performed on the surroundings by an amount equal to $a \left\{ \dfrac{V_2 - V_1}{V_1 V_2} \right\}$. This quantity of energy represents the "internal work" performed in separating the molecules.

Similar expressions can be derived from other equations of state.

An Adiabatic Expansion

By definition, this is a change in which no heat is absorbed.

A Polytropic Change

Consider the expansion of one mole of ideal gas from p_1, V_1, T_1 to p_2, V_2, T_2.

$$\Delta U = C_v(T_2 - T_1).$$

The most convenient expression for the work performed is equation (5,21)

$$w = \frac{R(T_1 - T_2)}{\sigma - 1},$$

so that

$$q = C_v(T_2 - T_1) + \frac{R(T_1 - T_2)}{\sigma - 1}.$$

Hence

$$q = \frac{(T_1 - T_2)}{\sigma - 1}(C_p - \sigma C_v). \quad \ldots \ldots \quad (5,24)$$

Ideal Gases Involved in Cyclic Operations

It happens to be particularly useful to the development of thermodynamic theory to consider the quantities of heat and work involved when a quantity of ideal gas undergoes a cyclic series of operations. The most important series of operations is one in which all processes involved take place reversibly, and in which the complete cycle consists of two isothermal processes (taking place at different temperatures) separated by two adiabatics. Such a cycle was studied by the French engineer SADI CARNOT early in the 19th century and is usually known by his name. A

Carnot cycle in which one mole of ideal gas is caused to undergo a series of expansions and compressions is illustrated by Figure 5,1.

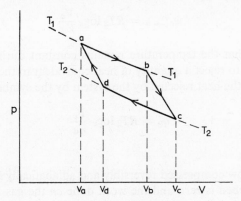

Figure 5,1. A Carnot cycle.

Process $a \longrightarrow b$

We imagine the gas to be initially at temperature T_1 and to occupy volume V_a. Its state is represented therefore by the point a in Figure 5,1. We now permit the gas to absorb a quantity of heat equal to q_1, and to expand reversibly and isothermally to volume V_b. We denote the work performed on the surroundings by the symbol $w_{a \rightarrow b}$. It follows from (5,16) that

$$w_{a \rightarrow b} = RT_1 \log_e \frac{V_b}{V_a}.$$

Since the internal energy of the gas is independent of the volume it occupies, the work performed must equal the heat absorbed, i.e.

$$q_1 = RT_1 \log_e \frac{V_b}{V_a}.$$

Process $b \longrightarrow c$

We now permit the gas to expand reversibly and adiabatically from V_b to V_c, and suppose that during this process the temperature drops from T_1 to T_2. The heat absorbed is zero, but (from (5,19)) the work performed is given by the equation

$$w_{b \rightarrow c} = C_v(T_1 - T_2).$$

Process $c \longrightarrow d$

The gas is now compressed reversibly from V_c to V_d (the actual value of V_d is determined by the requirement that the next stage $d \longrightarrow a$

D

completes the cycle), under such conditions that the temperature T_2 remains constant. The work done *on* the gas $w_{c \to d}$ is given by the equation

$$w_{c \to d} = RT_2 \log_e \frac{V_c}{V_d},$$

and in order that the temperature remains constant during this process the system has to reject a quantity of heat equivalent to the work done on it. We denote the heat rejected by the system by the symbol q_2', and write

$$q_2' = RT_2 \log_e \frac{V_c}{V_d}.$$

Process $d \to a$

The gas is now compressed reversibly and adiabatically from V_d to V_a. The heat absorbed is zero and the work done *on* the gas is given by the equation

$$w_{d \to a} = C_v(T_1 - T_2).$$

By applying equation (5,14) to the two adiabatic processes $b \to c$ and $d \to a$ we see that

$$\frac{T_1}{T_2} = \left(\frac{V_c}{V_b}\right)^{\gamma-1} = \left(\frac{V_d}{V_a}\right)^{\gamma-1}$$

i.e.

$$\frac{V_c}{V_d} = \frac{V_b}{V_a}.$$

It therefore follows that in this particular cycle the ratio of the heat absorbed by the system during one stage to the heat rejected at another is given by the ratio of the temperatures of the system during the stages concerned:

$$\frac{q_1}{q_2'} = \frac{RT_1 \log_e \dfrac{V_b}{V_a}}{RT_2 \log_e \dfrac{V_c}{V_d}} = \frac{T_1}{T_2}. \qquad \qquad \text{. . . .} \quad (5,25)$$

The nett work performed by the system during the complete cycle of operations is obviously

$$w = w_{a \to b} + w_{b \to c} - w_{c \to d} - w_{d \to a},$$

and since we see from above that $w_{b \to c}$ and $w_{d \to a}$ are equal, it follows that

$$w = RT_1 \log_e \frac{V_b}{V_a} - RT_2 \log_e \frac{V_c}{V_d},$$

and that the ratio $\dfrac{w}{q_1}$ is given by the equation

$$\frac{w}{q_1} = \frac{RT_1 \log_e \dfrac{V_b}{V_a} - RT_2 \log_e \dfrac{V_c}{V_d}}{RT_1 \log_e \dfrac{V_b}{V_a}} = \frac{T_1 - T_2}{T_1}. \quad . \quad . \quad (5,26)$$

Use will be made of equations (5,25) and (5,26) in Chapter 7.

A heat engine in its simplest form consists of a quantity of liquid or gas (usually called "the working substance") contained in a cylinder closed by a smooth tightly fitting piston. The function of the engine is for the working substance to absorb energy available only as heat, to expand and cause the piston to move against an external resistance and so perform work. In order that the engine may perform work continuously the working substance has to undergo a series of cyclic operations.

If an engine were designed so as to contain a gas approaching ideal behaviour and to undergo a series of operations such as those detailed above, we see from (5,26) that the nett work performed by the engine in one cycle is always less than the heat absorbed because the temperature at which the heat is absorbed T_1 cannot be infinite, and that at which heat is rejected T_2 cannot be zero.

EXERCISES 5

5,1. Four litres of a gas at 127° C exert a pressure of 75 mm Hg. Calculate the number of moles concerned, assuming the gas to be ideal.

5,2. One mole of ideal gas at 27° C and 10 atmospheres pressure expands isothermally to 1 atmosphere pressure;
  (*a*) reversibly;
  (*b*) against a constant pressure of 1 atmosphere.
Calculate the work done by the gas and the heat absorbed in each case.

5,3. Assuming ideal behaviour, what is the minimum work in ergs required to compress 1 kgm of air consisting of 20% by volume of oxygen and 80% nitrogen from 1 to 200 atmospheres at 0° C.

5,4. A quantity of air initially at 25° C is compressed adiabatically and reversibly from a volume of 10 litres to 1 litre. Assuming ideal behaviour and taking C_v for air at 5 cal deg^{-1} mole^{-1}, calculate the final temperature.

5,5. A fully resisted adiabatic expansion of helium gas results in a fall of temperature from 0° to −230° C. What is the ratio of the initial to the final pressure?

5,6. A gas is found to obey the van der Waals equation for which the constant $a = 1\cdot4 \times 10^{12}$ dyne-cm^4 and $b = 32$ cm^3 per mole. One mole is found to occupy 44·00 litres at 400° K. Calculate the pressure under which it is confined.

5,7. A vessel volume V_1 containing air at pressure p_1 is joined by means of a tap to one of volume V_2 at pressure p_2 and equilibrium conditions attained. The tap is then closed, and the vessel V_2 removed. A vessel of volume V_3 at pressure p_3 is now attached, and the process repeated. A large number of vessels are brought up to the first, one at a time, and the pressure shared as above. The temperature is kept constant throughout. If $V_1 = 2V_2 = 4V_3 = 8V_4 \ldots$, and $p_2 = p_3 = p_4 \ldots = 0$, show that the ultimate pressure attained in the vessel V_1 is

$$p_1 \times \tfrac{2}{3} \times \tfrac{4}{5} \times \tfrac{8}{9} \times \tfrac{16}{17} \ldots$$

5,8. The molecular weight of mercury vapour is 200 and at low pressures its specific heat at constant pressure is 0.025 cal deg^{-1} gm^{-1}. Calculate the ratio of its principal specific heats.

5,9. Calculate the molar thermal capacities of a polyatomic gas for which the ratio of principal specific heats is 1.30.

5,10. In a Diesel engine air is drawn into the cylinder at $27°$ C, and compressed adiabatically from an initial volume V_1 at atmospheric pressure to a final volume V_2, at which stage heavy oil is injected into it. If the spontaneous ignition temperature of air and oil is $480°$ C, calculate the minimum possible value of the compression ratio V_1/V_2, which will ensure that this temperature is reached during the compression stroke.

5,11. Four litres of a diatomic gas at 1 atmosphere pressure and $27°$ C expand reversibly according to the equation $pV^{0.5} =$ constant to a volume of 16 litres. Calculate:

(a) the pressure and temperature in the final state;
(b) the work done by the gas; and
(c) the heat absorbed.

The gas may be assumed to be ideal.

5,12. Calculate the maximum work performed when one mole of an ideal diatomic gas initially at $0°$ C expands from 1 to 10 litres:

(a) isothermally;
(b) adiabatically.

The answers should be given in joules.

5,13. Calculate the power of an engine required to produce 1000 litres of air at 10 atmospheres pressure per hour if the air is taken in at 1 atmosphere. Assume that the compression process is isothermal.

5,14. An airgun consists of a smooth cylinder 1 cm^2 cross-section closed at one end. The bullet is at first held with its base 2 cm from the closed end. Air is pumped into the space between the closed end and the base of the bullet until it is at 60 atmospheres. The pressure in the open portion of the tube and in the surroundings is 1 atmosphere. Neglecting friction, leakage, heat exchange and the kinetic energy of the air, calculate the length of tube which will impart the maximum final velocity to the bullet after it has been released.

5,15. By arbitrarily assigning the value zero to the enthalpy of a certain pure substance in a particular state, it is found that its molar enthalpy may be approximately related to its pressure p and molar volume V by the equation

$$H = 3 \cdot 5pV - 65 \cdot 5$$

where H and the product pV are both in calories. What is the relationship between p, V and the molar internal energy?

The substance is compressed adiabatically and reversibly. It is then cooled at constant pressure until its volume is halved. Finally, it passes through a throttle-valve on the down-side of which it is in its original state. Sketch the cycle on $p - V$, $H - p$ and $U - V$ diagrams identifying the points. Show that the compression process is governed by the equation

$$pV^{1 \cdot 4} = \text{constant.}$$

What is the highest pressure experienced in the cycle if the lowest pressure is 1 atmosphere?

5,16. Show that the molar internal energy of an ideal gas at pressure p and volume V is given by the equation

$$U - E_0^0 = \frac{pV}{\gamma - 1}$$

where E_0^0 is its energy at absolute zero.

5,17. One litre of air at 15° C and at 5 atmospheres pressure is heated to 200° C at constant pressure. It then expands adiabatically until the temperature falls to 100° C, is then cooled at constant volume to 15° C and compressed isothermally to its initial state. Calculate the work done by the gas in one cycle assuming air to behave as an ideal diatomic gas.

5,18. Natural gas flows slowly and steadily from a large subterranean source at a depth of 10,000 metres into evacuated storage tanks at ground level. The gas is found to be at a temperature of about 100° C when it enters the storage tanks. Its molecular weight is found to be 40 and the ratio of its specific heats 1·2.

Assuming that heat losses are negligible during the flow process estimate the temperature of the gas in the subterranean regions. The value of the gravitational constant is 981 cm sec^{-2}.

(Hint: apply equation 4,25.)

CHAPTER 6

THE FIRST LAW AND THE ENERGETICS OF CHEMICAL REACTIONS

In almost all instances a chemical reaction taking place in an adiabatic container leads either to a rise or fall in temperature of the system. We describe those reactions which, when carried out adiabatically, lead to a rise in temperature as EXOTHERMIC, and those which lead to a fall in temperature as ENDOTHERMIC. When an exothermic reaction takes place under such conditions that the temperature of the reaction products is the same as the initial temperature of the reactants, heat is given out by the system to the surroundings, and when an endothermic reaction takes place under the same conditions heat is absorbed by the system.

The quantity of heat given out or absorbed during a chemical reaction depends on the conditions under which the reaction takes place and the quantities of reagents involved. If we denote any reaction by the equation

$$a\mathrm{A} + b\mathrm{B} \ldots \longrightarrow c\mathrm{C} + d\mathrm{D} \ldots$$

the quantity of heat given out or absorbed when a moles of A and b moles of B . . . react to give c moles of C and d moles of D . . . *at the same temperature* is called the HEAT OF REACTION. In fact, this definition is still imprecise. The heat exchanged between the system and the surroundings depends on the conditions under which the reaction proceeds: it will depend on whether or not the system is allowed to expand against the surroundings or not. We take this factor into account by defining two quantities for each reaction: the HEAT OF REACTION AT CONSTANT PRESSURE and the HEAT OF REACTION AT CONSTANT VOLUME. It is unfortunate that two conventions exist regarding the *signs* associated with these quantities. The older convention, which stems from the early days of thermochemistry describes the heat of reaction of an exothermic reaction as positive and that of an endothermic reaction as negative: it denotes a reaction by such an equation as

$$2\mathrm{H}_{2(g)} + \mathrm{O}_{2(g)} \longrightarrow 2\mathrm{H}_2\mathrm{O}_{(\mathrm{liq})} + 136{,}640 \text{ cal.} \quad . \quad . \quad (6,1)$$

This equation means that when two moles of gaseous hydrogen react with one mole of gaseous oxygen to give two moles of liquid water at the same temperature (and at constant pressure), 136,640 cal pass to the surroundings. Recently the opposite convention has found favour, the heat of reaction of an endothermic reaction is associated with a positive sign (because the system absorbs a quantity of heat), and that of an exothermic reaction with a negative sign. This convention happens to be more convenient than the first in thermodynamics, and will for that reason be used in this book.

We now consider the reaction between two moles of hydrogen and one mole of oxygen taking place in a constant volume container. The heat given out when this reaction takes place at 25° C is 134,870 cal. But for any process

$$q = \Delta U + w,$$

and for a process in which no work is performed (in this case, any constant volume process)

$$q_v = \Delta U.$$

It follows that the heat of reaction at constant volume equals the increase in internal energy of the system. We may therefore formally denote the reaction by the expression

$$2H_{2(g)} + O_{2(g)} \longrightarrow H_2O_{(liq)}, \Delta U = -134,870 \text{ cal.} \quad . \quad (6,2)$$

We now consider the same reaction taking place at constant pressure. In Chapter 4 it was shown that the heat absorbed by a system during a constant pressure process in which no work other than expansion work is performed equals the increase in enthalpy. It follows that if we denote the heat of reaction at constant pressure by q_p,

$$q_p = \Delta H.$$

We may therefore make use of the value of the heat of reaction at constant pressure given above and write

$$2H_{2(g)} + O_{2(g)} \longrightarrow H_2O_{(liq)}, \Delta H = -136,640 \text{ cal.} \quad . \quad (6,3)$$

We shall invariably use the convention illustrated by equations (6,2) and (6,3) rather than that illustrated by equation (6,1).

The Measurement of Heats of Reaction

The fact that (using the convention agreed above) we define a heat of reaction as that quantity of heat absorbed by the system when reaction products are formed *at the same temperature* as that of the reactants from which they have come does not require the reaction actually to take place at constant temperature. Consider an endothermic reaction taking place in a constant volume container. We assume that we require to measure its heat of reaction at constant volume at 25° C. Two ways in which it might be done are described below. In the first the reaction vessel and its contents initially at 25° C is efficiently lagged so that the reaction proceeds adiabatically: as a result the temperature falls. At the end of the reaction we determine the quantity of heat which must be supplied to the system to raise its temperature to 25° C (this would be done most efficiently by using an electrical heating coil and calculating the heat supplied in terms of the current passed and voltage applied). In the second method heat is supplied by the coil *throughout the reaction* at just the right rate to maintain the temperature at 25° C. In the second method the reaction takes place at constant temperature, while in the first method it does not; but the quantities of heat supplied in the two methods *prove to be the same*. This is because the quantities of heat equal the change in a thermodynamic property of the system (in this case, the internal energy), and such a change is dependent only on the initial and final states of the system, and is independent of the path by which the process takes place.

The same conclusions apply to an exothermic reaction. A very popular method used to determine a heat of reaction, particularly one which involves a combustion process, is to use a Bomb Calorimeter, of which there are various models on the market, for example, the Berthelot–Mahler, the Griffon–Sutton and that made by Baird and Tatlock. They differ slightly in detail but not in principle.

They all contain:

(a) a metal calorimeter containing water, some stirring device and a thermometer;

(b) an air jacket and outer water jacket to shield the calorimeter from external temperature changes; and

(c) a steel bomb fitted with an oxygen inlet valve, electrical firing leads and a crucible.

Each apparatus is designed to hold a particular mass of water, and the total thermal capacity of the calorimeter and contents is determined by burning in it a given mass of a pure substance of known calorific value. Benzoic acid, which can be purified readily is popularly used. When the test reaction takes place the temperature of the calorimeter and contents rises or falls (the quantities of reactant are so arranged that the change in temperature is only of the order of 1 or 2 degrees), and the heat of reaction is calculated from that quantity of heat which would be required to bring about the change in temperature experienced. For the experimental details of this method and those based on other pieces of apparatus the student is referred to textbooks on Practical Physical Chemistry.

The Connection between Heats of Reaction at Constant Pressure and those at Constant Volume

Since $$H = U + pV,$$

it follows that for a reaction at constant pressure and constant temperature

$$\Delta H_{p,\,T} = \Delta U_{p,\,T} + (p\Delta V)_T. \qquad \ldots \quad (6,4)$$

The quantity $\Delta H_{p,\,T}$ is, of course, the heat of reaction at constant pressure. The quantity $\Delta U_{p,\,T}$ is *not*, however, quite the same as $\Delta U_{v,\,T}$, which is the heat of reaction at constant volume, except for reactions involving only gases approaching ideal behaviour, for which the internal energy is independent of the pressure and volume of the system. It is quite an easy matter to investigate the difference between $\Delta U_{p,\,T}$ and $\Delta U_{v,\,T}$ theoretically or indeed to determine the difference experimentally in the case of a particular chemical reaction, and it proves that except in those cases where the reaction at constant volume leads to the establishment in the constant volume calorimeter of extremely high pressures, the difference is so small as to be without practical significance.

This means that equation (6,4) can be written

$$\Delta H_{p,\,T} \simeq \Delta U_{v,\,T} + (p\Delta V)_T. \qquad \ldots \quad (6,5)$$

If we apply (6,5) to reactions which take place completely in a condensed phase, that is reactions which involve only solids or liquids, the change in volume occasioned by the reaction is likely to be so small that the quantity $p\Delta V$ is negligible and we can write

$$\Delta H_{p,\,T} \simeq \Delta U_{v,\,T}, \qquad \ldots \quad (6,6)$$

which is the same as saying that for such reactions the heat of reaction is the same whether measured at constant volume or at constant pressure.

The same statement is true for those reactions which involve gases but which do not lead to a change in the number of gas molecules present. The reaction

$$C + O_2 \longrightarrow CO_2$$

is an example. The statement is not true, however, for the reaction

$$C_7H_{16(g)} + 11O_2 \longrightarrow 7CO_2 + 8H_2O_{(g)}$$

where for the sake of argument we choose to carry out the reaction at such a temperature that all the components concerned are gases. In the reaction 12 moles of gas react to form 15, so that if the reaction takes place at constant pressure the work performed by the system expanding against the surroundings equals

$$p(V_{15 \text{ moles}} - V_{12 \text{ moles}})_T$$

If we assume that all the gases concerned approximate to ideal behaviour

$$pV_{15 \text{ moles}} = 15RT$$

and $$pV_{12 \text{ moles}} = 12RT,$$

so that the $(p\Delta V)_T$ term in (6,5) equals nRT where n represents the increase in number of gas moles concerned, in this case three. We therefore write

$$\Delta H_{p,\,T} \backsimeq \Delta U_{v,\,T} + nRT. \quad . \quad . \quad . \quad . \quad (6,7)$$

It is pointed out that the value of n depends on the conditions under which the reaction takes place. If the reaction considered takes place at 25° C the heptane and water will both be liquids, so that n assumes the value -4.

Although (6,7) is based on two assumptions, one that $\Delta U_{p,\,T} \backsimeq \Delta U_{v,\,T}$ and the second, that any gases concerned approximate to ideal behaviour, it is accurate enough for most purposes, simply because the inaccuracies introduced are so small compared to ΔH or ΔU that they may be ignored: in most cases they are, in fact, very much smaller than those introduced as the result of experimental error. This is made clear in the following example, in which it is shown that the nRT term itself is so small compared with ΔU that even a 10% error in the former renders the error in the calculation of ΔH negligible:

The heat of combustion at constant volume of naphthalene carried out at 288° K in a bomb calorimeter is $-1,234,600$ cal mole^{-1}. It is required to calculate the increase in enthalpy.

$$C_{10}H_{8(s)} + 12O_{2(g)} \longrightarrow 10CO_{2(g)} + 4H_2O_{(liq)}$$

At this temperature the naphthalene is solid and the water liquid, so that n assumes the value -2.

$$\Delta U = -1,234,600 \text{ cal mole}^{-1}.$$

Hence $$\Delta H = \Delta U - 2RT$$
$$= -1,234,600 - 2 \times 1 \cdot 987 \times 288$$
$$= -1,235,700 \text{ cal mole}^{-1}.$$

This particular example is typical of those for which equation (6,7) is used. Heats of reaction at constant volume can in many cases be carried out in a bomb calorimeter much more accurately than can the corresponding heats of reaction at constant pressure in a constant pressure calorimeter. On the other hand, it is the latter quantity that is more frequently required. Equation (6,7) is used to calculate ΔH from the experimental value of ΔU.

Hess's Law of Heat Summation

The reaction at constant pressure between one gm atom of carbon and one mole of oxygen to form one mole of carbon dioxide can proceed in two ways.

The first consists of the direct process represented by the equation

$$C + O_2 \longrightarrow CO_2, \quad \Delta H_1 = x.$$

The second consists of two stages: during one, only one-half of the available oxygen reacts, so that carbon monoxide is formed:

$$C + \tfrac{1}{2}O_2 \longrightarrow CO, \quad \Delta H_{2(1)} = y,$$

and during the second, the remaining oxygen is used to oxidise the carbon monoxide to carbon dioxide:

$$CO + \tfrac{1}{2}O_2 \longrightarrow CO_2, \quad \Delta H_{2(2)} = z.$$

The initial and final values of the enthalpy of the system depend only on the initial and final states, so that the increase in enthalpy resultant upon the complete reaction is independent of the path by which the change of state proceeds: i.e.

$$\Delta H_1 = \Delta H_{2(1)} + \Delta H_{2(2)} \quad . \quad . \quad . \quad . \quad . \quad (6,8)$$

or
$$x = y + z$$

This conclusion, which we have deduced from the fact that heats of reaction are equal to changes in a particular thermodynamic property of the system, was in fact discovered empirically by G. H. Hess in 1840. It is known as the LAW OF CONSTANT HEAT SUMMATION, and is usually stated in the form *the resultant heat change, at constant pressure or constant volume, in a given chemical reaction is the same whether it takes place in one or in several stages.*

This law is an extremely useful one because it permits the calculation of ΔH or ΔU for reactions for which these quantities cannot be *directly* measured. An example will make this clear. We require to know ΔH for the reaction

$$C + 2H_2 \longrightarrow CH_4 \text{ at } 25° \text{ C.}$$

We cannot determine this quantity directly simply because the reaction will not go. The quantity can, however, be calculated from the heats of combustion at constant pressure of methane, carbon and hydrogen: thus, measurements in a bomb calorimeter at 25° C and the application of equation (6,7) leads to the following values of ΔH:

(i) $CH_4 + 2O_2 \longrightarrow 2H_2O_{(liq)} + CO_2$, $\quad \Delta H_1 = -212,800$ cal

(ii) $C + O_2 \longrightarrow CO_2$, $\qquad\qquad\qquad \Delta H_2 = -94,050$ cal

(iii) $H_2 + \frac{1}{2}O_2 \longrightarrow H_2O_{(liq)}$, $\qquad\quad \Delta H_3 = -68,320$ cal

If we double (iii) add (ii) and subtract[1] (i) we obtain the equation

$$C + 2H_2 \longrightarrow CH_4, \quad \Delta H = 2\Delta H_3 + \Delta H_2 - \Delta H_1 = -17,890 \text{ cal}$$

The quantity $-17,890$ cal is usually called the ENTHALPY OF FORMATION of methane and is given the symbol ΔH_f. The enthalpy of formation of a compound is the increase in enthalpy occasioned by the formation of one mole of the compound from its constituent elements *in their natural state* under the conditions specified.

The enthalpy of formation is a particularly useful quantity for tabulation purposes[2]: usually the values at 25° C being given. If the values of the molar enthalpies of formation for all the reagents concerned are known, the heat of reaction of any given reaction can be calculated with ease. We take as example the reaction

$$NO_2 + SO_2 \longrightarrow NO + SO_3,$$

the molar enthalpies of formation at 25° C for the gases NO_2, SO_2, NO and SO_3 being 8090, $-70,960$, 21,600 and $-94,450$ cal respectively. The enthalpy of reaction equals the sum of the enthalpies of formation of the reaction products less that of the reactants, i.e.

$$\Delta H = -9980 \text{ cal.}$$

Kirchhoff's Laws

We have by this time seen that ΔH or ΔU can usually be obtained for any reaction as the result of calorimetric measurements. It may well be, however, that we require values of ΔH or ΔU at some temperature other than that at which the determination can be carried out conveniently. It is usually most convenient to carry out calorimetric measurements at 25° C, but we often require values of ΔH and ΔU at much more elevated temperatures.

---

[1] In order to subtract (i) we are using the fact that ΔH for a process equals $-\Delta H$ for the reverse process. The justification for this is obvious, it depends simply on the fact that ΔH is the change in a thermodynamic property. It is, however, of interest that the principle was established empirically in 1780 by Lavoisier and Laplace, who showed that the quantity of heat which must be supplied to decompose a compound into its elements is equal to the heat evolved when the compound is formed from its elements.

[2] See Table 12,I, page 209.

Kirchhoff's Laws show how ΔH and ΔU may be calculated at any temperature as long as their value at one temperature is known. The Laws are established as follows:

Consider the reaction

$$A \longrightarrow B.$$

$\Delta U = U_B - U_A$ where U_A and U_B are the molar internal energies of A and B.

and

$$\left(\frac{\partial(\Delta U)}{\partial T}\right)_v = \left(\frac{\partial U_B}{\partial T}\right)_v - \left(\frac{\partial U_A}{\partial T}\right)_v$$

$$= C_{v_B} - C_{v_A}.$$

Hence

$$\int d(\Delta U) = \int (C_{v_B} - C_{v_A})dT,$$

i.e.

$$\Delta U = \int (C_{v_B} - C_{v_A})dT + I \quad . \quad . \quad . \quad . \quad (6,9)$$

where I is an integration constant.

Molar thermal capacities are usually functions of temperature. If, however, the integration takes place over a temperature range so small that the various values of C_v change only to a negligible degree, equation (6,9) may be integrated to give

$$\Delta U = \Sigma C_v T + I,$$

where the symbol ΣC_v denotes the molar thermal capacities of the reaction products less those of the reactants. The value of ΔU at any one temperature then permits the calculation of the integration constant, so that the evaluation of ΔU at any other temperature becomes possible.

The variation in molar thermal capacities must usually be taken into account. Their dependence on temperature can always be represented by equations of the type

$$\left. \begin{array}{l} C_{v_B} = \alpha + \beta T + \gamma T^2 \ldots \\ C_{v_A} = \alpha' + \beta' T + \gamma' T^2 \ldots \end{array} \right\} \quad . \quad . \quad . \quad . \quad (6,10)$$

The constants α, β, γ, etc., are determined by actual measurement of C_v over the desired temperature range and by calculating values of the constants to fit the results. The equations produced are valid only for the temperature range over which the measurements of C_v are carried out. Insertion of such values into equation (6,9) yields the following equation

$$\int d(\Delta U) = \int \{(\alpha - \alpha') + (\beta - \beta')T + (\gamma - \gamma')T^2 \ldots\}dT.$$

Hence

$$\Delta U = (\alpha - \alpha')T + \frac{\beta - \beta'}{2}T^2 + \frac{\gamma - \gamma'}{3}T^3 \ldots + I. \qquad (6,11)$$

Knowledge of one value of ΔU determined at a convenient temperature T permits the calculation of I, so that ΔU may be evaluated at any other temperature.

The corresponding equation relating to the change in enthalpy is derived in the same way. In this case we require expressions for the dependence of C_p on temperature:

$$\begin{aligned} C_{p_B} &= a + bT + cT^2 \ldots \\ C_{p_A} &= a' + b'T + c'T^2 \ldots, \end{aligned} \qquad \qquad (6,12)$$

then since

$$\left(\frac{\partial(\Delta H)}{\partial T}\right)_p = \left(\frac{\partial H_B}{\partial T}\right)_p - \left(\frac{\partial H_A}{\partial T}\right)_p$$

$$= C_{p_B} - C_{p_A},$$

we arrive at the equation

$$\Delta H = (a - a')T + \frac{(b - b')}{2}T^2 + \frac{(c - c')}{3}T^3 \ldots + I', \qquad (6,13)^1$$

or a more general equation

$$\Delta H = \Sigma a T + \frac{\Sigma b}{2}T^2 + \frac{\Sigma c}{3}T^3 + \ldots + I'. \qquad (6,14)$$

An example of the use of equation (6,14) is given below:

The heat of reaction at constant pressure for

$$H_{2(g)} + \tfrac{1}{2}O_{2(g)} \longrightarrow H_2O_{(g)} \text{ at } 15^\circ \text{ C is } -57,780 \text{ cal.}$$

It is required to calculate ΔH for the reaction at 1000° K.

Over this temperature range the molar thermal capacities at constant pressure may be represented by the equations:

$$H_2, \quad C_p = 6 \cdot 50 + 0 \cdot 0009T \text{ cal deg}^{-1}.$$
$$O_2, \quad C_p = 6 \cdot 50 + 0 \cdot 0010T \text{ cal deg}^{-1}.$$
$$H_2O_{(g)}, \quad C_p = 8 \cdot 81 - 0 \cdot 0019T + 0 \cdot 00000222T^2 \text{ cal deg}^{-1}.$$

$$\int d(\Delta H) = \int (C_{p_{H_2O(g)}} - C_{p_{H_2}} - \tfrac{1}{2}C_{p_{O_2}})dT.$$

---

[1] The integration constant I' is often written ΔH_0, and is sometimes described as the enthalpy of reaction at the absolute zero. This description is not in fact correct. The reason for this is that the expressions for C_p (equations (6,12)) do not extend to the absolute zero. As a substance approaches the absolute zero its molar thermal capacity becomes closely represented by the Debye expression

$$C = \alpha T^3.$$

Hence

$$\Delta H = (8\cdot81 - 6\cdot50 - \tfrac{1}{2} \times 6\cdot50)T - \frac{(0\cdot0019 + 0\cdot0009 + 0\cdot0005)T^2}{2}$$
$$+ \frac{0\cdot00000222T^3}{3} + I'.$$

But at 288° K, $\Delta H = -57{,}780$ cal

Hence

$$-57{,}780 = -0\cdot94 \times 288 - 0\cdot00165 \times 288^2 + 0\cdot00000074 \times 288^3 + I',$$

so that $I' = -57{,}393$,
and the general expression for ΔH becomes

$$\Delta H = -0\cdot94T - 0\cdot00165T^2 + 0\cdot00000074T^3 - 57{,}393,$$

so that when $T = 1000°$ K,

$$\Delta H = -60{,}243 \text{ cal.}$$

The above calculations become, of course, very much easier when the variation of ΔU or ΔH is required over a temperature range over which the molar thermal capacities may reasonably be considered constant. For example, at and around 100° C the molar thermal capacity at constant pressure of water is 17·82 cal deg^{-1} mole^{-1}, and that of steam is 8·37 cal deg^{-1} mole^{-1}. At 100° C the latent heat of evaporation of water is 9650 cal mole^{-1}, i.e. for the reaction

$$H_2O_{(liq)} \longrightarrow H_2O_{(g)} \text{ at } 373° \text{ K}, \Delta H = 9{,}650 \text{ cal}$$

TABLE 6,I

Molar Thermal Capacities of Gases at Constant Pressure, over the Range 300–1500° K

$(C_p = a + bT + cT^2 \text{ cal deg}^{-1} \text{ mole}^{-1})$

	a	$b \times 10^3$	$c \times 10^7$
CO_2	6·214	10·4	−35·4
CO	6·42	1·66	−1·96
Cl_2	7·57	2·42	−9·65
H_2	6·95	−0·20	4·8
HCl	6·73	0·43	3·7
CH_4	3·38	18·0	−43·0
N_2	6·5	1·25	−0·01
O_2	6·15	3·1	−9·23
H_2O (gas)	7·256	2·3	2·83
NH_3	8·04	0·7	51

We calculate the value at $110°$ C as follows:

$$\left(\frac{\partial(\Delta H)}{\partial T}\right)_p = C_{p(g)} - C_{p(liq)}$$

$$= 8 \cdot 37 - 17 \cdot 82$$

$$= -9 \cdot 45 \text{ cal deg}^{-1} \text{ mole}^{-1}.$$

$$\Delta H = -9 \cdot 45 T + I$$

$$I = 9650 + 9 \cdot 45 \times 373$$

Hence ΔH at $383°$ K equals 9555 cal mole^{-1}.

Details of a power series which may be used to calculate the molar thermal capacities at constant pressure for some common gases over the temperature range $300–1500°$ K are given in Table 6,I.

Maximum Explosion and Flame Temperatures

When an exothermic reaction such as a combustion process takes place so quickly that an explosion or flame results, the process approximates to an adiabatic one, simply because there is insufficient time during the reaction for the reacting system to lose very much energy in the form of heat. We will here use the word explosion to denote such a process which takes place in a constant volume container, and the word flame to denote the process which takes place in open atmosphere, so that to all intents and purposes, the only difference between an explosion and a flame, in the sense that we are using the words, is that the first describes a rapid exothermic reaction carried out adiabatically at constant volume, and the second a rapid exothermic reaction carried out adiabatically at constant pressure.

It is a simple matter to calculate the theoretical *maximum* temperature which can be reached in a flame or in an explosion. The maximum temperature so calculated will in many cases exceed the actual temperature for various reasons which will be indicated in due course. Nevertheless, the calculation of the theoretical maximum temperature in a particular combustion process is of considerable interest. The method used is demonstrated by considering the combustion of hydrogen under various conditions.

1. The Temperature of a Hydrogen Flame Burning in Air at One Atmospheric Pressure

The approximate volume composition of air is 20% oxygen and 80% nitrogen, so that we may regard the combustion process in air as one mole of hydrogen plus one-half mole of oxygen plus two moles of nitrogen all at temperature T_1, changing to one mole of water vapour plus two moles of nitrogen all at temperature T_2, the change being both adiabatic and at constant pressure. It follows that the change in enthalpy is zero. Since the change in enthalpy is independent of the path connecting the initial and final states, we are free to choose that path which makes the calculation the simplest; we choose therefore to consider the complete process in two stages:

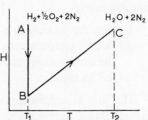

(a) an isothermal isobaric combustion to water vapour at temperature T_1, during which process we may imagine the energy released stored in some convenient thermal reservoir; and

(b) the absorption of this quantity of heat by the reaction products (including the nitrogen) resulting in the rise in temperature from T_1 to T_2.

Figure 6,1. The combustion of hydrogen burning in air.

The two stages are illustrated in Figure 6,1: the first stage being represented by line AB, and the second by line BC.

$$\Delta H = H_C - H_A = (H_C - H_B) + (H_B - H_A)$$

$$= \int_{T_1}^{T_2} \Sigma C_{p(H_2O + 2N_2)} dT + (H_B - H_A). \quad (6,15)$$

The quantity $(H_B - H_A)$ is the enthalpy of formation of water vapour at temperature T_1, and is known, as is C_p for water vapour and nitrogen, and since for the complete process ΔH is zero, the final temperature T_2 can be calculated from the equation:

$$\int_{T_1}^{T_2} \Sigma C_{p(H_2O + 2N_2)} dT = -\Delta H_{f H_2O(g)}^{T_1} \quad . \quad . \quad (6,16)$$

At 300° K, the enthalpy of formation of water vapour is —57,800 cal mole⁻¹, and the molar thermal capacities of water vapour and nitrogen are represented from 300° to 3000° K by the equations

$$C_{pH_2O(g)} = 7 \cdot 219 + 2 \cdot 374 \times 10^{-3}T + 0 \cdot 27 \times 10^{-6}T^2$$

and

$$C_{pN_2} = 6 \cdot 449 + 1 \cdot 425 \times 10^{-3}T - 0 \cdot 08 \times 10^{-6}T^2$$

the values being given in cal deg⁻¹.

Hence $\Sigma C_p = 20 \cdot 117 + 5 \cdot 224 \times 10^{-3}T + 0 \cdot 11 \times 10^{-6}T^2,$

so that if the initial temperature of the hydrogen and air is 300° K, the maximum flame temperature T_2 is given by the equation:

$$20 \cdot 117(T_2 - 300) + 2 \cdot 612 \times 10^{-3}(T_2^2 - 300^2) + 0 \cdot 037 \times 10^{-6}(T_2^3 - 300^3)$$
$$= 57,800$$

from which T_2 is found to be about 2400° K.

The validity of the method demonstrated above depends on two assumptions:

(i) that the process in a flame is truly adiabatic; and
(ii) that at temperatures approaching the maximum flame temperature, the combustion process $H_2 + \frac{1}{2}O_2 \longrightarrow H_2O_{(g)}$ goes completely from left to right.

The first assumption is certainly not really true, and will result in the actual flame temperature measured being slightly lower than that predicted. The second assumption is, however, the more important. For the sake of argument let us now assume that the equilibrium constant for the above reaction is such that at 2400° K one-quarter of the hydrogen remains unburnt. The flame gas will now be a mixture not of steam and nitrogen in the proportions one mole to two, but a mixture of steam, nitrogen and unreacted hydrogen and oxygen in the proportions one mole of steam to two and a half moles of nitrogen to a quarter mole of hydrogen and one-eighth mole of oxygen; and the maximum flame temperature will be given, not by equation (6,16) but by equation:

$$\int_{T_1}^{T_2} \Sigma C_{p(H_2O + 2\frac{1}{2}N_2 + \frac{1}{4}H_2 + \frac{1}{8}O_2)} dT = -\Delta H_{f H_2O(g)}^{T_1}. \quad . \quad (6,17)$$

The value of T_2 will be considerably less than that calculated earlier. In fact, the equilibrium constant for the reaction concerned happens to be such that between 2000° and 2400° K the assumption that the reaction goes to completion introduces very little error indeed into the calculation of the maximum flame temperature for hydrogen burning in air, but the same is not true in the cases we shall now discuss, simply because the temperatures concerned are much higher.

2. The Temperature of a Hydrogen Flame Burning in Pure Oxygen

If here we first assume that the reaction goes to completion, the maximum flame temperature will be given by the equation

$$\int_{T_1}^{T_2} C_{p H_2O(g)} dT = -\Delta H_{f H_2O(g)}^{T_1}. \quad . \quad . \quad (6,18)$$

If we make use of the same figures as before we find that the value of T_2 is about $5500°$ K. The dissociation of water vapour becomes appreciable long before such temperatures are reached, so that it is evident that this value is very much too high. The actual temperature can be computed from a knowledge of the equilibrium constant for water vapour at elevated temperatures, but this will not be done here.

3. The Maximum Explosion Temperature of a Hydrogen Air Mixture

We now consider a quantity of hydrogen and just sufficient air to ensure complete combustion exploded in a closed vessel. Since the process is one at constant volume, we are here concerned with changes in internal energy and with values of C_v rather than C_p. If again we assume that the explosion is adiabatic, and that the reaction proceeds to completion, the maximum explosion temperature T_2 is given by the expression

$$\int_{T_1}^{T_2} \Sigma C_{v(\text{H}_2\text{O} + 2\text{N}_2)} dT = -\Delta U_{f\text{H}_2\text{O}(g)}^{T_1}. \quad . \quad . \quad . \quad (6,19)$$

Since $\Delta H = \Delta U + nRT$
and since in the reaction

$$\text{H}_2 + \tfrac{1}{2}\text{O}_2 \longrightarrow \text{H}_2\text{O}_{(g)}, \quad n = -\tfrac{1}{2},$$

at $300°$ K $\Delta U_f = \Delta H_f + 300 = -57,500$ cal.
The values of C_v are given approximately by the equations:

$$C_{v\text{H}_2\text{O}(g)} = 5 \cdot 22 + 2 \cdot 4 \times 10^{-3}T \text{ cal deg}^{-1}$$

and $\qquad\qquad C_{v\text{N}_2} = 4 \cdot 5 + 1 \cdot 4 \times 10^{-3}T \text{ cal deg}^{-1},$

from which it can be shown that if $T_1 = 300°$ K, the value of T_2 is about $3000°$ K. As was explained earlier, this value will be higher than the experimental value because of the appreciable dissociation of water vapour.

By comparing equations (6,16) and (6,19), we can, however, see that the maximum explosion temperature for a particular combustion process will always be higher than the corresponding maximum flame temperature, simply because the ΣC_v term is always less than the corresponding ΣC_p term, whereas the difference between ΔU and ΔH will be in most cases so small as to be without real significance.

The effect of preheating the reactants will always be to increase the maximum flame or explosion temperature, even though the value of $-\Delta H$ or $-\Delta U$ for the combustion process may be lower at the higher temperature. We establish this theorem by calculating the maximum explosion temperature of a hydrogen–air mixture preheated from T_1 to

T_1^*. We denote the maximum explosion temperature under these conditions by the symbol T_2^*.

Equation (6,19) now becomes

$$\int_{T_1^*}^{T_2^*} \Sigma C_{v(H_2O + 2N_2)} dT = -\Delta U_{fH_2O(g)}^{T_1^*},$$

but from Kirchhoff's Law we can write

$$\Delta U_{fH_2O(g)}^{T_1^*} = \Delta U_{fH_2O(g)}^{T_1} + \int_{T_1}^{T_1^*} C_{v(H_2O)(g)} dT - \int_{T_1}^{T_1^*} \Sigma C_{v(H_2 + \frac{1}{2}O_2)} dT,$$

therefore

$$\int_{T_1^*}^{T_2^*} \Sigma C_{v(H_2O + 2N_2)} dT = -\Delta U_{fH_2O(g)}^{T_1} - \int_{T_1}^{T_1^*} C_{v(H_2O)(g)} dT$$

$$+ \int_{T_1}^{T_1^*} \Sigma C_{v(H_2 + \frac{1}{2}O_2)} dT,$$

i.e.

$$\int_{T_1}^{T_2^*} C_{v(H_2O)} + \int_{T_1^*}^{T_2^*} C_{v(2N_2)} dT = -\Delta U_{fH_2O(g)}^{T_1}$$

$$+ \int_{T_1}^{T_1^*} \Sigma C_{v(H_2 + \frac{1}{2}O_2)} dT. \quad (6,20)$$

The quantity represented by the last term of the right-hand side must always be positive, and it therefore is clear by comparing (6,20) with (6,19) that T_2^* is greater than T_2, i.e. that the maximum explosion temperature is higher as the result of pre-heating the reactants from T_1 to T_1^*.

This principle is of great importance in the functioning of an internal combustion engine.

The processes which take place in a cylinder of a spark-ignition engine such as that using petrol approximate to those shown in Figure 6,2. Process $a \longrightarrow b$ represents the intake stroke in which petrol vapour and the theoretical quantity of air required for its complete combustion is drawn into the cylinder at atmospheric pressure. Process $b \longrightarrow c$ is the compression stroke in which the gas is compressed

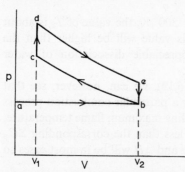

Figure 6,2. A pressure–volume diagram showing the processes which take place in a spark-ignition engine.

adiabatically from V_2 to V_1, and process $c \longrightarrow d$ represents the combustion process. The adiabatic compression from V_2 to V_1 will lead to a rise in temperature from T_1 to T_1^* which (assuming ideal behaviour of the gases concerned) can be calculated from the equation

$$\frac{T_1^*}{T_1} = \left(\frac{V_2}{V_1}\right)^{\gamma-1}.$$

The compression ratio $\dfrac{V_2}{V_1}$ in a modern engine of this type is about ten, and if we assume that the ratio of specific heats for the gas mixture is about 1·4, we see that the ratio of T_1^* to T_1 is about two and a half. In practice this means that the reacting gases are, in effect, preheated from about 300° to 750° K. The maximum explosion temperature T_d and the maximum explosion pressure p_d will thus be very much greater than those that would have been reached had no preheating by adiabatic compression occurred.

EXERCISES 6

6,1. Under particular conditions the heat of combustion of acetylene to carbon dioxide and liquid water is −310,400 cal, the enthalpy of formation of carbon dioxide is −96,000 cal and that of liquid water −68,000 cal. Calculate the enthalpy of formation of acetylene under the same conditions.

6,2. At 25° C the enthalpy of formation of ethane is −20,240 cal, that of carbon dioxide −94,260 cal and that of liquid water −68,320 cal. Calculate the heat of combustion of ethane under the same conditions.

6,3. The enthalpies of formation of the following compounds at 15° C are PbO, −50·30 kcal; SO_2, −70·92 kcal; PbS, +19·30 kcal. Calculate ΔH and ΔU for the reaction

$$PbS + 2PbO \longrightarrow 3Pb + SO_2$$

at the same temperature.

6,4. 0·8723 gm of a solid organic compound of molecular weight 122·1 evolved 5511 cal on complete combustion at constant volume at 18° C. Analysis of the products gave 2·200 gm of CO_2 and 0·386 gm of water. Calculate the molecular formula and the heat of combustion at constant pressure and enthalpy of formation of the compound, given that at this temperature the enthalpy of formation of carbon dioxide is −94,000 cal and that of liquid water −67,000 cal.

6,5. In this question the symbol HCl,yH_2O is used to denote 1 mole of HCl in v moles of water.
Assuming that NaCl, HCl and NaOH are completely ionised at infinite

dilution, calculate the heat of ionisation of water, i.e. the value of ΔH for the reaction

$$H_2O_{(liq)} \longrightarrow H^+_{(aq)}, \infty H_2O, \quad +OH^-_{(aq)}, \infty H_2O$$

from the following values of heats of dilution and reaction:

(1) HCl, 46·5 H$_2$O + NaOH, 1065·5 H$_2$O $\longrightarrow$ NaCl, 1113 H$_2$O,
$$\Delta H = -13·83 \text{ kcal}$$

(2) HCl, 46·5 H$_2$O + 1065·5 H$_2$O $\longrightarrow$ HCl, 1112 H$_2$O,
$$\Delta H = -0·35 \text{ kcal}$$

(3) HCl, 1112 H$_2$O + ∞H$_2$O $\longrightarrow$ HCl, ∞H$_2$O, $\quad \Delta H = -0·10$ kcal

(4) NaOH, 1065·5 H$_2$O + ∞H$_2$O $\longrightarrow$ NaOH, ∞H$_2$O,
$$\Delta H = -0·09 \text{ kcal}$$

(5) NaCl, 1113 H$_2$O + ∞H$_2$O $\longrightarrow$ NaCl, ∞H$_2$O, $\quad \Delta H = -0·07$ kcal

(This question is discussed in Appendix 1, page 416.)

6,6. Calculate the heat of formation of solid aluminium chloride (Al$_2$Cl$_6$) from the following data:

$$Al_{(s)} + 3HCl_{(aq)} \longrightarrow AlCl_{3(aq)} + \tfrac{3}{2}H_{2(g)}, \quad \Delta H = -127·0 \text{ kcal}$$

$$H_{2(g)} + Cl_{2(g)} \longrightarrow 2HCl_{(g)}, \quad \Delta H = -44·0 \text{ kcal}$$

$$HCl_{(g)} + aq \longrightarrow HCl_{(aq)}, \quad \Delta H = -17·5 \text{ kcal}$$

$$Al_2Cl_6 + aq \longrightarrow 2AlCl_{3(aq)}, \quad \Delta H = -155·8 \text{ kcal}$$

6,7. Given that the molar thermal capacity of oxygen at constant pressure over the temperature range concerned may be represented by the equation

$$C_p = 6·100 + 3·25 \times 10^{-3}T - 1·02 \times 10^{-6}T^2 \text{ cal deg}^{-1} \text{ mole}^{-1},$$

determine the quantity of heat required to raise the temperature of one mole of oxygen from 27° C to 127° C at 1 atmosphere pressure.

6,8. At temperatures around 100° C the molar thermal capacity of liquid water is 17·82 cal deg^{-1} mole^{-1}, and that of steam at constant pressure 8·37 cal deg^{-1} mole^{-1}. The latent heat of evaporation of water at 100° C is 536 cal gm^{-1}. Calculate its value at 120° C.

6,9. Over the temperature range 0–1000° C the molar thermal capacities of the following gases may be expressed by the equations:

$$H_2O_{(g)}, \ C_p = 8·8 - 0·002T \text{ cal deg}^{-1}$$
$$H_2, \quad C_p = 6·5 + 0·001T \text{ cal deg}^{-1}$$
$$O_2, \quad C_p = 6·4 + 0·002T \text{ cal deg}^{-1}.$$

The enthalpy of formation of steam at 0° C is $-57,780$ cal. Calculate its value at 1000° C.

6,10. Derive a general expression for the heat of reaction

$$C_{(graphite)} + H_2O_{(g)} \longrightarrow CO_{(g)} + H_{2(g)}$$

at constant pressure, as a function of temperature, given the following molar thermal capacity data:

$C_{(graphite)}$, $C_p = 2\cdot673 + 2\cdot62 \times 10^{-3}T + 1\cdot17 \times 10^5 T^{-2}$ cal deg^{-1}

$H_2O_{(g)}$, $C_p = 7\cdot219 + 2\cdot374 \times 10^{-3}T + 0\cdot267 \times 10^{-6}T^2$ cal deg^{-1}

H_2, $C_p = 6\cdot947 - 0\cdot200 \times 10^{-3}T + 0\cdot4808 \times 10^{-6}T^2$ cal deg^{-1}

CO, $C_p = 6\cdot342 + 1\cdot836 \times 10^{-3}T - 0\cdot2801 \times 10^{-6}T^2$ cal deg^{-1}

and the following standard heats of formation at 25° C

$$H_2O_{(g)}, \quad -57,800 \text{ cal}; \quad CO, \quad -26,200 \text{ cal}$$

6,11. The heat evolved in the solution of one mole of iron in dilute hydrochloric acid at constant pressure is 20,800 cal at 18° C. What is the change in internal energy of the system?

6,12. The heat of combustion of heptane (C_7H_{16}) at 27° C determined in a constant volume bomb calorimeter is -1100 kcal mole^{-1}. What is the heat of combustion at constant pressure?

6,13. The increase in enthalpy during the reaction

$$CaCO_3 \longrightarrow CaO + CO_2$$

is 42,900 cal mole^{-1} at 15° C. Given that over the temperature range concerned the molar thermal capacities are almost independent of temperature and are given by the equations:

CaO, $C_p = 12\cdot27$ cal deg^{-1}

$CaCO_3$, $C_p = 26\cdot37$ cal deg^{-1}

CO_2, $C_p = 7\cdot30$ cal deg^{-1}

calculate the values of ΔH and ΔU at 600° C.

6,14. Explain precisely the conditions which must operate if the enthalpy of a reaction is independent of temperature over the temperature range T_1 to T_2.

CHAPTER 7

THE SECOND LAW OF THERMODYNAMICS

The Second Law of Thermodynamics, like the Zeroth and First Laws, is a postulate which we accept, not because it can be verified directly, but because it makes predictions which are verified by experiment. No instance of its contravention has ever been recognised. It is the most famous of all scientific laws, owing its unique position to the fact that it has something to say about any event that can take place. There are many ways in which it can be stated. We shall now choose some of those ways and show that they are equivalent.

Perhaps the most homely and most descriptive way in which the Second Law may be expressed is to say that THE CLOCK CAN NEVER BE PUT BACK. In other words, THE EFFECT OF NO NATURAL SPONTANEOUS PROCESS CAN EVER BE COMPLETELY ERASED. We have already discussed a word which enables us to express the last statement with greater economy. In Chapter 4 we defined an IRREVERSIBLE PROCESS as one which cannot be reversed without bringing about permanent changes in the surroundings. We now express the Second Law in terms of this word, and postulate that ALL NATURAL SPONTANEOUS CHANGES ARE IRREVERSIBLE.

We have now made three statements which are plainly equivalent. We will not question at present whether or not they are true, but will rest content with the knowledge that they will lead to predictions which may all be verified by experiment.

We now select two natural spontaneous changes and investigate the reason why they cannot be reversed and leave no trace that they ever took place. Although the two changes we choose to investigate are quite different, we shall find that when we attempt to erase them we come up against the same difficulty in both cases. Both changes that we shall study involve the exchange of energy between the system and the surroundings, and we remember that energy is transferred from one body to another either as heat or as work. We therefore require to have available as part of the surroundings the following pieces of apparatus:

1. Thermal reservoirs at whatever temperatures we require to which heat may be rejected by the system, or from which heat may be

supplied. We stipulate that the thermal reservoirs are such that they can absorb quantities of heat without rise in temperature. (A thermal reservoir at 0° C might, for example, consist of a quantity of ice and water. When heat is absorbed some ice melts, but the temperature remains constant.)

2. An apparatus capable of performing work on the system, or on which the system itself may perform work. Since all work processes can be resolved into the ability to raise or lower a weight, the apparatus selected can be as simple as a weight over a pulley; when the system does work on the apparatus the weight is raised, and when the apparatus does work on the system the weight is lowered.

The first natural spontaneous process which we study is the adiabatic expansion of an ideal gas into a vacuum.

Consider for convenience one mole of an ideal gas confined in a cylinder at pressure p_1, occupying a volume V_1 at temperature T, the gas being

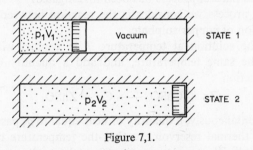

Figure 7,1.

separated from a vacuum by a weightless frictionless piston, the cylinder being completely lagged from the surroundings, so that any reaction which occurs is adiabatic. When we permit the piston to move, the gas expands into the vacuum until it occupies a volume V_2 and exerts a pressure p_2. The process is illustrated by Figure 7,1. Since the expansion is made into a vacuum, no work is done against the surroundings, and since the system is lagged, no heat is absorbed. We have seen, incidentally, in Chapter 5 that if the gas is ideal there will be, under these conditions, no change in temperature.

We now proceed to reverse the process; to convert the gas from state 2 (p_2, V_2, T) to state 1 (p_1, V_1, T). This constitutes an isothermal compression. We therefore remove the lagging from the cylinder, place it in contact with a thermal reservoir at temperature T and permit the piston to be pushed back to its original position by means of the weight and pulley.

From the calculations carried out in Chapter 5 we know that the amount of work required to be done by the weight equals $RT \log_e \dfrac{V_2}{V_1}$. At the end of the operation the weight is therefore hanging lower than it was initially. Since the temperature of the system remains constant throughout the compression process a quantity of heat also equal to $RT \log_e \frac{V_2}{V_1}$ must be rejected by the system to the thermal reservoir.

We have now succeeded in restoring the system to its original state. What changes have occurred in the surroundings? Firstly, the weight is in a lower position than it was initially, and requires a quantity of work equal to $RT \log_e \frac{V_2}{V_1}$ to raise it to its original position; and secondly, the thermal reservoir has received a quantity of heat equal to $RT \log_e \frac{V_2}{V_1}$. Obviously, if we can convert this quantity of heat into work we have reversed the natural spontaneous expansion process and have left the surroundings unchanged. We postpone further discussion of the problem until the second natural process has been investigated.

The second process we consider is the reaction between zinc and an aqueous solution of copper sulphate.

We place the solution at temperature T in contact with a thermal reservoir at the same temperature, and add a quantity of zinc. The exothermic reaction

$$Zn + CuSO_4 \longrightarrow Cu + ZnSO_4$$

takes place spontaneously, a quantity of heat equal to q_1 passing from the system to the thermal reservoir, so that the temperature of the system remains constant. We now require to reverse the process.

We can do this by electrolysing the mixture: we connect the precipitated copper to the positive electrode of a direct current generator, insert a negative electrode into the solution and pass a particular quantity of electricity through the solution at the required e.m.f., the electric current being produced as the result of work performed in the generator by a falling weight. We find that the quantity of work required to be performed by the weight on the generator in order to produce the necessary current at the required e.m.f. equals w. The weight now hangs a certain distance lower than it did before. During the electrolysis we find that a quantity of heat q_2 passes from the system to the thermal reservoir at temperature T.

We have now restored the system completely to its original state. The surroundings have, however, suffered the following changes:

(1) the weight is in a lower position than it was initially, and requires a quantity of work equal to w to restore it to its original position; and
(2) the thermal reservoir has received a total quantity of heat equal to $q_1 + q_2$.

We find on inspection that

$$w = q_1 + q_2.$$

We have reached the same conclusion as that reached in the last example. We have found that in both cases, a system and its surroundings can only be restored to their original state after a natural spontaneous process, if it is possible to convert a quantity of energy available only as heat into mechanical work without leaving further permanent changes in the surroundings. We have analysed only two processes. The same conclusions would have been reached whatever examples we had chosen.

We now require therefore to investigate the conditions under which energy available only as heat can be converted into mechanical work. In general there is only one way in which this can be done: heat is passed to some material known as the *working substance*, which expands against a resistance, so that work is performed. This is the principle on which heat engines are designed, whether of the piston or turbine type. We select the simplest example of all, in which the working substance is a fluid contained in a cylinder fitted with a frictionless piston. We suppose the cylinder and its working substance to be initially at temperature T, place it in contact with a thermal reservoir at a temperature only infinitesimally higher, and suppose that a quantity of heat q_1 flows from reservoir to working substance. The latter expands, so performing work.

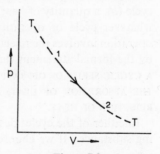

Figure 7,2.

Such an operation is illustrated in Figure 7,2, where as the result of the absorption of heat and the performance of work, the working substance is shown to change from state 1 (p_1, V_1, T) to state 2 (p_2, V_2, T). During this operation heat has been converted into work; in fact, if the working substance is a gas approaching ideal behaviour the quantity of work performed is precisely the same as the quantity of heat absorbed. The difficulty which arises is that the working substance is now in a different state. By the very nature of our previous arguments we require not only heat to be converted into work but also that after the operation the working substance should be returned to its original state. It is obviously necessary therefore that the working substance must undergo some sort of *cyclic* series of operations which return it eventually to its initial state. Two such simple cyclic operations are shown in Figure 7,3.

Process 1 ⟶ 2 is the same in each case, and is the isothermal expansion described above. In example (*a*) process 2 ⟶ 3 consists of an adiabatic expansion (during which the temperature falls from T to T_2), and 3 $\longrightarrow$ 1 some non-isothermal compression process. Example (*b*) consists of an adiabatic expansion 2 $\longrightarrow$ 3 (during which the temperature falls from T to T_2), an isothermal compression from 3 $\longrightarrow$ 4 and an adiabatic compression 4 $\longrightarrow$ 1. This particular cycle is a very famous one; it is the CARNOT CYCLE which we have already met in Chapter 5.

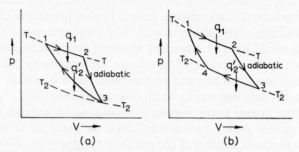

Figure 7,3. Two simple cyclic operations.

The two cycles (*a*) and (*b*) have this in common: during one operation in each case, operation 3 $\longrightarrow$ 1 in cycle (*a*) and operation 3 $\longrightarrow$ 4 in cycle (*b*), a quantity of heat is rejected by the working substance. In fact, whatever cycle of operations be chosen it is found that at least one operation involves the rejection of heat. These findings can be summarised by the formal statement that NO SUBSTANCE CAN BE CAUSED TO UNDERGO A CYCLIC SERIES OF OPERATIONS UNLESS AT LEAST ONE OPERATION INVOLVES THE ABSORPTION OF HEAT, AND AT LEAST ONE OPERATION INVOLVES THE REJECTION OF HEAT.

In either of the cycles described above work is performed by the working substance. If we choose any such cycle and designate:

(*a*) the nett work performed by the working substance over the complete cycle by the symbol w;

(*b*) the heat absorbed by the working substance by the symbol q_1; and

(*c*) the heat rejected by the symbol q'_2,

then since in a complete cycle of operations the energy put in must equal the energy taken out, we can write

$$w = q_1 - q'_2. \qquad \qquad \text{(7,1)}$$

It is clear from our previous argument that a natural process can only be reversed, leaving the surroundings unchanged if a quantity of energy available only as heat (the quantity q_1 in equation 7,1) can be converted entirely into work (the quantity w). We now see that this cannot be done:

we see therefore why natural spontaneous processes are irreversible, why the clock can never be put back.

Clearly the statements that ALL NATURAL SPONTANEOUS CHANGES ARE IRREVERSIBLE and that NO SUBSTANCE CAN BE CAUSED TO UNDERGO A CYCLIC SERIES OF OPERATIONS UNLESS AT LEAST ONE OPERATION INVOLVES THE ABSORPTION OF HEAT, AND AT LEAST ONE OPERATION THE REJECTION OF HEAT are equivalent. The latter is, in fact, the way in which the Second Law is usually expressed by engineers, because it relates more closely to the problems with which they are concerned. It is closely related to statements of the Second Law made in the last century by Kelvin and Planck. We can go farther: the engineer's statement of the Second Law is obviously equivalent to one which states that NO TWO ADIABATIC PROCESSES INVOLVING THE SAME SUBSTANCE WHEN SHOWN ON THE SAME DIAGRAM CAN CROSS. If they could, a cycle could be devised using two adiabatics and only one process in which heat is absorbed. This last statement is the basis of a mathematical approach to the Second Law made by Carathéodory.

We now require to express the irreversibility of all natural spontaneous processes mathematically. We do this by establishing the existence of a thermodynamic property which always changes in the same way during any natural spontaneous process. The property is called ENTROPY. It was first recognised in the last century by Clausius, and the argument which we shall use to establish its identity and characteristics is much the same as that used by him. The argument is a long and detailed one: for convenience we divide it into four stages.

Stage 1. The Carnot Theorem and its Consequences

We have already seen that if a system undergoes any complete cycle of operations the nett work performed by it must equal the heat absorbed minus the heat rejected, i.e.

$$w = q_1 - q'_2. \qquad \ldots \ldots \qquad (7,1)$$

In a particular cycle of operations first studied by the French engineer Carnot early in the 19th century and called a CARNOT CYCLE, a simple relationship was found to exist between the quantity of heat absorbed, the quantity rejected and the temperatures at which the absorption and rejection take place. This relationship will now be established.

A Carnot cycle consists of any two isothermal processes *carried out reversibly*, so that the maximum quantity of work will be performed, separated by two *reversible* adiabatic processes. The type of system and the nature of the actual series of operations concerned is not important.

That portrayed in Figure 7,4 represents the expansion and contraction of an ideal gas, process $1 \longrightarrow 2$ being the isothermal expansion at temperature T_1, process $2 \longrightarrow 3$ an adiabatic expansion from T_1 to T_2, process $3 \longrightarrow 4$ an isothermal compression at T_2 and process $4 \longrightarrow 1$ an adiabatic compression to the original state at T_1, but it could be quite different. It could, for example, be a lead accumulator discharging first reversibly and isothermally at T_1, then reversibly and adiabatically from T_1 to T_2 followed by an isothermal charging process at T_2 and an adiabatic charging process from T_2 to T_1.

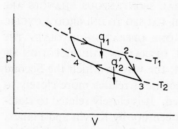

Figure 7,4. A Carnot cycle.

The CARNOT THEOREM states that the thermal efficiency of the cycle defined by the equation

$$\eta = \frac{w}{q_1} \qquad \qquad (7,2)$$

is independent of the nature of the system concerned and the type of operation involved, and is determined solely by the two temperatures T_1 and T_2 between which the cycle operates.

We establish the theorem in the following way:

We suppose that the theorem is not correct and devise two cycles of operations involving different substances working between the same two temperatures. We designate one cycle A and the other B, and suppose that the thermal efficiency of A is greater than that of B. It follows from (7,1) and (7,2) that we may write

$$\eta_A = \frac{w_A}{q_{1_A}} = \frac{q_{1_A} - q'_{2_A}}{q_{1_A}}$$

and

$$\eta_B = \frac{w_B}{q_{1_B}} = \frac{q_{1_B} - q'_{2_B}}{q_{1_B}}.$$

We now regulate the cycles so that the heat rejected in both cases is the same, i.e.

$$q'_{2_A} = q'_{2_B}.$$

Under these circumstances it follows that if

$$\eta_A > \eta_B,$$
$$q_{1_A} > q_{1_B},$$

and

$$w_A > w_B.$$

We now arrange to operate cycle A between the two temperatures T_1 and T_2, so that the working substance absorbs a quantity of heat q_{1_A} from a heat reservoir at T_1 and rejects a quantity of heat q'_{2_A} to a heat reservoir at T_2, but utilise some of the work which becomes available to carry out the second cycle of operations in the *reverse direction*, so that the working substance in B absorbs a quantity of heat q'_{2_B} from the reservoir at T_2, and rejects a quantity of heat q_{1_B} to the reservoir at T_1. The work required to do this, w_B is less than the work available w_A, so we have available some device such as a weight and pulley on which the "excess" work $w_A - w_B$ can be expended. The complete device, the two thermal reservoirs, the two systems A and B, and the weight and pulley may now be made to operate as an isolated unit as shown in Figure 7,5.

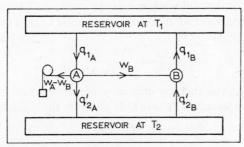

Figure 7,5.

As the result of the operations carried out the following changes have been achieved in the various parts of the system:

(*a*) the reservoir at T_2 is unchanged; it received a quantity of heat q'_{2_A} from system A, but lost the same quantity of heat q'_{2_B} to system B;

(*b*) the reservoir at T_1 has lost a quantity of heat equal to q_{1_A}, but has gained a quantity of heat equal to q_{1_B}. Since, however, we have shown that if q'_{2_A} equals q'_{2_B}, q_{1_A} must be greater than q_{1_B}; it is evident that the reservoir has suffered a nett loss equal to $q_{1_A} - q_{1_B}$;

(*c*) a quantity of work w_B has been expended by one system on the other, but a quantity equal to $w_A - w_B$ has been performed on the weight and pulley.

Since
$$w_A = q_{1_A} - q'_{2_A}$$

and
$$w_B = q_{1_B} - q'_{2_B}$$

it follows, since we arranged that
$$q'_{2_A} = q'_{2_B},$$

that
$$w_A - w_B = (q_{1_A} - q'_{2_A}) - (q_{1_B} - q'_{2_B})$$
$$= q_{1_A} - q_{1_B}$$

We appear to have succeeded in converting a quantity of heat equal to $q_{1_A} - q_{1_B}$ into an equivalent quantity of work $w_A - w_B$ without causing changes in the surroundings. This conclusion is contrary to the Second Law. It follows that the original premise upon which the argument is based that we might suppose that the thermal efficiency of one Carnot cycle is greater than that of the other is incorrect.

Since we have shown that the thermal efficiency of any Carnot cycle working between the same thermal reservoirs is independent of the nature of the system concerned and the type of operations involved, we are at liberty to choose the simplest possible system in order to obtain an expression for the thermal efficiency of the cycle. In Chapter 5 we chose to imagine the transport of an ideal gas around a Carnot cycle and found (equation 5,26) that

$$\frac{w}{q_1} = \frac{T_1 - T_2}{T_1}.$$

It follows that the thermal efficiency of *any* Carnot cycle operating between two temperatures T_1 and T_2 is given by the equation

$$\eta = \frac{T_1 - T_2}{T_1}, \qquad \ldots \ldots \quad (7,3)$$

irrespective of the nature of the substance involved and the actual operations to which it is subjected, as long as the processes involved are all carried out reversibly.

From (7,1), (7,2) and (7,3) it follows that for any Carnot cycle

$$\frac{q_1 - q'_2}{q_1} = \frac{T_1 - T_2}{T_1}$$

i.e.
$$\frac{q_1}{T_1} = \frac{q'_2}{T_2}. \qquad \ldots \ldots \ldots \quad (7,4)$$

We now require to consider the modifications which must be made to this equation if one or more operations in the cycle are permitted to take place irreversibly. We therefore compare two cycles: one a reversible Carnot cycle in which a quantity of heat q_1 is absorbed at temperature T_1, a quantity of heat q'_2 rejected at temperature T_2 and a quantity of work w_c performed on the surroundings; and the second, a cycle in which one or more processes take place irreversibly, so that a quantity of heat $q_{1_{\text{irrev}}}$ is absorbed at temperature T_1, a quantity of heat $q'_{2_{\text{irrev}}}$ rejected at temperature T_2 and a quantity of work w_{irrev} performed.

The two cycles are therefore represented by the two equations

$$\eta_c = \frac{q_1 - q_2'}{q_1} = \frac{w_c}{q_1}$$

and

$$\eta_{\text{irrev}} = \frac{q_{1\text{irrev}} - q_{2\text{irrev}}'}{q_{1\text{irrev}}} = \frac{w_{\text{irrev}}}{q_{1\text{irrev}}}.$$

We remember from Chapter 4 that any irreversible process performs less than the maximum possible quantity of work from the same change of state, so that if we arrange that in the irreversible cycle the quantity of heat absorbed is the same as that absorbed in the Carnot cycle, the nett work performed w_{irrev} must be less than w_c, so that

$$\eta_{\text{irrev}} < \eta_c.$$

It follows that

$$\frac{q_{1\text{irrev}} - q_{2\text{irrev}}'}{q_{1\text{irrev}}} < \frac{T_1 - T_2}{T_1}.$$

$$\frac{q_{2\text{irrev}}'}{q_{1\text{irrev}}} > \frac{T_2}{T_1}.$$

or that

$$\frac{q_{1\text{irrev}}}{T_1} < \frac{q_{2\text{irrev}}'}{T_2}. \qquad \cdots \cdots \quad (7,5)$$

A Digression on the Establishment of the Thermodynamic Scale of Temperature

In equation (7,4) we have two quantities q_1 and q_2' which depend only on temperature and are independent of the particular characteristics of the working substance involved. We may regard, therefore, the two temperatures T_1 and T_2 as *defined* by equation (7,4).

This, in fact, is what we were seeking in Chapter 3 when we attempted to discriminate between one property and another in order to establish an absolute scale of temperature. The scale on which two temperatures T_1 and T_2 are related to the heat absorbed and the heat rejected in a Carnot cycle by the equation

$$\frac{q_1}{q_2'} = \frac{T_1}{T_2}$$

is called the Thermodynamic or Kelvin Absolute Temperature Scale.

It is only on the Ideal Gas scale of temperature that Boyle's and Charles's Laws and the combined equation $pv = RT$ apply. Since we used these laws in the derivation of the equation

$$\eta = 1 - \frac{T_2}{T_1}$$

E

in Chapter 5, it must follow that T_1 and T_2 represent temperatures on the Ideal Gas scale. The Ideal Gas scale and the Thermodynamic scale of temperature are therefore identical.

A Change of Symbols

The quantities q_2' and $q_{2\text{irrev}}'$ were defined in the argument given above as the heats *rejected* by the system at temperature T_2. It is convenient at this stage to define two quantities q_2 and $q_{2\text{irrev}}$ as the heats *absorbed* by the system at T_2; so that

$$q_2 = -q_2'$$

and
$$q_{2\text{irrev}} = -q_{2\text{irrev}}'.$$

We can then summarise the findings of the first stage in our argument by the following statement:

If any cycle of operations consists of the absorption of a quantity of heat q_1 at temperature T_1, and the absorption of a (negative) quantity of heat q_2 at a lower temperature T_2

$$\frac{q_1}{T_1} + \frac{q_2}{T_2} \leqslant 0, \quad \cdot \quad \cdot \quad \cdot \quad \cdot \quad \cdot \quad \cdot \quad (7,6)$$

the equality sign applying to a cycle in which all operations are performed reversibly, and the inequality sign to a cycle in which one or more operations are performed irreversibly.

Stage 2. The Clausius Inequality

The heavy continuous line in Figure 7,6 represents any *reversible* cycle of operations. Superimposed on the diagram are a series of curves representing adiabatics (ad, $ebhc$, fg, etc.) and a series of curves (ab, dc, ef, hg, etc.) representing isothermal processes at temperatures $T_1, T_2, T_3 \ldots$ Clearly $abcd$ represents one Carnot cycle, $efgh$ a second and so on.

If we imagine that in these Carnot cycles quantities of heat q_1, q_2, q_3, q_4, etc., are absorbed along the isothermals $T_1, T_2, T_3, T_4 \ldots$ we may write

$$\frac{q_1}{T_1} + \frac{q_2}{T_2} = 0$$

$$\frac{q_3}{T_3} + \frac{q_4}{T_4} = 0 \ldots$$

It is clear that if the adiabatics are placed sufficiently close together, the cycle represented by the heavy continuous line can be superimposed

precisely by a series of Carnot cycles in juxtaposition.[1] It follows therefore that for any reversible cycle

$$\frac{q_1}{T_1} + \frac{q_2}{T_2} + \frac{q_3}{T_3} + \frac{q_4}{T_4} \ldots = 0$$

i.e.
$$\sum \left(\frac{q}{T}\right)_{rev} = 0. \qquad \ldots \quad \ldots \quad (7,7)$$

We now consider a similar cycle of operations in which one or more
processes take place irreversibly. If we now attempt to superimpose on

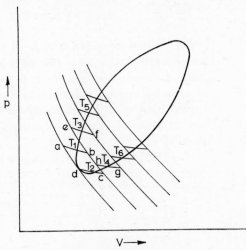

Figure 7,6.

the diagram of such a cycle a series of adiabatics and isothermals which
precisely reproduce the cycle, clearly some of these, too, must represent
irreversible processes. We know from (7,6) that for any elementary cycle
consisting of two isothermals and two adiabatics of which any one process
is irreversible

$$\frac{q_i}{T_i} + \frac{q_j}{T_j} < 0,$$

it therefore follows that the sum of such quantities must also be negative,
i.e. that for any irreversible cycle

$$\sum \left(\frac{q}{T}\right)_{irrev} < 0. \qquad \ldots \quad \ldots \quad (7,8)$$

[1] It can, in fact, be formally proved that for any reversible process no matter how the
temperature may change, it is always possible to find a reversible zigzag path between
the same two states, consisting of two adiabatics separated by an isothermal such that
the heat absorbed during the isothermal process is the same as that absorbed during the
original process. (See Zermansky, *Heat and Thermodynamics*, 3rd edition.)

Equation (7,7) and inequality (7,8) may be summarised by the statement that "whenever a system executes a complete cyclic process the sum of $\frac{q}{T}$ around the cycle is less than zero if the cycle is irreversible or equal to zero if the cycle is carried out reversibly".

i.e.
$$\oint \left(\frac{q}{T}\right) \leqslant 0. \qquad \ldots \ldots \ldots \quad (7,9)$$

This statement is known as the INEQUALITY OF CLAUSIUS.

Stage 3. Entropy

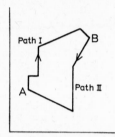

Figure 7,7.

Let us now consider a cycle of operations in which a substance is taken reversibly from an initial state A to some second state B by a series of changes collectively described as PATH I, and returned from state B to the original state A by a second series of changes collectively described as PATH II.

If we stipulate that each change is carried out reversibly then we may say that for the complete cycle

$$\oint_A^A \left(\frac{q}{T}\right)_{rev} = 0. \qquad \ldots \ldots \quad (7,7)$$

The complete cycle may, however, be divided artificially into two portions A to B by Path I and B to A by Path II, so that equation (7,7) becomes

$$\sum_A^B \left(\frac{q}{T}\right)_{rev\,Path\,I} + \sum_B^A \left(\frac{q}{T}\right)_{rev\,Path\,II} = 0.$$

Since each change is reversible this becomes

$$\sum_A^B \left(\frac{q}{T}\right)_{rev\,Path\,I} - \sum_A^B \left(\frac{q}{T}\right)_{rev\,Path\,II} = 0,$$

i.e.
$$\sum_A^B \left(\frac{q}{T}\right)_{rev\,Path\,I} = \sum_A^B \left(\frac{q}{T}\right)_{rev\,Path\,II} \qquad \ldots \ldots \quad (7,10)$$

We have imposed no conditions regarding Path I or Path II except that all changes therein are reversible; we may therefore say that if a system changes from state A to state B by any reversible path,

$$\sum_A^B \left(\frac{q}{T}\right)_{rev} \text{ is a constant.}$$

This quantity therefore depends only on the initial and final states A and B. Therefore, there would appear to exist some property of a system such that when the system changes reversibly from state A to state B the property changes by an amount equal to $\sum_A^B \left(\frac{q}{T}\right)_{rev}$.

This property is called the ENTROPY of the system, and is denoted by the symbol S. We may therefore say that when a system changes from state A to state B the increase in entropy equals

$$\Delta S = S_B - S_A = \sum_A^B \left(\frac{q}{T}\right)_{rev} \quad . \quad . \quad . \quad . \quad (7,11)$$

For an infinitesimal reversible change we may write

$$dS = \frac{q_{rev}}{T} \quad . \quad . \quad . \quad . \quad . \quad . \quad (7,12)$$

We complete our proof that entropy is indeed a property of the system, and hence is a quantity which has a fixed and definite value corresponding to any particular state by the following argument.

If we consider a system initially at state A undergoing any reversible cycle of operations it follows from equation (7,7) that

$$\Delta S = \sum_A^A \left(\frac{q}{T}\right)_{rev} < 0. \quad . \quad . \quad . \quad . \quad (7,13)$$

The value of S when the system is in state A must therefore be independent of the past history of the system and must depend solely on its state.

We will now consider a system changing from state A to state B by a path the whole or part of which is irreversible, and we shall show that the quantity $\sum_A^B \left(\frac{q}{T}\right)_{irrev}$ is less than that quantity relating to the reversible path.

This may be proved in the general case from the Clausius Inequality. Figure 7,8 shows a cycle ABA, in which the change A to B is carried out by a series of operations, one or more of which are irreversible, but the return process

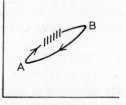

Figure 7,8.

B to A is reversible throughout. Since any cycle is irreversible, if any portion of it is not reversible, we may say from (7,8) that

$$\sum_A^A \left(\frac{q}{T}\right)_{\text{irrev}} < 0,$$

and dividing the path into two portions A–B and B–A

$$\sum_A^B \left(\frac{q}{T}\right)_{\text{irrev}} + \sum_B^A \left(\frac{q}{T}\right)_{\text{rev}} < 0.$$

Reversing the portion B–A

$$\sum_A^B \left(\frac{q}{T}\right)_{\text{irrev}} - \sum_A^B \left(\frac{q}{T}\right)_{\text{rev}} < 0.$$

Hence

$$\sum_A^B \left(\frac{q}{T}\right)_{\text{irrev}} < \sum_A^B \left(\frac{q}{T}\right)_{\text{rev}}.$$

Therefore

$$\Delta S = S_B - S_A > \sum_A^B \left(\frac{q}{T}\right)_{\text{irrev}}. \quad . \quad . \quad . \quad (7,14)$$

or for an infinitesimal irreversible change

$$dS > \frac{q_{\text{irrev}}}{T} \quad . \quad . \quad . \quad . \quad . \quad (7,15)$$

Stage 4. The Entropy Principle

So far in this chapter our interest has been focused on the change in entropy of the system, and we have seen (combining equation 7,12 and inequality 7,15), that when a system undergoes an infinitesimal change accompanied by the absorption of a quantity of heat q, its change in entropy is given by the expression

$$dS_{\text{system}} \geqslant \frac{q}{T}, \quad . \quad . \quad . \quad . \quad . \quad (7,16)$$

the equality sign being applicable when the change takes place reversibly and the inequality sign being applicable to a natural spontaneous change. We note particularly that in the case of a reversible *adiabatic* process

$$dS_{\text{system}} = 0 \quad . \quad . \quad . \quad . \quad . \quad (7,17)$$

and that in the case of a natural spontaneous adiabatic process

$$dS_{system} > 0. \quad . \quad . \quad . \quad . \quad . \quad . \quad (7,18)$$

It is now necessary to consider not only the change in entropy of the system in which the process takes place but also the change in entropy of the surroundings.

We consider first a system in thermal equilibrium with the surroundings and suppose that a reversible process takes place to an infinitesimal degree, and is accompanied by the passage of a quantity of heat q from surroundings to system. Since the system absorbs a quantity of heat as part of a reversible process, its entropy increases by an amount equal to $\frac{q}{T}$. Since the surroundings lose the same quantity of heat at the same temperature, its entropy decreases by an amount equal to $\frac{q}{T}$. It follows that the total entropy of the system and surroundings *considered together* is unchanged, so that

$$dS_{total} = dS_{system} + dS_{surroundings} = 0. \quad . \quad . \quad (7,19)$$

This statement represents the most important characteristic of a reversible change.

We now consider a natural spontaneous process.

We can proceed in various ways. The most general way is that illustrated by Figure 7,9. Represented therein is a system which in due course will undergo a natural spontaneous change. Here we place no restrictions on the relationship between the system and the surroundings. They need not be in thermal equilibrium, neither need they be in mechanical equilibrium. At some considerable distance from the system we build an adiabatic wall, so far away indeed that we may assume that its presence will have no effect on the course of the change in the system. The immediate surroundings (those enclosed within the wall) will, of course, be effected by the natural spontaneous change in the system; the remote surroundings will not.

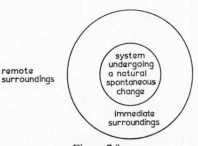

Figure 7,9.

We now designate the system and the immediate surroundings taken together the "super-system", and permit the natural spontaneous change in the system to take place. Since the super-system is by definition isolated from the remote surroundings, any change within becomes adiabatic, and it follows from (17,18) that since the process taking place is a natural spontaneous one, that

$$dS_{\text{super-system}} = dS_{\text{system}} + dS_{\text{immediate surroundings}} > 0. \quad (7,20)$$

The entropy of the remote surroundings is unchanged, so that we may write

$$dS_{\text{total}} = dS_{\text{system}} + dS_{\substack{\text{immediate} \\ \text{surroundings}}} + dS_{\substack{\text{remote} \\ \text{surroundings}}} > 0. \quad (7,21)$$

We now cease to consider the division of the surroundings into two areas and write

$$dS_{\text{total}} = dS_{\text{system}} + dS_{\text{surroundings}} > 0. \quad . \quad . \quad (7,22)$$

In other words, we have shown that the total entropy of the system and surroundings considered together increases. *This statement represents the most important characteristic of a natural spontaneous process.*

Statement (7,22) may possibly be understood more clearly if it is demonstrated by some specific cases. Two should suffice: Figure 7,10 illustrates a spontaneous irreversible chemical reaction occurring to an infinitesimal degree in a system requiring the absorption of q units of heat. The system is in thermal equilibrium, with a heat reservoir of such a type that the loss of a small quantity of heat will result in no change in temperature. Both the system and the heat reservoir are at the same temperature. As the result of the spontaneous process occurring in the system we can write

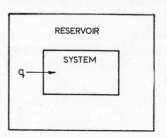

Figure 7,10.

$$dS_{\text{system}} > \frac{q}{T}.$$

The heat q has, however, passed from reservoir to system reversibly because there is no temperature difference between the two. Therefore, the decrease in entropy of the reservoir equals $\frac{q}{T}$, and the increase in entropy of system and reservoir considered together must therefore be $dS_{\text{system}} - \frac{q}{T}$, which is some positive quantity.

We choose as our second example two thermal reservoirs, one at temperature T_1, and one at a lower temperature T_2. On connecting the reservoirs by some thermal conductor, heat flows spontaneously from the hot to the colder reservoir. If the hot reservoir loses q units of heat at temperature T_1, the decrease in entropy equals $\dfrac{q}{T_1}$. The cold reservoir gains q units of heat at temperature T_2, so that its increase in entropy equals $\dfrac{q}{T_2}$. The overall increase in entropy of the complete system is $\dfrac{q}{T_2} - \dfrac{q}{T_1}$, which, since T_2 is less than T_1, is some positive quantity.

We summarise the above by the statement that *when a system undergoes a reversible change, the total entropy of the system and surroundings remains constant, but that when a system undergoes a natural spontaneous change, the total entropy of the system and surroundings increases.*

Combining expressions (7,19) and (7,22) we write

It follows that for a finite change

$$dS_{\text{total}} \geqslant 0.$$
$$\left. \begin{array}{c} \\ \\ \end{array} \right\} \qquad \cdots \qquad (7,23)$$
$$\Delta S_{\text{total}} \geqslant 0.$$

The foregoing argument completes the establishment of the following facts:

1. There exists a thermodynamic property which we call ENTROPY.

2. The entropy of an isolated system can never decrease. Whatever be the nature of the change which an isolated system may undergo, its entropy can only increase if the change takes place along a natural path, or remains constant if the change takes place reversibly.

3. Interaction between a system and its surroundings can never lead to a decrease in the total entropy, where we use the expression total entropy to mean the sum of the entropy of the system and that of its surroundings. The total entropy can only increase during a natural change, or remain constant if the change takes place reversibly.

The Second Law: General Discussion

At the beginning of this chapter we chose to express the Second Law by postulating the irreversibility of all natural spontaneous changes, and demonstrated that the reason why the effect of no natural process can ever be completely erased is that it appears impossible to convert a quantity of energy available only as heat into mechanical work without bringing about other changes of state in other bodies. We then sought to express the irreversibility of all natural spontaneous processes in terms of thermodynamic quantities. That we have now done. The irreversibility of all natural spontaneous processes is characterised by the increase in entropy that results. This statement, which is perhaps the most useful expression of the Second Law, is also called the ENTROPY PRINCIPLE. It is the most important principle established in this book: it is possibly the most important yet established in science.

We should at this stage recognise the fundamental difference between the First and Second Laws. The First Law is concerned with the *conservancy* of energy: the fact that the total energy of the universe remains constant no matter what processes occur. The Second Law establishes a quantity which is not conserved, but which is continuously increased. Since natural changes continuously occur there is more entropy in the universe today than there was yesterday; there will be more tomorrow than there is today. Its increase is the very epitome of natural change.[1]

From the point of view of the chemist, the Entropy Principle is that which we have been seeking. We require to know whether a particular reaction

$$A \rightleftharpoons B$$

will, under the conditions we find convenient to apply, proceed from left to right or right to left. We now have the answer: *The reaction will proceed in that direction which coincides with an increase in the total entropy of the universe.*

The importance of the correct understanding of this last sentence cannot be over-emphasised. Too often the student understands the Second Law to mean that a natural spontaneous process leads to an increase in entropy, and assumes that this necessarily means an increase in entropy of the system alone. This is correct *if, and only if,* the system is isolated from the surroundings, so that the entropy of the latter is unchanged. It is rare that reactions are studied under circumstances such as these. Usually a reaction is studied under such circumstances that the system concerned is free to exchange energy with the surroundings, such as happens when a system reacts at constant temperature and pressure. Under such circumstances the Second Law says nothing about the change in entropy of the system *alone*, but states only that the *sum* of the entropies of the system and surroundings must increase. In fact, in the case of many spontaneous exothermic reactions such as

$$H_2 + \tfrac{1}{2}O_2 \longrightarrow H_2O_{(liq)}$$

carried out at room temperature, the reacting system suffers a considerable decrease in entropy. The increase in entropy of the surroundings is, however, so large that the total entropy of the universe, i.e. that of the system and surroundings taken together, is increased.

[1] The word entropy comes from the Greek word for transformation. It was chosen by Clausius to describe the "transformation content" of a system.

Entropy and Thermodynamic Probability

We end this chapter by discussing not what entropy *does* but what it *is*. To this question classical thermodynamics does not provide an answer; it limits itself to expressions concerning the *change in entropy*, and shows how the change in entropy of a system is related to other quantities, and how such changes may be calculated. In fact, it limits itself to such statements that in an infinitesimal change in which a system absorbs a quantity of heat q, the entropy of the system increases by an amount dS related to q by the expression

$$dS \geqslant \frac{q}{T}.$$

Of the nature of entropy it has nothing to say.

To provide an answer we have to engage the services of another branch of science, now generally called STATISTICAL THERMODYNAMICS. We have already explained in Chapter 2 that in the statistical treatment the system under discussion is examined particle by particle, and the thermodynamic properties of the system evaluated by considering the contribution made by each constituent particle of the system in turn.

To illustrate the principles involved we consider a system consisting of a particular quantity of gas maintained in a particular thermodynamic state. Its internal energy at any particular moment will equal the sum of the energies possessed by the individual molecules. Although we may isolate the system, and so ensure that its internal energy remains constant, it is clear that intermolecular collisions will result in continual changes in the quantity of energy possessed by any one molecule, and if it were possible to examine the system at successive moments and obtain a series of instantaneous photomicrographs of the system as a whole, we should find that each differed from the rest *in detail*. Each photograph would represent a different *micro-state*, the energies and dispositions of the individual molecules in each micro-state differing from those in another.

This means that to any one thermodynamic state defined by such quantities as internal energy, pressure, temperature and so on, obtained by large-scale measurements carried out on the system as a whole, there corresponds a large number of different micro-states revealed only when the system is subjected to examination molecule by molecule. The number of micro-states which correspond to a particular thermodynamic state is called the THERMODYNAMIC PROBABILITY of the system, and is assigned the symbol W. It is a matter merely of statistical argument, as we shall show in Chapter 13, that *if it is assumed that all possible micro-states are equally accessible to the system*, the most probable thermodynamic state which a system will assume under given conditions is that which encompasses the maximum number of micro-states, simply because it is more likely that a system will find itself in a thermodynamic state which can be attained by a large number of possible micro-states, than that it will assume a thermodynamic state which can be attained only by a small number of possible molecular arrangements.

We may assume therefore that when an unstable isolated[1] system proceeds to equilibrium it changes to a state of greater thermodynamic probability. In other words, a natural spontaneous process in an isolated system leads to an increase in its W value. We have already seen, however, that when an isolated system undergoes a natural spontaneous change its entropy increases. We have therefore two quantities, the entropy of the system and its W value, both of which increase during a natural spontaneous change. We suspect therefore either that the two quantities are the same or that one is some function of the other varying monotonously with it.

We shall show in Chapter 13 that the connection between the two quantities is logarithmic, that

$$S = k \log_e W \qquad \qquad (7,24)$$

where k is a quantity known as the Boltzmann Constant. We shall not explore this matter further at this stage, but have introduced the concept of the entropy of a system as a measure of the number of possible micro-states available to it, merely in order to give it some physical reality.

EXERCISES 7

7,1. An engineering firm issues a prospectus giving details of a new design of engine and electrical generator. The engine derives energy from a slow combustion chamber in which a new solid fuel is burnt, the calorific value of which is 6000 cal gm^{-1}. 3·6 kgm of fuel are burnt per hour, at which rate the maximum temperature of the combustion chamber is maintained at 425° C. The engine exhausts to the atmosphere which may be assumed to be at 17° C.

The prospectus claims that the generator will maintain an output of 15 kwatt.

Do you recommend investment?

7,2. The changes in pressure and volume which take place in the cylinder of a spark-ignition engine such as that using petrol approximate to those shown in Figure 6,2. Process $a \longrightarrow b$ represents the intake stroke in which petrol vapour and air are drawn into the cylinder, and process

---

[1] We consider an isolated system at this stage only because of its simplicity. The same principles apply to changes which occur in a system which is permitted to interact with the surroundings, but in such cases we have to consider changes in the surroundings as well.

$b \longrightarrow c$ the compression stroke in which the gas is compressed adiabatically from V_2 to V_1. Process $c \longrightarrow d$ corresponds to the combustion process, and is equivalent to the absorption of a quantity of heat q_1 sufficient to raise the temperature of the gas from T_c to T_d. Process $d \longrightarrow e$ is an adiabatic expansion, and process $e \longrightarrow b$ corresponds to the decrease in pressure within the cylinder consequent upon opening the exhaust valve. This process is equivalent to the rejection of a quantity of heat q_2 sufficient to raise the temperature of the gas from T_b to T_e. Process $b \longrightarrow a$ is the exhaust stroke.

Assuming that the molar thermal capacity of the gas in the system is independent of temperature, prove that the thermal efficiency of the cycle is given by the equation

$$\eta = 1 - \left(\frac{1}{r}\right)^{\gamma-1}$$

where r is the compression ratio V_2/V_1 and γ the ratio of principal molar thermal capacities of the gas.

Prove that this efficiency is necessarily less than that of a Carnot engine working between the highest temperature (T_d) and the lowest (T_b).

7,3. A series of Carnot engines are arranged, so that each engine absorbs the heat rejected by the preceding one at the temperature at which it was rejected. If each engine performs the same amount of work, show that the difference between the temperatures of heat absorption and heat rejection is the same for all engines.

7,4. A reversible engine, the working substance in which is an ideal diatomic gas, operates in a cycle which when represented on a $p - V$ diagram is a rectangle, the sides of which are parallel to the p and V axes. If p_1 and p_2 are the lower and higher pressures, and V_1 and V_2 the lower and higher volumes, and if $p_2 = 2p_1$ and $V_2 = 2V_1$, show that the efficiency of the engine is $\frac{2}{19}$.

7,5. A spring is placed in a large thermostat at $300°$ K and is stretched isothermally and reversibly from its original length L_1 (in which its tension is zero) to length L_2, during which it is found that $2·00$ cal of heat are absorbed by the spring. The stretched spring is then released and allowed to collapse to its initial length, during which process $5·00$ cal of heat are given up to the thermostat. The spring is now again in its initial state.

Calculate the work performed *on* the spring and its change in entropy during the stretching process, then the change in its entropy during the collapse, and finally, the change in entropy of the universe during the overall process.

7,6. Elaborate on the statement that the entropy change during a particular process depends only on the initial and final states of the system, whereas the heat absorbed during the process does not.

7,7. The form of the Second Law favoured by Clausius is that *heat will not pass spontaneously from one body to another at higher temperature.* Use this statement to prove the Carnot theorem. (Hint: the method used is similar to that used on page 98, except that the two cycles are now regulated so that the work performed is the same in each case.)

7,8. Show that the Clausius statement of the Second Law quoted above is equivalent to the statement that *it is impossible by making use of any cyclic series of operations any number of times to convert completely a quantity of energy available only as heat into mechanical work.*

CHAPTER 8

THE CALCULATION OF ENTROPY CHANGES

We have shown that the increase in entropy of a system concerned in some infinitesimal change is given by the expression

$$dS_{\text{system}} \geqslant \frac{q}{T} \qquad \qquad (8,1)$$

and that the change in entropy of the system and surroundings is governed by the expression

$$dS_{\text{total}} = dS_{\text{system}} + dS_{\text{surrounding}} \geqslant 0. \qquad (8,2)$$

Finite changes are described by the expressions

$$\Delta S_{\text{system}} \geqslant \sum \frac{q}{T} \qquad \qquad (8,3)$$

and
$$\Delta S_{\text{total}} = \Delta S_{\text{system}} + \Delta S_{\text{surroundings}} \geqslant 0. \qquad (8,4)$$

We will first calculate the change in entropy of systems during simple finite processes *which we will assume can be carried out reversibly*, so that we may use the equation

$$\Delta S_{\text{system}} = \sum \frac{q}{T}, \qquad \qquad (8,5)$$

and later in the chapter will consider the bearing that such results have on processes which must necessarily proceed by natural spontaneous, i.e. irreversible, paths.

(1) The Fusion of a Solid

Consider a system consisting of a solid and liquid in equilibrium at temperature T. If the system be maintained at constant pressure, the absorption of a quantity of heat L_f, known as the Molar Latent Heat of Fusion, leads to the fusion of one mole of solid.

$$\Delta S = S_{1 \text{ mole of liquid}} - S_{1 \text{ mole of solid}} = \frac{L_f}{T}. \qquad (8,6)$$
$$ {\scriptstyle\text{at temperature } T} {\scriptstyle\text{at temperature } T}$$

For example, the molar latent heat of fusion of ice at 273·15° K is 1435·7 cal, therefore the molar entropy of fusion

$$\Delta S = \frac{1435\cdot7}{273\cdot15} \text{ cal deg}^{-1} \text{ mole}^{-1}.$$

(2) The Evaporation of a Liquid

The absorption of a quantity of heat L_e, known as the Molar Latent Heat of Evaporation, leads to the evaporation at constant pressure of one mole of liquid.

$$\Delta S = S_{1 \text{ mole of vapour} \atop \text{at temperature } T} - S_{1 \text{ mole of liquid} \atop \text{at temperature } T} = \frac{L_e}{T}. \quad . \quad . \quad (8,7)$$

For example, at 373·15° K the molar latent heat of evaporation of water is 9720 cal, and therefore the molar entropy of evaporation

$$\Delta S = \frac{9720}{373\cdot15} \text{ cal deg}^{-1} \text{ mole}^{-1}.$$

(3) Polymorphic Phase Changes

The conversion of rhombic sulphur into monoclinic at temperature T is accompanied by the absorption of a quantity of heat analogous to the latent heat of fusion or evaporation. Denoting the molar quantity by the symbol L_p, the change in entropy per mole is given by the equation

$$\Delta S = \frac{L_p}{T}. \quad . \quad . \quad . \quad . \quad . \quad (8,8)$$

(4) The Rise in Temperature of a Body from T_1 to T_2

Consider first a system maintained at constant volume. The quantity of heat required to raise the temperature of one mole of substance from temperature T to temperature $T + dT$ equals $C_v dT$, where C_v is the molar thermal capacity at constant volume.

The increase in entropy of the system during the rise in temperature from T_1 to T_2 is therefore given by the expression

$$\Delta S = \int_{T_1}^{T_2} \frac{C_v}{T} dT. \quad . \quad . \quad . \quad . \quad (8,9)$$

If, over the temperature range concerned, C_v remains independent of temperature, equation (8,9) integrates to give

$$\Delta S = C_v \log_e \frac{T_2}{T_1}. \quad . \quad . \quad . \quad (8,10)$$

If the molar thermal capacity changes with temperature, it may, as explained in Chapter 4, be expressed by some equation of the form

$$C_v = \alpha + \beta T + \gamma T^2 \ldots$$

and the constants α, β and γ determined by experiment. In this case

$$\Delta S = \int_{T_1}^{T_2} \left(\frac{\alpha}{T} + \beta + \gamma T \ldots \right) dT$$

i.e. $$\Delta S = \alpha \log_e \frac{T_2}{T_1} + \beta(T_2 - T_1) + \frac{\gamma}{2}(T_2{}^2 - T_1{}^2) \ldots \qquad (8,11)$$

If the system be maintained at constant pressure, the corresponding equations are

$$\Delta S = C_p \log_e \frac{T_2}{T_1} \quad \cdot \quad \cdot \quad \cdot \quad \cdot \quad \cdot \quad (8,12)$$

and $$C_p = a + bT + cT^2 \ldots$$

so that

$$\Delta S = a \log_e \frac{T_2}{T_1} + b(T_2 - T_1) + \frac{c}{2}(T_2{}^2 - T_1{}^2) \ldots \qquad (8,13)$$

(5) General Expressions for Reversible Changes in an Ideal Gas

Consider one mole of gas changing reversibly from p_1, V_1, T_1 to p_2, V_2, T_2. For an infinitesimal change

$$dS = \frac{q}{T} \quad \text{or} \quad q = TdS.$$

But for a reversible change in which no work other than expansion work is performed

$$q = dU + pdV$$

so that $$dS = \frac{dU}{T} + \frac{p}{T}dV$$

but since $$dU = C_v dT \quad \text{and} \quad \frac{p}{T} = \frac{R}{V}$$

$$dS = \frac{C_v dT}{T} + R\frac{dV}{V} \quad \cdot \quad \cdot \quad \cdot \quad \cdot \quad \cdot \quad (8,14)$$

Alternative forms of equation (8,14) may be obtained as follows:

since $\qquad pV = RT$ and $d(pV) = RdT,$

$$dS = C_v \frac{d(pV)}{pV} + R\frac{dV}{V} \quad . \quad . \quad . \quad . \quad . \quad . \quad (8,15)$$

Hence $\qquad dS = C_v \frac{(pdV + Vdp)}{pV} + R\frac{dV}{V}$

$$= C_v\frac{dV}{V} + C_v\frac{dp}{p} + R\frac{dV}{V}$$

$$= C_p\frac{dV}{V} + C_v\frac{dp}{p}. \quad . \quad . \quad . \quad . \quad . \quad (8,16)$$

Also $\qquad RdT = pdV + Vdp,$

therefore $\qquad \dfrac{dT}{T} = \dfrac{p}{RT}dV + \dfrac{V}{RT}dp$

i.e. $\qquad \dfrac{dT}{T} = \dfrac{dV}{V} + \dfrac{dp}{p},$

so that $\qquad \dfrac{dV}{T} = \dfrac{dT}{T} - \dfrac{dp}{p}.$

Therefore $\qquad dS = C_v\dfrac{dT}{T} + R\dfrac{dT}{T} - R\dfrac{dp}{p}$

$$= C_p\frac{dT}{T} - R\frac{dp}{p}. \quad . \quad . \quad . \quad . \quad . \quad (8,17)$$

The corresponding integral forms are

$$S_2 - S_1 = \Delta S = C_v \log_e \frac{T_2}{T_1} + R \log_e \frac{V_2}{V_1} \quad . \quad . \quad (8,14a)$$

$$= C_v \log_e \frac{p_2 V_2}{p_1 V_1} + R \log_e \frac{V_2}{V_1} \quad . \quad . \quad (8,15a)$$

$$= C_p \log_e \frac{V_2}{V_1} + C_v \log_e \frac{p_2}{p_1} \quad . \quad . \quad (8,16a)$$

$$= C_p \log_e \frac{T_2}{T_1} - R \log_e \frac{p_2}{p_1} \quad . \quad . \quad (8,17a)$$

(6) The Reversible Isothermal Expansion of an Ideal Gas

Consider one mole of an ideal gas expanding from $p_1 V_1$ to $p_2 V_2$. The heat absorbed during the expansion is $RT \log_e \dfrac{V_2}{V_1}$

and therefore $\quad \Delta S = \dfrac{q}{T} = R \log_e \dfrac{V_2}{V_1} = R \log_e \dfrac{p_1}{p_2}.$ $\quad . \quad . \quad .$ (8,18)

This result may of course be obtained from equation (8,14a) since for an isothermal change $T_1 = T_2$.

We shall see in Chapter 12 that in order to use the Third Law of Thermodynamics we require to know the difference between the molar entropy of a pure substance at some elevated temperature and that at the absolute zero of temperature. Such values are obtained by making use of the equations we have already discussed, from measurements of molar thermal capacities and molar latent heats.

We will illustrate the methods used by discussing the determination of the difference between the molar entropy of ethylene at 25° C (298·15° K) and 1 atmosphere pressure, and that at absolute zero, and will use for this purpose the data provided by Egan and Kemp.[1]

Since ethylene is a gas at 25° C and at 1 atmosphere pressure, the process requires the measurement of

(1) the molar thermal capacity at constant pressure of ethylene from 298·15° K to its boiling point (169·40° K);
(2) the molar latent heat of evaporation at 169·40° K;
(3) the molar thermal capacity of liquid ethylene from 169·40° K to its melting point at 1 atmosphere pressure (103·95° K);
(4) the molar latent heat of fusion at 103·95° K; and
(5) the molar thermal capacity of solid ethylene from 103·95° K to a temperature as close to absolute zero as it is convenient to reach.

The change in entropy will then be calculated from the equation

$\Delta S = S^{298 \cdot 15} - S^0$

$$= \int_{169 \cdot 40}^{298 \cdot 15} \frac{C_{p(g)}}{T} dT + \frac{L_e}{169 \cdot 40} + \int_{103 \cdot 95}^{169 \cdot 40} \frac{C_{p(\text{liq})}}{T} dT$$

$$+ \frac{L_f}{103 \cdot 95} + \int_0^{103 \cdot 95} \frac{C_{p_s}}{T} dT. \quad . \quad . \quad (8,19)$$

The first term can be evaluated in two ways. The first is to express the molar thermal capacity as a function of temperature and integrate direct. The second (and more usual) way is to use graphical methods and plot $\dfrac{C_p}{T}$

[1] Egan and Kemp, *J. Am. Chem. Soc.*, 1937, **59**, 1264.

against T or C_p against $\log_e T$, as shown in Figure 8,1.

Since
$$\int_{T_1}^{T_2} \frac{C_p}{T} dT = \int_{T_1}^{T_2} C_p d \log_e T$$

it is evident that the value of the first term is given by the area under the curve in both cases.

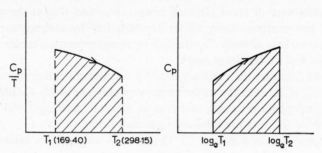

Figure 8,1.

The evaluation of the fifth term is, however, less simple. It was found practicable to determine the molar thermal capacity of solid ethylene only from its melting point (103·95° K) to 15° K.

The values obtained permit the evaluation of the integral $\int_{15}^{103\cdot95} \frac{C_{p_s}}{T} dT$,

but there remains the problem of the evaluation of the integral $\int_{0}^{15} \frac{C_{p_s}}{T} dT$.

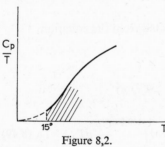

Figure 8,2.

It will be seen from Figure 8,2 that the molar thermal capacity of ethylene (like that of most solids) decreases rapidly as the temperature falls to 15° K. The Debye Theory of Specific Heats suggests that molar thermal capacities of crystalline solids approach zero as the temperature falls to absolute zero, and that over a temperature range close to absolute zero are proportional to the cube of the absolute temperature, i.e. that close to the absolute zero

$$C_p = \alpha T^3 \quad . \quad . \quad . \quad . \quad . \quad . \quad (8,20)$$

If we assume that this equation holds from 0° K to 15° K, the value of α may be calculated by making use of the value of C_p at the lowest temperature at which it was determined, and the integral in which we are interested evaluated, since

$$\int_0^{15} \frac{C_{p_s}}{T}dT = \int_0^{15} \alpha T^2 dT = 1125\alpha. \quad . \quad . \quad . \quad (8,21)$$

The work of Egan and Kemp provides the following results:

$$\int_{169\cdot40}^{298\cdot15} \frac{C_{p_g}}{T}dT \qquad 5\cdot12 \text{ cal deg}^{-1}$$

$$\frac{L_e}{169\cdot40} \qquad 19\cdot11 \text{ cal deg}^{-1}$$

$$\int_{103\cdot95}^{169\cdot40} \frac{C_{p_{liq}}}{T}dT \qquad 7\cdot92 \text{ cal deg}^{-1}$$

$$\frac{L_f}{103\cdot95} \qquad 7\cdot70 \text{ cal deg}^{-1}$$

$$\int_{15}^{103\cdot95} \frac{C_{p_s}}{T}dT \qquad 12\cdot23 \text{ cal deg}^{-1}$$

$$\int_0^{15} \alpha T^2 dT \qquad 0\cdot25 \text{ cal deg}^{-1}$$

i.e. $\Delta S = S^{298\cdot15} - S^0 = 52\cdot33 \text{ cal deg}^{-1}.$

It is clear that the value of the Debye term ($0\cdot25$ cal deg^{-1}) is so small in comparison with the other terms that an appreciable error in it will lead to little change in the value of ΔS.

For certain reasons which will be clear in Chapters 13 and 14, it is desirable to have available entropy differences which would exist if the gas concerned were of ideal behaviour. The corrections to be applied can be evaluated from any one of the equations of state selected. In the case of ethylene Egan and Kemp chose the Berthelot Equation and calculated the correction to be $0\cdot15$ cal deg^{-1}.

We obtain therefore the value for the difference between ethylene as an ideal gas at 25° C and 1 atmosphere pressure and as a solid at absolute zero

$$\Delta S = S^{298\cdot15} - S^0 = 52\cdot48 \text{ cal deg}^{-1} \text{ mole}^{-1}.$$

The difference between the molar entropy of water vapour in the hypothetical standard state of 298·15° K and 1 atmosphere pressure and ice at the absolute zero was determined with great accuracy by Giauque and Strut.[1]

The values they obtained at each stage of the investigation are as shown below:

1. The lowest temperature at which the molar thermal capacity of ice was measured was 10° K. The value of $\int_0^{10} \frac{C_{p_{ice}}}{T} dT$ was therefore obtained by means of the Debye equation to give the value 0·022 cal deg⁻¹.

2. The experimental values of the molar thermal capacity of ice from 10° to 273·15° yields a value of $\int_{10}^{273·15} \frac{C_{p_{ice}}}{T} dT$ of 9·081 cal deg⁻¹.

3. The latent heat of fusion at 273·15° was found to be 1435·7 cal, giving the value of the entropy of fusion as 5·257 cal deg⁻¹.

4. The value of $\int_{273·15}^{298·15} \frac{C_{p_{water}}}{T} dT$ was obtained graphically and proved to be 1·580 cal deg⁻¹.

5. The molar latent heat of evaporation at 298·15° is 10,499 cal, so that the entropy of evaporation is 35·220 cal deg⁻¹.

6. Evaporation at 298·15° K yields water vapour at 23·756 mm pressure. In order to obtain the value for water vapour in the hypothetical state of 298·15° and 1 atmosphere pressure, we have to calculate the change in entropy which would result from the isothermal compression of the gas. If we treat the gas as ideal, it is clear from equation (8,18) that

$$\Delta S = S_{760\,mm} - S_{23·756\,mm}$$

$$= R \log_e \frac{23·756}{760}$$

$$= -6·886 \text{ cal deg}^{-1}.$$

The correction for gas imperfections proves to be 0·002 cal deg⁻¹.

From these results it follows that the difference between the molar entropy of water vapour in the hypothetical state of 1 atmosphere pressure and 298·15° K and that of ice at absolute zero is 44·28 cal deg⁻¹.

The student might well question the significance of the result obtained in view of the fact that water vapour cannot exist at 298·15° K and at 1 atmosphere pressure. The answer is that it is convenient to tabulate thermodynamic properties of all liquids and gases under the same

[1] Giauque and Strut, *J. Am. Chem. Soc.*, 1936, **58**, 1144.

conditions, that is, to tabulate thermodynamic properties of substances in some *standard state*. The standard state chosen as the most convenient is that of an ideal gas at 298·15° K and at 1 atmosphere pressure. Such tabulated values may not have any *real* significance in the sense that they apply to a real situation, but they are of the greatest possible practical value, because values of the same thermodynamic properties in a real situation can be calculated from them. We may, for example, require in a practical problem to know the change in entropy when ice at 0° K changes to steam at 600° K and 1 atmosphere pressure (a *real* situation). This may be calculated from the tabulated value as follows:

$$S_{1\,\text{atm}}^{600} - S^\circ = \{S_{1\,\text{atm}}^{600} - S_{1\,\text{atm}}^{298\cdot15}\} + \{S_{1\,\text{atm}}^{298\cdot15} - S^\circ\}$$

$$= \int_{298\cdot15}^{600} \frac{C_p}{T}dT + 44\cdot28.$$

The evaluation of the integral requires merely the knowledge of C_p over the temperature range concerned.

It is necessary to point out that in some instances a change of state from absolute zero to some elevated temperature is not always as simple as that described. Many solids undergo phase changes at definite temperatures. In such cases extra terms must be added to equation (8,19).

The Calculation of Entropy Changes in Irreversible Processes

So far in this chapter we have considered entropy changes in reversible processes. We now require to consider changes of state which are brought about by natural spontaneous (i.e. irreversible) processes.

The Second Law states that for a finite irreversible change

$$\Delta S_{\text{system}} \geqslant \sum \frac{q_{\text{irrev}}}{T} \quad \cdot \quad \cdot \quad \cdot \quad \cdot \quad \cdot \quad (8,3)$$

and that

$$\Delta S_{\text{total}} = \Delta S_{\text{system}} + \Delta S_{\text{surroundings}} \geqslant 0. \quad \cdot \quad \cdot \quad \cdot \quad (8,4)$$

Such an irreversible process in which a system changes from state 1 to state 2 is shown in Figure 8,3 by the broken line which we have called Path I. We may measure the quantities of heat absorbed by the system during this change, but it is evident from expression (8,3) that such quantities cannot be used in the calculation of ΔS unless we have reason to suppose that the heat absorbed by the irreversible process is the same as that which would be

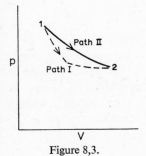

Figure 8,3.

absorbed along the corresponding reversible path. Usually this will not be the case.

If, however, we can devise some convenient reversible path such as that shown as Path II in Figure 8,3, and if we can calculate the quantities of heat which would be absorbed along this path, we may calculate ΔS from the expression

$$\Delta S = \sum \frac{q_{\text{rev}}}{T}.$$

The value of ΔS is independent of path because

$$\Delta S = S_2 - S_1$$

and S_1 and S_2 have unique values determined solely by the initial and final states of the system.

In principle therefore we calculate the change in entropy brought about by an irreversible change from the heats which would be absorbed if we linked the initial and final states by any convenient reversible path.

In some cases this is particularly simple. We may imagine the spontaneous expansion of one mole of an ideal gas from an initial state defined by the properties p_1, V_1, T_1 to a final state defined by the properties p_2, V_2, T_2. The process is represented by the broken line $1 \longrightarrow 2$ in Figure 8,4. We do not interest ourselves in the heat actually absorbed in the spontaneous process; instead, we select some reversible path between the initial and final states. The simplest path is a reversible isothermal expansion at T_1, from V_1 to some intermediate volume V_3, followed by a reversible adiabatic expansion from V_3 to V_2.

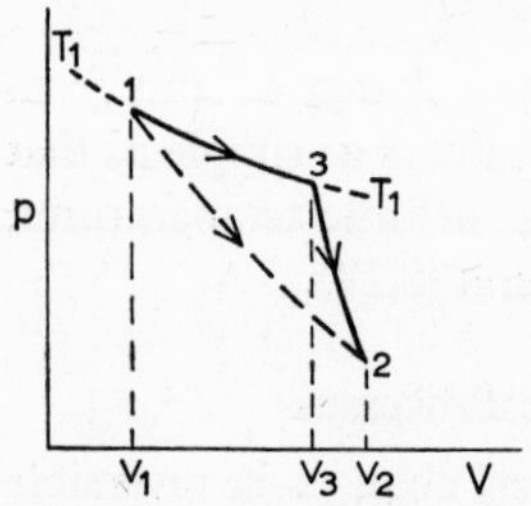

Figure 8,4. The irreversible expansion of an ideal gas.

The heat absorbed in process $1 \longrightarrow 3$ is

$$RT_1 \log_e \frac{V_3}{V_1}$$

and

$$S_3 - S_1 = R \log_e \frac{V_3}{V_1}.$$

The heat absorbed in process $3 \longrightarrow 2$ is zero, and since the process is reversible, $S_2 - S_3 = 0$.

The change in entropy from state 1 to state 2 is therefore given by the equation

$$S_2 - S_1 = R \log_e \frac{V_3}{V_1}.$$

We now require to eliminate V_3 from the result. Since process $3 \longrightarrow 2$ is reversible and adiabatic

$$T_1 V_3{}^{\gamma-1} = T_2 V_2{}^{\gamma-1}$$

i.e.
$$V_3 = V_2\left(\frac{T_2}{T_1}\right)^{\frac{1}{\gamma-1}}.$$

Since $R = C_p - C_v$ and $\gamma = \dfrac{C_p}{C_v}$

$$\Delta S = S_2 - S_1 = R \log_e \frac{V_2}{V_1} + C_v \log_e \frac{T_2}{T_1}.$$

which result is of course identical with that given in equation (8,14a).

We now investigate those changes of state in which the quantity of heat absorbed by the system from the surroundings is the same whether the process is reversible or not. As an example of such a process we consider the fusion of one mole of a solid such as ice at constant pressure. In order to consider the process taking place under reversible conditions we imagine that the system consisting of a quantity of ice is maintained at 273·15° K and under a pressure of 1 atmosphere in contact with the surroundings (a thermal reservoir), also at 273·15° K. We now imagine that a quantity of heat equal to 1435·7 cal flows from the thermal reservoir to the system; resulting in the fusion of one mole of ice.

$$\Delta S_{\text{system}} = \frac{1435 \cdot 7}{273 \cdot 15} \text{ cal deg}^{-1}$$

$$\Delta S_{\text{surroundings}} = -\frac{1435 \cdot 7}{273 \cdot 16} \text{ cal deg}^{-1}$$

$$\Delta S_{\text{total}} = \Delta S_{\text{system}} + \Delta S_{\text{surroundings}} = 0.$$

It is useful to note that the quantity of heat absorbed by the system represents its increase in enthalpy, that is to say, the difference between the molar enthalpy of water at 273·15° K and that of ice at the same temperature is 1435·7 cal.

We now consider the same process carried out under irreversible conditions. We again therefore choose a system consisting of a quantity of ice at 273·15° K and under a pressure of 1 atmosphere, but choose now to place the system in contact with a thermal reservoir at some higher temperature T. The flow of heat from the reservoir at temperature T to the system at the lower temperature 273·15° K is an irreversible process, but we find that precisely the same quantity of heat is absorbed by the system in order to fuse one mole of ice as that found before. This is because the quantity of heat required is the difference between the molar enthalpy of water at 273·15° K and that of ice at the same temperature, and is a quantity which is independent of the method by which the heat is supplied.

ΔS_{system} is therefore the same as before, i.e $\dfrac{1435\cdot7}{273\cdot15}$ cal deg^{-1}

$$\Delta S_{\text{surroundings}} = -\frac{1435\cdot7}{T}$$

and $$\Delta S_{\text{total}} = \frac{1435\cdot7}{273\cdot16} - \frac{1435\cdot7}{T}.$$

This quantity is of course greater than zero because T is greater than 273·15° K.

What we have demonstrated in the above argument is that the entropy of fusion of a solid is the same whether the overall fusion process be reversible or not; the increase in the total entropy of the system and surroundings in the irreversible process being accounted for by the fact that the decrease in entropy of the surroundings is less than it is in the case when the heat transfer takes place under reversible conditions.

The same is true of processes in which the absorption of heat by a system at constant pressure or at constant volume results in a rise in temperature, evaporation or other phase change. The methods used earlier in the chapter to calculate the change in entropy of ethylene and water are therefore justified.

We have now considered the calculation of entropy changes in natural spontaneous processes which owe their irreversibility to the fact that the system and surroundings do not remain in equilibrium throughout. There remains that most important group of natural spontaneous processes, chemical reactions, in which the system may remain in mechanical and thermal equilibrium with the surroundings throughout, but which owe their irreversibility to changes in composition. In principle the change in entropy due to a chemical reaction is calculated in the same way as that discussed above. We do not attempt to make calculations along the natural irreversible path, but select an alternative reversible path. The selection of a reversible path, however, presents considerable difficulties, and in fact, can only be done with the help of the Third Law. The principles involved will be discussed in Chapter 12.

EXERCISES 8

8,1. Over the temperature range 0–2000° C, C_p for water vapour may be represented by the equation

$$C_p = 8.81 - 1.9 \times 10^{-3}T + 2.22 \times 10^{-6}T^2 \text{ cal deg}^{-1}.$$

Calculate the entropy change of the system when the temperature of one mole of steam is raised at 1 atmosphere pressure from 150° to 200° C.

8,2. Calculate the entropy change involved in converting two moles of hydrogen from 30 litres at 2 atmospheres pressure to 100 litres at 1 atmosphere pressure. (Assume C_p to be 7.4 cal deg^{-1}.)

8,3. Calculate the change in entropy when one mole of water at 0° C is heated at 1 atmosphere to form steam at 100° C. Assume that the average specific heat of water is 0.98 cal deg^{-1} gm^{-1}, and that the heat of evaporation at 1 atmosphere pressure is 536 cal gm^{-1}.

8,4. Supercooled water at $-10°$ C and at 1 atmosphere pressure in an adiabatic container is seeded. Ice spontaneously appears. Calculate the change in entropy per mole of water present. The only information required is the molar thermal capacity of supercooled water, which may be assumed to be 18 cal deg^{-1} mole^{-1}.

8,5. A system consists of m_1 gm of water initially at temperature T_1 separated from m_2 gm of water initially at T_2. Show that if the two liquids are maintained at constant pressure but allowed to mix adiabatically the entropy of the system increases by an amount equal to

$$c_p \log_e \left[\left\{ \frac{m_1 T_1 + m_2 T_2}{T_1(m_1 + m_2)} \right\}^{m_1} \times \left\{ \frac{m_1 T_1 + m_2 T_2}{(m_1 + m_2)T_2} \right\}^{m_2} \right]$$

It may be assumed that the specific heat of water is independent of temperature over the range concerned.

CHAPTER 9

THE COMBINATION OF THE FIRST AND SECOND LAWS AND THE IDENTIFICATION OF THE THERMODYNAMIC POTENTIALS

Since for an infinitesimal *reversible* change in a static system the First Law may be described by the equation

$$q_{rev} = dU + w_{max},$$

and since the Second Law states that

$$dS = \frac{q_{rev}}{T},$$

the two laws may be combined in the equation

$$TdS = dU + w_{max}.$$

For the present we concern ourselves only with those processes in which the work performed by the system is that performed by expansion, that is to say with those processes for which

$$w_{max} = pdV.$$

Such changes are therefore described by the equation

$$TdS = dU + pdV. \quad . \quad . \quad . \quad . \quad . \quad . \quad (9,1)$$

We now require to consider natural spontaneous (i.e. irreversible) changes. For these the Second Law states that

$$dS \geqslant \frac{q_{irrev}}{T}. \quad . \quad . \quad . \quad . \quad . \quad . \quad (9,2)$$

We find it convenient to convert this expression into an equality by writing

$$dS = \frac{q_{irrev}}{T} + dS_{irrev}. \quad . \quad . \quad . \quad . \quad (9,3)$$

We are not concerned at present with the nature or physical meaning of the quantity dS_{irrev} just introduced. We merely observe by comparison of

(9,2) and (9,3) that irrespective of whether the heat absorbed in the process is positive or negative, the quantity dS_{irrev} must always be positive or zero. It is zero for all irreversible processes in which

$$dS = \frac{q_{\text{irrev}}}{T},$$

and greater than zero for all changes in which

$$dS > \frac{q_{\text{irrev}}}{T}.$$

We now wish to apply equation (9,3) to the various types of irreversible processes discussed in the last chapter. We first consider physical processes taking place at constant pressure, so that the system is at all times in mechanical equilibrium with the surroundings, such processes as the fusion of a solid, the evaporation of a liquid or a rise in temperature of the system. The irreversibility of such processes depends solely on the fact that the system and surroundings are not in thermal equilibrium; in other words, the temperature of the surroundings is higher than that of the system undergoing the change of state. Under such conditions the First Law equation assumes the form

$$q_{\text{irrev}} = dU + pdV,$$

where we denote the irreversibility of the overall process by the use of the suffix irrev, but denote the expansion work performed by the term pdV because the system and surroundings are in mechanical equilibrium. We showed in the last chapter that the quantity of heat required to bring about a particular change of state of this sort (the latent heat of fusion, or evaporation, or the molar thermal capacity), is the same whether the system is in thermal equilibrium with the source of heat or not, and is therefore the same whether the overall process is reversible or not. In other words these are the changes for which

$$dS_{\text{system}} = \frac{q_{\text{irrev}}}{T}.$$

For such changes it is evident from (9,3) that the term dS_{irrev} is zero, and that the First and Second Law expressions can be combined to give the equation

$$TdS = dU + pdV,$$

which is the same as that derived for the reversible process. The same argument applies to irreversible thermal processes carried out at constant volume.

We now consider that group of spontaneous physical processes in which the irreversibility is due to the fact that the system and surroundings are not in mechanical equilibrium. In other words, the pressure of the system is higher than the pressure of the surroundings by a finite amount, so that when the system expands, less than the maximum possible quantity of work is performed and less than the maximum possible quantity of heat is absorbed. For such a process the First Law is expressed by the equation

$$q_{\text{irrev}} = dU + w_{\text{irrev}}.$$

Substituting in (9,3) and rearranging, we obtain the equality

$$TdS = dU + w_{\text{irrev}} + TdS_{\text{irrev}}. \quad . \quad . \quad . \quad (9,4)$$

This equation can be simplified by the following argument. The same change of state resulting in the same change in internal energy can be brought about by an irreversible process described by the equation

$$q_{\text{irrev}} = dU + w_{\text{irrev}},$$

or by a reversible process described by the equation

$$q_{\text{rev}} = dU + w_{\text{max}},$$

so that
$$q_{\text{rev}} - q_{\text{irrev}} = w_{\text{max}} - w_{\text{irrev}},$$

but since $q_{\text{rev}} = TdS$, and for the type of process with which we are at present concerned $w_{\text{max}} = pdV$,

$$TdS - q_{\text{irrev}} = pdV - w_{\text{irrev}}.$$

Equation (9,3) may be rearranged to read

$$q_{\text{irrev}} = TdS - TdS_{\text{irrev}}$$

from which it follows that

$$TdS_{\text{irrev}} + w_{\text{irrev}} = pdV.$$

Substituting in (9,4) we obtain the equation

$$TdS = dU + pdV.$$

We reach the important conclusion that the equation

$$TdS = dU + pdV \quad . \quad . \quad . \quad . \quad . \quad (9,1)$$

describes not only a reversible process but also an irreversible process in which the irreversibility is due to lack of thermal or mechanical equilibrium between the system and surroundings (as long as the only form of work performed by the system is that of expansion).

We now require to discuss the thermodynamics of a chemical reaction. A chemical reaction can proceed reversibly only if:

(a) the system and surroundings remain in thermal and mechanical equilibrium; and
(b) the components of the system are in internal chemical equilibrium throughout.

Reactions which proceed naturally and spontaneously are irreversible, even though the system and surroundings may remain in thermal and mechanical equilibrium, simply because condition (b) is not satisfied. In other words, *a natural spontaneous chemical reaction is irreversible because of the changes in composition which result.*

Since it is this aspect of a chemical reaction which we wish to investigate, we consider a reaction proceeding to an infinitesimal degree in a system which is both in thermal and mechanical equilibrium with the surroundings. We therefore apply the First Law to the reaction in the form

$$q_{irrev} = dU + pdV$$

where we describe the heat absorbed as q_{irrev} because the overall process is irreversible, but denote the reversible expansion work by pdV. Substituting in (9,3) and rearranging, we obtain the equation

$$TdS = dU + pdV + TdS_{irrev}. \quad . \quad . \quad . \quad (9,5)$$

We now remember that whatever circumstances exist, the quantity TsS_{irrev} can never be negative, and rewrite (9,5) in the form

$$\boxed{TdS_{irrev} = TdS - dU - pdV \geqslant 0.} \quad . \quad . \quad (9,6)$$

From this expression it is clear that the term dS_{irrev} represents that quantity of entropy *produced* by a natural spontaneous irreversible process.

Expression (9,6) contains the essence of all that has so far been discussed in this book. It is the fundamental equation of Chemical Thermodynamics and it is from this expression that many of the equations used later are derived.

Equation (9,1) applicable to physical changes, and expression (9,6) applicable to processes involving changes in composition are a sufficient description of all changes which take place in systems capable of performing on the surroundings no work other than expansion work. These are the circumstances under which most physical and chemical processes take place. In some instances, however, work other than expansion work may be performed. If, for example, a chemical reaction takes place in a chemical cell, an electrical charge dQ is transferred from one part of the system to another at different electrical potential. In this case a quantity of work equal to $\mathbf{E}dQ$, where $\mathbf{E}$ represents the potential difference through which the charge is transferred, may be performed. Similarly, a reaction may result in the expansion of a surface film; in which case a quantity of work equal to τda (the product of the surface tension and the increase in area of the film) may be done. In such special cases as these equation (9,1) and expression (9,6) have to be complicated by the inclusion of extra terms, $\mathbf{E}dQ$ or τda as the case may be. We shall not, however, consider these special reactions at this stage. Physical processes described by equation (9,1) will be discussed in the next chapter. Our immediate concern is with expression (9,6).

The Direction Assumed by a Spontaneous Chemical Reaction

Consider a mixture of reactants A, B, C and D, at temperature T and pressure p, capable of interacting according to the chemical equation

$$a\text{A} + b\text{B} \rightleftharpoons c\text{C} + d\text{D}.$$

We wish to know whether some of A and B will turn spontaneously into C and D, or whether some of C and D will turn spontaneously into A and B. For simplicity we suppose that no work other than expansion work is possible. It follows from (9,6) that if the conversion of infinitesimal quantities of A and B into C and D would lead to such changes in S, U and V that

$$TdS - dU - pdV > 0 \quad . \quad . \quad . \quad . \quad (9,7)$$

there is no thermodynamic reason why the reaction should not proceed from left to right. If, however, the changes in these quantities are such that

$$TdS - dU - pdV < 0$$

we conclude that the reaction may not proceed from left to right, but may proceed from right to left. If the changes are such that

$$TdS - dU - pdV = 0$$

no irreversible process is possible in either direction; and we conclude that the system is already in a state of chemical equilibrium.

Expressions (9,6) and (9,7) apply under all circumstances (as long as no work other than expansion work is possible). If we wish to use them to determine whether or not a particular chemical reaction will proceed *to a finite extent*, it is necessary that they be integrated. This will be difficult in the most general case simply because the reaction may result in changes in all the quantities concerned, T, S, U, p and V.

Fortunately, we are rarely concerned as to whether or not a reaction will take place under *general* conditions, but whether or not it will take place under *particular* conditions. In fact, we are usually interested in whether or not a reaction will take place either (i) at constant temperature and at constant volume, or (ii) at constant temperature and at constant pressure. If we restrict ourselves to these conditions we can derive expressions from (9,6) which are simpler to use.

(1) *Reactions at constant temperature and volume*

Under these circumstances

$$TdS = d(TS)_T \quad \text{and} \quad pdV = 0;$$

the expression $TdS_{\text{irrev}} = TdS - dU - pdV \geqslant 0$

therefore reduces to the form

$$TdS_{\text{irrev}} = -d(U - TS)_{T, V} \geqslant 0. \quad . \quad . \quad . \quad (9,8)$$

The quantity $(U - TS)$ must be a property of the system, because it is an arithmetic combination of other properties U, T and S. It is called the HELMHOLTZ AVAILABLE WORK FUNCTION or simply the WORK FUNCTION, is given the symbol A, and is defined by the equation

$$A = U - TS. \quad . \quad . \quad . \quad . \quad (9,9)$$

It follows from this definition and from (9,8) that a reaction at constant temperature and at constant volume will proceed in such a direction that the Work Function of the system is decreased.

(2) *Reactions at constant temperature and pressure*

Under these circumstances

$$TdS = d(TS)_T \quad \text{and} \quad pdV = d(pV)_p$$

The expression

$$TdS_{\text{irrev}} = TdS - dU - pdV \geqslant 0$$

therefore assumes the form

$$TdS_{\text{irrev}} = -d(U + pV - TS)_{T, p} \geqslant 0. \quad . \quad . \quad (9,10)$$

The quantity $(U + pV - TS)$ must be a property of the system because it is an arithmetic combination of others. It is called the GIBBS FREE ENERGY or simply the FREE ENERGY, is given the symbol G, and is defined by the equation

$$G = U + pV - TS. \quad . \quad . \quad . \quad (9,11)$$

Since, however, $H = U + pV$

F

we may also define the Free Energy by the equation

$$G = H - TS. \qquad \qquad (9,12)$$

It follows from (9,10) and (9,11) that a reaction at constant temperature and pressure will take place in that direction that leads to a decrease in the Free Energy of the system.

Earlier in this book we stated that one of the most important questions that thermodynamics would answer was whether or not a particular reaction was possible under the conditions applied. We have now established two criteria which provide the answer: the reaction is possible if

$$dA_{T,V} \leqslant 0, \qquad \qquad (9,13)$$

or if

$$dG_{T,p} \leqslant 0. \qquad \qquad (9,14)$$

Both of these expressions may be integrated under their own restrictive conditions to give

$$\Delta A_{T,V} \leqslant 0, \qquad \qquad (9,13a)$$

and

$$\Delta G_{T,p} \leqslant 0. \qquad \qquad (9,14a)$$

These criteria determine whether or not a reaction is possible to a finite extent. A reaction $aA + bB \longrightarrow cC + dD$ will proceed at constant temperature and volume if a finite decrease in Work Function results. The reaction will proceed at constant temperature and pressure if it is accompanied by a decrease in Free Energy. Clearly, therefore, the measurement of the change in Work Function or Free Energy is a matter of great importance. We now show how this may be done.

Since

$$A = U - TS$$

$$dA = dU - TdS - SdT,$$

and for changes at constant temperature,

$$dA = dU - TdS.$$

This may be integrated for finite changes at constant temperature to give

$$\Delta A = \Delta U - T\Delta S. \qquad \qquad (9,15)$$

For any chemical reaction at constant temperature and constant volume, ΔU is easily determined. As will be remembered from Chapter 4, it is equal to the heat of reaction at constant volume. It may therefore be determined directly or indirectly from calorimetric measurements as described in Chapter 6. There remains the calculation of ΔS. The Second Law states that for a natural spontaneous reaction

$$\Delta S \geqslant \frac{q}{T},$$

so that it is evident that ΔS cannot be calculated from the heat of reaction. Solution of the problem requires the Third Law of Thermodynamics, and further discussion will be delayed until Chapter 12.

The determination of the change in Free Energy for a reaction taking place at constant temperature and pressure follows precisely the same pattern. Since

$$G = H - TS$$
$$dG = dH - TdS - SdT,$$

and for changes at constant temperature

$$dG = dH - TdS.$$

This may be integrated for finite changes at constant temperature to give

$$\Delta G = \Delta H - T\Delta S. \quad . \quad . \quad . \quad . \quad . \quad (9,16)$$

For any reaction at constant temperature and pressure ΔH equals the heat of reaction at constant pressure. Its determination has been described in Chapter 6.

The importance of the concepts of the Work Function and Free Energy cannot be over-emphasised, and equations (9,15) and (9,16), which are true for all isothermal processes, are two of the most important equations derived in this book. It so happens that the chemist is usually more interested in Free Energy than in the Work Function simply because it is more usual to carry out reactions at constant pressure than at constant volume. For just the same reason we are usually more interested in changes in enthalpy than changes in internal energy.

The Physical Significance of the Work Function and Free Energy

Strictly speaking it is unnecessary to attempt to give physical significance to any thermodynamic property of a system. They are mathematical quantities which are important simply because they are state functions, and because mathematical expressions exist connecting one with another. The fact remains, however, that the student often finds their significance easier to grasp if they are given some physical form.

The Work Function is defined by the equation

$$A = U - TS. \quad . \quad . \quad . \quad . \quad . \quad . \quad (9,9)$$

A simultaneous infinitesimal change in U, T and S results in a change in A given by the equation

$$dA = dU - TdS - SdT.$$

An infinitesimal reversible process is described by the equations

$$q_{rev} = dU + w_{max}$$

and
$$dS = \frac{q_{rev}}{T},$$

so that
$$dU - TdS = -w_{max}$$

and
$$dA = -w_{max} - SdT. \quad . \quad . \quad . \quad . \quad (9,17)$$

This equation holds for a reversible change under all conditions. If we now consider a change at constant temperature, the last term vanishes and we can write

$$dA_T = -w_{max}. \quad . \quad . \quad . \quad . \quad (9,18)$$

This equation may be integrated to give

$$\Delta A_T = -w_{max}, \quad . \quad . \quad . \quad . \quad (9,19)$$

so that we see that the decrease in Work Function experienced by a system during an isothermal process equals the maximum work which can be performed on the surroundings. This explains the name given to the property. For a natural spontaneous process between the same initial and final states, the decrease in the Work Function is the same, but the work performed will be less than the maximum work, so we write

$$\Delta A_T > -w. \quad . \quad . \quad . \quad . \quad (9,20)$$

The Free Energy of a system is defined by the equation

$$G = U + pV - TS. \quad . \quad . \quad . \quad (9,11)$$

A simultaneous infinitesimal change in U, p, V, T and S results in a change in G given by the equation

$$dG = dU + pdV + Vdp - TdS - SdT.$$

As we saw earlier, a reversible infinitesimal change is also described by the equation

$$dU - TdS = -w_{max},$$

so that

$$dG = -w_{max} + pdV + Vdp - SdT. \quad . \quad . \quad (9,21)$$

This equation holds for a reversible change under all conditions. If, however, we consider a change at constant pressure and at constant temperature, the last two terms vanish, and we can write

$$dG_{T,p} = -(w_{max} - pdV). \qquad (9,22)$$

This equation may be integrated to give

$$\Delta G_{T,p} = -(w_{max} - p\Delta V), \qquad (9,23)$$

so that the decrease in Free Energy experienced by a system during an isothermal process at constant pressure equals the maximum work which can be performed on the surroundings *less the expansion work which necessarily has to be carried out.*

We have already discussed in Chapter 4 the significance of the maximum work available during a reaction, but it may be useful to reconsider the question in terms of the concepts developed above.

When any change takes place the work performed may be of various sorts; it may be expansion work, electrical work, surface work and so on. If the change takes place reversibly the work performed is the maximum possible which can be obtained from the process: this is the quantity w_{max}. The quantity $(w_{max} - \int pdV)$ is the maximum work less that expansion work which necessarily has to be performed against the surroundings.

We consider two examples. We first consider the reaction

$$C_7H_{16} + 11O_2 \longrightarrow 7CO_2 + 8H_2O$$

proceeding at constant pressure and at some constant temperature so elevated that all the molecular species are gases. Whether the reaction proceeds irreversibly or reversibly a quantity of work equal to $3RT$ is performed against the surroundings when one mole of heptane reacts, because the reaction leads to an increase of three moles of gas.

If the reaction proceeds as a normal combustion process this quantity of work is all that is performed. It is possible, however, to carry out the reaction reversibly using the same sort of arrangement as that discussed on page 48 in Chapter 4. Under these conditions a very much greater quantity of work will be performed. This quantity is the quantity w_{max} for the process, and represents the difference between the Work Function for seven moles of CO_2 and eight moles of steam, and that for one mole of heptane and eleven moles of oxygen. Of this total amount, the quantity $3RT$ is still performed as expansion work against the surroundings; but the quantity $(w_{max} - p\Delta V)$, in this case $(w_{max} - 3RT)$, is energy available for work other than that necessarily performed due to the expansion of the system. It is this quantity which represents the decrease in Free Energy.

We now consider the reaction which takes place at constant temperature and pressure between hydrogen and silver chloride when the reagents are arranged in the form of the cell

$$H_2Pt \mid HCl_{aq} \qquad AgCl \mid Ag.$$

When a conductor is placed across the electrodes the reaction

$$H_2 + 2AgCl \longrightarrow 2HCl + 2Ag$$

takes place, and a potential difference **E** is established across the cell. During the course of the reaction both expansion and electrical work will be performed (actually, the expansion work performed by the system will be negative because the reaction leads to a diminution in volume) so that the operative expression is

$$TdS_{irrev} = TdS - dU - pdV - \mathbf{E}dQ \geqslant 0. \quad . \quad . \quad (9,24)$$

Since the reaction takes place at constant temperature and pressure, this expression reduces to

$$TdS_{irrev} = -dG - \mathbf{E}dQ \geqslant 0.$$

If the reaction is allowed to proceed to a finite extent the amount of electrical work performed will depend on the extent to which the passage of electricity between the electrodes is opposed. If the cell is made to work against an external e.m.f. only infinitesimally less than the e.m.f. established by the cell, the maximum work will be obtained *and the reaction will proceed reversibly*. Under these circumstances the term $TdS_{irrev} = 0$, and the infinitesimal process will be described by the equation

$$-dG = \mathbf{E}dQ.$$

As will be seen in a later chapter, the e.m.f. established by the cell depends on such factors as the concentration of the reactants. If we consider a cell so large that the concentration of the reactants is virtually unchanged when one mole of hydrogen reacts with two moles of silver chloride, so that the e.m.f. established remains constant throughout, the molar decrease in Free Energy is given by the equation

$$-\Delta G = \mathbf{E}\Delta Q,$$

where ΔQ is the total quantity of electricity transported across the cell. The principles of electrochemistry show that this quantity equals two Faradays ($2 \times 96,487$ coulomb), so that we may write

$$-\Delta G = 2\mathbf{E}F.$$

From (9,23) it follows that $2\mathbf{E}\mathbf{F}$ represents the quantity $(w_{max} - p\Delta V)$. We observe that in a cell such as the Daniell Cell

$$Zn \mid ZnSO_{4_{aq}} \;\vdots\; CuSO_{4_{aq}} \mid Cu$$

which depends on the reaction

$$Zn + CuSO_4 \longrightarrow ZnSO_4 + Cu$$

that since the reaction leads virtually to no change in volume, the expansion work term vanishes.

A More Generalised Approach to the Thermodynamics of Chemical Reactions

Earlier in this chapter it was shown that any infinitesimal process in which the only form of work performed is expansion work is described by the expression

$$TdS_{irrev} = TdS - dU - pdV \geqslant 0. \qquad . \quad . \quad . \quad (9,6)$$

Alternative statements may be obtained as follows:

Since $\qquad\qquad d(pV) = pdV + Vdp,$

$$pdV + Vdp - d(pV) = 0.$$

Adding this quantity to the right-hand side of the equation in (9,6) we obtain

$$TdS_{irrev} = TdS - dU - d(pV) + Vdp \geqslant 0,$$

or, since $\qquad dU + d(pV) = dH,$

$$TdS_{irrev} = TdS - dH + Vdp \geqslant 0, \qquad . \quad . \quad . \quad (9,25)$$

or, since $\qquad d(TS) = TdS - SdT,$

we may add $\qquad d(TS) - TdS - SdT$

and obtain $\qquad TdS_{irrev} = -SdT - pdV - dU + d(TS),$

but $\qquad\qquad dA = dU - d(TS),$

so that $\qquad\qquad TdS_{irrev} = -SdT - dA - pdV \geqslant 0. \quad . \quad . \quad (9,26)$

We may also add $d(TS) - TdS - SdT$ to the right-hand side of the equation in (9,25) and obtain

$$TdS_{irrev} = -SdT + Vdp - dH + d(TS),$$

but $\qquad\qquad dG = dH - d(TS),$

so that

$$TdS_{irrev} = -SdT - dG + Vdp \geqslant 0. \qquad . \quad . \quad . \quad (9,27)$$

The four expressions

$$TdS_{\text{irrev}} = TdS - dU - pdV \geqslant 0 \quad . \quad . \quad . \quad (9,6)$$

$$TdS_{\text{irrev}} = TdS - dH + Vdp \geqslant 0 \quad . \quad . \quad . \quad (9,25)$$

$$TdS_{\text{irrev}} = -SdT - dA - pdV \geqslant 0 \quad . \quad . \quad . \quad (9,26)$$

$$TdS_{\text{irrev}} = -SdT - dG + Vdp \geqslant 0 \quad . \quad . \quad . \quad (9,27)$$

are equivalent. That which we choose to use to investigate the progress of a natural spontaneous change depends solely on the conditions under which the change takes place.

It follows from this expression that for any natural spontaneous process

$$TdS_{\text{irrev}} = -dU_{S,V} = -dH_{S,p} = -dA_{T,V} = -dG_{T,p} \geqslant 0 \quad (9,28)$$

and that

$$dU_{S,V} \leqslant 0 \quad . \quad . \quad . \quad . \quad (9,29)$$

$$dH_{S,p} \leqslant 0 \quad . \quad . \quad . \quad . \quad (9,30)$$

$$dA_{V,T} \leqslant 0 \quad . \quad . \quad . \quad . \quad (9,31)$$

$$dG_{p,T} \leqslant 0. \quad . \quad . \quad . \quad . \quad (9,32)$$

By this generalised treatment we have shown that four criteria determine the direction chosen by a natural spontaneous process. The last two are, of course, the same as those derived by the more specialised arguments earlier in the chapter. They happen to be of much greater practical importance than the first two, simply because the conditions under which they apply are just the conditions under which we wish to study a chemical reaction; whereas conditions under which we attempted to keep the entropy constant would be most difficult to devise. As explained earlier, it so happens that we are usually more interested in studying a reaction at constant pressure than at constant volume, so that the last criterion,

$$dG_{T,p} \leqslant 0$$

becomes of much greater practical importance than the other three.

The student will remember that in any purely mechanical process a system tends to choose that direction which leads to a reduction in potential energy. The quantities U, H, A and G are therefore often called the four THERMODYNAMIC POTENTIALS, because under the appropriate conditions natural spontaneous processes take place in that direction which leads to their reduction.

The Thermodynamic Criteria for Equilibrium

Any infinitesimal process that takes place in a system which is maintained in thermodynamic equilibrium must necessarily be reversible. The term TdS_{irrev} is therefore zero, and it follows from expressions (9,6), (9,25), (9,26) and (9,27) that the process is described by any of the equations

$$dU = TdS - pdV \quad . \quad . \quad . \quad (9,33)$$

$$dH = TdS + Vdp \quad . \quad . \quad . \quad (9,34)$$

$$dA = -SdT - pdV \quad . \quad . \quad . \quad (9,35)$$

$$\text{and } dG = -SdT + Vdp. \quad . \quad . \quad . \quad (9,36)$$

It follows that equilibrium conditions are characterised by the equations

$$dU_{S,V} = 0 \quad . \quad . \quad . \quad . \quad . \quad . \quad (9,37)$$

$$dH_{S,p} = 0 \quad . \quad . \quad . \quad . \quad . \quad . \quad (9,38)$$

$$dA_{T,V} = 0 \quad . \quad . \quad . \quad . \quad . \quad . \quad (9,39)$$

$$dG_{T,p} = 0. \quad . \quad . \quad . \quad . \quad . \quad . \quad (9,40)$$

We have already shown that during a natural spontaneous process $U_{S,V}$, $H_{S,p}$, $A_{T,V}$ and $G_{T,p}$ decrease. It follows therefore that at equilibrium under the appropriate conditions U, H, A and G are at a minimum.

EXERCISES 9

9,1. Under what circumstances is the free energy change in a chemical reaction equal to the change in the Helmholtz available work function?

9,2. The standard molar free energies of formation, molar enthalpies of formation and molar entropies of nitric oxide, nitrogen dioxide, sulphur dioxide and sulphur trioxide at 25° C are given in Table 12.I.

Use these values to determine (a) the change in entropy of the system when one mole of sulphur dioxide and one mole of nitrogen dioxide react at 25° C and at 1 atmosphere pressure to form sulphur trioxide and nitric oxide; (b) the entropy change in the surroundings (assuming that they, too, are at 25° C); and (c) the *entropy produced* in the system as the result of the reaction. What is the increase in entropy of the universe as the result of the reaction having taken place?

9,3. Expression (9,29) shows that a spontaneous reaction taking place *at constant entropy and constant volume* leads to a decrease in internal energy. Explain how you might carry out a reaction so that the entropy and volume of the system is the same at the beginning and the end, and show that the decrease in internal energy follows as a natural consequence.

9,4. A system is maintained at constant pressure throughout the operations described. The first operation consists of the spontaneous conversion of a quantity of substances A and B into C at constant temperature. The second operation consists of the absorption or loss of a quantity of heat so that the entropy of the system in its final state is the same as that in its initial state. Compare the quantity of heat absorbed or given out in the first operation with that absorbed or given out in the second.

CHAPTER 10

FURTHER RELATIONSHIPS BETWEEN THERMO-DYNAMIC PROPERTIES AND SOME OF THEIR APPLICATIONS

It has been shown that any infinitesimal process which takes place in a system at equilibrium, and in which no work other than expansion work is possible, is described by the following equations:

$$dU = TdS - pdV \qquad \cdots \quad \cdots \quad (9,33)$$

$$dH = TdS + Vdp \qquad \cdots \quad \cdots \quad (9,34)$$

$$dA = -SdT - pdV \qquad \cdots \quad \cdots \quad (9,35)$$

and
$$dG = -SdT + Vdp. \qquad \cdots \quad \cdots \quad (9,36)$$

Further relationships derive as follows:

From (9,33)
$$\left(\frac{\partial U}{\partial S}\right)_v = T \qquad \cdots \quad \cdots \quad (10,1)$$

and
$$\left(\frac{\partial U}{\partial V}\right)_s = -p. \qquad \cdots \quad \cdots \quad (10,2)$$

From (9,34)
$$\left(\frac{\partial H}{\partial S}\right)_p = T \qquad \cdots \quad \cdots \quad (10,3)$$

and
$$\left(\frac{\partial H}{\partial p}\right)_s = V. \qquad \cdots \quad \cdots \quad (10,4)$$

From (9,35)
$$\left(\frac{\partial A}{\partial V}\right)_T = -p \qquad \cdots \quad \cdots \quad (10,5)$$

and
$$\left(\frac{\partial A}{\partial T}\right)_v = -S. \qquad \cdots \quad \cdots \quad (10,6)$$

From (9,36)
$$\left(\frac{\partial G}{\partial p}\right)_T = V \qquad \cdots \quad \cdots \quad (10,7)$$

and
$$\left(\frac{\partial G}{\partial T}\right)_p = -S. \qquad \cdots \quad \cdots \quad (10,8)$$

Differentiating (10,1) with respect to V at constant S, and (10,2) with respect to S at constant V, we obtain

$$\left\{\frac{\partial\left(\frac{\partial U}{\partial S}\right)_v}{\partial V}\right\}_S = \frac{\partial^2 U}{\partial S \partial V} = \left(\frac{\partial T}{\partial V}\right)_S \quad \ldots \quad (10,9)$$

and

$$\left\{\frac{\partial\left(\frac{\partial U}{\partial V}\right)_S}{\partial S}\right\}_V = \frac{\partial^2 U}{\partial V \partial S} = -\left(\frac{\partial p}{\partial S}\right)_V \ldots \quad (10,10)$$

It follows that

$$\left(\frac{\partial T}{\partial V}\right)_S = -\left(\frac{\partial p}{\partial S}\right)_V \ldots \ldots \quad (10,11)$$

By following the same procedure with equations (10,3) to (10,8) we obtain three more relationships:

$$\left(\frac{\partial T}{\partial p}\right)_S = \left(\frac{\partial V}{\partial S}\right)_p \quad \ldots \ldots \quad (10,12)$$

$$\left(\frac{\partial p}{\partial T}\right)_V = \left(\frac{\partial S}{\partial V}\right)_T \quad \ldots \ldots \quad (10,13)$$

and

$$\left(\frac{\partial V}{\partial T}\right)_p = -\left(\frac{\partial S}{\partial p}\right)_T \quad \ldots \ldots \quad (10,14)$$

Equations[1] (10,11) to (10,14) were first derived by Maxwell, and are known as MAXWELL'S RELATIONS. Some applications of these equations follow.

The Thermodynamic Criterion of an Ideal Gas

From (9,33) it follows that

$$\left(\frac{\partial U}{\partial V}\right)_T = T\left(\frac{\partial S}{\partial V}\right)_T - p,$$

but

$$\left(\frac{\partial p}{\partial T}\right)_V = \left(\frac{\partial S}{\partial V}\right)_T \quad \ldots \ldots \quad (10,13)$$

therefore

$$p = T\left(\frac{\partial p}{\partial T}\right)_V - \left(\frac{\partial U}{\partial V}\right)_T \quad \ldots \quad (10,15)$$

---

[1] These equations may also be derived by applying Theorem 4, given on page xv, to equations (9,33) to (9,36), since Theorem 4 states that if

$$dA = BdC + DdE,$$
$$\left(\frac{\partial D}{\partial C}\right)_E = \left(\frac{\partial B}{\partial E}\right)_C.$$

For a substance obeying the equation

$$pV = nRT$$

$$\left(\frac{\partial p}{\partial T}\right)_V = \frac{nR}{V} = \frac{p}{T}.$$

Substitution in (10,15) shows that

$$\left(\frac{\partial U}{\partial V}\right)_T = 0, \quad \dots \dots \dots \dots \quad (10,16)$$

and from (9,34) it follows that

$$\left(\frac{\partial H}{\partial p}\right)_T = T\left(\frac{\partial S}{\partial p}\right)_T + V$$

but

$$-\left(\frac{\partial S}{\partial p}\right)_T = \left(\frac{\partial V}{\partial T}\right)_p \quad \dots \dots \dots \dots \quad (10,14)$$

so that

$$V = T\left(\frac{\partial V}{\partial T}\right)_p + \left(\frac{\partial H}{\partial p}\right)_T. \quad \dots \dots \quad (10,17)$$

For a substance obeying the equation

$$pV = nRT,$$

$$\left(\frac{\partial V}{\partial T}\right)_p = \frac{nR}{p} = \frac{V}{T}.$$

Substitution in (10,17) shows that

$$\left(\frac{\partial H}{\partial p}\right)_T = 0. \quad \dots \dots \dots \quad (10,18)$$

For a substance obeying the equation

$$pV = nRT,$$

$$U = H - nRT.$$

So from (10,16)

$$\left(\frac{\partial (H - nRT)}{\partial V}\right)_T = 0$$

i.e.

$$\left(\frac{\partial H}{\partial V}\right)_T = 0, \quad \dots \dots \dots \quad (10,19)$$

and from (10,18)

$$\left(\frac{\partial (U + nRT)}{\partial p}\right)_T = 0$$

so that

$$\left(\frac{\partial U}{\partial p}\right)_T = 0. \quad \dots \dots \dots \quad (10,20)$$

The relationship $pV = nRT$ is the criterion of an ideal gas which derives from kinetic theory; we see that for such a substance the thermodynamic criteria are the expressions

$$\left(\frac{\partial U}{\partial V}\right)_T = 0, \quad \left(\frac{\partial H}{\partial p}\right)_T = 0, \quad \left(\frac{\partial H}{\partial V}\right)_T = 0, \quad \left(\frac{\partial U}{\partial p}\right)_T = 0. \quad (10,21)$$

It will be remembered that in Chapter 5 these relationships were accepted as an empirical consequence of the Joule experiment; we have now shown their theoretical origin.

It should be noted that we have incidentally derived the equation

$$p = T\left(\frac{\partial p}{\partial T}\right)_V - \left(\frac{\partial U}{\partial V}\right)_T. \quad \cdot \quad \cdot \quad \cdot \quad (10,15)$$

referred to and used in Chapter 5.

A General Expression for the Difference in Principal Molar Thermal Capacities

In Chapter 4 we derived the general equation

$$C_p - C_v = \left\{p + \left(\frac{\partial U}{\partial V}\right)_T\right\}\left(\frac{\partial V}{\partial T}\right)_p \quad \cdot \quad \cdot \quad \cdot \quad (4,21)$$

where the symbols U and V denote the molar internal energy and volume. We can now put this equation into a more useful form:

from (9,33)
$$\left(\frac{\partial U}{\partial V}\right)_T = T\left(\frac{\partial S}{\partial V}\right)_T - p$$

where S is the molar entropy of the substance.

It follows that
$$C_p - C_v = T\left(\frac{\partial S}{\partial V}\right)_T\left(\frac{\partial V}{\partial T}\right)_p$$

but since
$$\left(\frac{\partial p}{\partial T}\right)_V = \left(\frac{\partial S}{\partial V}\right)_T \quad \cdot \quad \cdot \quad \cdot \quad \cdot \quad \cdot \quad (10.13)$$

$$C_p - C_v = T\left(\frac{\partial p}{\partial T}\right)_V\left(\frac{\partial V}{\partial T}\right)_p.$$

From Theorem 3, page xv,

$$\left(\frac{\partial p}{\partial T}\right)_V\left(\frac{\partial T}{\partial V}\right)_p\left(\frac{\partial V}{\partial p}\right)_T = -1$$

so that
$$\left(\frac{\partial p}{\partial T}\right)_V = -\left(\frac{\partial V}{\partial T}\right)_p\left(\frac{\partial p}{\partial V}\right)_T.$$

Therefore
$$C_p - C_v = -\frac{T\left(\frac{\partial V}{\partial T}\right)_p^2}{\left(\frac{\partial V}{\partial p}\right)_T}. \quad \ldots \ldots \quad (10,22)$$

For any substance the quantities $\left(\frac{\partial V}{\partial T}\right)_p$ and $\left(\frac{\partial V}{\partial p}\right)_T$ can be measured directly without undue difficulty. We have therefore a means of determining the quantity $C_p - C_v$.

Equation (10,22) is one of great practical importance. The quantity C_p may, in the case of liquids and solids, be measured directly with ease, but the direct determination of the quantity C_v is virtually impossible for obvious reasons. The quantity C_v is, however, required particularly to test the theories of Solid State Physics; it is calculated therefore from equation (10,22). It is usual to express (10,22) in terms of α the volume coefficient of thermal expansion, and β the isothermal compressibility coefficient:

$$\alpha = \frac{1}{V}\left(\frac{\partial V}{\partial T}\right)_p$$

and
$$\beta = -\frac{1}{V}\left(\frac{\partial V}{\partial p}\right)_T,$$

so that (10,22) becomes

$$C_p - C_v = \frac{TV\alpha^2}{\beta} \quad \ldots \ldots \quad (10,23)$$

where V equals the molar volume.

Clearly, if v' equals the specific volume of the substance under investigation, the difference in principal specific heats is given by the equation

$$c_p - c_v = \frac{Tv'\alpha^2}{\beta}. \quad \ldots \ldots \quad (10,24)$$

General Expressions for the Changes in Thermodynamic Properties over Ranges of Temperature and Pressure

Since the internal energy and enthalpy of an ideal gas is dependent only on temperature, the changes in internal energy and enthalpy when one mole of ideal gas changes from state 1 defined by temperature T_1 and pressure p_1 to state 2 defined by temperature T_2 and pressure p_2 are given by the equations

$$\Delta U = U_2 - U_1 = \int_{T_1}^{T_2} C_v dT$$

and
$$\Delta H = H_2 - H_1 = \int_{T_1}^{T_2} C_p dT.$$

We have also seen that the change in molar entropy is given by the equation

$$\Delta S = S_2 - S_1 = \int_{T_1}^{T_2} \frac{C_p}{T} dT - R \int_{p_1}^{p_2} \frac{dp}{p}.$$

The corresponding equations for substances other than ideal gases are complicated by the dependence of the internal energy and enthalpy on the pressure of the system as well as on the temperature.

A general expression for ΔH, i.e. $H_{T_2, p_2} - H_{T_1, p_1}$ applicable to all substances may be obtained as follows: The general equation

$$dH = TdS + Vdp$$

is written in the form

$$dH = T\left\{\left(\frac{\partial S}{\partial T}\right)_p dT + \left(\frac{\partial S}{\partial p}\right)_T dp\right\} + Vdp.$$

Since

$$\left(\frac{\partial S}{\partial T}\right)_p = \frac{C_p}{T}$$

and

$$\left(\frac{\partial S}{\partial p}\right)_T = -\left(\frac{\partial V}{\partial T}\right)_p \quad . \quad . \quad . \quad . \quad (10,14)$$

$$dH = C_p dT + \left\{V - T\left(\frac{\partial V}{\partial T}\right)_p\right\}dp$$

$$= C_p dT + V(1 - \alpha T)dp$$

where α is the volume coefficient of thermal expansion. It follows that

$$\Delta H = H_2 - H_1 = \int_{T_1}^{T_2} C_p dT + \int_{p_1}^{p_2} V(1 - \alpha T)dp.$$

A general expression for ΔS may be obtained as follows:
Since S is a function of temperature and pressure

$$dS = \left(\frac{\partial S}{\partial T}\right)_p dT + \left(\frac{\partial S}{\partial p}\right)_T dp$$

$$= C_p \frac{dT}{T} - \left(\frac{\partial V}{\partial T}\right)_p dp$$

$$= C_p \frac{dT}{T} - \alpha Vdp$$

and

$$\Delta S = S_2 - S_1 = \int_{T_1}^{T_2} \frac{C_p}{T} dT - \int_{p_1}^{p_2} \alpha Vdp.$$

These equations are of considerable practical importance, particularly in the field of mechanical engineering. The analysis of steam turbines requires the knowledge of the specific enthalpy and entropy of water and steam over a large temperature and pressure range. The absolute value of these quantities is not required, so for tabulation purposes the convention is adopted that both the specific enthalpy and specific entropy of water at the triple point is zero, so that the tabulated value of $H_{T,p}$ is really $H_{T,p} - H_{\text{Triple point}}$ and the tabulated value of $S_{T,p}$ really $S_{T,p} - S_{\text{Triple point}}$. These quantities are calculated by means of the expressions derived above, and depend on the measurement of the specific heat and the volume coefficient of thermal expansion. The tabulated results are called STEAM TABLES, the best known of which were produced first by H. L. Callendar in the United Kingdom, and later by J. H. Keenan and F. G. Keyes in the U.S.A. Extracts from these are published in a very convenient form in *Thermodynamic Tables and Other Data* by the Cambridge University Press. Similar information is required for common refrigerants such as carbon dioxide, ammonia, Freon12 (CCl_2F_2) and methyl chloride. For these the arbitrary datum state for zero enthalpy and entropy is that of the liquid at $-40°$ F.

Phase Changes: The Clausius–Clapeyron Equation

For any physical change in which no work other than expansion work is performed we know that at equilibrium

$$\left(\frac{\partial p}{\partial T}\right)_V = \left(\frac{\partial S}{\partial V}\right)_T. \qquad \ldots \ldots \quad (10,13)$$

Consider now a system consisting of a liquid and vapour in equilibrium at temperature T. The vapour pressure p is dependent only on the temperature, and is independent of the quantity of liquid present and therefore of the volume. The quantity $\left(\frac{\partial p}{\partial T}\right)_V$ may therefore be replaced by $\frac{dp}{dT}$.

The increases in entropy and volume resulting from the evaporation of dn moles of liquid at temperature T are given by the equations

$$dS = \frac{L_e dn}{T}$$

and
$$dV = (V_g - V_{\text{liq}})dn$$

where L_e is the molar latent heat of evaporation, and V_g and V_{liq} are the molar volumes at the same temperature.

Hence
$$\left(\frac{\partial S}{\partial V}\right)_T = \frac{L_e}{T(V_g - V_{\text{liq}})}$$

and
$$\frac{dp}{dT} = \frac{L_e}{T(V_g - V_{liq})}. \qquad \ldots \ldots \quad (10,25)$$

This equation is known as the Clausius–Clapeyron Equation. It permits the calculation of the variation of vapour pressure with temperature, or, as is seen more clearly, by rewriting the equation in the form

$$\frac{dT_b}{dp} = \frac{T_b(V_g - V_{liq})}{L_e} \qquad \ldots \ldots \quad (10,26)$$

where we have used the symbol T_b to denote the boiling point, it permits calculation of the variation of boiling point with pressure.

An approximation to (10,25) which is useful under certain circumstances is obtained as follows:

At temperatures well below the critical point, the molar volume of the liquid is very small compared to that of the vapour, and if we make the assumption that the vapour obeys the gas law $pV = RT$, we obtain the equation

$$\frac{dp}{dT} = \frac{L_e p}{RT^2}$$

or
$$\frac{d \log_e p}{dT} = \frac{L_e}{RT^2}. \qquad \ldots \ldots \quad (10,27)$$

This equation may be integrated over a temperature range small enough for us permissibly to assume the independence of L_e to give the equation

$$\log_e p = -\frac{L_e}{RT} + b, \qquad \ldots \ldots \quad (10,28)$$

where b is the integration constant.
This equation may be put in the form

$$\log_e p = b - \frac{a}{T}, \qquad \ldots \ldots \quad (10,29)$$

so that the determination of the vapour pressure of a liquid at two temperatures permits the evaluation of the constants a and b, and the calculation therefrom of the vapour pressure of the liquid at any other temperature within the range concerned.

We point out that whereas equation (10,25) is *exact*, the assumptions made in the derivation therefrom of equation (10,29) are such that the latter is of limited application.

Equivalent expressions to (10,25) can be deduced to describe the variation of vapour pressure of a solid with respect to temperature in terms of the molar latent heat of sublimation L_s

$$\frac{dp}{dT} = \frac{L_s}{T(V_g - V_s)}, \qquad \ldots \ldots \quad (10,30)$$

the variation of melting point of a solid with temperature, in terms of the molar heat of fusion L_f

$$\frac{dp}{dT} = \frac{L_f}{T(V_{\text{liq}} - V_s)}, \quad \cdots \quad \cdots \quad (10,31)$$

or the variation with pressure of the transition temperature between two crystalline forms of the same substance in terms of the molar heat of transformation L_p

$$\frac{dp}{dT} = \frac{L_{p\alpha \longrightarrow \beta}}{T(V_\beta - V_\alpha)}. \quad \cdots \quad \cdots \quad (10,32)$$

We illustrate the use of these equations by calculating the dependence of the melting point of ice on the pressure applied.

At $273 \cdot 1°$ K $V_{\text{water}} = 18 \cdot 002$ cc. mole^{-1}

$$V_{\text{ice}} = 19 \cdot 633 \text{ cc. mole}^{-1}$$

$$L_f = 1435 \cdot 7 \text{ cal mole}^{-1}$$

$$= 1435 \cdot 7 \times 4 \cdot 184 \times 10^7 \text{ erg mole}^{-1}$$

$$\frac{dT}{dp} = \frac{273 \cdot 1 \times (-1 \cdot 631)}{1435 \cdot 7 \times 4 \cdot 184 \times 10^7} \text{ degrees dyne}^{-1} \text{ cm}^2$$

but 1 atmosphere equals $1 \cdot 013 \times 10^6$ dynes cm^{-2}, therefore at $273 \cdot 1°$ K

$$\frac{dT}{dp} = -\frac{273 \cdot 1 \times 1 \cdot 631 \times 1 \cdot 013 \times 10^6}{1435 \cdot 7 \times 4 \cdot 184 \times 10^7} \text{ degrees atm}^{-1}$$

$$= -0 \cdot 0075 \text{ degrees atm}^{-1}.$$

If the melting point at some definite pressure is required the student may prefer the following method:

Equation (10,31) is written in the form

$$\frac{d \log_e T}{dp} = \frac{V_{\text{liq}} - V_s}{L_f}.$$

The quantity on the right-hand side is almost independent of pressure, so that this equation can be integrated between limits $T_1 p_1$ and $T_2 p_2$ to give

$$\log_e \frac{T_2}{T_1} = \frac{V_{\text{liq}} - V_s}{L_f}(p_2 - p_1).$$

This equation will be used to determine the melting point of ice at 100 atmospheres pressure, using the values for the molar volumes of water and ice and that for the latent heat of fusion at $273 \cdot 1°$ K.

$$\log_{10} \frac{T_2}{273 \cdot 1} = -\frac{1 \cdot 631 \times 1 \cdot 013 \times 10^6 (100 - 1)}{2 \cdot 303 \times 1435 \cdot 7 \times 4 \cdot 184 \times 10^7}$$

$$= -0 \cdot 001183.$$

It follows that $T_2 = 272 \cdot 35°$ K. The student should note that in the above T_2/T_1 is so close to unity that seven figure logarithms should be used in calculations of this sort.

The Gibbs–Helmholtz Equation

In the last chapter we emphasised the importance of the determination of the change in free energy of a system as the result of a chemical reaction. The actual calculation from thermal data requires the Third Law, and is described in Chapter 12. Usually, the thermal data available for the calculation applies to 25° C, and results in the evaluation of ΔG at this temperature.

An equation known as the GIBBS–HELMHOLTZ EQUATION permits the calculation of ΔG at any temperature from its value at one particular temperature.

Consider a chemical reaction

$$A \longrightarrow B$$

taking place at constant temperature and pressure.

$$\Delta G = G_B - G_A$$

and

$$\Delta S = S_B - S_A.$$

We earlier showed that

$$\left(\frac{\partial G}{\partial T}\right)_p = -S. \qquad \dots \qquad (10,8)$$

It therefore follows that the rate of change of ΔG with respect to temperature is given by the expression

$$\left(\frac{\partial(\Delta G)}{\partial T}\right)_p = \left(\frac{\partial(G_B - G_A)}{\partial T}\right)_p = -S_B + S_A = -\Delta S.$$

We have already seen that for a process at constant temperature

$$\Delta G = \Delta H - T\Delta S. \qquad \dots \qquad (9,16)$$

It follows therefore that

$$\Delta G = \Delta H + T\left\{\frac{\partial(\Delta G)}{\partial T}\right\}_p. \qquad \dots \qquad (10,33)$$

This equation may be put into a form which is, for some purposes, more convenient:

$$\left\{\frac{\partial\left(\frac{\Delta G}{T}\right)}{\partial T}\right\}_p = \Delta G\frac{d\left(\frac{1}{T}\right)}{dT} + \frac{1}{T}\left(\frac{\partial(\Delta G)}{\partial T}\right)_p$$

$$= \frac{1}{T}\left(\frac{\partial(\Delta G)}{\partial T}\right)_p - \frac{\Delta G}{T^2}.$$

It follows that

$$T^2\left\{\frac{\partial\left(\frac{\Delta G}{T}\right)}{\partial T}\right\}_p = T\left\{\frac{\partial(\Delta G)}{\partial T}\right\}_p - \Delta G,$$

and from (10,33) it is evident that the right-hand side of this equation equals $-\Delta H$, so that we may write

$$\left\{\frac{\partial\left(\frac{\Delta G}{T}\right)}{\partial T}\right\}_p = -\frac{\Delta H}{T^2}. \quad\quad\quad (10,34)$$

Equations (10,33) and (10,34) are known as the GIBBS–HELMHOLTZ EQUATION. Similar equations can be derived showing the variation with temperature of the Work Function; the equation corresponding to (10,34) being

$$\left\{\frac{\partial\left(\frac{\Delta A}{T}\right)}{\partial T}\right\}_V = -\frac{\Delta U}{T^2}. \quad\quad\quad (10,35)$$

The Integration of the Gibbs–Helmholtz Equation

From (10,34) it follows that

$$\int d\left(\frac{\Delta G}{T}\right)_p = -\int\frac{\Delta H}{T^2}dT. \quad\quad\quad (10,36)$$

If over the temperature range concerned ΔH does not change appreciably we obtain on integration the equation

$$\frac{\Delta G}{T} \simeq \frac{\Delta H}{T} + I^*,$$

where I^* is the integration constant, so that

$$\Delta G \simeq \Delta H + I^*T. \quad\quad\quad (10,37)[1]$$

If therefore ΔG is known at any one temperature, I^* can be calculated, so that the value of ΔG at any other temperature can be obtained. It is stressed that relationship (10,37) is an approximate one only, and that the temperature range over which it can be expected to hold is very small, being limited to that range over which ΔH (and therefore I^*) does not appreciably change.

---

[1] If the approximate equation $\Delta G \simeq \Delta H + I^*T$ is compared with (9,16), $\Delta G = \Delta H - T\Delta S$, it will be seen that $I \simeq -\Delta S$. It is clear therefore that (10,37) can hold only over such a temperature range that the change in ΔS is negligible.

The accurate solution of (10,36) requires us to take into account the variation of ΔH with temperature. We proceed as follows:

We saw in Chapter 6 that the variation of ΔH with temperature can be expressed in terms of the molar thermal capacities of the reactants and reaction products.

For the reaction $n_1A + n_2B \longrightarrow n_3C + n_4D$

$$\left(\frac{\partial(\Delta H)}{\partial T}\right)_p = n_3 C_{p_C} + n_4 C_{p_D} - n_1 C_{p_A} - n_2 C_{p_B}$$

the various values of C_p can be expressed as functions of temperature, e.g.

$$C_{p_A} = a + bT + cT^2 \ldots \qquad \qquad \text{(6,12)}$$

so that $\left\{\dfrac{\partial(\Delta H)}{\partial T}\right\}_p = \Sigma a + \Sigma bT + \Sigma cT^2 \ldots$

and therefore $\Delta H = \Sigma aT + \dfrac{\Sigma b}{2}T^2 + \dfrac{\Sigma c}{3}T^3 \ldots + I'. \qquad \text{(6,14)}$

It follows that over the same temperature range as equations (6,12) are valid

$$\int d\left(\frac{\Delta G}{T}\right)_p = -\int \frac{\Sigma aT + \dfrac{\Sigma b}{2}T^2 + \dfrac{\Sigma c}{3}T^3 \ldots + I'}{T^2} dT$$

and $\dfrac{\Delta G}{T} = -\Sigma a \log_e T - \dfrac{\Sigma b}{2}T - \dfrac{\Sigma c}{6}T^2 \ldots + \dfrac{I'}{T} + I,$

where I is the second integration constant, i.e.

$$\Delta G = -\Sigma aT \log_e T - \frac{\Sigma b}{2}T^2 - \frac{\Sigma c}{6}T^3 \ldots + I' + IT. \quad \text{(10,38)}$$

It should be noted that two integration constants appear in the last equation, I' the integration constant of equation (6,14) and I which appears in the last step. I' can of course be evaluated if the heat of reaction at any one given temperature is known. Similarly, if ΔG is known at any one temperature, the constant I can be calculated, so that ΔG can then be evaluated at any other temperature. It is important to note that equation (10,38) can be used only over that temperature range for which the constants a, b, $c \ldots$ in equation (6,12) have been experimentally established.

Example. For the reaction

$$H_2 + \tfrac{1}{2}O_2 \longrightarrow H_2O_{(g)}$$

at $288°$ K $\Delta H = -57,780$ calories, and at $298°$ K $\Delta G = -54,590$ calories.

It is required to calculate ΔG at 1000° K, given that over the temperature range 288–1000° K the molar thermal capacities at constant pressure of the reactants are described by the equations

$$H_2, \; C_p = 6\cdot50 + 0\cdot0009T \text{ cal mole}^{-1}$$

$$O_2, \; C_p = 6\cdot50 + 0\cdot0010T \text{ cal mole}^{-1}$$

$$H_2O_{(g)}, \; C_p = 8\cdot81 - 0\cdot0019T + 0\cdot00000222T^2 \text{ cal mole}^{-1}.$$

From these values it follows that

$$\Delta H = -0\cdot94T - 0\cdot00165T^2 + 0\cdot000,000,74T^3 + I'.$$

Substituting the value $\Delta H = -57,780$ cal at $T = 288°$, it follows that $I' = -57,393$ cal, so that the general expression for the variation of ΔH over this temperature range is given by the equation

$$\Delta H = -0\cdot94T - 0\cdot00165T^2 + 0\cdot000,000,74T^3 - 57,393.$$

This equation corresponds to (6,14). Substituting in (10,36) gives

$$\int d\left(\frac{\Delta G}{T}\right)_p = \int \left\{\frac{0\cdot94}{T} + 0\cdot00165 - 0\cdot000,000,74T + \frac{57,393}{T^2}\right\}dT$$

i.e. $\quad \dfrac{\Delta G}{T} = 0\cdot94 \log_e T + 0\cdot00165T - 0\cdot000,000,37T^2 - \dfrac{57,393}{T} + I$

or $\quad \Delta G = 0\cdot94T \log_e T + 0\cdot00165T^2 - 0\cdot000,000,37T^3 - 57,393 + IT.$

Substituting the value $\Delta G = -54,590$ cal at $T = 298°$, shows that $I = 3\cdot6$. The general expression for ΔG is therefore

$$\Delta G = 0\cdot94T \log_e T + 0\cdot00165T^2 - 0\cdot000,000,37T^3 - 57,393 + 3\cdot6T$$

so that $\quad$ at $T = 1000°$ K, $\quad \Delta G = -46,017$ cal.

We point out that equation (10,33)

$$\Delta G = \Delta H + T\left\{\frac{\partial(\Delta G)}{\partial T}\right\}_p$$

permits the calculation of ΔH if the value of ΔG and its rate of change with temperature is known. For the majority of chemical reactions this is not very useful, simply because values of ΔH can be determined directly from thermal measurements much more easily than can values of ΔG, but the same is not true of reactions which take place in electro-chemical cells. In such cases (as has been shown already) the value of ΔG can be determined easily from the e.m.f. of the cell, but the evaluation of ΔH

from thermal data is not possible,[1] and the evaluation of ΔH depends on equation (10,33). An example of the use of this equation for this purpose is given in Chapter 17.

EXERCISES 10

10,1. As explained earlier in the book the work performed by a system such as a fibre or rubber band when stretched is given by the equation

$$w = -\phi dL$$

where ϕ is the tension on the band, and L its length. The change in volume of such a system on stretching and hence the pdV work concerned is negligible and a reversible change is therefore described by the equation

$$TdS = dU - \phi dL.$$

Show that such a process carried out at constant pressure is governed by the equations

$$dG = -SdT + \phi dL$$

$$\left(\frac{\partial S}{\partial L}\right)_T = -\left(\frac{\partial \phi}{\partial T}\right)_L$$

and
$$\left(\frac{\partial U}{\partial L}\right)_T = \phi - T\left(\frac{\partial \phi}{\partial T}\right)_L.$$

If you are told that the tension of a piece of rubber maintained at constant length is directly proportional to the absolute temperature, what conclusion can you reach regarding the function of the work performed on the system when the rubber is stretched?

10,2. The vapour pressure of a liquid is 8·75 cm of mercury at 48·9° C, 11·49 cm at 54·4° C and 14·94 cm at 60·0° C. Its latent heat of evaporation at 54·4° C is 566 cal gm^{-1}, the specific volume of its vapour 9·72 litres gm^{-1}, and that of the liquid so small that it may be neglected.

Estimate the absolute zero of temperature on the Celsius scale.

10,3. Establish the relation

$$C_p - C_v = T\left(\frac{\partial p}{\partial T}\right)_v\left(\frac{\partial V}{\partial T}\right)_p$$

and show that the difference in C_p and C_v for a van der Waals gas is given by the expression

$$\frac{R}{1 - \dfrac{2a(V-b)^2}{V^3RT}}$$

where the symbols have their usual significance.

---

[1] ΔH is not equal to the heat absorbed because work other than expansion work is performed.

10,4. A gas is found to obey the equation of state

$$pV = RT + Bp$$

where V is its molar volume and B is a constant independent of temperature. Show that the internal energy of the gas is independent of the pressure and volume of the system, but that the enthalpy is not. Show that the increase in entropy of one mole of such a gas when it expands from T_1, p_1, V_1 to T_2, p_2, V_2 is given by the expression

$$\Delta S = C_v \log_e \frac{T_2}{T_1} + R \log_e \frac{V_2 - B}{V_1 - B}.$$

10,5. The cell

$$\text{Zn} \mid \text{ZnCl}_{2(aq)} \qquad \text{AgCl}_{(sat)} \mid \text{Ag}$$

depends on the reaction

$$\text{Zn} + 2\text{AgCl} \longrightarrow \text{ZnCl}_2 + 2\text{Ag}.$$

Its e.m.f. at 25° C is 1·005 volt and $\left(\dfrac{\partial E}{\partial T}\right)_p = -0\cdot0004$ volt deg^{-1}.

Calculate ΔG, ΔH and ΔS for the reaction at 25° C. Calculate also the heat absorbed by the cell if the cell is allowed to give current for a period long enough to permit one mole of zinc to pass into solution. Explain why this quantity is not the same as ΔH.

10,6. Rhombic and monoclinic sulphur are in equilibrium at 95·4° C and at 1 atmosphere pressure. It will be made clear in the next chapter that under such circumstances the chemical potential and hence the molar free energy of each species is the same, so that the free energy of transformation is zero at this temperature. The molar thermal capacities of the two substances are given by the expressions

$$S_r, \; C_p = 4\cdot12 + 0\cdot0047T \text{ cal deg}^{-1}$$

$$S_m, \; C_p = 3\cdot62 + 0\cdot0072T \text{ cal deg}^{-1}.$$

The enthalpy change for the reaction

$$S_r \longrightarrow S_m \text{ is } 77\cdot0 \text{ cal at } 0° \text{ C}.$$

Show that the free energy change for the reaction at any temperature covered by the expressions for C_p is given by the equation

$$\Delta G = 120 + 0\cdot50T \log_e T - 0\cdot00125T^2 - 2\cdot82T.$$

10,7. The quantities α the volume coefficient of thermal expansion, and β the isothermal compressibility coefficient were defined on page 147.

Prove that $\qquad\qquad -\left(\dfrac{\partial \beta}{\partial T}\right)_p = \left(\dfrac{\partial \alpha}{\partial p}\right)_T.$

CHAPTER 11

THE AFFINITY OF REACTION AND CHEMICAL POTENTIALS

The *affinity of reaction* is an expression which has been used for over a hundred years to describe qualitatively "the tendency for a reaction to go". In recent years the Belgian chemist de Donder[1] has shown how this concept may be expressed in quantitative terms.

One of the most important facts we have so far established is that any natural spontaneous process leading to changes in the composition of the system results in the production of entropy, and that, according to the conditions under which the process takes place, the entropy produced is related to changes in the thermodynamic potentials given by the equations

$$TdS_{\text{irrev}} = -dU_{S,V} = -dH_{S,p} = -dA_{T,V} = -dG_{T,p}. \quad (9,28)$$

The de Donder concept rests on the postulate that *the tendency for a reaction to proceed is proportional to the quantity of entropy produced.*

The establishment of this concept requires the definition of a parameter called the *extent of reaction*. Consider a reaction described by the equation

$$a\text{A} + b\text{B} \ldots \longrightarrow c\text{C} + d\text{D} \ldots$$

If dn_a moles of A react with dn_b moles of B . . . to form dn_c moles of C and dn_d moles of D . . . it follows from the Law of Definite Proportions that

$$\frac{dn_a}{a} = \frac{dn_b}{b} = \frac{dn_c}{c} = \frac{dn_d}{d} = \text{constant.}$$

We assign the symbol $d\xi$ to the constant concerned and call ξ *the extent of reaction*. It follows that $-ad\xi$, $-bd\xi$, . . . $cd\xi$ and $dd\xi$ . . . represent the increase in the amount of components A, B, C and D present in the reaction system when the reaction proceeds to the extent described, so that if initially a system consists of n_a moles of A and n_b moles of B, but no C and D ($\xi = 0$), and after a certain time the reaction has proceeded to an extent ξ, the composition of the system is given by $n_a - a\xi$ moles of A,

[1] de Donder, *L'Affinité* (Paris, 1927, 1931, 1934).

$n_b - b\xi$ moles of B, $c\xi$ moles of C and $d\xi$ moles of D. It should be noted that ξ is not dimensionless but is expressed in moles.

We note, too, that when the reaction has proceeded from an initial state $\xi = 0$ to a final state $\xi = 1$, a moles of A have reacted with b moles of B . . . to form c moles of C and d moles of D . . ., and we also observe that the extent of reaction provides a convenient co-ordinate by which to express the rate of reaction since, denoting the rate of reaction at time t by the symbol $\mathbf{V}_{(t)}$

$$\mathbf{V}_{(t)} = \frac{d\xi_{(t)}}{dt}. \qquad \qquad (11,1)$$

We are now in a position to express the affinity of reaction in quantitative terms:

IF A NATURAL SPONTANEOUS REACTION AT TEMPERATURE T PROCEEDS BY AN AMOUNT $d\xi$, SO THAT THE ENTROPY PRODUCED EQUALS dS_{irrev}, THE AFFINITY OF REACTION $\mathbf{A}$ IS DEFINED BY THE EQUATION

$$\mathbf{A}d\xi = TdS_{\text{irrev}}. \qquad \qquad (11,2)$$

From (11,1) and (11,2) it follows that

$$\mathbf{A}_{(t)}\mathbf{V}_{(t)} = T\frac{dS_{\text{irrev}}}{dt}, \qquad \qquad (11,3)$$

where the symbols $\mathbf{A}_{(t)}$ and $\mathbf{V}_{(t)}$ denote the affinity and rate of reaction at time t. The rate of production of entropy must be positive throughout the course of reaction and must reduce to zero when chemical equilibrium is reached. We may therefore write

$$\mathbf{A}_{(t)}\mathbf{V}_{(t)} \geqslant 0, \qquad \qquad (11,4)$$

where the inequality sign refers to any moment during the course of the reaction and the equality sign to that time when chemical equilibrium has been reached.

Expression (11,4) is clearly satisfied by either of the following conditions:[1]

(i) That $\mathbf{V}_{(t)} = 0$ and $\mathbf{A}_{(t)} = 0$, which condition applies when chemical equilibrium has been attained. *The condition $\mathbf{A}_{(t)} = 0$ is the most important criterion of chemical equilibrium.*

(ii) That both the velocity and affinity of reaction are finite and have the same sign. In other words, a reaction will take place so that $\mathbf{V}_{(t)}$ is positive *if, and only if, the affinity of reaction in that direction is positive.* This is the most important criterion governing the course of a chemical reaction.

---

[1] It will be observed that expression (11,4) is also satisfied mathematically by the conditions

$$\mathbf{V}_{(t)} > 0, \mathbf{A}_{(t)} = 0$$

or

$$\mathbf{V}_{(t)} = 0, \mathbf{A}_{(t)} > 0.$$

The first condition does not apply to a real situation (the student should satisfy himself

We have now established that the affinity of reaction is a measure of its tendency to proceed. At any particular moment it depends on the thermodynamic state of the system at the time. It follows from (9,28) and (11,2) that it is related to changes in the thermodynamic potentials by the equations

$$\mathbf{A} = -\left(\frac{\partial U}{\partial \xi}\right)_{S,V} = -\left(\frac{\partial H}{\partial \xi}\right)_{S,p} = -\left(\frac{\partial A}{\partial \xi}\right)_{T,V} = -\left(\frac{\partial G}{\partial \xi}\right)_{T,p} \quad (11,5)$$

Of these equations the most important, simply because we usually wish to study reactions at constant temperature and pressure, is the last,

$$\mathbf{A} = -\left(\frac{\partial G}{\partial \xi}\right)_{T,p} \quad . \quad . \quad . \quad . \quad . \quad (11,6)$$

It is opportune at this stage to mention the problem of *coupled* simultaneous reactions. Simultaneous reactions taking place in a system are said to be *coupled* if one or more reactant is common to each, so that the course of one is influenced by the course of the other. If at time t the affinity and rate of reaction of one is denoted by $\mathbf{A}'$ and $\mathbf{V}'$, and the affinity and reaction rate of the second by $\mathbf{A}''$ and $\mathbf{V}''$, it follows from (11,3) that

$$T\frac{dS_{\text{irrev}}}{dT} = \mathbf{A}'\mathbf{V}' + \mathbf{A}''\mathbf{V}'' \geqslant 0.$$

It would appear at first sight that both reactions can take place (i.e. both $\mathbf{V}'$ and $\mathbf{V}''$ may be positive) even if $\mathbf{A}''$ is negative as long as

$$\mathbf{A}' > \left|\frac{\mathbf{A}''\mathbf{V}''}{\mathbf{V}'}\right|.$$

In other words, it would appear that a reaction may proceed simultaneously with another, although it would not occur if the other were not taking place. This hypothesis was considered to be of great importance to biological systems[1] because it was thought to explain the occurrence of complex syntheses which would, if studied in isolation, prove thermo-

---

why this should be), but the second does. It describes that situation in which there is no thermodynamic reason why the reaction should not proceed (i.e. a shift in composition from left to right would lead to the production of entropy), but for some reason or other the reaction does not appear to take place. It corresponds therefore to some state of metastable equilibrium, in which the system is frozen, or to some state in which the rate of reaction is too small to be observed. A system consisting of carbon and oxygen at room temperature is an example. Combination to form carbon dioxide would result in the production of entropy, but the reaction is so slow that no change can be detected in the composition of the system over a great period of time.

[1] See van Rysselberghe, *Bull. classe. sci. acad. roy. Belg.*, 1936, (5) **22**, 1330, and 1937, (5) **23**, 416.

dynamically highly improbable. It has, however, been shown recently that this hypothesis is probably incorrect.[1]

Chemical Potentials

In Chapter 9 it was shown that an irreversible process in which no work other than expansion work is possible may be described by the equations

$$TdS_{irrev} = TdS - dU - pdV$$

$$TdS_{irrev} = TdS - dH + Vdp$$

$$TdS_{irrev} = -SdT - dA - pdV$$

and
$$TdS_{irrev} = -SdT - dG + Vdp,$$

and in the present chapter we have shown how the affinity of reaction may be defined in terms of TdS_{irrev}. We now show how the quantities TdS_{irrev} and the affinity of reaction may be expressed in terms of the changes in composition which result within the system.

Consider a system containing

$$
\begin{array}{lll}
n_1 \text{ moles of component} & & 1 \\
n_2 \quad\;\; ,, \qquad\;\; ,, & & 2 \\
\cdot \qquad ,, \qquad\;\; ,, & & \cdot \\
\cdot \qquad ,, \qquad\;\; ,, & & \cdot \\
\cdot \qquad ,, \qquad\;\; ,, & & \cdot \\
n_i \qquad ,, \qquad\;\; ,, & & i \\
\cdot \qquad ,, \qquad\;\; ,, & & \cdot \\
\cdot \qquad ,, \qquad\;\; ,, & & \cdot \\
\cdot \qquad ,, \qquad\;\; ,, & & \cdot \text{ and so on.}
\end{array}
$$

The internal energy of the system may be expressed as a function of any two thermodynamic properties (H, S, A, G, T, p or V) and the composition terms. Choosing S and V as the two dependent properties we write

$$U = f(S, V, n_1, n_2, \ldots n_i, \ldots) \quad \ldots \quad (11,8)$$

Any variation in the system (including changes in composition) is described by the equation

$$dU = \left(\frac{\partial U}{\partial S}\right)_{V, n_1, n_2, \ldots n_i, \ldots} dS + \left(\frac{\partial U}{\partial V}\right)_{S, n_1, n_2, \ldots n_i, \ldots} dV$$

$$+ \left(\frac{\partial U}{\partial n_1}\right)_{V, S, n_2, \ldots n_i, \ldots} dn_1 + \left(\frac{\partial U}{\partial n_2}\right)_{V, S, n_1, \ldots n_i, \ldots} dn_2 \ldots$$

$$+ \left(\frac{\partial U}{\partial n_i}\right)_{V, S, n_1, \ldots n_{i-1}, n_{i+1}, \ldots} dn_i + \ldots \quad \ldots \quad (11,9)$$

[1] See Koenig *et al.*, *J. Am. Chem. Soc.*, 1961, **83**, 1029.

The terms $\left(\dfrac{\partial U}{\partial S}\right)_{V,\,n_1,\,n_2,\,\ldots\,n_i,\,\ldots}$ and $\left(\dfrac{\partial U}{\partial V}\right)_{S,\,n_1,\,n_2,\,\ldots\,n_i,\,\ldots}$ represent changes in U *at constant composition*, and under such conditions we know that

$$\left(\frac{\partial U}{\partial S}\right)_V = T \qquad\qquad (10,1)$$

and

$$\left(\frac{\partial U}{\partial V}\right)_S = -p. \qquad\qquad (10,2)$$

Substituting in equation (11,9) we obtain

$$dU = TdS - pdV$$
$$+ \left(\frac{\partial U}{\partial n_1}\right)_{V,\,S,\,n_2,\,\ldots\,n_i,\,\ldots} dn_1 + \left(\frac{\partial U}{\partial n_2}\right)_{V,\,S,\,n_1,\,\ldots\,n_i,\,\ldots} dn_2 \ldots$$
$$\ldots + \left(\frac{\partial U}{\partial n_i}\right)_{V,\,S,\,n_1,\,n_2,\,\ldots\,n_{i-1},\,n_{i+1},\,\ldots} dn_i + \ldots \quad (11,10)$$

We now express the quantity $\left(\dfrac{\partial U}{\partial n_1}\right)_{V,\,S,\,n_2,\,\ldots\,n_i,\,\ldots}$ by the symbol μ_1, the

quantity $\left(\dfrac{\partial U}{\partial n_2}\right)_{V,\,S,\,n_1,\,\ldots\,n_i,\,\ldots}$ by the symbol μ_2, and the quantity

$\left(\dfrac{\partial U}{\partial n_i}\right)_{V,\,S,\,n_1,\,n_2,\,\ldots\,n_{i-1},\,\ldots\,n_{i+1}}$ by the symbol μ_i, obtaining the equation

$$dU = TdS - pdV + \mu_1 dn_1 + \mu_2 dn_2 \ldots + \mu_i dn_i \ldots \quad (11,11)$$

The quantities $\mu_1, \mu_2, \ldots \mu_i \ldots$ are called the CHEMICAL POTENTIALS of components $1, 2, \ldots i \ldots$

Equation (11,11) may be integrated at constant temperature, pressure and composition to give

$$U = TS - pV + \mu_1 n_1 + \mu_2 n_2 \ldots + \mu_i n_i \ldots \quad (11,12)$$

Since H, A and G are defined by the equations

$$U = H - pV$$
$$= A + TS$$
$$= G + TS - pV$$

it follows that

$$H = TS + \mu_1 n_1 + \mu_2 n_2 \ldots + \mu_i n_i \ldots \quad (11,13)$$
$$A = -pV + \mu_1 n_1 + \mu_2 n_2 \ldots + \mu_i n_i \ldots \quad (11,14)$$

and

$$G = \mu_1 n_1 + \mu_2 n_2 \ldots + \mu_i n_i \ldots \quad (11,15)$$

We have defined the quantity μ_i by the equation

$$\mu_i = \left(\frac{\partial U}{\partial n_i}\right)_{V,\,S,\,n_1,\,n_2,\,\ldots\,n_{i-1},\,n_{i+1},\,\ldots}$$

but now wish to prove that the same quantity may be defined by the equation

$$\mu_i = \left(\frac{\partial G}{\partial n_i}\right)_{p,\,T,\,n_1,\,n_2,\,\ldots\,n_{i-1},\,n_{i+1},\,\ldots}$$

Considering the system as before, we express the Free Energy of the system in terms of the pressure, temperature and the composition terms, i.e.

$$G = f(T, p, n_1, n_2, \ldots n_i, \ldots). \qquad \ldots \quad (11,16)$$

Hence

$$dG = \left(\frac{\partial G}{\partial T}\right)_{p,\,n_1,\,n_2,\,\ldots\,n_i,\,\ldots} dT + \left(\frac{\partial G}{\partial p}\right)_{T,\,n_i,\,n_2,\,\ldots\,n_i,\,\ldots} dp$$

$$+ \left(\frac{\partial G}{\partial n_1}\right)_{p,\,T,\,n_2,\,\ldots\,n_i,\,\ldots} dn_1 + \left(\frac{\partial G}{\partial n_2}\right)_{p,\,T,\,n_1,\,\ldots\,n_i,\,\ldots} dn_2 \ldots$$

$$\ldots + \left(\frac{\partial G}{\partial n_i}\right)_{p,\,T,\,n_1,\,\ldots\,n_{i-1},\,n_{i+1}} dn_i \ldots \qquad \ldots \quad (11,17)$$

The terms $\left(\frac{\partial G}{\partial T}\right)_{p,\,n_1,\,n_2,\,\ldots\,n_i,\,\ldots}$ and $\left(\frac{\partial G}{\partial p}\right)_{T,\,n_1,\,n_2,\,\ldots\,n_i,\,\ldots}$ represent

changes in G *at constant composition*, and under such conditions we know that

$$\left(\frac{\partial G}{\partial p}\right)_T = V \quad . \quad . \quad . \quad . \quad . \quad . \quad (10,7)$$

and

$$\left(\frac{\partial G}{\partial T}\right)_p = -S. \quad . \quad . \quad . \quad . \quad . \quad (10,8)$$

Substituting in (11,17) and expressing $\left(\frac{\partial G}{\partial n_1}\right)_{p,\,T,\,n_2,\,\ldots\,n_i,\,\ldots}$ as μ'_1, etc., we

obtain

$$dG = -SdT + Vdp + \mu'_1 dn_1 + \mu'_2 dn_2 \ldots + \mu'_i dn_i \ldots \quad (11,18)$$

Now $\qquad G = U + pV - TS$

and $\qquad dG = dU + pdV + Vdp - TdS - SdT.$

Substituting in (11,18) we obtain

$$dU = TdS - pdV + \mu'_1 dn_1 + \mu'_2 dn_2 \ldots + \mu'_i dn_i \ldots \quad (11,19)$$

Comparison of (11,11) and (11,19) shows that

$$\mu = \mu'$$

i.e. that $\mu_i = \left(\dfrac{\partial G}{\partial n_i}\right)_{p,\ T,\ n_1,\ n_2,\ \ldots\ n_{i-1},\ n_{i+1},\ \ldots}$

We may therefore write

$$dG = -SdT + Vdp + \mu_1 dn_1 + \mu_2 dn_2 \ldots + \mu_i dn_i \ldots \quad (11,20)$$

By considering

$$H = f(S, p, n_1, n_2, \ldots n_i, \ldots)$$

and

$$A = f(T, V, n_1, n_2, \ldots n_i, \ldots)$$

it can in the same way be shown that

$$dH = TdS + Vdp + \mu_1 dn_1 + \mu_2 dn_2 \ldots + \mu_i dn_i \ldots \quad (11,21)$$

and that

$$dA = -SdT - pdV + \mu_1 dn_1 + \mu_2 dn_2 \ldots + \mu_i dn_i \ldots \quad (11,22)$$

i.e. that

$$\mu_i = \left(\frac{\partial H}{\partial n_i}\right)_{S,\ p,\ n_1,\ \ldots\ n_{i-1},\ n_{i+1},\ \ldots} = \left(\frac{\partial A}{\partial n_i}\right)_{T,\ V,\ n_1,\ \ldots\ n_{i-1},\ n_{i+1},\ \ldots}$$

We obtain therefore a complete set of equalities

$$\left.\begin{aligned}
\mu_i &= \left(\frac{\partial U}{\partial n_i}\right)_{S,\ V,\ n_1,\ \cdots\ n_{i-1},\ n_{i+1},\ \cdots} \\[2mm]
\mu_i &= \left(\frac{\partial H}{\partial n_i}\right)_{S,\ p,\ n_1,\ \cdots\ n_{i-1},\ n_{i+1},\ \cdots} \\[2mm]
\mu_i &= \left(\frac{\partial A}{\partial n_i}\right)_{T,\ V,\ n_1,\ \cdots\ n_{i-1},\ n_{i+1},\ \cdots} \\[2mm]
\mu_i &= \left(\frac{\partial G}{\partial n_i}\right)_{p,\ T,\ n_1,\ \cdots\ n_{i-1},\ n_{i+1},\ \cdots}
\end{aligned}\right\} \quad (11,23)$$

The most important of these relationships is the last

$$\mu_i = \left(\frac{\partial G}{\partial n_i}\right)_{p,\ T,\ n_1,\ \cdots\ n_{i-1},\ n_{i+1},\ \cdots} \quad (11,24)$$

There are two reasons for this: the first is that more often than not we require to study reactions at constant temperature and pressure, and the second is due to the uniqueness of the equation

$$G = \mu_1 n_1 + \mu_2 n_2 \ldots + \mu_i n_i \ldots \qquad \ldots \quad (11,15)$$

compared with equations (11,12), (11,13) and (11,14).

If we consider a system consisting simply of n moles of a pure substance, it is evident from (11,15) that

$$G = \mu n \qquad . \quad . \quad . \quad . \quad . \quad . \quad (11,25)$$

so that the chemical potential of a *pure* substance equals its MOLAR FREE ENERGY. The physical significance of the chemical potential of a component in a mixture is not quite the same because its value depends on the *concentration* of the component and hence on the quantities of other components present. It can best be comprehended by considering a mixture of n_1, n_2, ... n_i, ... moles of components 1, 2, ... i, ..., and supposing that the quantity of one component i is increased by an amount δn_i moles, while the temperature, pressure and quantities of other components remain the same. If the resultant increase in Free Energy of the system is δG, the mean value of μ_i is given by the equation

$$\bar{\mu}_i = \frac{\delta G}{\delta n_i}$$

and the true value of μ_i at any point by the limiting value of $\bar{\mu}_i$ as δn_i approaches 0.

Clearly, too, if we imagine a system so large that the increase of component i by an amount equal to one mole does not appreciably alter the *concentrations* of the other components, μ_i equals the increase in Free Energy of the system due to the addition of one mole of component i. For this reason the quantity μ_i is sometimes called the PARTIAL MOLAR FREE ENERGY of the component. We shall not, however, use this term, but shall always use the term CHEMICAL POTENTIAL, because as will be seen shortly, this term more dramatically describes the nature and power of the function. It should be noted that the chemical potential is an *intensive* property.

If equation (11,15) is differentiated generally we obtain

$$dG = \mu_1 dn_1 + \mu_2 dn_2 \ldots + \mu_i dn_i \ldots + n_1 d\mu_1$$
$$+ n_2 d\mu_2 \ldots + n_i d\mu_i \ldots \quad (11,26)$$

Comparing this with (11,20) we see that

$$-SdT + Vdp - n_1 d\mu_1 - n_2 d\mu_2 \ldots + n_i d\mu_i = 0. \qquad (11,27)$$

G

This expression is known as the GIBBS–DUHEM EQUATION. We shall not use this equation at present, but merely note that it shows the inter-dependence of the intensive variables $T, p, \mu_1, \mu_2 \ldots \mu_i \ldots$

The Dependence of the Chemical Potential of a Component on Temperature, Pressure and Concentration

Later in this chapter we shall show how elegantly and simply the physical and chemical behaviour of a multi-component system may be expressed in terms of the chemical potentials of the components. In fact, the concept of chemical potential proves to be one of the most powerful in chemistry. Before demonstrating this we must show the dependence of chemical potential on temperature, pressure and concentration.

The Dependence of μ_i on Temperature

We have shown that under all circumstances

$$dG = -SdT + Vdp + \mu_1 dn_1 + \mu_2 dn_2 \ldots + \mu_i dn_i \ldots \quad (11,20)$$

If the pressure and all quantities $n_1, n_2 \ldots$ except n_i remain constant,

$$dG = -SdT + \mu_i dn_i$$

and from Theorem 4, page xv, it follows that

$$\left(\frac{\partial \mu_i}{\partial T}\right)_{p,\, n_1,\, n_2,\, \cdots\, n_i,\, \cdots} = -\left(\frac{\partial S}{\partial n_i}\right)_{p,\, T,\, n_1,\, \cdots\, n_{i-1},\, n_{i+1},\, \cdots} \quad (11,28)$$

The quantity $\left(\dfrac{\partial S}{\partial n_i}\right)_{p,\, T,\, n_1,\, \cdots\, n_{i-1},\, n_{i+1},\, \cdots}$ is defined as the PARTIAL MOLAR ENTROPY of the component i and is given the symbol $\bar{s}_i$. We may therefore write

$$\left(\frac{\partial \mu_i}{\partial T}\right)_{p,\, n_1,\, \cdots} = -\bar{s}_i$$

so that integrating under the conditions indicated

$$\mu_{i T_2} - \mu_{i T_1} = -\int_{T_1}^{T_2} \bar{s}_i dT \quad \cdot\ \cdot\ \cdot\ \cdot \quad (11,29)$$

An alternative expression for the variation of μ_i with temperature may be obtained as follows:

$$\left(\frac{\partial\left(\frac{\mu_i}{T}\right)}{\partial T}\right)_{p,\,n_1,\,n_2,\,\cdots} = \frac{1}{T}\left(\frac{\partial\mu_i}{\partial T}\right)_{p,\,n_1,\,n_2,\,\cdots} - \frac{\mu_i}{T^2}$$

$$= -\frac{\bar{s}_i}{T} - \frac{\mu_i}{T^2}$$

$$= -\frac{1}{T^2}(\mu_i + T\bar{s}_i).$$

Now $$H = G + TS.$$

Therefore

$$\left(\frac{\partial H}{\partial n_i}\right)_{p,\,T,\,n_1,\,\cdots\,n_{i-1},\,n_{i+1},\,\cdots} =$$

$$\left(\frac{\partial G}{\partial n_i}\right)_{p,\,T,\,n_1,\,\cdots\,n_{i-1},\,n_{i+1},\,\cdots} + T\left(\frac{\partial S}{\partial n_i}\right)_{p,\,T,\,n_1,\,\cdots\,n_{i-1},\,n_{i+1},\,\cdots}$$

$$= \mu_i + T\bar{s}_i. \quad \cdots \quad \cdots \quad (11,30)$$

The quantity $\left(\dfrac{\partial H}{\partial n_i}\right)_{p,\,T,\,n_1,\,\cdots\,n_{i-1},\,n_{i+1},\,\cdots}$ is called the PARTIAL MOLAR

ENTHALPY[1] of the component i and is given the symbol $\bar{h}_i$. We may therefore write

$$\left(\frac{\partial\left(\frac{\mu_i}{T}\right)}{\partial T}\right)_{p,\,n_1,\,n_2,\,\cdots} = -\frac{\bar{h}_i}{T^2}, \quad \cdots \quad \cdots \quad (11,31)$$

so that integrating under the conditions indicated we obtain the equation

$$\frac{\mu_i}{T} = I - \int\frac{\bar{h}_i}{T^2}dT, \quad \cdots \quad \cdots \quad (11,32)$$

where I is an integration constant.

Equations (11,31) and (11,32) are of course analogous to the Gibbs–Helmholtz equation for a pure substance.

The Dependence of μ_i on Pressure

If the temperature and all quantities $n_1, n_2 \ldots$ except n_i remain constant, equation (11,20) reduces to

$$dG = Vdp + \mu_i dn_i \quad \cdots \quad \cdots \quad (11,33)$$

---

[1] The student should note carefully the difference between

$$\left(\frac{\partial H}{\partial n_i}\right)_{p,\,T,\,n_1,\,\ldots\,n_{i-1},\,n_{i+1},\,\ldots} \quad \text{and} \quad \left(\frac{\partial H}{\partial n_i}\right)_{S,\,p,\,n_1,\,\ldots\,n_{i-1},\,n_{i+1}}.$$

The first is by definition $\bar{h}_i$ and the second μ_i (see equation (11,23)).

and from Theorem 4, page xv, it follows that

$$\left(\frac{\partial \mu_i}{\partial p}\right)_{T,\,n_1,\,n_2,\,\cdots} = \left(\frac{\partial V}{\partial n_i}\right)_{p,\,T,\,n_1,\,\cdots\,n_{i-1},\,n_{i+1},\,\cdots} \qquad (11,34)$$

The quantity $\left(\dfrac{\partial V}{\partial n_i}\right)_{p,\,T,\,n_1,\,\cdots\,n_{i-1},\,n_{i+1}}$ is defined as the PARTIAL MOLAR
VOLUME of the component and is given the symbol $\bar{v}_i$.

It follows that
$$\int d\mu_i = \int \bar{v}_i dp, \qquad \cdots \cdots \quad (11,35)$$

so that
$$\mu_{i p_2} - \mu_{i p_1} = \int_{p_1}^{p_2} \bar{v}_i dp.$$

This equation can be applied either to a *pure* substance in the gaseous, liquid or solid states, in which we may omit the suffix i, and in which the partial molar volume $\bar{v}_i$ becomes the molar volume $\bar{V}$,[1] or to a component of a mixture. We consider a pure substance first.

An Ideal Gas

Since the molar volume of an ideal gas is given by the equation

$$\bar{V} = \frac{RT}{p}$$

it follows from (11,35) that

$$\mu = RT \log_e p + I \qquad \cdots \cdots \quad (11,36)$$

where I is an integration constant.

It is evident that I is the value of the chemical potential of the gas at *unit pressure*, so that if we denote the chemical potential of the gas at unit pressure by the symbol μ_0 we may write

$$\mu = \mu_0 + RT \log_e p \qquad \cdots \cdots \quad (11,37)$$

Obviously the value of μ_0 depends on the units in which the pressure is measured. It is customary to say that a gas is in a *standard state* when under a pressure of one atmosphere, and to describe μ_0 as its *standard chemical potential*. The definition of the standard state requires that the pressure in (11,37) is expressed in atmospheres also.

It should be noted that the standard chemical potential of the gas is itself independent of pressure and dependent only on temperature, whereas the chemical potential of a gas at any other pressure is a function

---

[1] We have previously denoted the molar volume of a pure substance by the symbol V. We use the symbol $\bar{V}$ in the present section to distinguish it from the V in equations (11,33) and (11,34) which denotes the volume of the system as a whole.

both of temperature and pressure. These facts may be registered by writing (11,37) in the form

$$\mu(T, p) = \mu_0(T) + RT \log_e p \quad . \quad . \quad . \quad . \quad (11,38)$$

where the symbols (T, p) and (T) denote the fact that the preceding quantity is so dependent.

Real Gases

One method that we might use to obtain for a real gas an equation equivalent to (11,37) would be to express the molar volume at temperature T in terms of some power series of the sort

$$\bar{V} = \frac{RT}{p}(a + bp + cp^2 \ldots)$$

determine the constants a, b, and c by experiment, introduce into equation (11,35), and integrate. The resultant expression for μ would be perfectly sound, but would be very complicated and difficult to handle.

It is obviously desirable to be able to describe the chemical potential of a real gas by equations which have the same *form* as those which describe the ideal gas, and this is achieved by constructing quantities known as the FUGACITY and FUGACITY COEFFICIENT first introduced by G. N. Lewis. The fugacity of a gas may be regarded as a sort of corrected pressure, and the fugacity coefficient as a measure of the departure of the gas from ideal behaviour. It is an experimental fact that the behaviour of any gas approaches ideality at very low pressures, so that the fugacity and the pressure become the same under these conditions. The fugacity is given the symbol p^* and the fugacity coefficient the symbol γ, and they are formally defined by the expressions

$$\left. \begin{array}{ll} \mu = \mu_0^* + RT \log_e p^* & \text{(i)} \\\\ \dfrac{p^*}{p} = \gamma & \text{(ii)} \\\\ \gamma \longrightarrow 1 \text{ as } p \longrightarrow 0 & \text{(iii)} \end{array} \right\} \quad . \quad . \quad . \quad (11,39)$$

It should be noted that the standard state to which the term μ_0^* refers is that of unit fugacity and not unit pressure. Since μ_0^* is a function of temperature but is independent of pressure, and since $p^* = \gamma p$, we may write

$$\mu(T, p) = \mu_0^*(T) + RT \log_e p^* \quad . \quad . \quad . \quad (11,40)$$

or $\quad\quad \mu(T, p) = \mu_0^*(T) + RT \log_e \gamma p. \quad . \quad . \quad . \quad (11,41)$

Methods by which the fugacity coefficient may be determined for a gas at any temperature and pressure are described in Chapter 18.

Liquids and Solids

The molar volume of a liquid or solid is almost independent of pressure. We may therefore integrate equation (11,35) to obtain

$$\mu_{p_2} - \mu_{p_1} = \bar{V}(p_2 - p_1). \quad \ldots \quad (11,42)$$

We register the fact that μ is a function of both temperature and pressure by writing (11,42) in the form

$$\mu_{p_2}(T, p) - \mu_{p_1}(T, p) = \bar{V}(p_2 - p_1). \quad \ldots \quad (11,43)$$

Mixtures: The Dependence of μ_i on Concentration
Ideal Gas Mixtures

It follows from (11,37) that the chemical potential of a component of an ideal gas mixture may be expressed in terms of its partial pressure by the equation

$$\mu_i = \mu_0 + RT \log_e p_i \quad \ldots \quad (11,44)$$

where μ_0 is the standard chemical potential of the component *as a pure gas at one atmosphere pressure and at temperature T.*

As before, we register the fact that μ_i is dependent on both temperature and pressure and μ_0 is dependent on temperature alone by writing

$$\mu_i(T, p) = \mu_0(T) + RT \log_e p_i. \quad \ldots \quad (11,45)$$

An Alternative Expression for μ_i

In certain cases it is convenient to express the chemical potential of a component of a mixture of gases in terms of its mole fraction. If a gas mixture contains n_1 moles of component 1, n_2 moles of component 2 ... the mole fraction of component 1 is defined by the equation

$$y_1 = \frac{n_1}{n_1 + n_2 \ldots},$$

that of component 2 by the equation

$$y_2 = \frac{n_2}{n_1 + n_2 \ldots}, \text{ and so on.}$$

Clearly,
$$y_1 + y_2 \ldots = 1.$$

In an ideal gas mixture the partial pressure of a component is related to its mole fraction and the total pressure exerted by the mixture by the equation

$$p_i = y_i p \quad \ldots \quad \ldots \quad (11,46)$$

so that (11,45) may be written in the form

$$\mu_i(T, p) = \mu_0(T) + RT \log_e p + RT \log_e y_i.$$

The quantity $\mu_0(T) + RT \log_e p$ is independent of the mole fraction of the gas and may be given the symbol μ_{0_y}, so that

$$\mu_i(T, p) = \mu_{0_y}(T, p) + RT \log_e y_i. \quad . \quad . \quad . \quad (11,47)$$

It should be noted carefully that the value of μ_{0_y} differs from that of μ_0 in (11,45). The term μ_0 is the chemical potential of the pure gas at unit pressure, and is therefore independent of pressure and dependent only on T, whereas μ_{0_y} is the chemical potential of the pure gas at pressure p and dependent on both T and p.

Real Gas Mixtures

Here again we follow G. N. Lewis and replace partial pressures by partial fugacities so that equation (11,44) becomes

$$\mu_i = \mu_\circ^* + RT \log_e p_i^* \quad . \quad . \quad . \quad . \quad (11,48)$$

where $\mu_\circ^*$ is the standard chemical potential of the component *as a pure gas at unit fugacity and at temperature T*.

The mole fraction of a component in a gas mixture which is not ideal is related to its partial fugacity and the fugacity of the mixture as a whole by the equation

$$p_i^* = y_i p^*$$

so that (11,48) can be written in the form

$$\mu_i = \mu_\circ^* + RT \log_e p^* + RT \log_e y_i.$$

The term $\mu_\circ^* + RT \log_e p^*$ can be written $\mu_{\circ y}^*$. so as to obtain the equation

$$\mu_i(T, p) = \mu_{\circ y}^*(T, p) + RT \log_e y_i. \quad . \quad . \quad (11,49)$$

It should be remarked that the departure of most real gases from ideal behaviour is appreciable only at very high pressures, so that under all other circumstances the inaccuracy which results from using pressures instead of fugacities, and partial pressures instead of partial fugacities is very small indeed.

Ideal Liquid Mixtures

Consider a homogeneous liquid mixture containing n_1 moles of component 1, n_2 moles of component 2 . . . in equilibrium with its supernatant vapour. A component in such a mixture is said to behave ideally if it obeys Raoult's Law, that is to say, if its partial vapour pressure p_i, its mole fraction *in the liquid phase* x_i and p_i^o the vapour pressure it would exert at the same temperature *as a pure substance*, are connected by the equation

$$p_i = x_i p_i^o. \qquad \ldots \ldots \quad (11,50)$$

A liquid mixture is said to be ideal if all the components therein behave ideally.

If the vapour of a component i behaves as an ideal gas it follows from (11,44) that its chemical potential *in the vapour phase* may be described by the equation

$$\mu_{i(g)} = \mu_{0_{i(g)}} + RT \log_e p_i.$$

We now make use of (11,50) and write

$$\mu_{i(g)} = \mu_{0_{i(g)}} + RT \log_e p_i^o + RT \log_e x_i.$$

The quantity $\mu_{0_{i(g)}} + RT \log_e p_i^o$ is independent of the concentration of the component and is denoted by the symbol μ_{0_x}, so that we write

$$\mu_{i(g)} = \mu_{0_x} + RT \log_e x_i. \qquad \ldots \quad (11,51)$$

Later in this chapter we shall show that if a component is present in more than one phase in a multiphase system at equilibrium, its chemical potential is the same in each phase. In the system under consideration the component in the liquid phase is in equilibrium with its supernatant vapour, so that

$$\mu_{i(\text{liq})} = \mu_{i(g)}.$$

We may therefore write

$$\mu_{i(\text{liq})} = \mu_{0_x} + RT \log_e x_i.$$

It follows that μ_{0_x} is the chemical potential of the pure liquid ($x_i = 1$) at the pressure and temperature to which the mixture is subjected, and is the same as the chemical potential of the vapour in equilibrium with the pure liquid at the same temperature and pressure. Since the vapour pressure of a liquid is dependent on both temperature and the externally applied pressure, μ_{0_x} must be a function of both temperature and pressure. This fact is registered by writing the last equation in the form

$$\mu_{i(\text{liq})}(T, p) = \mu_{0_x}(T, p) + RT \log_e x_i. \qquad \ldots \quad (11,52)$$

Before proceeding farther the student should be sure that he understands the difference between equations (11,50) and (11,51) on the one hand, and (11,46) and (11,47) on the other. Firstly, the term p in (11,46) is the total pressure of the gas mixture, whereas the term p_i^o in (11,50) is the vapour pressure of the pure component, and secondly, the symbol ν_i

denotes the mole fraction of a component in a *gas phase*, whereas the symbol x_i denotes the mole fraction of a component in a *liquid mixture*. The mole fractions of the components in a liquid mixture are not (except in certain special circumstances explained in Chapter 15) the same as those in the supernatant vapour. The terms μ_{o_x} and $\log_e x_i$ in equation (11,51) are quite different therefore from the terms μ_{o_y} and $\log_e y_i$ in (11,47).

The term "homogeneous liquid mixture" is usually used to describe a single phase containing two or more components in more or less comparable amounts, whereas if the quantity of one component present is very much greater than the quantities of the others we normally use the word *solution* instead, and refer to the component present in greater quantity as the solvent, and to those present in less as the solutes. For example, we would refer to a liquid phase containing one mole of water, two moles of ethyl alcohol and two moles of acetic acid as a homogeneous liquid mixture, and to a liquid phase containing forty moles of water, two moles of ethyl alcohol and two moles of acetic acid as a solution of ethyl alcohol and acetic acid in water, and refer to the water as the solvent and the other components as solutes. The use of the various terms is only a matter of custom, no difference in principle exists. Neither is there any difference in principle if one or more components are so-called "involatile". The word "involatile" applied to a solid or liquid merely implies that its vapour pressure under the conditions existing is too small to be significant, not that it does not exist. It therefore follows that the expressions we have derived for the chemical potential of a component of a homogeneous liquid mixture are applicable to any component of a solution of any nature.

The mole fraction is a convenient measure of the concentration of a component only if it is present to an appreciable extent. For rather dilute solutions two other conventions for expressing the quantities of solutes are more convenient. These are *molar concentrations* C, where C_i represents the number of moles of component i in 1 litre of solution, and *molal concentrations* m, where m_i represents the number of moles of component i in 1000 gm of pure solvent. The connection between x_i and m_i is purely arithmetic: if, for example, we consider a solution of glucose in water of molality $m_{(gl)}$

$$x_{(gl)} = \frac{m_{(gl)}}{\frac{1000}{18} + m_{(gl)}}.$$

For very dilute aqueous solutions C_i and m_i are very nearly the same, but for more concentrated aqueous solutions and solutions in other solvents the connections between C_i, m_i and x_i are more complicated, depending of course on the density of the solution and therefore on temperature. We need not, in fact, concern ourselves overmuch with molar concentrations, their dependence on temperature is such a disadvantage that they are now rarely used in thermodynamic calculations. We shall find it convenient to use mole fractions in some cases and molalities in others.

Since for a given solution the connection between x_i, C_i and m_i is purely arithmetic, it follows from (11,52) that we may express the chemical potential of a component i in an ideal solution in three ways:

$$\mu_i(T, p) = \mu_{0_x}(T, p) + RT \log_e x_i \quad . \quad . \quad . \quad (11,53)$$

$$\mu_i(T, p) = \mu_{0_c}(T, p) + RT \log_e C_i \quad . \quad . \quad . \quad (11,54)$$

$$\mu_i(T, p) = \mu_{0_m}(T, p) + RT \log_e m_i \quad . \quad . \quad . \quad (11,55)$$

μ_{0_x} is, of course, the chemical potential of the component in the pure state ($x_i = 1$) at temperature T and pressure p, μ_{0_c} the chemical potential of the component *in solution* at unit molar concentration and at temperature T and pressure p, and μ_{0_m} the chemical potential of the component *in solution* at unit molal concentration and at temperature T and pressure p. Since the standard state selected differs in each case, the actual values of μ_{0_x}, μ_{0_c} and μ_{0_m} are correspondingly different. For any particular problem we select the standard state which proves the most convenient.

Real Solutions

Raoult's Law is obeyed by very few real solutions except those approaching "infinite dilution". Here again, G. N. Lewis suggested that, rather than to attempt "corrections" for Raoult's Law, we define for real solutions a term known as the ACTIVITY[1] of the component, the activity being a sort of "corrected" or "idealised" concentration which approaches the same numerical value as the stoichiometric concentration only as the solution approaches ideal behaviour. The activity of a component in terms of mole fractions is denoted by the symbol a_x, and by the symbols a_c and a_m in terms of molar concentrations and molalities.

We must be clear about the conditions under which a solution approaches ideal behaviour, because these conditions complete the formal

[1] The Lewis concept of activity is not the only procedure which has been suggested to cover the application of thermodynamic equations to real solutions. Bjerrum and Guggenheim have suggested the use of ϕ the OSMOTIC COEFFICIENT. This is defined by the equation

$$\mu_A = \mu_{0_{x_A}}(T, p) + \phi_x RT \log_e x_A.$$

Here ϕ_x is the Osmotic Coefficient referred to mole fractions; similar quantities ϕ_c and ϕ_m apply to systems in which concentration terms are expressed in molarities and molalities.

definition of the activity of each component. It is an experimental fact that a solution approaches ideal behaviour when it approaches infinite dilution: in other words, when the mole fraction of the solvent approaches unity and the mole fraction of the solute approaches zero. We define therefore the activity of the solvent in terms of mole fractions by the joint equations

$$\left. \begin{array}{l} \mu = \mu_{0_{a_x}} + RT \log_e a_x \\[2mm] \dfrac{a_x}{x} = \gamma_x \longrightarrow 1 \text{ as } x \longrightarrow 1 \end{array} \right\} \quad . \quad . \quad . \quad (11,56)$$

but we define the activity of the solute by the joint equations

$$\left. \begin{array}{l} \mu = \mu_{0_{a_x}} + RT \log_e a_x \\[2mm] \dfrac{a_x}{x} = \gamma_x \longrightarrow 1 \text{ as } x \longrightarrow 0 \end{array} \right\} \quad . \quad . \quad . \quad (11,57)$$

The term γ_x is the ACTIVITY COEFFICIENT measured in terms of mole fractions. When we express the concentration of one component in terms of molarities or molalities, we define the activity and the activity coefficient by the equations

$$\left. \begin{array}{l} \mu = \mu_{0_{a_c}} + RT \log_e a_c \\[2mm] \dfrac{a_c}{C} = \gamma_c \longrightarrow 1 \text{ as } C \longrightarrow 0 \end{array} \right\} \quad . \quad . \quad . \quad (11,58)$$

or

$$\left. \begin{array}{l} \mu = \mu_{0_{a_m}} + RT \log_e a_m \\[2mm] \dfrac{a_m}{m} = \gamma_m \longrightarrow 1 \text{ as } m \longrightarrow 0 \end{array} \right\} \quad . \quad . \quad . \quad (11,59)$$

the terms γ_c and γ_m being the activity coefficients measured in terms of molar concentrations and molalities respectively. Activity Coefficients are quantities which can be determined precisely by many methods. These will be explored in Chapter 18.

It is not the function of chemical thermodynamics to *explain* the divergence of activity coefficients from unity, that is to explain why, in solution, a component behaves as though it is at some concentration other than its true stoichiometric one. Many factors contribute to this particular fact. We are reminded that one of the best-known theories of modern chemistry, the Debye–Huckel Theory of Electrolytes traces the divergence of γ from unity in the case of solutions of electrolytes to interionic and ionic–solvent attractions. Reference will be made to this theory in Chapter 16.

Further Discussion of the Significance of Standard States

The equations we have derived for the chemical potential of a single gas, of a component of a gaseous mixture or of a component of a solution show remarkable similarity and remarkable simplicity.

The chemical potential of a single ideal gas at temperature T and pressure p (expressed in atmospheres) is represented by the equation

$$\mu = \mu_0 + RT \log_e p \quad . \quad . \quad . \quad . \quad (11,37)$$

where μ_0 is a quantity which is independent of pressure. Because of the form of equation (11,37) μ_0 happens to be the value of the chemical potential of the gas at temperature T and at 1 atmosphere pressure. We therefore select the condition of a pressure of 1 atmosphere as representing a *standard state* with which all other conditions of the gas can be compared, simply because such a selection permits us to use equation (11,37).

We have shown also that the chemical potential of a component of an ideal gas mixture at temperature T is given by the equation

$$\mu_i = \mu_0 + RT \log_e p_i \quad . \quad . \quad . \quad . \quad . \quad (11,44)$$

where p_i is the partial pressure of the component (expressed in atmospheres) and μ_0 has precisely the same significance as that explained above: it is the value of the chemical potential of the component *as a pure gas* at 1 atmosphere pressure and at temperature T.

Under certain circumstances it is more convenient to express the chemical potential of a component of a gas mixture in terms of its mole fraction y_i. In this case we arrive at the equation

$$\mu_i(T, p) = \mu_{0_y}(T, p) + RT \log_e y_i. \quad . \quad . \quad (11,47)$$

Here again the chemical potential of the component is expressed as the sum of two terms, one independent of its mole fraction and the other dependent on it. In this case the term μ_{0_y} is the value of the chemical potential of the component i *as a pure gas at temperature T and pressure p.* It is clear that the standard state to which μ_{0_y} refers is quite different from the standard state chosen in equation (11,44). The point we wish to stress is that there is nothing mysterious or even fundamental about the choice and designation of a standard state. *We select, in a particular problem, that particular standard state which happens to lead to the simplest equations.*

Precisely the same procedure is adopted in selecting the standard state of a component in solution. For a solution in which all components are present in comparable amounts the concentration of any one is probably best expressed in terms of its mole fraction x_i. In this case the dependence of its chemical potential on concentration is given by the equation

$$\mu_i = \mu_{0_x} + RT \log_e x_i \quad . \quad . \quad . \quad . \quad (11,53)$$

where μ_{0_x} is the chemical potential of the component as a pure liquid at the temperature and pressure to which the mixture is subjected, and the standard state concerned is that of the pure liquid under the same conditions. If, however, one component is present in a much smaller quantity than any other, it is more convenient to express its concentration in terms of molar or molal units. In such cases the dependence of its chemical potential on concentration is given by the equations

$$\mu_i = \mu_{0_c} + RT \log_e C_i \quad . \quad . \quad . \quad . \quad (11,54)$$

and
$$\mu_i = \mu_{0_m} + RT \log_e m_i \quad . \quad . \quad . \quad . \quad (11,55)$$

and the standard state selected for the component is, in the first case, a solution of concentration one mole per litre, and in the second, a solution containing one mole per 1000 gm of solvent.

The argument is precisely the same for gases and the components of solutions, the behaviour of which is far from ideal: the standard state selected is defined in terms of fugacities and activity terms, so that the essential form of the equations given above is preserved.

We point out that the standard state selected for a particular component may sometimes be a hypothetical one, unattainable in practice. We should, for example, describe the chemical potential of silver chloride in aqueous solution by equation (11,55). In this case the term μ_{0_m} refers to the chemical potential of silver chloride at unit molality, although we know that such a condition can never be attained. In the same way we would select the standard state of water vapour at 25° C as 1 atmosphere pressure, although we know that the minimum temperature at which water vapour can exert a pressure of 1 atmosphere is 100° C. The utility of a particular standard state is not reduced by its unattainability.

We have not yet considered the question of the standard state for a pure liquid or pure solid. Consider a pure liquid or pure solid in equilibrium with its supernatant vapour. The chemical potential of the vapour is given by the equation

$$\mu_{(g)} = \mu_0 + RT \log_e p$$

where p is its vapour pressure and μ_0 its standard chemical potential.

Since the chemical potential of the liquid or solid is the same as that of the vapour in equilibrium with it, we may write

$$\mu_{(liq)} = \mu_{(g)} = \mu_0 + RT \log_e p$$

and

$$\mu_{(s)} = \mu_{(g)} = \mu_0 + RT \log_e p.$$

The vapour pressure of a pure liquid or solid at a particular temperature is independent of the quantity of liquid or solid present, so that $\mu_{(liq)}$ or $\mu_{(s)}$ is similarly independent. It follows that a pure liquid or pure solid may be regarded as being in its standard state, so that we may write

$$\left. \begin{array}{l} \mu_{(liq)} = \mu_{0(liq)} \\[2mm] \mu_{(s)} = \mu_{0(s)}. \end{array} \right\} \qquad . \quad . \quad . \quad . \quad . \quad (11,60)$$

or

We shall find later that this is important when we consider a reaction of type

$$CaCO_{3(s)} \longrightarrow CaO_{(s)} + CO_2.$$

The calcium carbonate and calcium oxide form separate solid phases, and their chemical potentials remain the same throughout the course of the reaction.

The Significance of Chemical Potentials and their Connection with the Affinity of Reaction

We have said earlier that the concept of chemical potentials is one of the most useful so far developed. This statement will now be demonstrated by showing how postulates can be formulated in terms of chemical potentials which simply and elegantly describe a wide range of physical and chemical phenomena.

We consider in turn:

  (i) phase equilibria;
 (ii) diffusion processes; and
(iii) spontaneous chemical reactions proceeding to equilibrium.

(i) Phase Equilibria

Consider a system in which a component is present in two phases α and β in equilibrium at constant temperature and pressure. The system may consist of a pure substance present as both solid and liquid, such as a mixture of ice and water at $0°$ C and at 1 atmosphere pressure; a pure substance present as both liquid and vapour, such as water and steam at $100°$ C and at 1 atmosphere pressure; a solid in equilibrium with its saturated solution and so on.

We now keep the temperature and pressure constant, but permit a small quantity of material in one phase to pass to the other; we might, for example, permit a system consisting of ice and water to absorb a small quantity of heat so that dn moles of ice melt to give dn moles of water. It follows that the decrease in the number of moles present in one phase must equal the increase in the second, i.e.

$$-dn_\alpha = dn_\beta.$$

Since no change in temperature or pressure takes place, equation (11,20) reduces to the form

$$dG_{T,\,p} = \mu_\alpha dn_\alpha + \mu_\beta dn_\beta$$

and since the system remains in equilibrium

$$dG_{T,\,p} = 0.$$

It follows that

$$\mu_\alpha = \mu_\beta. \qquad . \quad . \quad . \quad . \quad . \quad (11,61)$$

We deduce the general statement that

IF A PARTICULAR COMPONENT IS PRESENT IN MORE THAN ONE PHASE IN AN EQUILIBRIUM SYSTEM, ITS CHEMICAL POTENTIAL IS THE SAME IN EACH PHASE

This statement is of great importance. We call it THE FIRST STATEMENT OF CHEMICAL POTENTIALS. We shall use it in later chapters to derive the Phase Rule, the Distribution Law and the Donnan Membrane Equilibrium Equation, and to obtain a thermodynamic interpretation of osmotic pressure. It will be remembered that we have already used it to derive the expression for the chemical potential of a component in solution in terms of its concentration.

(ii) Diffusion Processes

We now consider a system which is maintained at constant temperature and pressure, but which has not yet reached internal equilibrium because diffusion processes are still in progress from one part of the system to another. Such a system is easily devised. We might choose a vessel containing in its lower half a concentrated solution of sugar in water and carefully pour pure water on top. After some

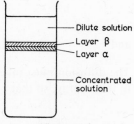

Figure 11,1.

time a concentration gradient will be established throughout, the more concentrated solution lying at the bottom of the vessel, the more dilute at the top. We select two adjacent portions of the system and call one layer α and the other layer β as shown in Figure 11,1. We observe the diffusion of dn moles of sugar from layer α to layer β. The change in free energy may be described in terms of the chemical potential of the sugar in both layers by the equation

$$dG_{T, p} = \mu_\alpha dn_\alpha + \mu_\beta dn_\beta$$

and we note that

$$dn_\beta = -dn_\alpha$$

and that dn_β is positive and dn_α is negative. Since the diffusion process is a natural spontaneous one, it must be accompanied by a decrease in free energy. It follows that

$$\mu_\alpha > \mu_\beta.$$

We deduce the general statement that

DIFFUSION OCCURS FROM THAT PORTION OF THE SYSTEM IN WHICH THE COMPONENT CONCERNED HAS THE HIGHER CHEMICAL POTENTIAL TO THAT IN WHICH IT HAS THE LOWER.

We call this THE SECOND STATEMENT OF CHEMICAL POTENTIALS.

It is of interest to observe that although we deduced the Second Statement from the observation that in a system at constant temperature and pressure diffusion of a component takes place from a point of higher concentration to one of lower, we could have made the deduction without this knowledge. We select two portions of the solution and call one portion α and the other β, and describe the concentration of the solute in one by the term C_α and that in the other by the term C_β. It follows from (11,54) that the chemical potential of the solute in the two portions of the system may be described by the equations

$$\mu_\alpha = \mu_0 + RT \log_e C_\alpha$$

and

$$\mu_\beta = \mu_0 + RT \log_e C_\beta.$$

The diffusion must take place in that direction which leads to a decrease in free energy, so that

$$dG_{T, p} = \mu_\alpha dn_\alpha + \mu_\beta dn_\beta < 0.$$

Since $dn_\alpha = -dn_\beta$, we can write

$$\{(\mu_0 + RT \log_e C_\alpha) - (\mu_0 + RT \log_e C_\beta)\}dn_\alpha < 0$$

i.e.

$$dn_\alpha RT \log_e \frac{C_\alpha}{C_\beta} < 0.$$

It follows that diffusion will take place at constant temperature and pressure from α to β (i.e. dn_α is negative) only if

$$\frac{C_\alpha}{C_\beta} > 1.$$

By this method we have shown that the fact that at constant temperature and pressure diffusion of a component occurs from a point at which it is at the higher concentration to one at which it is at a lower is itself a consequence of the general expressions we have deduced.

It should be pointed out that this conclusion is true only if the system is at constant temperature and pressure. If a temperature gradient is established across a solution diffusion takes place until the concentration at one end differs from that at the other. This phenomenon was discovered in the last century by Soret, and is known as the SORET EFFECT. The investigation of this effect is one of the most interesting developments in modern thermodynamics.[1]

(iii) A Spontaneous Chemical Reaction Leading to Chemical Equilibrium

This is one of the most important sections in the whole book. In it we show how the entropy produced in a chemical reaction and the affinity at any moment during the reaction may be expressed in terms of the chemical potentials of the reactants and reaction products.

We consider a system at temperature T and pressure p containing substances A, B, C and D . . . capable of interacting according to the equation

$$a\text{A} + b\text{B} \ldots \rightleftharpoons c\text{C} + d\text{D} \ldots$$

The reaction may be homogeneous (i.e. take place completely in the gaseous phase or in solution), or be heterogeneous such as a reaction between a gas and a solid.

We now suppose that the reaction proceeds from left to right by an amount $d\xi$. This will be accompanied by the production of a quantity of entropy given by equation

$$\mathbf{A}d\xi = TdS_{\text{irrev}} \quad . \quad . \quad . \quad . \quad . \quad (11,2)$$

and by an increase in A, B, C and D of da, db, dc and dd moles respectively

---

[1] See de Groot, S. R., *L'Effet Soret* (North Holland, Amsterdam). Agar, J. N., *The Structure of Electrolytic Solutions* (edr. W. J. Hamer), p. 200 (John Wiley, New York, 1959). Tyrrell, H. J. V., *Diffusion and Heat Flow in Liquids* (Butterworths, 1961).

(we note that da and db are negative increments and dc and dd positive). We know also that

$$da = -ad\xi$$
$$db = -bd\xi$$
$$dc = cd\xi$$

and
$$dd = dd\xi.$$

It is possible to describe the reaction by two sets of equations: the first are those equations which were derived in Chapter 9:

$$dU = TdS - pdV - TdS_{irrev}$$
$$dH = TdS + Vdp - TdS_{irrev}$$
$$dA = -SdT - pdV - TdS_{irrev}$$

and
$$dG = -SdT + Vdp - TdS_{irrev},$$

and the second, those equations which derive from (11,11), (11,21), (11,22) and (11,20)

$$dU = TdS - pdV - (a\mu_A + b\mu_B - c\mu_C - d\mu_D \ldots)d\xi \qquad (11,62)$$
$$dH = TdS + Vdp - (a\mu_A + b\mu_B - c\mu_C - d\mu_D \ldots)d\xi \qquad (11,63)$$
$$dA = -SdT - pdV - (a\mu_A + b\mu_B - c\mu_C - d\mu_D \ldots)d\xi \qquad (11,64)$$

and
$$dG = -SdT + Vdp - (a\mu_A + b\mu_B - c\mu_C - d\mu_D \ldots)d\xi. \qquad (11,65)$$

We see that

$$TdS_{irrev} = (a\mu_A + b\mu_B - c\mu_C - d\mu_D \ldots)d\xi \ . \quad . \quad (11,66)$$

and that

$$\boxed{\mathbf{A} = a\mu_A + b\mu_B - c\mu_C - d\mu_D \ldots} \quad . \quad . \quad (11,67)$$

Since the affinity of reaction is greater than zero, a necessary condition for the reaction to proceed from left to right is that

$$\boxed{a\mu_A + b\mu_B \ldots > c\mu_C - d\mu_D \ldots} \quad . \quad . \quad (11,68)$$

We deduce the general statement that

A CHEMICAL REACTION WILL PROCEED ONLY IF THE SUM OF THE CHEMICAL POTENTIALS OF THE REACTING SPECIES IS GREATER THAN THE SUM OF THE CHEMICAL POTENTIALS OF THE SPECIES PRODUCED.

We call this THE THIRD STATEMENT OF CHEMICAL POTENTIALS.

We observe that expressions (11,66), (11,67) and (11,68) are general expressions which are independent of any special conditions imposed on the reacting system. Only if we require to calculate the effect of a finite change such that a moles of A and b moles of B . . . react to form c moles of C and d moles of D . . . do we require to consider the conditions imposed. It then follows from equations (11,62) to (11,65) that

$$-\Delta U_{S,\,v} = (a\mu_{A_{in}} + b\mu_{B_{in}} \ldots) - (c\mu_{C_f} + d\mu_{D_f} \ldots) \quad (11,69)$$

$$-\Delta H_{S,\,p} = (a\mu_{A_{in}} + b\mu_{B_{in}} \ldots) - (c\mu_{C_f} + d\mu_{D_f} \ldots) \quad (11,70)$$

$$-\Delta A_{T,\,v} = (a\mu_{A_{in}} + b\mu_{B_{in}} \ldots) - (c\mu_{C_f} + d\mu_{D_f} \ldots) \quad (11,71)$$

$$-\Delta G_{T,\,p} = (a\mu_{A_{in}} + b\mu_{B_{in}} \ldots) - (c\mu_{C_f} + d\mu_{D_f} \ldots) \quad (11,72)$$

We have denoted the fact that μ_A and μ_B in this last set of equations are the chemical potentials of A and B in their initial state (i.e. before reaction) by the suffix in, and the fact that μ_C and μ_D are the chemical potentials of C and D in their final state (i.e. when the reaction is complete) by the suffix f.

Of this last set of equations the most important is (11,72); we shall use it shortly to derive the Reaction Isotherm.

We now imagine that the reaction

$$a\text{A} + b\text{B} \ldots \longrightarrow c\text{C} + d\text{D} \ldots$$

has proceeded to such an extent that a state of chemical equilibrium has been established. At equilibrium the affinity is zero, and it follows from (11,67) that

$$\boxed{a\mu_{A_{eq}} + b\mu_{B_{eq}} \ldots = c\mu_{C_{eq}} + d\mu_{D_{eq}} \ldots} \quad . \quad (11,73)$$

We deduce the general statement that

AT EQUILIBRIUM THE SUMS OF THE CHEMICAL POTENTIALS OF THE REACTING SPECIES ON BOTH SIDES OF THE CHEMICAL EQUATION ARE EQUAL.

We call this THE FOURTH STATEMENT OF CHEMICAL POTENTIALS.

Some Applications of Chemical Potentials to Chemical Reactions

(i) The Law of Mass Action

We first consider a chemical reaction

$$a\text{A} + b\text{B} \ldots \rightleftharpoons c\text{C} + d\text{D} \ldots$$

in which the chemical species are gases, the behaviour of which is ideal.

We express the chemical potential of each component at equilibrium in terms of its equilibrium partial pressure, i.e.

$$\mu_{A_{eq}} = \mu_{o_A} + RT \log_e p_{A_{eq}} \quad \cdots \quad (11,44)$$

Substituting in (11,73) and rearranging, we see that

$$RT \log_e \frac{p_{C_{eq}}^c p_{D_{eq}}^d}{p_{A_{eq}}^a p_{B_{eq}}^b} = a\mu_{o_A} + b\mu_{o_B} \cdots - c\mu_{o_C} - d\mu_{o_D} \cdots$$

The terms on the right-hand side are dependent only on temperature. If we represent their sum by the term $\Sigma\mu_0$ we may write

$$\frac{p_{C_{eq}}^c p_{D_{eq}}^d}{p_{A_{eq}}^a p_{B_{eq}}^b} = e^{\frac{\Sigma\mu_0}{RT}} \quad \cdots \quad (11,74)$$

The term $e^{\frac{\Sigma\mu_0}{RT}}$ is usually given the symbol K_p, and is known as the *Equilibrium Constant in terms of partial pressures*, so that we may write

$$\frac{p_{C_{eq}}^c p_{D_{eq}}^d}{p_{A_{eq}}^a p_{B_{eq}}^b} = K_p(T). \quad \cdots \quad (11,75)$$

The symbol (T) is included to denote that K_p is a function of temperature. Equation (11,75) will be familiar as one form of the Law of Mass Action. Since the terms $\mu_{o_A}, \mu_{o_B}, \ldots$ are independent of pressure, the value of K_p for a reaction involving only ideal gases is independent of the pressure to which the system is subjected.

For some purposes it is convenient to express the Law of Mass Action in terms of the mole fractions of the components at equilibrium. We now use (11,47) and write

$$\mu_{A_{eq}} = \mu_{o_{y_A}}(T, p) + RT \log_e y_{A_{eq}}$$

where $\mu_{o_{y_A}}$ is the chemical potential of component A as a pure gas at pressure p and temperature T.

Proceeding as before we obtain the equation

$$\frac{y_{C_{eq}}^c y_{D_{eq}}^d}{y_{A_{eq}}^a y_{B_{eq}}^b} = K_y(T,p). \quad . \quad . \quad . \quad . \quad (11,76)$$

Since the standard chemical potentials in terms of mole fractions are functions of pressure and temperature, so the value of K_y depends on the temperature and pressure to which the system is subjected. This fact is registered by the inclusion of the symbol (T,p).

The relationship between K_y and K_p is easily obtained. Since the partial pressure of a component is related to the total pressure of the system by the equation

$$p_i = y_i p \quad . \quad . \quad . \quad . \quad . \quad . \quad (11,46)$$

it follows that

$$K_y = K_p \times p^{a+b-c-d} \quad . \quad . \quad . \quad . \quad (11,77)$$

so that K_y is the same as K_p only

   (i) if the system is at unit pressure; or
   (ii) if $a + b \ldots = c + d \ldots$

Since K_p is independent of pressure it follows from (11,77) that

$$\frac{K_{y_{p_2}}}{K_{y_{p_1}}} = \left(\frac{p_2}{p_1}\right)^{a+b-c-d} \quad . \quad . \quad . \quad . \quad (11,78)$$

so that increase in pressure will lead to an increase in the value of K_y for a reaction such as

$$N_2 + 3H_2 \rightleftharpoons 2NH_3$$

but the value of K_y for a reaction such as

$$H_2 + Br_2 \rightleftharpoons 2HBr$$

is independent of pressure. It is evident that equation (11,78) is an example of Le Chatalier's Principle.

For systems involving gases which are not ideal, the partial pressure terms in the above equations must be replaced by partial fugacities, so that equation (11,75) becomes

$$\frac{p^{*c}_{C_{eq}} p^{*d}_{D_{eq}}}{p^{*a}_{A_{eq}} p^{*b}_{B_{eq}}} = K_{p*}(T). \quad . \quad . \quad . \quad . \quad (11,79)$$

We must now consider the reaction

$$aA + bB \ldots \rightleftharpoons cC + dD \ldots$$

taking place in solution. The argument used is the same as that given above. If the solution is ideal the equilibrium concentration of each component can be represented in terms of mole fractions, molar concentrations or molalities, so that the following expressions are obtained:

$$\frac{x_{C_{eq}}^c x_{D_{eq}}^d}{x_{A_{eq}}^a x_{B_{eq}}^b} = K_x(T, p) \quad \ldots \quad \ldots \quad (11,80)$$

$$\frac{C_{C_{eq}}^c C_{D_{eq}}^d}{C_{A_{eq}}^a C_{B_{eq}}^b} = K_c(T, p) \quad \ldots \quad \ldots \quad (11,81)$$

$$\frac{m_{C_{eq}}^c m_{D_{eq}}^d}{m_{A_{eq}}^a m_{B_{eq}}^b} = K_m(T, p). \quad \ldots \quad \ldots \quad (11,82)$$

If the solution is not ideal, activities must be used instead of concentrations. We then obtain the equations

$$\frac{a_{x_{C_{eq}}}^a a_{x_{D_{eq}}}^d}{a_{x_{A_{eq}}}^a a_{x_{B_{eq}}}^b} = K_{a_x}(T, p) \quad \ldots \quad \ldots \quad (11,83)$$

$$\frac{a_{c_{C_{eq}}}^c a_{c_{D_{eq}}}^d}{a_{c_{A_{eq}}}^a a_{c_{B_{eq}}}^b} = K_{a_c}(T, p) \quad \ldots \quad \ldots \quad (11,84)$$

and

$$\frac{a_{m_{C_{eq}}}^c a_{m_{D_{eq}}}^d}{a_{m_{A_{eq}}}^a a_{m_{B_{eq}}}^b} = K_{a_m}(T, p). \quad \ldots \quad \ldots \quad (11,85)$$

We must now consider equilibrium in a heterogeneous system, choosing as example the reaction

$$CaCO_{3(s)} \rightleftharpoons CaO_{(s)} + CO_2.$$

At equilibrium

$$\mu_{CaCO_{3_{eq}}} = \mu_{CaO_{eq}} + \mu_{CO_{2_{eq}}}.$$

We have already shown that the chemical potential of a pure solid or liquid is dependent on the temperature and pressure but is independent of the quantity present, so that we may write

$$\mu_{CaCO_{3_{eq}}} = \mu_{0_{CaCO_3}}$$

and

$$\mu_{CaO_{eq}} = \mu_{0_{CaO}}.$$

If we assume that the behaviour of carbon dioxide is ideal we may write

$$\mu_{CO_{2eq}} = \mu_{0CO_2} + RT \log_e p_{CO_{2eq}}$$

so that at equilibrium

$$RT \log_e p_{CO_{2eq}} = \mu_{0CaCO_3} - \mu_{0CaO} - \mu_{0CO_2}.$$

Since all terms on the right-hand side are independent of concentration we may write

$$p_{CO_{2eq}} = K_p(T, p). \quad . \quad . \quad . \quad . \quad (11,86)$$

It will be noted that the solid components do not figure in the last equation, but that K_p is shown to be a function of pressure as well as temperature because the terms μ_{0CaCO_3} and μ_{0CaO} are so dependent. It should also be noted that the solid components would figure in the final equation if they formed a true solid solution with each other, because their chemical potentials at equilibrium would then depend on their relative concentrations.

Although the symbol (T, p) has been used in equations (11,80) to (11,86) to denote the fact that the equilibrium constants for condensed systems are dependent on both temperature and pressure, it should be understood that in fact their dependence on pressure is of relatively little importance. The argument is the same whichever constant we consider. Thus for the reaction

$$aA + bB \ldots \rightleftharpoons cC + dD \ldots$$

$$RT \log_e K_x = a\mu_{0x_A} + b\mu_{0x_B} \ldots - c\mu_{0x_C} - d\mu_{0x_D} \ldots$$

so that $\quad RT \left(\dfrac{\partial \log_e K_x}{\partial p} \right)_T = a \left(\dfrac{\partial \mu_{0x_A}}{\partial p} \right)_T + b \left(\dfrac{\partial \mu_{0x_B}}{\partial p} \right)_T \ldots$

$$- c \left(\frac{\partial \mu_{0x_C}}{\partial p} \right)_T - d \left(\frac{\partial \mu_{0x_D}}{\partial p} \right)_T \ldots$$

$$= a\bar{v}_A + b\bar{v}_B \ldots - c\bar{v}_C - d\bar{v}_D \ldots \quad (11,87)$$

It follows that increase in pressure will lead to an increase in the value of the equilibrium constant if the sum of the partial molar volumes of the reactants is greater than that of the reaction products. Since the difference between these quantities is extremely small in the case of a condensed system, the effect of change in pressure on the value of the equilibrium constant is in fact very small indeed.

The impression may have been given in what has gone before that it is necessary always to express the concentration of each component in a reacting system in the same way, i.e. all in mole fractions, or all in molalities, and so on. This is not the case at all, the concentration of each component may be expressed in whichever way is the most convenient. Thus, one of the most important reactions in electro-chemistry is that in which hydrogen reacts with a saturated solution of silver chloride in water containing hydrochloric acid. The reaction is

$$H_2 + 2Ag^+ \longrightarrow 2Ag + 2H^+.$$

The equilibrium concentration of hydrogen is expressed in terms of its partial pressure, and that of the silver and hydrogen ions in terms of molal activities, so that the equilibrium constant is given by the equation

$$\frac{a^2 m_{H^+eq}}{p_{H_2eq} a^2 m_{Ag^+eq}} = K.$$

We have here a *mixed* equilibrium constant which has resulted purely and simply as the result of our selecting the most convenient expression for the equilibrium concentration of each species.

The Variation of the Equilibrium Constant with Temperature

It follows from equation (11,74) and from the subsequent argument that the equilibrium constant for any reaction

$$aA + bB \ldots \rightleftharpoons cC + dD \ldots$$

may be represented by the equation

$$\log_e K = \frac{1}{RT}\{a\mu_{o_A} + b\mu_{o_B} \ldots - c\mu_{o_C} - d\mu_{o_D} \ldots\}$$

so that
$$R\left(\frac{\partial \log_e K}{\partial T}\right)_p = a\left\{\frac{\partial\left(\frac{\mu_{o_A}}{T}\right)}{\partial T}\right\}_p + b\left\{\frac{\partial\left(\frac{\mu_{o_B}}{T}\right)}{\partial T}\right\}_p \ldots$$

It follows from (11,31) that

$$R\left(\frac{\partial \log_e K}{\partial T}\right)_p = \frac{1}{T^2}\{-a\bar{h}_{o_A} - b\bar{h}_{o_B} \ldots + c\bar{h}_{o_C} + d\bar{h}_{o_D} \ldots\}$$

where h_o denotes the standard partial molar enthalpy of each component. The sum in the last bracket equals ΔH_o, the standard heat of reaction, i.e. the heat absorbed at constant pressure when the reactants originally in their standard states form reaction products in their standard states. We may therefore write

$$\left(\frac{\partial \log_e K}{\partial T}\right)_p = \frac{\Delta H_o}{RT^2} \ldots \qquad \ldots \qquad . \qquad . \qquad . \qquad (11,88)$$

In many cases the heat of reaction does not vary very much with the concentration of the reactants, and we may replace ΔH_0 by ΔH, the heat of reaction at arbitrary concentrations, and write

$$\boxed{\left(\frac{\partial \log_e K}{\partial T}\right)_p = \frac{\Delta H}{RT^2}} \quad \cdots \cdots \quad (11,89)$$

For a temperature range so small that ΔH may be assumed to remain constant this equation may be integrated to give

$$\log_e K = -\frac{\Delta H}{RT} + I \quad \cdots \cdots \quad (11,90)$$

where I is the integration constant. The equilibrium constant can be calculated at any temperature within the range if its value at any one temperature and the value of the heat of reaction are known. Alternatively we note that the knowledge of K at two temperatures permits the calculation of the heat of reaction.

If we require to integrate (11,89) over a temperature range so great that the variation in ΔH must be taken into account, Kirchhoff's Law must be used to construct an expression for ΔH as a function of temperature. The way this is done is explained in Chapter 6, a typical expression being

$$\Delta H = \Sigma a T + \frac{\Sigma b}{2} T^2 + \frac{\Sigma c}{3} T^3 \ldots + I'. \quad \cdots \quad (6,14)$$

Substituting in (11,89) and integrating, we obtain the equation

$$\log_e K = \frac{\Sigma a}{R} \log_e T + \frac{\Sigma b}{2R} T + \frac{\Sigma c}{6R} T^2 \cdots - \frac{I'}{RT} - \frac{I}{R}$$

where $-I$ is the second integration constant.

Hence $\quad RT \log_e K = \Sigma a T \log_e T + \frac{\Sigma b}{2} T^2 + \frac{\Sigma c}{6} T^3 - I' - IT.$ (11,91)

We note that the right-hand side of this equation is identical with the right-hand side of the integrated form of the Gibbs–Helmholtz equation (10,38), except that all the signs are changed. The student will be clear on the reason for this in the next section. We also point out that all terms on the right-hand side of (11,91) except the last integration constant I are obtainable from thermal data (see Chapter 6), but that the evaluation of I can only be achieved using thermal data with the help of the Third Law. We return to this problem in the next chapter. We also point out that the equation can be used only over that temperature range over which the thermal capacity constants $a, b, c \ldots$ have been experimentally established.

Equation (11,89) was originally derived by van't Hoff and is usually known as the *van't Hoff Equation*.

(ii) The Reaction Isotherm

Earlier in this chapter we showed that when a reaction

$$a\text{A} + b\text{B} \ldots \longrightarrow c\text{C} + d\text{D} \ldots$$

proceeds to the extent that a moles of A and b moles of B react to form c moles of C and d moles of D at the same temperature and pressure, the decrease in free energy is given by the equation

$$-\Delta G_{T,\, p} = (a\mu_\text{A} + b\mu_\text{B} \ldots) - (c\mu_\text{C} + d\mu_\text{D} \ldots) \qquad (11,72)$$

μ_A and μ_B being the chemical potentials of A and B in the initial state, and μ_C and μ_D being the chemical potentials of C and D in the final state.

For a reaction in which the chemical species are all gases the behaviour of which is ideal

$$\mu_\text{A} = \mu_{o_\text{A}} + RT \log_e p_{\text{A}_{in}}$$

$$\mu_\text{B} = \mu_{o_\text{B}} + RT \log_e p_{\text{B}_{in}}$$

$$\mu_\text{C} = \mu_{o_\text{C}} + RT \log_e p_{\text{C}_f}$$

$$\mu_\text{D} = \mu_{o_\text{D}} + RT \log_e p_{\text{D}_f}$$

It follows that

$$-\Delta G_{T,\, p} = (a\mu_{o_\text{A}} + b\mu_{o_\text{B}} \ldots - c\mu_{o_\text{C}} - d\mu_{o_\text{D}} \ldots)$$

$$- RT \log_e \frac{p_{\text{C}_f}^c p_{\text{D}_f}^d}{p_{\text{A}_{in}}^a p_{\text{B}_{in}}^b} \qquad (11,92)$$

Since $\qquad a\mu_{o_\text{A}} + b\mu_{o_\text{B}} \ldots - c\mu_{o_\text{C}} - d\mu_{o_\text{D}} \ldots = RT \log_e K_p \qquad (11,74)$

we may write

$$-\Delta G_{T,\, p} = RT \log_e K_p - RT \log_e \frac{p_{\text{C}_f}^c p_{\text{D}_f}^d}{p_{\text{A}_{in}}^a p_{\text{B}_{in}}^b} \quad . \quad . \quad (11,93)$$

If in a particular reaction the initial partial pressures of A and B are 1 atmosphere, and the final partial pressures of both C and D are 1 atmosphere, so that A and B are initially in their standard states, and C and D finally in their standard states, the free energy change becomes the *Standard Free Energy Change*, and is denoted by the symbol ΔG_o. Since under these conditions the last term in (11,93) vanishes,

$$\boxed{-\Delta G_o = RT \log_e K_p} \quad . \quad . \quad . \quad . \quad (11,97)$$

We also note that

$$-\Delta G_0 = a\mu_{0_A} + b\mu_{0_B} \ldots - c\mu_{0_C} - d\mu_{0_D} \ldots \qquad (11,98)$$

So far we have considered only a gas reaction, and have chosen to express the chemical potential of each component in terms of its partial pressure, which is the same as choosing its standard state as that of the pure gas at 1 atmosphere pressure. Similar equations may be produced for a gaseous system in which we choose to express the chemical potential of each component in terms of its mole fraction, or for a system in solution in which we express the chemical potential of each component in terms of its mole fraction, molar concentration or molality. For a system which is far from ideal, partial pressures must be replaced by partial fugacities, and other concentration terms replaced by activities. The values of ΔG_0, K, μ_{0_A}, μ_{0_B} . . . will depend on the system used.

Equations (11,93) and (11,97) are usually called the *Reaction Isotherm*. They were first derived by van't Hoff.

The important fact which emerges from these equations is that if for any reaction K or its corresponding standard free energy change $-\Delta G_0$ is known, the free energy change can be calculated whatever be the initial and final states of the reactants and reaction products. Conversely, the measurement of the free energy change under arbitrary conditions, as has been discussed in Chapter 9 and will be discussed again in Chapter 12, permits the calculation of ΔG_0 and K_p.

Earlier in this book we stated that the two most interesting questions to which thermodynamics would provide an answer were (1) whether or not a reaction would proceed under the conditions we wished to apply, and if so (2) how completely would it go. Clearly we are now very near to giving the complete answer to both questions. When, in the next chapter, we see how the Third Law of Thermodynamics may be used to determine the free energy change for a chemical reaction from thermal data, we shall be able not only to say whether ΔG is positive or negative, which answers the first question, but to calculate the value of the equilibrium constant, which answers the second.

(iii) The Calculation of the Affinity of Reaction

We now show how it is possible, using the concept of chemical potentials, to calculate the affinity of reaction at any stage during its course.

We first consider a reaction

$$A \rightleftharpoons B$$

proceeding in solution at constant temperature and pressure. We shall later apply some of the conclusions of this section to a study of chemical kinetics, and since it is an experimental fact that reaction *rates* are proportional to the molar concentrations of the reactants, we choose in this section to express the concentration of reactants in molar quantities, and for simplicity to suppose that the solution is ideal throughout the course of reaction and that it undergoes no change of volume. We suppose that the system consists of 1 litre of solution containing initially one mole of substance A but none of substance B. We denote the start of the reaction by the parameter $\xi = 0$, and observe that if the reaction proceeds completely so that all of A converts to B, the value of the parameter changes to $\xi = 1$.

At any point during the reaction the affinity is given by the equation

$$\mathbf{A} = \mu_A - \mu_B.$$

We use (11,54) to express μ_A and μ_B in terms of molar concentrations and obtain the equation

$$\mathbf{A} = \{\mu_{0_{C_A}} + RT \log_e C_A\} - \{\mu_{0_{C_B}} + RT \log_e C_B\}$$

When the reaction has proceeded to extent ξ, the molar concentration of component A becomes equal to $(1 - \xi)$ and that of B to ξ; and since from (11,98) it is clear that

$$\mu_{0_{C_A}} - \mu_{0_{C_B}} = -\Delta G_0$$

the affinity of reaction at extent ξ is given by the equation

$$\mathbf{A} = -\Delta G_0 + RT \log_e \frac{1 - \xi}{\xi}. \qquad . \quad . \quad . \quad (11,99)$$

This equation permits the calculation of the affinity at any stage in the reaction if ΔG_0 is known.

TABLE 11,I

ξ	$\mathbf{A} = 1000 + RT \log_e \dfrac{1 - \xi}{\xi}$
0	∞
0·02	3330 cal
0·05	2770
0·1	2316
0·2	1831
0·3	1507
0·4	1243
0·5	1000
0·6	757
0·7	493
0·8	169
0·9	−316
0·95	−770
0·98	−1330
1·0	−∞

Table 11,I shows the values of the affinity of the reaction

$$A \rightleftharpoons B$$

at 300° K, at which temperature we choose to assign $-\Delta G_0$ the value 1000 cal.

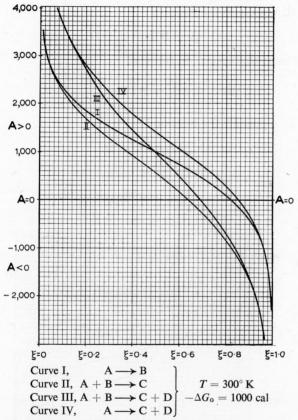

Curve I,   A ⟶ B ⎫
Curve II, A + B ⟶ C ⎪ $T = 300°$ K
Curve III, A + B ⟶ C + D ⎬ $-\Delta G_0 = 1000$ cal
Curve IV,   A ⟶ C + D ⎭

System consists of one litre of solution containing initially one mole of each reactant on the left-hand side of the equation.

Figure 11,2. The variation of Affinity with extent of reaction.

The graph of **A** against ξ is shown as Curve I in Figure 11,2. We note that chemical equilibrium is reached when $\xi = 0.82$, so that the part of the curve from $\xi = 0.82$ to $\xi = 1$ is unreal.

Curve II represents the course of the reaction

$$A + B \rightleftharpoons C$$

in which we choose an ideal solution which at $\xi = 0$ contains one mole of

A and one mole of B. In this case the affinity of reaction is given by the equation

$$\mathbf{A} = -\Delta G_0 + RT \log_e \frac{(1-\xi)^2}{\xi}. \quad . \quad . \quad . \quad (11,100)$$

We again choose to assign $-\Delta G_0$ the value 1000 cal.

Curve III represents the reaction

$$A + B \rightleftharpoons C + D$$

under the same conditions. In this case

$$\mathbf{A} = -\Delta G_0 + RT \log_e \frac{(1-\xi)^2}{\xi^2}. \quad . \quad . \quad (11,101)$$

Curve IV represents the reaction

$$A \rightleftharpoons C + D$$

for which

$$\mathbf{A} = -\Delta G_0 + RT \log_e \frac{(1-\xi)}{\xi^2}. \quad . \quad . \quad (11,102)$$

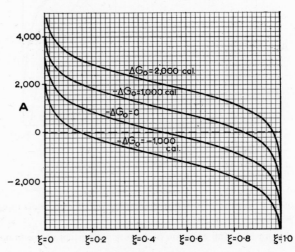

Figure 11,3. Curves of **A** against ξ for reactions of the same molecularity at different values of ΔG_0.

The curves shown in Figure 11,2 are of great interest. The following observations are made:

1. The actual curve of **A** against ξ and so the dependence of the affinity on the extent of reaction, is determined solely by the molecularity of

the reaction as long as the system remains thermodynamically ideal; and for reactions of the same molecularity carried out at the same temperature, the position of the curve above the axis $\mathbf{A} = 0$ is determined solely by the value of ΔG_0. In Figure 11,3 we show the curves for four reactions of the same molecularity at different values of ΔG_0.

2. The effect of changing the temperature at which the reaction proceeds is two-fold. It first changes ΔG_0, and secondly changes the slope of the curve at all points. The second effect will usually be much greater than the first, the slope at all points being directly proportional to the absolute temperature.

3. Probably the most interesting observation is that at no point during any reaction does $\left(\dfrac{\partial \mathbf{A}}{\partial \xi}\right)_{T,\,p}$ become equal to zero.

Since, from (11,6), $\mathbf{A} = -\left(\dfrac{\partial G}{\partial \xi}\right)_{T,\,p}$, we see that as the equilibrium point is approached in a reaction at constant temperature and pressure $\left(\dfrac{\partial G}{\partial \xi}\right)_{T,\,p}$ approaches zero, so that the graph of G against ξ for the forward and back reactions forms a continuous curve as shown in Figure 11,4 (a).

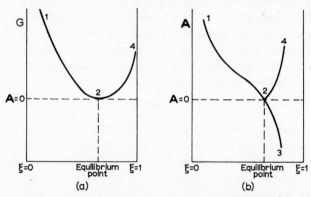

Figure 11,4. (a) The change in free energy of the system during the course of reaction. (b) The change in affinity during the course of reaction.

We might suppose that the curve of $\mathbf{A}$ against ξ would be of the same shape. In fact, as shown in Figure 11,4 (b), we find that at the equilibrium point ($\mathbf{A} = 0$), $\left(\dfrac{\partial \mathbf{A}}{\partial \xi}\right)_{\mathbf{A}=0}$ which equals $\left(\dfrac{\partial^2 G}{\partial \xi^2}\right)_{\mathbf{A}=0}$ is finite, and that the curve of the forward reaction $1 \longrightarrow 2$ abruptly joins that of the reverse reaction $4 \longrightarrow 2$. (The portion $4 \longrightarrow 2$ is, of course, the "real" mirror image of the unreal curve $2 \longrightarrow 3$.)

The value of $\left(\dfrac{\partial \mathbf{A}}{\partial \xi}\right)$ can be evaluated from whichever equation (11,99) to (11,102) is applicable. For the reaction

$$A \rightleftharpoons B$$

$$\left(\frac{\partial \mathbf{A}}{\partial \xi}\right)_{T,\,p} = -\frac{RT}{\xi(1-\xi)} \quad \cdots \quad (11,103)$$

and since it follows from (11,99) that when $\mathbf{A} = 0$, $RT \log_e \dfrac{1-\xi_{eq}}{\xi_{eq}} = \Delta G_0$ it can be shown quite easily that the slope as equilibrium is approached is given by the equation

$$\left(\frac{\partial \mathbf{A}}{\partial \xi}\right)_{\substack{T,\,p \\ \mathbf{A}=0}} = -\frac{RT\left\{1 + e^{\frac{\Delta G_0}{RT}}\right\}^2}{e^{\frac{\Delta G_0}{RT}}}. \quad \cdots \quad (11,104)$$

Thermodynamics and Chemical Kinetics

Since it has been established that the affinity of reaction at any moment in the course of a reaction is a measure of its tendency to proceed, it would not be unreasonable to suppose that some relationship might be established between the affinity and the velocity of reaction that might permit the calculation of velocity constants from thermodynamic data. Some aspects of this problem will now be discussed, but it must be explained at the beginning that despite considerable efforts which have been made in this direction,[1] little success has been attained.

We shall here discuss only a reaction

$$A \rightleftharpoons B$$

which we shall suppose to be a First Order reaction both in the forward and reverse directions. If we assume that initially the system consists of one litre of solution containing one mole of reagent A, and none of reagent B, the velocity of reaction may be expressed in terms of the extent of reaction by the equation

$$\mathbf{V}_{(\xi)} = k_1(1-\xi) - k_2\xi \quad \cdots \quad (11,105)$$

where k_1 and k_2 are the velocity constants of the forward and back reactions. This equation may be simplified as follows:

At equilibrium

$$k_1(1 - \xi_{eq}) = k_2\xi_{eq}$$

[1] See, for example: Prigogine, Outer and Herbo, *J. Phys. Chem.*, 1948, **52**, 321. Manes, Hofer and Weller, *J. Chem. Phys.*, 1950, **18**, 1355. Denbigh, *Trans. Farad. Soc.*, 1952, **48**, 389.

so that

$$\mathbf{V}_{(\xi)} = k_1 \left\{ 1 - \frac{\xi}{\xi_{eq}} \right\}. \quad \ldots \quad (11,106)$$

We know, too, that the affinity of reaction may be expressed by the equation

$$\mathbf{A}_{(\xi)} = -\Delta G_0 + RT \log_e \frac{1 - \xi}{\xi}. \quad \ldots \quad (11,99)$$

Calculation of the velocity constant from thermodynamic data would be possible if it were possible to equate some function of $\mathbf{V}$ with $\mathbf{A}$. This has not been found possible. For many physical processes such as diffusion, thermal and electrical conduction and so on, the rate of change proves to be directly proportional to the driving force concerned, but it can be shown easily that this is not so in the case of a chemical reaction. If the relationship between $\mathbf{V}$ and $\mathbf{A}$ were a simple linear one it would be possible to find some proportionality constant y such that the curves of $\mathbf{A}$ against ξ and $y\mathbf{V}$ against ξ coincide at all points. That this is not possible is seen clearly by comparing the expression for $\left(\frac{\partial \mathbf{V}}{\partial \xi} \right)_{T, p}$ with that for $\left(\frac{\partial \mathbf{A}}{\partial \xi} \right)_{T, p}$. From (11,106) it follows that

$$\left(\frac{\partial \mathbf{V}}{\partial \xi} \right)_{T, p} = -\frac{k_1}{\xi_{eq}}$$

and is therefore independent of the extent of reaction, while it follows from (11,99) and from the curves shown in Figure 11,2 that $\left(\frac{\partial \mathbf{A}}{\partial \xi} \right)_{T, p}$ is a function of the extent of reaction.

Since any graph of $y\mathbf{V}$ against ξ must be a straight line passing through the point $\mathbf{A} = 0$, $\xi = \xi_{eq}$, it is clear from Figure 11,2 that it can coincide with the curve of $\mathbf{A}$ against ξ only in the immediate vicinity of the equilibrium point. This conclusion is perhaps demonstrated more elegantly by the following argument due essentially to Denbigh.[1]

At some point during the course of the reaction let the concentration of A be C_A and that of B be C_B, and their chemical potentials be μ_A and μ_B. When equilibrium is reached we may write

$$\mu_{A_{eq}} = \mu_{B_{eq}}$$

so that

$$\mu_A - \mu_B = (\mu_A - \mu_{A_{eq}}) - (\mu_B - \mu_{B_{eq}})$$

$$= RT \log_e \frac{C_A}{C_{A_{eq}}} - RT \log_e \frac{C_B}{C_{B_{eq}}}.$$

[1] *Trans. Farad. Soc.*, 1952, **48**, 389.

H

The equilibrium constant K may be expressed as the ratio of the velocity constant for the forward reaction to that of the back reaction, so that

$$\frac{C_{B_{eq}}}{C_{A_{eq}}} = K = \frac{k_1}{k_2}.$$

Therefore, the affinity of reaction at any moment is given by the expression

$$\mathbf{A} = \mu_A - \mu_B = RT \log_e \frac{k_1 C_A}{k_2 C_B}.$$

Since

$$\mathbf{V} = k_1 C_A - k_2 C_B$$

it follows that $\mathbf{V}$ is proportional to $\mathbf{A}$ only if

$$k_1 C_A - k_2 C_B = \frac{RT}{y} \log_e \frac{k_1 C_A}{k_2 C_B}$$

where y is a proportionality constant.

This can be true only if it is permissible to expand the right-hand side of the equation as follows:

$$\frac{RT}{y} \log_e \frac{k_1 C_A}{k_2 C_B} = \frac{RT}{y} \log_e \left\{ 1 + \left(\frac{k_1 C_A}{k_2 C_B} - 1 \right) \right\}$$

$$\simeq \frac{RT}{y} \left\{ \frac{k_1 C_A}{k_2 C_B} - 1 \right\}$$

$$\simeq \frac{RT}{y k_2 C_B} \{ k_1 C_A - k_2 C_B \}.$$

The second step in this expansion is permissible only if $\frac{k_1 C_A}{k_2 C_B}$ is very nearly equal to unity, so that $k_1 C_A$ is very nearly the same as $k_2 C_B$. This condition clearly applies only when the reaction is extremely close to equilibrium.

EXERCISES 11

11,1. The free energy change accompanying a given process is $-20 \cdot 5$ kcal mole^{-1} at 25° C, while at 35° C it is $-20 \cdot 0$ kcal mole^{-1}. Calculate the approximate change in entropy and enthalpy for the process at 30° C.

11,2. The dissociation pressure of the system

$$Ca(OH)_{2(s)} \rightleftharpoons CaO_{(s)} + H_2O_{(g)}$$

is $10 \cdot 5$ mm Hg at $340 \cdot 6°$ C and $101 \cdot 2$ mm Hg at $421 \cdot 3°$ C. Use the van't Hoff equation to calculate the mean heat of hydration of calcium oxide over this temperature range.

11,3. The standard free energy of formation of nitric oxide is given as a function of temperature by the equation

$$\Delta G_0 = 21,600 - 2 \cdot 50T \text{ cal mole}^{-1}.$$

Calculate the percentage of oxygen converted into nitric oxide when air containing 20% oxygen by volume is heated to 2000° C at 1 atmosphere pressure.

11,4. The equilibrium constant for the reaction

$$H_{2(g)} + \tfrac{1}{2}S_{2(g)} \rightleftharpoons H_2S_{(g)}$$

has the following values

$T°$ K	1173	1273	1373	1473	1573
K_p (atm$^{-\frac{1}{2}}$)	28·25	13·74	7·48	4·38	2·77

Determine the mean heat of reaction over this temperature range and evaluate the standard entropy change for the reaction at 1373° K.

11,5. The standard free energies of formation, enthalpies of formation and molar thermal capacities of $BaCO_3$, BaO and CO_2 at 300° K are

	ΔG_{o_f}	ΔH_{o_f}	C_p
$BaCO_3$	−272 kcal	−291 kcal	21·6 cal deg^{-1}
BaO	−126 kcal	−133 kcal	10·4 cal deg^{-1}
CO_2	−94·3 kcal	−94·1 kcal	9·0 cal deg^{-1}

Show that the temperature at which the vapour pressure of CO_2 in equilibrium with barium carbonate and barium oxide is one atmosphere lies between 1500° K and 2000° K.

(Hint: since the equilibrium constant for the reaction is the partial pressure of CO_2, the temperature at which the partial pressure is 1 atmosphere is that temperature at which the standard free energy change for the reaction

$$BaCO_3 \longrightarrow BaO + CO_2$$

is zero. An expression for ΔG_0 in terms of temperature may be obtained using Kirchhoff's Law and the Gibbs–Helmholtz equation. This expression will show that ΔG_0 is positive when $T = 1500°$ K and negative when $T = 2000°$ K.)

11,6. A substance such as calcium carbonate will spontaneously dissociate when its dissociation pressure of CO_2 exceeds the partial pressure of CO_2 in the atmosphere above it. In the dissociation of calcium carbonate the dissociation pressure at 500° C is 0·11 mm Hg.

What is the lowest temperature at which calcium carbonate will dissociate completely in an atmosphere containing 0·03% by volume of CO_2 when the barometer reads 759 mm Hg?

The mean value of ΔH for the reaction

$$CaCO_3 \longrightarrow CaO + CO_2$$

over the temperature range concerned is 41,340 cal.

11,7. The point of inflexion of the curves shown in Figure 11,2 is that point at which

$$\left(\frac{\partial^2 \mathbf{A}}{\partial \xi^2}\right)_{T, p} = 0.$$

It denotes the extent of reaction at which the affinity decreases with increase in ξ more slowly than at any other. Show that for reactions I and III it occurs at $\xi = 0.5$, for reaction II at $\xi = \sqrt{2} - 1$, i.e. 0·414, and for reaction IV at $\xi = 2 - \sqrt{2}$, i.e. 0·586.

CHAPTER 12

THE THIRD LAW OF THERMODYNAMICS AND THE CALCULATION OF FREE ENERGY CHANGES AND EQUILIBRIUM CONSTANTS FROM THERMAL DATA

The student is reminded of the following definitions:

The Standard Free Energy Change ΔG_0 in the reaction

$$a\text{A} + b\text{B} \ldots \longrightarrow c\text{C} + d\text{D} \ldots$$

is the increase in free energy of the system when a moles of reactant A and b moles of reactant B ... *in their standard states* react to form c moles of C and d moles of D ... *in their standard states* the temperature and pressure remaining constant. This quantity is related to the Equilibrium Constant for the reaction by the equation

$$-\Delta G_0 = RT \log_e K,$$

so that, in effect, the calculation of the standard free energy change is equivalent to the calculation of the equilibrium constant.

The free energy change involved when the reactants are in arbitrary rather than standard states is given by the reaction isotherm

$$\Delta G = \Delta G_0 + RT \log_e \frac{[\text{C}]^c_{\text{final}} \times [\text{D}]^d_{\text{final}} \cdots}{[\text{A}]^a_{\text{initial}} \times [\text{B}]^b_{\text{initial}} \cdots}$$

where the symbols $[\text{A}]_{\text{initial}} \cdots [\text{C}]_{\text{final}} \cdots$ denote the arbitrary concentrations of reactants in their initial states and reaction products in their final states in terms of partial pressures, molal concentrations, molal activities or whatever unit is used to define the standard state.

Clearly the first two equations can be combined to give

$$-\Delta G = RT \log_e K - RT \log_e \frac{[\text{C}]^c_{\text{final}} \times [\text{D}]^d_{\text{final}}}{[\text{A}]^a_{\text{initial}} \times [\text{B}]^b_{\text{initial}}}.$$

It follows that if the free energy change is measured under whatever conditions are convenient, the standard free energy change and the equilibrium constant can be calculated. On the other hand, once the standard free energy change or the equilibrium constant is known, the free energy change under any other circumstances can be easily evaluated.

The determination of free energy changes from thermal data depends essentially on the equation

$$\Delta G = \Delta H - T\Delta S \qquad . \quad . \quad . \quad . \quad . \quad (9,16)$$

which applies to any reaction at constant temperature. The determination of ΔH is purely a First Law problem; it has been discussed in Chapters 4 and 6. There remains the problem of the determination of ΔS. The Second Law of Thermodynamics provides no guidance on the calculation of ΔS from thermal data, because a chemical change is thermodynamically irreversible, and therefore the change in entropy is related to the heat absorbed only by the inequality

$$\Delta S > \sum \frac{q}{T}.$$

The Third Law of Thermodynamics shows how ΔS may be determined in other ways.

The Experimental Origin of the Third Law

Earlier in this book we showed that the free energy change for a chemical reaction which takes place in an electrochemical cell can be determined directly from the e.m.f. of the cell at constant pressure, and that the change in enthalpy can be calculated using equation (10,33). The methods involved will be discussed in more detail in Chapter 17.

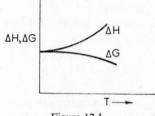

Figure 12,1.

In 1902 T. W. Richards [1] carried out such determinations over a fairly large temperature range, and showed that the values of ΔG and ΔH for any particular reaction approach each other at low temperatures.

In 1906 Nernst [2] put forward the hypothesis that the curves of ΔG and ΔH against temperature become tangential to each other as absolute zero is approached, as illustrated in Figure 12,1.

In other words the Nernst hypothesis is that as absolute zero is approached, not only does

$$\text{(i)} \quad \Delta G - \Delta H \longrightarrow 0 \qquad . \quad . \quad . \quad . \quad (12,1)[3]$$

[1] T. W. Richards, *Z. Physical Chem.*, 1902, **42**, 129.
[2] W. Nernst, *Nachr. Ges. Wiss. Gottingen* (1906).
[3] It should be clear that there is no suggestion that either ΔH or ΔG approach zero as absolute zero is approached. ΔH and ΔG remain (positive or negative) *finite* quantities.

but also   (ii) $\left\{\dfrac{\partial(\Delta H)}{\partial T}\right\}_p \longrightarrow 0$ . . . . . . (12,2)

and   (iii) $\left\{\dfrac{\partial(\Delta G)}{\partial T}\right\}_p \longrightarrow 0.$ . . . . . . (12,3)

The implications of both (ii) and (iii) are of great interest. It will be remembered that Kirchhoff's Law states that for a reaction

$$A \longrightarrow B$$

$$\left\{\dfrac{\partial(\Delta H)}{\partial T}\right\}_p = C_{p_B} - C_{p_A}.$$

The Nernst hypothesis is therefore equivalent to the prediction that molar thermal capacities of all substances become equal as absolute zero is approached. This prediction, in fact, foreshadowed Einstein's theory of specific heats based on Quantum Theory and Statistical Thermodynamics, in which he showed that the molar thermal capacities of all crystalline solids approach zero at absolute zero.

Our immediate concern is, however, not with (ii) but with (iii). Since for a reaction at constant temperature

$$\Delta H - \Delta G = T\Delta S = -T\left\{\dfrac{\partial(\Delta G)}{\partial T}\right\}_p$$

(iii) is equivalent to the hypothesis that as absolute zero is approached

$$\Delta S \longrightarrow 0 \qquad . \quad . \quad . \quad . \quad . \quad (12,4)$$

in other words, the hypothesis suggests that in the reaction

$$A \longrightarrow B$$

$$S_A^0 = S_B^0. \qquad . \quad . \quad . \quad . \quad . \quad (12,5)$$

Before discussing the implications of (12,5) we must inquire whether it can possibly apply to all reactions irrespective of the physical state of the reactants and reaction products. We choose to consider the possibility that reactant A can exist in two physical forms at absolute zero, firstly, as a stable crystal, and secondly, as a supercooled liquid. If this possibility is accepted, equation (12,5) would imply that both

$$S_{A_{crystal}}^0 = S_B^0$$

and $$S_{A_{supercooled\ liquid}}^0 = S_B^0.$$

Both equations can be true only if

$$S^0_{A\text{crystal}} = S^0_{A\text{supercooled liquid}}. \quad \cdot \quad \cdot \quad \cdot \quad \cdot \quad (12,6)$$

Equation (12,6) is open to experimental proof.

Process $1 \longrightarrow 2$ in Figure 12,2 represents the fusion of one mole of a pure crystalline compound at temperature T. The entropy of fusion can

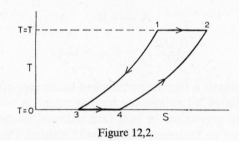

Figure 12,2.

be determined directly from the latent heat of fusion at the same temperature, since

$$\Delta S_{\text{fusion}} = S_2 - S_1 = \frac{L_f}{T}.$$

Processes $1 \longrightarrow 3 \longrightarrow 4 \longrightarrow 2$, however, represent a second possible path that the fusion process might take, process $1 \longrightarrow 3$ representing the cooling of the solid from temperature T to absolute zero, $3 \longrightarrow 4$ the fusion at absolute zero, and $4 \longrightarrow 2$ the rise in temperature of the super-cooled liquid from absolute zero to temperature T. The overall change in entropy from state 1 to state 2 must be independent of the path chosen, so that

$$\frac{L_f}{T} = (S_2 - S_4) + (S_4 - S_3) - (S_1 - S_3), \quad \cdot \quad \cdot \quad (12,6)$$

where $(S_2 - S_4)$ equals $(S^T - S^0)_{\text{supercooled liquid}}$ and can be calculated from measurements of the molar thermal capacity of the supercooled liquid from temperature T to absolute zero, and $(S_1 - S_3)$ equals $(S^T - S^0)_{\text{crystal}}$ and can be calculated from measurements of the molar thermal capacity of the crystalline form.

Such measurements as these were carried out by Gibson and Giauque[1] on glycerol. They showed that

$$\frac{L_f}{T} > (S_2 - S_4) - (S_1 - S_3)$$

[1] Gibson and Giauque, *J. Am. Chem. Soc.*, 1923, **45**, 93.

and therefore that $(S_4 - S_3)$, the entropy of fusion at absolute zero is a finite positive quantity. In other words, the entropies of a supercooled liquid and the stable crystalline form at absolute zero are not the same.

We might also suppose that if equation (12,5) holds for a reaction in which one reactant is in the solid state, it is unlikely to hold when the same reactant is in solution, because we would expect an entropy increase when a solution is formed from its components. There is reason, too, to believe that the entropy of a crystalline solid is, at any particular temperature, always less than that of the same substance in an amorphous state, and it was shown by Simon and Lange[1] that this difference persists in the case of silica at temperatures only slightly above absolute zero.

Experiment, in fact, shows that equation (12,5) holds only for reactions between crystalline solids.[2]

The formal statement that

THE ENTROPY CHANGE IN A REACTION BETWEEN PURE CRYSTALLINE SOLIDS APPROACHES ZERO AS THE TEMPERATURE FALLS TO ABSOLUTE ZERO

is known as the *Nernst Heat Theorem*.

It is one, and perhaps as far as the chemist is concerned, the most useful form in which the Third Law can be expressed.

Application of equation (12,5) to several reactions

$$C + O_2 \longrightarrow CO_2$$

$$CCl_4 \longrightarrow 2Cl_2 + C$$

$$Zn + Cl_2 \longrightarrow ZnCl_2$$

and so on, leads to a corresponding series of equations

$$S_C^0 + S_{O_2}^0 = S_{CO_2}^0$$

$$S_{CCl_4}^0 = 2S_{Cl_2}^0 + S_C^0$$

$$S_{Zn}^0 + S_{Cl_2}^0 = S_{ZnCl_2}^0.$$

These equations are satisfied by an infinite number of sets of solutions, and we have no evidence why one set should be preferred to any other. In other words, we have no information as to the *real* and absolute[3] value

---

[1] Simon and Lange, *Z. Physik.*, 1926, **38**, 227.

[2] We point out without discussion that equation (12,5) is untrue for reactions involving "special" substances such as CO, H_2, N_2O and H_2O, even though they may be in a stable crystalline form. The reason for this will be made clear in Chapter 14.

[3] This question is discussed again in Chapter 13 in terms of Statistical Thermodynamics.

of any of the individual terms S_C^0, S_{Zn}^0 . . ., and are therefore perfectly free to ascribe any conventional values which are convenient and self-consistent. We choose the conventional value

$$S^0 = 0$$

for all perfect crystalline bodies,[1] and permit the term $S_{A_{cal}}^T$ defined by the equation

$$S_{A_{cal}}^T = S_A^T - S_A^0$$

to be called the (conventional) absolute entropy of substance A at temperature T.

The Use of the Third Law for the Determination of the Entropy Change Resulting from a Chemical Reaction at Some Temperature other than Absolute Zero

As was explained earlier, the entropy change resulting from a chemical reaction

$$A \longrightarrow B \text{ at temperature } T,$$

i.e. $$\Delta S = S_B^T - S_A^T$$

cannot be calculated from the heat of reaction because the reaction proceeds irreversibly.

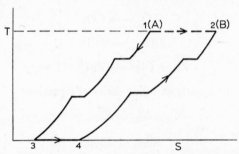

Figure 12,3. For representation purposes it has been supposed that both substances A and B are gases at temperature T, so that the horizontal portions of the curves $1 \longrightarrow 3$ and $4 \longrightarrow 2$ represent fusions and evaporations. It has also been supposed that $S_B^T > S_A^T$: there is, of course, no reason why this should be, and the argument is the same if the opposite is the case.

The natural reaction $A \longrightarrow B$ is shown by the hatched line $1 \longrightarrow 2$ in Figure 12,3.

In an earlier chapter we demonstrated that although the entropy change during an irreversible process usually cannot be calculated directly from

[1] With the exception of the "special" substances mentioned in footnote 2 on the previous page.

thermal measurements made during the change itself, it can always be calculated if the initial and final states of the system are known, and if these states can be linked by any convenient reversible path.

In the case under discussion the initial state is that of one mole of reactant A at temperature T, and the final state that of one mole of B at the same temperature; and we show, connecting them, a path consisting of three parts:

$1 \longrightarrow 3$ represents one mole of substance A being cooled from temperature T to absolute zero, $3 \longrightarrow 4$ represents the chemical reaction at absolute zero, and $4 \longrightarrow 2$ represents the rise in temperature of one mole of substance B from absolute zero to temperature T.

$$S_B^T - S_A^T = (S_B^T - S_B^0) + (S_B^0 - S_A^0) + (S_A^0 - S_A^T) \quad . \quad (12,7)$$

$$= S_{Bcal}^T + (S_B^0 - S_A^0) - S_{Acal}^T.$$

S_{Acal}^T and S_{Bcal}^T can be calculated if the molar thermal capacities and any necessary latent heat terms relating to the substances A and B are known. (Two such quantities were evaluated in Chapter 8, one for ethylene based on the data of Egan and Kemp, and one for water based on the data of Giauque and Strut.) The Third Law states that as long as A and B are pure crystalline solids at absolute zero, the value of the second bracket is zero. In fact, the Third Law states that for such solids Figure 12,3 is incorrect; points 3 and 4 on the entropy axis coincide and the path $1 \longrightarrow 3 \longrightarrow 4 \longrightarrow 2$ simplifies to that shown in Figure 12,4.

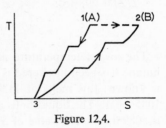

Figure 12,4.

As an example of the use of the Third Law to determine the free energy change of a reaction, and hence its equilibrium constant, from thermal data, we choose the isomeric transformation of *n*-butane into *iso*butane at 298·15° K. The data from which the entropy values are calculated are those of Aston and Messerley[1] and Aston, Kennedy and Schumann.[2]

The lowest temperature at which the molar thermal capacity of solid *n*-butane has been measured is 10° K. The change in entropy from absolute zero to 10° K is calculated therefore using the Debye equation. At 107·55° K crystalline butane undergoes a change of structure for which the molar latent heat of transformation is 494 cal. The second crystalline modification fuses at 134·89° K, the latent heat of fusion being

[1] *J. Am. Chem. Soc.*, 1940, **62**, 1917.   [2] *Ibid.*, 1940, **62**, 2059.

1113·7 cal. The liquid boils at 272·66° K and its corresponding latent heat term is 5351 cal.

S_{cal} for *n*-butane at 298·15° K is therefore given by the following summation

		ΔS
0–10° K	Debye extrapolation	0·15
10–107·55°	$\int C_p d \log_e T$	14·534
107·55°	Polymorphic change	4·593
107·55–134·89°	$\int C_p d \log_e T$	4·520
134·89°	Fusion	8·255
134·89–272·66°	$\int C_p d \log_e T$	20·203
272·66°	Evaporation	19·62
272·66–298·15°	$\int C_p d \log_e T$	1·95

$$S_{cal}^{298·15} = S^{298·15} - S^0 = 74·0 \text{ cal deg}^{-1} \text{ mole}^{-1}$$

The lowest temperature at which the molar thermal capacity of *iso*-butane has been measured is 12·53° K. Only one crystalline modification is known: this melts at 113·74° and the molar latent heat of fusion is 1085·4 cal. The liquid boils at 261·44° and the latent heat of evaporation is 5089·6 cal. The value of $S_{cal}^{298·15}$ is therefore given by the summation:

		ΔS
0–12·53° K	Debye extrapolation	0·247
12·53–113·74°	$\int C_p d \log_e T$	16·115
113·74°	Fusion	9·543
113·74–261·44°	$\int C_p d \log_e T$	22·030
261·44°	Evaporation	19·468
261·44–298·15°	$\int C_p d \log_e T$	2·910

$$S_{cal}^{298·15} = S^{298·15} - S^0 = 70·4 \text{ cal deg}^{-1} \text{ mole}^{-1}$$

It follows that the standard entropy change at 298·15° K when one mole of *n*-butane at 1 atmosphere pressure forms *iso*butane at the same pressure is given by 70·4–74·0, i.e.

$$\Delta S_0 = -3·6 \text{ cal deg}^{-1}.$$

The value of ΔH_0 at 298·15° K may be determined from the heats of combustion of n-butane and *iso*butane, and gives the result

$$\Delta H_0 = -1630 \text{ cal.}$$

Hence at 298·15° K

$$\Delta G_0 = \Delta H_0 - T\Delta S_0$$

$$= -550 \text{ cal.}$$

Since $-\Delta G_0 = RT \log_e K$, we obtain the value $K = 2\cdot6$.

Thermodynamic Data Available in the Literature

The thermodynamic data which is found in the literature falls into two categories. The first is that which derives completely from Statistical Thermodynamics and will be described in Chapter 14. Typical of the second category is that information given in the volume entitled SELECTED VALUES OF CHEMICAL THERMODYNAMIC PROPERTIES published by THE NATIONAL BUREAU OF STANDARDS (U.S.A.) in CIRCULAR No. 500 (1952). Some of this information has been obtained from calorimetric measurements and some from statistical data. Extracts from this publication are given in Table 12,I.

TABLE 12,I

(Note: Values of ΔH_{0f}^0, ΔH_{0f}^{298}, ΔG_{0f}^{298}, are expressed in kcal mole^{-1}, and S_0^{298} and C_p^{298} in cal deg^{-1} mole^{-1}.)

	ΔH_{0f}^0	ΔH_{0f}^{298}	ΔG_{0f}^{298}	$\log_{10} K_f$ at 298° K	S_0^{298}	C_p^{298}
H_2	—	—	—	—	31·211	6·892
H_2O (g)	$-57\cdot107$	$-57\cdot798$	$-54\cdot636$	40·047	45·106	8·025
H_2O (liq)		$-68\cdot317$	$-56\cdot690$	41·553	16·716	17·996
C (graphite)	—				1·361	2·066
CO	$-27\cdot202$	$-26\cdot416$	$-32\cdot808$	24·048	47·301	6·965
N_2	—	—	—	—	45·767	6·960
NO	21·477	21·600	20·719	$-15\cdot187$	50·339	7·137
NO_2	8·682	8·091	12·390	$-9\cdot082$	57·47	9·06
NH_3 (g)	$-9\cdot368$	$-11\cdot04$	$-3\cdot976$	2·9144	46·01	8·523
O_2	—	—	—	—	49·003	7·017
SO_2		$-70\cdot96$	$-71\cdot79$	52·621	59·40	9·51
SO_3 (g)		$-94\cdot45$	$-88\cdot52$	64·884	61·24	12·10
Fe	—	—	—	—	6·49	6·03
FeO*		$-63\cdot7$	$-58\cdot4$	42·81	12·9	
Fe_3O_4		$-267\cdot0$	$-242\cdot4$	177·68	35·0	

* FeO is non-stoichiometric, and is actually $Fe_{0\cdot95}O$.

The quantity ΔH_{0f}^{298} (which is an abbreviation for $\Delta H_{0f}^{298\cdot15}$) is the STANDARD HEAT OF FORMATION of the compound at 25° C (298·15° K): it is the heat absorbed when one mole of the compound in its standard state at 25° C is formed from its constituent elements in their standard states at the same temperature. That of liquid water is $-68\cdot317$ kcal. This is the quantity of heat absorbed (note that the negative sign indicates that the reaction is exothermic), when one mole of liquid water at 25° C is formed from one mole of hydrogen at 1 atmosphere pressure, and at 25° C and half a mole of oxygen at the same temperature and pressure. Hess's Law permits these values to be used to calculate ΔH_0^{298} for any reaction required.

S_0^{298} is the entropy of one mole of the substance at 25° C calculated according to the convention that the entropy at 0° K is zero. In most cases therefore, S_0^{298} is the same as the quantity $S_0^{298} - S^0$, i.e. the quantity $S_{0\text{cal}}^{298}$. It will be noted, however, that the table contains three of the "special" substances, H_2, H_2O and CO mentioned in the footnote on page 205. In these cases the values S_0^{298} are somewhat greater than the quantities $S_{0\text{cal}}^{298}$. The reason for this difference will be given in Chapter 14.

ΔG_{0f}^{298} is the STANDARD FREE ENERGY OF FORMATION[1] of the compound under the same conditions as those operating in the case of ΔH_{0f}^{298}. Clearly ΔG_{0f}^{298} can be calculated from ΔH_{0f}^{298} and the appropriate values of S_0^{298}. For example, the free energy of formation of liquid water is calculated from ΔH_{0f}^{298} and the values of S_0^{298} for liquid water, hydrogen and oxygen,

$$\Delta G_{0f}^{298} = \Delta H_{0f}^{298} - 298\cdot15 \times 10^{-3}\,(16\cdot716 - 31\cdot211 - \tfrac{1}{2} \times 49\cdot003)$$

$$= -68\cdot3174 + 11\cdot627$$

$$= -56\cdot690 \text{ kcal.}$$

(The factor 10^{-3} arises in the above equation because of the units concerned.)

$Log_{10}\ K_f$ at 298° K is the logarithm of the equilibrium constant for the reaction

$$H_2 + \tfrac{1}{2}O_2 = H_2O_{liq}.$$

It is, of course, calculated from the Standard Free Energy of Formation by means of the equation

$$\log_{10} K_f = -\frac{\Delta G_{0f}^{298}}{2\cdot303RT}.$$

C_p^{298} is the molar thermal capacity of the substance in its standard state at 25° C.

---

[1] The student should note that in Circular No. 500, as in most American publications, the symbol F is used for Gibbs Free Energy rather than G.

$\Delta H_{0_f}^0$ is the STANDARD HEAT OF FORMATION at absolute zero (this quantity is required in some applications of Statistical Thermodynamics).

The publication mentioned above also lists the quantities ΔH, ΔS and ΔC_p of transition, fusion and evaporation.

We illustrate the various ways in which the information given in Table 12,I may be used by calculating the Standard Free Energy change and the equilibrium constant at 25° C for the reaction

$$SO_2 + NO_2 = NO + SO_{3(g)}.$$

Method I

From Hess's Law it follows that

$$\Delta H_0^{298} = \Sigma \Delta H_{0_f}^{298} \text{ (reaction products–reactants)}$$

$$= (21 \cdot 600 - 94 \cdot 450) - (8 \cdot 091 - 70 \cdot 96)$$

$$= -9 \cdot 981 \text{ kcal.}$$

$$\Delta S_0^{298} = (50 \cdot 339 + 61 \cdot 24) - (59 \cdot 40 + 57 \cdot 47)$$

$$= -5 \cdot 29 \text{ cal deg}^{-1}.$$

$$\Delta G_0^{298} = \Delta H_0^{298} - T \Delta S_0^{298}$$

$$= -9 \cdot 981 + 298 \cdot 15 \times 5 \cdot 29 \times 10^{-3}$$

$$= -8 \cdot 40 \text{ kcal.}$$

$$\log_{10} K = \frac{\Delta G_0^{298}}{2 \cdot 303 RT} = \frac{8 \cdot 40 \times 10^3}{2 \cdot 303 \times 1 \cdot 987 \times 298 \cdot 15}.$$

$$= 6 \cdot 158.$$

Method II

The same result can be obtained more simply from the Free Energies of Formation since

$$\Delta G_0^{298} = \Sigma \Delta G_{0_f}^{298} \text{ (reaction products–reactants)}$$

$$= -8 \cdot 40 \text{ kcal.}$$

Method III

Inspection shows that the equilibrium constant for the reaction

$$SO_2 + NO_2 = NO + SO_{3(g)}$$

is related to the respective equilibrium constants of formation of the reactants and reaction products by the equation

$$K = \frac{K_{f_{NO}} K_{f_{SO_3(g)}}}{K_{f_{SO_2}} K_{f_{NO_2}}}$$

i.e. $\qquad \log_{10} K = \Sigma \log_{10} K_f$

Hence $\qquad \log_{10} K = -15 \cdot 187 + 64 \cdot 884 - 52 \cdot 621 + 9 \cdot 082$

$$= 6 \cdot 158,$$

so that $\qquad \Delta G_0^{298} = -RT \log_e K$

$$= -1 \cdot 987 \times 10^{-3} \times 298 \cdot 15 \times 2 \cdot 303 \times 6 \cdot 158$$

$$= -8 \cdot 40 \text{ kcal.}$$

As has been explained, the quantities given in Table 12,I are those which relate to the substances concerned at 25° C and at a pressure of 1 atmosphere. We now demonstrate how these quantities may be used to give information on chemical reactions under other conditions. As an example we choose to calculate the mole fractions of nitrogen, hydrogen and ammonia resulting from the partial decomposition of ammonia at 700° K and 100 atmospheres pressure.

Essentially the problem is to calculate the value of the equilibrium constant expressed in terms of mole fractions (i.e. K_y) at this temperature and pressure for the reaction

$$2NH_3 \rightleftharpoons N_2 + 3H_2.$$

The method we choose consists of three steps:

(i) the calculation of K_p at 25° C and at 1 atmosphere pressure, using the data available in Table 12,I;

(ii) from this we calculate K_p at 700° K using the van't Hoff equation, Kirchhoff's Law and the thermal capacity data given in Table 6,I;

(iii) from this we estimate K_y at 700° K and 100 atmospheres pressure using equation (11,77). We point out that this equation holds strictly only for gases of ideal behaviour, and that at 100 atmospheres pressure the departure of the behaviour of nitrogen, hydrogen and ammonia from ideality is appreciable, so that some inaccuracy in the value of K_y will be expected.

(i) The Calculation of K_p at 25° C

For the reaction as written

$$\Delta H_0 = 11{,}040 \times 2 \text{ cal}$$

and

$$\Delta S_0 = 45 \cdot 767 + 3 \times 31 \cdot 211 - 2 \times 46 \cdot 01$$

$$= 47 \cdot 38 \text{ cal deg}^{-1}.$$

Hence

$$\Delta G_0 = 7{,}952 \text{ cal}$$

and

$$\log_{10} K_p^{298} = -\frac{7{,}952}{2 \cdot 303 RT} = -5 \cdot 828.$$

(Both the values of ΔG_0 and $\log_{10} K_p$ can, of course, be obtained more directly from columns 4 and 5 of Table 12,I. We have preferred to calculate from values of ΔH and ΔS because these are the fundamental quantities from which the figures in columns 4 and 5 were obtained.)

(ii) The Calculation of K_p at 700° K

It follows from equation (11,89) that

$$\log_e K_p^{700} - \log_e K_p^{298} = \int_{298}^{700} \frac{\Delta H_0}{RT^2} dT.$$

Table 6,I shows that over the temperature range 300–1500° K, the values of C_p for hydrogen, nitrogen and ammonia are given by the equations:

$$\text{H}_2 : C_p = 6 \cdot 95 - 0 \cdot 20 \times 10^{-3}T + 4 \cdot 8 \times 10^{-7}T^2 \text{ cal deg}^{-1} \text{ mole}^{-1}$$

$$\text{N}_2 : C_p = 6 \cdot 50 + 1 \cdot 25 \times 10^{-3}T \text{ cal deg}^{-1} \text{ mole}^{-1}$$

$$\text{NH}_3 : C_p = 8 \cdot 04 + 0 \cdot 70 \times 10^{-3}T + 51 \cdot 0 \times 10^{-7}T^2 \text{ cal deg}^{-1} \text{ mole}^{-1}.$$

So that

$$\Sigma C_p = C_{p_{\text{N}_2}} + 3C_{p_{\text{H}_2}} - 2C_{p_{\text{NH}_3}}$$

$$= 11 \cdot 27 - 0 \cdot 75 \times 10^{-3}T - 87 \cdot 6 \times 10^{-7}T^2 \text{ cal deg}^{-1}.$$

From Kirchhoff's Law

$$\Delta H_0 = \int (11 \cdot 27 - 0 \cdot 75 \times 10^{-3}T - 87 \cdot 6 \times 10^{-7}T^2) dT$$

$$= 11 \cdot 27T - 0 \cdot 375 \times 10^{-3}T^2 - 29 \cdot 2 \times 10^{-7}T^3 + I.$$

Making use of the value of ΔH_0 at 298°, i.e. 22,080 cal, we evaluate the integration constant I, and write the general expression for ΔH_0 in the form

$$\Delta H_0 = 11 \cdot 27T - 0 \cdot 375 \times 10^{-3}T^2 - 29 \cdot 2 \times 10^{-7}T^3 + 18,833 \text{ cal mole}^{-1}.$$

Hence

$$R \log_e K_p^{700} - R \log_e K_p^{298}$$

$$= \int_{298}^{700} \left(\frac{11 \cdot 27}{T} - 0 \cdot 375 \times 10^{-3} - 29 \cdot 2 \times 10^{-7}T + \frac{18,822}{T^2} \right) dT$$

$$= 45 \cdot 16 \text{ cal deg}^{-1}.$$

so that
$$\log_{10} K_p^{700} = \frac{45 \cdot 16}{2 \cdot 303R} + \log_{10} K_p^{298}$$

$$= 4 \cdot 04$$

i.e.
$$K_p^{700} = 1 \cdot 1 \times 10^4 \text{ atm}^2.$$

(iii) The Calculation of K_y at 700° K and at 100 Atmospheres Pressure

Since for the reaction

$$2NH_3 \rightleftharpoons N_2 + 3H_2$$

the increase in number of gas molecules is two it follows from equation (11,77) that

$$\frac{K_{y(100 \text{ atm})}^{700}}{K_p^{700}} = 100^{-2}$$

i.e.
$$K_{y(100 \text{ atm})}^{700} = 1 \cdot 1.$$

The mole fractions of the three components of the equilibrium mixture at 700° K and 100 atmospheres pressure are therefore determined by the three equations:

$$\frac{y_{N_2} y_{H_2}^3}{y_{NH_3}^2} = 1 \cdot 1$$

$$y_{H_2} = 3y_{N_2}$$

$$y_{N_2} + y_{H_2} + y_{NH_3} = 1.$$

The student will find that these equations are satisfied by the values

$$y_{N_2} = 0 \cdot 2$$

$$y_{H_2} = 0 \cdot 6$$

$$y_{NH_3} = 0 \cdot 2.$$

The Dependence of Yield on the Relative Initial Concentrations of the Reactants

The yield of reaction product in a chemical reaction is dependent not only upon the value of the equilibrium constant for the reaction at a given temperature and pressure but also on the relative initial concentrations of the reactants. This can be demonstrated by considering the gaseous reaction

$$a\text{A} + b\text{B} \rightleftharpoons c\text{C}$$

taking place at constant pressure. We will suppose that the system consists initially of n moles of A and yn moles of B. We require to establish the value of y which will produce at equilibrium the maximum yield of C.

Suppose that when equilibrium is reached a moles of A and b moles of B have reacted to form c moles of C. If the total pressure of the system is P, the equilibrium partial pressures of the species are connected by the equations

$$p_{\text{A}_{\text{eq}}} + p_{\text{B}_{\text{eq}}} = P - p_{\text{C}_{\text{eq}}}$$

$$p_{\text{A}_{\text{eq}}} = \frac{n - a}{n + yn - a - b}(P - p_{\text{C}_{\text{eq}}})$$

and

$$p_{\text{B}_{\text{eq}}} = \frac{yn - b}{n + yn - a - b}(P - p_{\text{C}_{\text{eq}}})$$

so that

$$K_p = \frac{p_{\text{C}_{\text{eq}}}^c}{\left\{\dfrac{n - a}{n + yn - a - b}(P - p_{\text{C}_{\text{eq}}})\right\}^a \left\{\dfrac{yn - b}{n + yn - a - b}(P - p_{\text{C}_{\text{eq}}})\right\}^b}.$$

Taking logarithms and rearranging we obtain the equation

$$\log_e \frac{p_{\text{C}_{\text{eq}}}^c}{(P - p_{\text{C}_{\text{eq}}})^{a+b}} = \log_e K_p + a \log_e (n - a) + b \log_e (yn - b)$$
$$- (a + b) \log_e (n + yn - a - b).$$

Clearly $p_{\text{C}_{\text{eq}}}$ is a maximum when the differential of either side of this equation with respect to y is equal to zero; i.e. when

$$\frac{bn}{yn - b} = \frac{(a + b)n}{n + yn - a - b}$$

i.e.

$$y = \frac{b}{a}.$$

From this we see that *the maximum yield is achieved when the initial concentrations of reactants* A *and* B *are in the ratio* $a:b$. This theorem may be extended to reactions involving any number of reactants.

In certain industrial processes the chemist may be less interested in the actual yield of reaction product and more interested in the prevention of waste of one reactant. The situation might easily arise that in a reaction

$$aA + bB \rightleftharpoons cC$$

reactant A is very much more expensive than reactant B, and that recovery of that amount of A which remains unconverted is difficult. Under such circumstances it would be uneconomical to arrange that the initial concentrations of A and B are in the ratio $a:b$. Inspection of the equilibrium equation

$$\frac{[C]_{eq}^c}{[A]_{eq}^a[B]_{eq}^b} = K$$

shows that the quantity of A left unconverted at equilibrium is the smaller, the greater be the ratio of the initial concentration of B to that of A.

The Significance of the Entropy of Mixing in the Establishment of the Equilibrium Point in a Chemical Reaction

So far in this book we have, when discussing the thermodynamics of a chemical reaction, accepted as an experimental *fact* the principle that a state of chemical equilibrium is always established in a closed system. We have therefore agreed that, since any natural spontaneous process at constant temperature and pressure leads to a decrease in free energy, the graph of the free energy of the system against extent of reaction is of that form shown in Figure 11,4 (a). In other words, we have agreed that because *chemical equilibrium is always established*, the equilibrium point must be that point at which the free energy of the system is at a minimum.

We now wish to pursue the argument in the opposite direction, and to demonstrate that the fact that in a closed system a reaction will not proceed to completion but to a state of balanced equilibrium, can itself be predicted by thermodynamic theory. The argument might perhaps have been presented in an earlier part of the book: we have left it to this stage so that we can make use of some of the data established in this chapter.

We consider first a natural spontaneous process in which two gases *mix* at constant pressure. For ease of argument we assume that their behaviour is ideal.

We suppose that n_1 moles of gas A and n_2 moles of gas B both at a pressure p and at the same temperature are allowed to mix, the temperature and total pressure remaining constant.

Since the gases are ideal the final partial pressure of component A is given by the equation

$$p_A = \frac{n_1}{n_1 + n_2} p,$$

and that of B by the equation

$$p_B = \frac{n_2}{n_1 + n_2} p.$$

Thermodynamically the diffusion process is precisely equivalent to an isothermal process in which component A expands from pressure p to pressure p_A, and in which component B expands from pressure p to pressure p_B. Since the enthalpy of an ideal gas is independent of pressure, it is clear that *the change in enthalpy is zero*, but that it follows from equation (8,17a) that the change in entropy of each component is given by the equations

$$\Delta S_A = -n_1 R \log_e \frac{p_A}{p}$$

and

$$\Delta S_B = -n_2 R \log_e \frac{p_B}{p}$$

so that the change in entropy of the system is given by the equations

$$\Delta S = \Delta S_A + \Delta S_B = -n_1 R \log_e \frac{p_A}{p} - n_2 R \log_e \frac{p_B}{p}$$

$$= -n_1 R \log_e \frac{n_1}{n_1 + n_2} - n_2 R \log_e \frac{n_2}{n_1 + n_2}$$

$$= -n_1 R \log_e y_1 - n_2 R \log_e y_2 \quad . \quad . \quad . \quad (12,8)$$

where y_1 and y_2 are the mole fractions of components A and B in the mixture. Since both y_1 and y_2 must necessarily be less than unity, the quantity ΔS which is called the *Entropy of Mixing* is always positive, as we would expect. We therefore enunciate the very important principle, that THE ENTROPY OF A MIXTURE OF IDEAL GASES IS ALWAYS GREATER THAN THE SUM OF THE ENTROPIES OF THE COMPONENTS AT THE SAME TEMPERATURE AND PRESSURE. A similar principle applies to the mixing of two components in solution. This will be discussed in Chapter 15.

Earlier in this chapter we studied the isomeric transformation of *n*-butane into *iso*butane at 25° C, and calculated the value of its equilibrium constant at this temperature and at a pressure of 1 atmosphere. We now calculate the total entropy, the enthalpy and hence the free energy of various mixtures of n-butane and *iso*butane ranging from $n_1 = 1$, $n_2 = 0$, to $n_1 = 0$, $n_2 = 1$, so that $n_1 + n_2 = 1$, under the same conditions.

We have already shown that the entropy of one mole of n-butane at 25° C and at 1 atmosphere pressure is 74·0 cal deg^{-1}, and that that of *iso*butane is 70·4. The total entropy of a mixture of n_1 moles of n-butane and n_2 moles of *iso*butane under the same conditions must be the sum of three terms, 74·0 n_1, 70·4 n_2 and the entropy of mixing. These values and those of TS where $T = 298 \cdot 15°$ K are given in Table 12,II.

We have shown that the enthalpy of mixing of two ideal gases is zero, so that the enthalpy of a mixture of two gases is merely the sum of the enthalpies of the two components at the same temperature. We do not know the absolute value of the molar standard enthalpy of n-butane or *iso*butane, but the change in enthalpy at 25° C for the reaction

$$n\text{-butane} \longrightarrow iso\text{butane}$$

is -1630 cal, so that

$$H_{O_{n\text{-butane}}} - H_{O_{iso\text{butane}}} = 1630 \text{ cal mole}^{-1},$$

and the enthalpy of a mixture of n_1 moles (i.e. $1 - n_2$ moles) of n-butane and n_2 moles of *iso*butane must be given by the equations

$$H = n_1 H_{O_{n\text{-butane}}} + n_2 H_{O_{iso\text{butane}}}$$

$$= (1 - n_2) H_{O_{n\text{-butane}}} + n_2 H_{O_{iso\text{butane}}}$$

$$= H_{O_{n\text{-butane}}} - n_2 (H_{O_{n\text{-butane}}} - H_{O_{iso\text{butane}}})$$

$$= H_{O_{n\text{-butane}}} - 1630 n_2.$$

These values are also listed in Table 12,II.

TABLE 12,II

(Values of S_O, ΔS_{mixing} and S in cal deg^{-1} and values of TS, H and G in cal.)

n_1	n_2	$n_1 S_{O1}$	$n_2 S_{O2}$	ΔS_{mixing}	S	TS	H		G
1·0	0	74·0	—	—	74·0	22,200	H_O		$H_O - 22,200$
0·95	0·05	70·3	3·52	0·40	74·22	22,266	$H_O -$	81	$H_O - 22,347$
0·9	0·1	66·6	7·04	0·65	74·29	22,287	$H_O -$	163	$H_O - 22,450$
0·8	0·2	59·2	14·08	1·00	74·28	22,284	$H_O -$	326	$H_O - 22,610$
0·7	0·3	51·8	21·12	1·22	74·14	22,242	$H_O -$	489	$H_O - 22,731$
0·6	0·4	44·4	28·16	1·34	73·90	22,170	$H_O -$	652	$H_O - 22,822$
0·5	0·5	37·0	35·20	1·38	73·58	22,074	$H_O -$	815	$H_O - 22,889$
0·4	0·6	29·6	42·24	1·34	73·18	21,954	$H_O -$	978	$H_O - 22,932$
0·3	0·7	22·2	49·28	1·22	72·70	21,810	$H_O - 1141$		$H_O - 22,951$
0·2	0·8	14·8	56·32	1·00	72·12	21,636	$H_O - 1304$		$H_O - 22,940$
0·1	0·9	7·4	63·36	0·65	71·41	21,423	$H_O - 1467$		$H_O - 22,890$
0·0	1·0	—	70·4	—	70·4	21,120	$H_O - 1630$		$H_O - 22,750$

Values of Thermodynamic Properties of mixtures of n-butane and *iso*butane at 25° C and at 1 atmosphere pressure.

Lastly we calculate the various values of G from the equation

$$G = H - TS.$$

The values of the total entropy and the free energy (in terms of H_0) are shown in Figure 12,5. We see that a mixture of 0·28 moles of n-butane

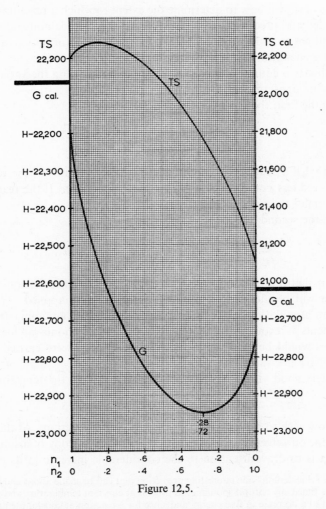

Figure 12,5.

and 0·72 moles of *iso*butane has a lower free energy than has a mixture of any other composition. We would expect, therefore, that a mixture of any composition other than that would change to this value, simply because such a change would result in a decrease in free energy. It should be noted that the value of the ratio n_2/n_1 at the point of minimum free energy is $0\cdot72/0\cdot28$, i.e. $2\cdot57$, the difference between this value and that of the equilibrium constant calculated earlier in this chapter ($2\cdot6$) is accounted for completely by arithmetical approximations.

Qualitative Generalisations

We have shown how to determine the extent to which a reaction will go by detailed and precise calculations. We now wish to demonstrate that it is sometimes possible to obtain a great deal of information about a particular chemical reaction without recourse to arithmetic.

The first two equations we consider are those showing the variation of equilibrium constant with temperature and pressure.

From the first, the van't Hoff equation

$$\left\{\frac{\partial \log_e K}{\partial T}\right\}_p = \frac{\Delta H}{RT^2} \quad \cdot \quad \cdot \quad \cdot \quad \cdot \quad (11,89)$$

we see that if a reaction is exothermic (i.e. ΔH is negative), the reaction will proceed less completely the higher the temperature. If the reaction is endothermic[1] the opposite is true.

From the second

$$\left(\frac{\partial \log_e K_x}{\partial p}\right)_T = a\bar{v}_A + b\bar{v}_B \ldots - c\bar{v}_C - d\bar{v}_D \ldots \quad (11,87)$$

it is clear that if a reaction leads to a decrease in volume, the equilibrium constant will be the greater, the greater the pressure applied. We have seen how useful this fact can be: the formation of ammonia from its constituents is exothermic, so that the yield of ammonia at high temperatures would be extremely small if the synthesis were carried out at atmospheric pressure. By carrying out the synthesis at high pressures, moderately good yields can be obtained even though the temperature is high.

We now wish to generalise about the entropy of reaction. At this stage we confine ourselves to one observation about the entropy of a substance, and that is to draw attention to the considerable increase in its entropy

---

[1] There is incidentally one interesting prediction that can be made about endothermic reactions. Since any natural spontaneous process at constant temperature and pressure must lead to a decrease in free energy and since for a reaction at constant temperature

$$-\Delta G = -\Delta H + T\Delta S$$

and since as absolute zero is approached the quantity $T\Delta S$ must according to the Third Law approach zero, the quantity $-\Delta H$ must be positive at very low temperatures. It would appear that the quantity ΔH for a reaction which is endothermic at ordinary temperatures, must decrease as the temperature is lowered, reach zero at some particular temperature and become negative as still lower temperatures are reached.

which results from evaporation. Latent heats of sublimation and evaporation are very much greater than latent heats of fusion, and the entropies of sublimation or evaporation[1] represent a very large part of the total entropy of a gas. The molar entropy of water at 100° C is about 20 cal deg^{-1}, the entropy of evaporation about 27 cal deg^{-1}; the entropy of liquid ethylene at its boiling point about 28, the entropy of evaporation about 19. The importance of this from our point of view is that in a reaction

$$a\text{A}_{\text{(liquid or solid)}} + b\text{B}_{\text{(gas)}} \longrightarrow c\text{C}_{\text{(liquid or solid)}} + d\text{D}_{\text{(gas)}}$$

the gas molecules involved play a much larger part in determining the total change in entropy than do the molecules present as solids or liquids. If the reaction leads to an increase in the number of gas molecules present the change in entropy of the system will almost always be positive, whereas a decrease in the number of gas molecules will almost always indicate a decrease in entropy.

It follows from this and from the equation

$$-\Delta G = -\Delta H + T\Delta S$$

that a reaction which is both exothermic and which results in an increase in the number of gas molecules concerned will almost certainly show a readiness to take place.

If the reaction is exothermic but results in a decrease in number of gas molecules, or if the reaction is endothermic but results in an increase in gas molecules, the matter is decided by the relative sizes of ΔH and $T\Delta S$. The reaction

$$2\text{H}_2 + \text{O}_2 \longrightarrow 2\text{H}_2\text{O}_{\text{(liq)}}$$

leads to a decrease in the number of gas molecules and hence to a considerable decrease in entropy (about 90 cal deg^{-1}), but the value of $-\Delta H$ is so high that it plays the decisive part in determining the fact that the reaction will go. On the other hand, the decomposition of ammonia at high temperatures

$$2\text{NH}_3 \longrightarrow \text{N}_2 + 3\text{H}_2$$

is readily brought about, although the reaction is endothermic, because the increase in entropy is so great that the term $T\Delta S$ is more important than ΔH.

---

[1] The student is reminded of Trouton's Rule, that for non-associated liquids $\dfrac{L_e}{T_b} \simeq 21$, where L_e is the latent heat of evaporation and T_b the boiling point, i.e. that for non-associated liquids the entropy of evaporation is about 21 cal deg^{-1}. Trouton's Rule is discussed further in Chapter 15.

We point out too that the relative importance of the $T\Delta S$ term in the equation

$$-\Delta G = -\Delta H + T\Delta S$$

is likely to increase, the greater the value of T. It may be that two or more reactions are possible between the reactants in a system, and that one brings about a greater increase in the number of gas molecules than the second. In this case it is likely that the first reaction will be favoured at higher temperatures. A case in point is the reaction between carbon and oxygen; one reaction

$$C + \tfrac{1}{2}O_2 \longrightarrow CO$$

leads to an increase in the number of gas molecules in the system; the second

$$C + O_2 \longrightarrow CO_2$$

does not. Our argument predicts that the first will be favoured at high temperatures. This prediction is of course confirmed by observation.

Empirical Relationships between the Entropy Values for Different Compounds

The precise determination of the entropy of a pure substance is a long and tedious process, so that over the years various attempts have been made to discover empirical relationships between the entropy values for known substances which would permit the values for others to be estimated.

Ionic Compounds

The approximate constancy in the difference in molar entropies for the pairs of salts in the following groups:

$$KCl - KF, \qquad 19 \cdot 76 - 15 \cdot 91 \;\; = 3 \cdot 8$$
$$\tfrac{1}{2}(MgCl_2 - MgF_2), \;\; \tfrac{1}{2}(21 \cdot 4 - 13 \cdot 7) \; = 3 \cdot 9$$

and

$$KI - KBr, \qquad 24 \cdot 94 - 23 \cdot 05 \;\; = 1 \cdot 9$$
$$CsI - CsBr, \qquad 31 \cdot \;\;\; - 29 \cdot \;\;\;\; = 2 \cdot 0$$
$$\tfrac{1}{2}(CaI_2 - CaBr_2), \, \tfrac{1}{2}(34 \cdot \;\;\; - 31 \cdot \;\;) = 1 \cdot 5$$

suggests:

  (i) that to a first approximation the constituent ions make independent contributions to the entropy of the whole; and
  (ii) that although we might suppose the entropy of a solid to be a function of both the masses of the constituent atoms and the forces acting between them, the effect of the first is of greater importance than that of the second.

The first attempt to correlate the results for ionic compounds was made by W. M. Latimer[1] in 1921. He suggested that the contribution of each cation to the entropy of the compound is given by the equation

$$S^{298} = \tfrac{3}{2}R \log_e \text{at. wt.} - 0.94.$$

This equation determines the dotted line in Figure 12,6.

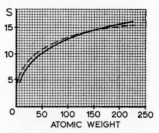

Figure 12,6. Entropies of elements in solid compounds as a function of atomic weight.

It was later shown that better results are obtained if some account is taken of the interionic forces. This results in the line being redrawn (as shown by the solid line in Figure 12,6[2]), so as to decrease slightly the contribution made by the lighter ions and to increase slightly that made by the heavier. Values taken from this curve are quite satisfactory as far as positive ions are concerned. Some of these values are shown in Table 12,III.

TABLE 12,III

Entropies of positive ions in solid compounds at 298° K

(Values in cal deg⁻¹)

Ag	12·8	K	9·2	Sn	13·1
Al	8·0	Li	3·5	Tl	15·4
Ca	9·3	Mg	7·6	U	16·0
Co	10·6	Mn	10·5	W	15·0
Cu	10·8	Pb	15·5	Zn	10·9

Results for negative ions were obtained by subtracting the values for positive ions from the entropies of the salts concerned. These results showed that the values obtained depend on the charge on the positive ion concerned, the greater the positive charge the smaller the apparent contributions by the negative ion. Some of the values obtained by Latimer are shown in Table 12,IV.

Values obtained for the entropies of salts by the use of the figures given in Tables 12,III and 12,IV rarely differ from the experimental values by more than 1 or 2 cal deg⁻¹. Thus the calculated value for silver chloride is 22·8, whereas the experimental value is 22·97; that of aluminium sulphate 57·1 compared with 57·2; that of potassium sulphate 40·4 compared with 42·0. It is unlikely that inaccuracies greater than these will be found except in those cases in which the degree of covalency in the salt is high.

[1] W. M. Latimer, *J. Am. Chem. Soc.*, 1921, **43**, 818.
[2] Figure 12,6 and the contents of Tables 12,III and 12,IV are reproduced by permission from Latimer, *Oxidation Potentials* (Prentice-Hall, 1952).

TABLE 12,IV

Entropies of negative ions in solid compounds at 298° K

(Values in cal deg^{-1})

Negative ion	Charge on positive ion		
	+1	+2	+3
Cl$^-$	10·0	8·1	6·9
Br$^-$	13·0	10·9	
I$^-$	14·6	13·6	12·5
OH$^-$	5·0	4·5	3·0
O^{--}	2·4	0·5	0·5
S^{--}	8·2	5·0	1·3
CO$_3$$^{--}$	15·2	11·4	
SO$_4$$^{--}$	22	17·2	13·7

Salt Hydrates

The contribution made by water of crystallisation to the entropy of a salt hydrate is approximately the same whatever the salt concerned. Thus the molar entropy of $MgCl_2.2H_2O$ at 25° C is 43·0 cal deg^{-1} and that of $MgCl_2.H_2O$ is 32·8, so that the contribution made by the second water molecule is 10·2 cal deg^{-1}; that of $CuSO_4.5H_2O$ is 73·0 and that of $CuSO_4.3H_2O$ 53·8, so that the fourth and fifth water molecules each appear to contribute about 9·6 cal deg^{-1} to the entropy of the higher hydrate. Out of eighteen pairs of hydrates chosen at random by the author thirteen gave values for the entropy of water of crystallisation lying between 9·1 and 10·7 cal deg^{-1} mole^{-1}, three values between 8·3 and 8·7, one 5·1 and the last 12·5. The average of these figures is 9·8. This figure is particularly interesting because it is the same as the hypothetical entropy of ice at 25° C obtained by extrapolation from 0° C.

Organic Compounds

It would be expected that the change in any thermodynamic property of a compound would be more or less regular as we pass from one member of a homologous series to another. This is in fact the case. R. H. Ewell[1] showed that the standard entropy of normal paraffins calculated as gases at 25° C and 1 atmosphere pressure may be represented fairly accurately by the equation

$$S_0^{298} = 35·6 + 9·7n$$

where n is the number of carbon atoms in the molecule. The entropy of the liquid under the same conditions is given by the equation

$$S_0^{298} = 25·0 + 7·7n$$

[1] R. H. Ewell, *Ind. and Eng. Chem.*, 1940, **32**, 778.

and that of the solid by the equation

$$S_0^{298} = 18 \cdot 0 + 5 \cdot 6n,$$

while that of a liquid branched-chain paraffin is given by the equation

$$S_0^{298} = 25 \cdot 0 + 7 \cdot 7n - 4 \cdot 5r$$

where r is the number of aliphatic branches on the main chain. Equations similar to these have been established for such quantities as free energies of formation[1] of members of other homologous series.

By far the most exhaustive study of empirical equations of this sort has been made by G. J. Janz.[1] The publication mentioned in the footnote provides tables showing the changes in entropy and free energy of formation resulting from the substitution of methyl groups in hydrocarbons by such groups as ^-OH, $^-NO_2$ and so on, and so permits the entropy and free energy of formation of complicated molecules to be estimated with fair accuracy.

In this respect it is pointed out that although it is obviously desirable that *accurate* values of the thermodynamic properties of all compounds are known, much valuable information can be deduced if, in the absence of such knowledge, estimated values are available, even though they may be inaccurate by as much as 5% or 10%.

Further Considerations of the Third Law

Earlier in this book it was said that the laws of thermodynamics are postulates which we accept, not so much because they are capable of direct verification, but because they make predictions, some of which can be tested by experiment. Thus, one reason why we accept the First Law is that it predicts that the heat absorbed or evolved during a chemical reaction is the same whether the reaction takes place in one or more stages. The prediction is found to be true. One reason why we accept the Second Law is that it leads to a relationship involving phase changes known as the Clausius–Clapeyron Equation enabling us, among other things, to predict the variation of melting point of a solid with pressure. The predicted variation and that established by experiment are found to agree.

By far the most impressive evidence for the truth of the Third Law comes from Statistical Thermodynamics, and will be discussed later.

In the present section we are concerned with what direct evidence in support of the Third Law can be obtained by classical considerations.

---

[1] C. L. Thomas, G. Egloff and J. C. Morrell, *Ind. and Eng. Chem.*, 1937, **19**, 1260; and P. F. Bruins and J. D. Czarnecki, *ibid.*, 1941, **33**, 201.

[2] G. J. Janz, *Estimation of Thermodynamic Properties* (Academic Press Inc., 1958).

One quite obvious method would be to use the Third Law to predict the value of the equilibrium constant for a particular reaction, and to compare the result with the value obtained by direct analysis of the equilibrium mixture. This is not, however, a method which is often used, mainly because of experimental difficulties. The most popular method of obtaining direct evidence is to use an electro-chemical cell. The thermodynamics of chemical cells have been mentioned earlier in this book, and will be discussed in considerable detail in Chapter 17. As far as we are concerned in the present context, the point of importance is that the entropy change in the chemical reaction upon which the cell depends can be determined directly (and with great accuracy) from measurements of the rate of change of e.m.f. with temperature. For example, the cell

$$Ag \mid AgCl_{(sat)} KCl_{(aq)} Hg_2Cl_{2(sat)} \mid Hg$$

depends on the reaction

$$Ag + \tfrac{1}{2}Hg_2Cl_2 \longrightarrow AgCl + Hg.$$

The molar increase in entropy is given by the equation

$$\Delta S = F\left(\frac{\partial \mathbf{E}}{\partial T}\right)_p$$

where F is the Faraday (96,487 coulomb) and $\mathbf{E}$ the e.m.f. of the cell (measured in volts). The rate of change of e.m.f. with temperature at temperatures around 25° C is found to be 0·00038 volt deg^{-1}, so that

$$\Delta S = \frac{96,487 \times 0\cdot00038}{4\cdot184} = 7\cdot8 \text{ cal deg}^{-1}.$$

ΔS may, however, be expressed in the form:

$$\Delta S = S^{298}_{AgCl} + S^{298}_{Hg} - S^{298}_{Ag} - \tfrac{1}{2}S^{298}_{Hg_2Cl_2}$$

or in the form:

$$\Delta S = (S^{298} - S^0)_{AgCl} + (S^{298} - S^0)_{Hg} - (S^{298} - S^0)_{Ag} - \tfrac{1}{2}(S^{298} - S^0)_{Hg_2Cl_2}$$
$$+ (S^0_{AgCl} + S^0_{Hg} - S^0_{Ag} - \tfrac{1}{2}S^0_{Hg_2Cl_2}) \quad (12,9)$$

The quantities in the first four brackets have been calculated from specific heat measurements on the substances concerned from 25° C to temperatures close to absolute zero: they are

$$(S^{298} - S^0)_{AgCl} = 23\cdot1$$

$$(S^{298} - S^0)_{Hg} = 17\cdot8$$

$$(S^{298} - S^0)_{Ag} = 10\cdot25$$

$$\tfrac{1}{2}(S^{298} - S^0)_{Hg_2Cl_2} = 22\cdot8,$$

so that the sum of the first four brackets comes to 7·85 cal deg⁻¹. Agreement between this value and that obtained for ΔS from e.m.f. measurements is sufficiently close to suggest that the quantity in the last bracket in equation (12,9) is indeed zero, as required by the Third Law. A similar result has been obtained by the use of other cells.

There is one other type of reaction from which we can obtain direct evidence for the Third Law. Two allotropic modifications of a crystalline substance are in equilibrium only at their transition temperature. At this point their chemical potentials, and therefore their molar free energies, are equal. The transition temperature between rhombic and monoclinic sulphur is 95·4° C (368·55° K). Denoting the thermodynamic properties of one by the suffix r and those of the other by the suffix m we may write:

$$\Delta G^{368 \cdot 55} = G_m - G_r = 0.$$

The heat of reaction from rhombic to monoclinic at this temperature has been measured. The value obtained is

$$\Delta H^{368 \cdot 55} = H_m - H_r = -95 \text{ cal}$$

from which

$$\Delta S = S_m^{368 \cdot 55} - S_r^{368 \cdot 55} = \frac{\Delta H - \Delta G}{T} = -0 \cdot 26 \text{ cal deg}^{-1}.$$

The values of $(S^{368 \cdot 5} - S^0)_m$ and $(S^{368 \cdot 5} - S^0)_r$ have been determined from specific heat measurements. The difference between the two is only $-0 \cdot 25$ cal deg⁻¹, showing again that within the limits of experimental error we may accept that

$$S_m^0 - S_r^0 = 0.$$

A More Formal Statement of the Third Law

The statement that THE ENTROPY CHANGE IN A REACTION BETWEEN PURE CRYSTALLINE SOLIDS APPROACHES ZERO AS ABSOLUTE ZERO IS APPROACHED is the most useful form of the Third Law for our purpose. It is not, however, a particularly satisfactory statement because, as has been stated earlier, it does not apply to reactions involving all pure crystalline bodies, and it is aesthetically unsatisfactory to make a statement of a scientific law which, one has to explain, applies to all reactions except those to which it does not. The manner in which we introduced the Third Law differs too from the manner in which the Zeroth, First and Second Laws were introduced: in those cases we made a formal and perfectly general postulate, and derived from it a mathematical expression suitable to the problem in hand. For example, we chose to introduce the Second Law in the form

of the postulate that ALL NATURAL SPONTANEOUS CHANGES ARE IRREVER-
SIBLE, and deduced from it the more readily applicable statement that the
entropy of an isolated system can only increase or remain constant.

We now propose to discuss the Third Law in the same way. We choose
as our formal postulate the statement that IT IS IMPOSSIBLE BY ANY PRO-
CEDURE, NO MATTER HOW IDEALISED, TO REDUCE ANY SYSTEM TO ABSOLUTE
ZERO IN A FINITE NUMBER OF OPERATIONS.

This is a statement of fact: absolute zero has never been reached, and
despite the successful efforts which have been made to reduce systems to
temperatures only about one-thousandth of a degree above absolute
zero, it appears that, though improved techniques may result in temperatures closer still to absolute zero being reached, the final goal will for
ever be denied.

We now proceed to deduce from this formal postulate a statement
concerning the change in entropy due to a reaction at absolute zero. We
consider first a chemical reaction represented by the equation

$$A \longrightarrow B$$

which is endothermic, and which if carried out at constant temperature is
accompanied by the absorption of a quantity of heat q from the surroundings. The entropy change resultant upon the reaction is

$$S_B^T - S_A^T = \Delta S \geqslant \frac{q}{T}$$

the equality sign applying if the reaction proceeds reversibly and the inequality sign applying to the natural spontaneous reaction. Since S_B^T
and S_A^T are independent of the path by which A transforms into B, the
heat absorbed must be greater when the change takes place reversibly than
when it proceeds by any natural irreversible path.

We now consider the same reaction in an adiabatic container. Since no
heat can be absorbed from the surroundings the reaction is accompanied
by a fall in temperature of the system itself. It follows from the argument
given above that the fall in temperature will be greater if the reaction is
carried out reversibly than when it proceeds by any irreversible path.

We now consider the possibility of starting with the reactant A in an
adiabatic container initially at some temperature T', so that the fall in
temperature brought about by the reaction is sufficient to bring the system
to the absolute zero. From what has gone before we realise that the
chance of success is best if we carry out the reaction reversibly; we therefore ignore any irreversible path. The fact that we cannot in practice carry
out a chemical reaction reversibly is irrelevent to the argument.

Consider first a system containing component A at some arbitrary temperature T_1, and permit the reaction to take place adiabatically and reversibly to give component B at temperature T_2. A reversible adiabatic change is accompanied by no change in entropy. Hence we may write

$$S_A^{T_1} = S_B^{T_2}.$$

But
$$S_A^{T_1} = S_A^0 + \int_0^{T_1} \frac{C_A}{T} dT$$

and
$$S_B^{T_2} = S_B^0 + \int_0^{T_2} \frac{C_B}{T} dT,$$

therefore
$$S_B^0 - S_A^0 = \int_0^{T_1} \frac{C_A}{T} dT - \int_0^{T_2} \frac{C_B}{T} dT.$$

The quantity $S_B^0 - S_A^0$ can be greater than, equal to, or less than zero. If this quantity is greater than zero it must be possible to select some real temperature T' such that

$$S_B^0 - S_A^0 = \int_0^{T'} \frac{C_A}{T} dT.$$

It follows that if the system containing component A at temperature T' be permitted to react adiabatically and reversibly, the temperature of the reaction product will be at the absolute zero. This conclusion is contrary to our experience and to the formal statement of the Third Law. It follows that the quantity $S_B^0 - S_A^0$ cannot be greater than zero.

We prove that $S_B^0 - S_A^0$ cannot be less than zero by considering the reverse reaction

$$B \longrightarrow A$$

and arguing in the same way.

Since S_B^0 is neither greater nor less than S_A^0 the two quantities must be equal, i.e.

$$S_A^0 = S_B^0. \qquad \cdots \qquad (12,10)$$

It is now necessary to reconsider the argument. We prove the statement that for the reaction

$$A \longrightarrow B \text{ at } 0° \text{ K}$$

there is no change in entropy, by considering a *reversible* change between A at one temperature and B at another. One assumption inherent in the choice of a reversible path is that the system remains in internal equilibrium throughout. If either A or B be in, not a stable crystalline form,

I

but some metastable state (such as a glass), no reversible process is possible, and the argument developed becomes null and void.

We see therefore that our formal postulate leads conclusively to the statement that for reactions between stable crystalline components at absolute zero ΔS is zero, but indicates that there is no reason why we should expect to find the same result if one or more of the components is in some metastable state.

EXERCISES 12

Except where otherwise stated solution of the following exercises requires reference to Tables 6,I; (page 83) 12,I; 12,III and 12,IV (pages 209, 223 and 224).

12,1. The following questions should be answered *without reference* to any tables of thermodynamic data:

1. What can be deduced regarding the free energy change for the exothermic reaction at 100° C and 1 atmosphere pressure

$$2H_2 + O_2 \longrightarrow 2H_2O_{(liq)} ?$$

   Would you expect the free energy change for this reaction to be the same, greater or less than that for the reaction

$$2H_2 + O_2 \longrightarrow 2H_2O_{(g)}$$

   under the same conditions?
2. Would you expect the percentage of carbon monoxide in the gaseous phase of the equilibrium system C, CO, CO_2 to increase or decrease with rise in temperature?
3. The decrease in free energy for the reaction

$$2Mg + O_2 \longrightarrow 2MgO$$

   at 200° C is positive. Would you expect $-\Delta G$ to increase or decrease with rise in temperature?

Reasons should be given for the conclusions reached.

12,2. The heat of reaction for the reaction

$$2NOCl \longrightarrow 2NO + Cl_2$$

is almost independent of temperature and for the reaction at constant pressure $\Delta H = 18,000$ cal. The standard entropies of the reactants at 25° C are

NOCl, 63·0; NO, 50·3; Cl_2, 53·3 cal deg^{-1} mole^{-1}.

Estimate the value of the equilibrium constant K_p at 200° C.

12,3. Calculate the value of the equilibrium constant at 1000° K and 1 atmosphere pressure for the reaction

$$2H_2 + O_2 \longrightarrow 2H_2O_{(g)}$$

using the value for ΔH_{of}^{298}, and the values for S_0^{298} given in Table 12,I, and the values for C_p given in Table 6,I.

12,4. Ammonia is kept at 1 atmosphere pressure and at 700° K for several hours. What is the value of the equilibrium constant under these conditions, and what percentage of ammonia would you expect to dissociate?

What would be the partial pressures of nitrogen, hydrogen and ammonia in the equilibrium mixture?

12,5. The Deacon process for the manufacture of chlorine depends on the reaction

$$2HCl_{(g)} + \tfrac{1}{2}O_2 \longrightarrow H_2O_{(g)} + Cl_2.$$

Derive an expression for the heat of reaction (ΔH) as a function of temperature. Hence derive an expression for $\log_{10} K$ as a function of temperature.

12,6. The standard enthalpy of formation of zinc oxide at 25° C is $-84\cdot0$ kcal, and the entropy of zinc is $9\cdot9$ cal deg^{-1} and that of zinc oxide $10\cdot4$. Calculate the standard free energy of formation of zinc oxide at 25° C. Hence find the free energy change for the reaction

$$ZnO + C \longrightarrow Zn + CO.$$

12,7. The free energy of formation of diamond from graphite at 25° C is $685\cdot0$ cal mole^{-1}. The molar entropies of graphite and diamond at 25° C are $1\cdot36$ and $0\cdot58$ cal deg^{-1} and their densities $2\cdot22$ gm cm^{-3} and $3\cdot51$ gm cm^{-3}.

Under what conditions might the formation of diamonds from graphite be thermodynamically possible?

12,8. Show that irrespective of the actual value of a heat of formation of a compound an error of about 60 cal mole^{-1} leads to an error in the calculation of an equilibrium constant concerning the compound of about 10%. Show that an equilibrium constant is uncertain to the same extent if one of the standard entropies concerned is uncertain to $0\cdot2$ cal deg^{-1} mole^{-1} at 25° C.

12,9. The values of ΔH for a reaction $A + B \longrightarrow C + D$ (in which the chemical species are all gases) carried out at atmospheric pressure at various temperatures are given below:

$T°$ K	300	400	500	600	700	800	900
ΔH kcal	41	20	7	$1\cdot8$	$-2\cdot0$	$-7\cdot0$	-19

Under what circumstances would you expect to obtain the maximum yield of C and D?

PART III

STATISTICAL THERMODYNAMICS

STATISTICAL THERMODYNAMICS: THERMO-DYNAMIC PROBABILITY, THE DISTRIBUTION LAW AND THE PARTITION FUNCTIONS

Classical thermodynamics identifies any particular equilibrium state of that portion of matter which it calls the system by large-scale or *macro*-measurements such as temperature, pressure and volume, and we have shown how thermodynamic theory may be developed and tested by making use of other large-scale measurements such as heats of reaction, thermal capacities, heats of fusion and so on, measurements which have been made either on the system as a whole, or on some convenient amount of the substances composing it. Neither the measurement of these quantities, nor indeed the thermodynamic theory to which they have been applied is concerned with the *nature* of the substances involved. We may at times have referred to atoms and molecules, but when we have done so it has been merely for convenience rather than necessity. In short, classical thermodynamics is not concerned with the intimate structure of the system to which it is applied.

Since, however, matter is composed of atoms and molecules, it might be reasoned that the same information as that obtained by large-scale measurements might be deduced by study and measurement of the individual particles comprising the system. Statistical Thermodynamics is based on this principle. It sets out to interpret the laws of thermodynamics by considering the behaviour of the individual particles concerned: and in particular shows how the thermodynamic properties of a system may be calculated from measurements which relate to the atoms and molecules therein.

Macro-states and Micro-states

The classical concept of a thermodynamic state would appear to imply that no change takes place in a system during such time as its thermodynamic properties remain constant, but that this concept is not correct is realised as soon as we subject the system to microscopic examination. Imagine that a system is maintained in a particular thermodynamic state for a considerable period (during which the value of all properties determined by macro-measurements remain constant), and that full sets of instantaneous micro-measurements are made at various times throughout. We should find that the instantaneous *micro-states* revealed by these measurements are all quite different, because the particles comprising the system will have moved from one position to another, and the distribution of energy between them will have continually changed. Evidently to what so far in this book we have called a thermodynamic state there corresponds a large number of different micro-states identifiable only by subjecting the system to a microscopic examination. The *number* of micro-states in which a system in a particular thermodynamic state may be found proves to be the most important single quantity known to Statistical Thermodynamics.

We can gain much information regarding the relationship between a thermodynamic state (or macro-state, as we shall call it in the next few pages) and the micro-states corresponding to it, by considering two simple models. The macro-measurements made on each model are those made on the system as a whole, i.e. the total number of particles therein, the total energy and so on, while the various micro-states concerned are revealed only by the examination of the individual particles comprising the system. We make our models subject to whatever conditions we find convenient, and assume that such measurements as we find appropriate, such as "the total energy of the system", can in fact be easily determined.

Model 1

We consider an isolated system consisting of a number of identical particles in a box, and suppose that each particle may be associated only with a whole number of units of energy. We imagine that the macroscopic tools which we use to examine the system are capable only of determining the number of particles present and the energy possessed by the whole. We use them and find that the system consists of five particles and possesses 5 joules. These facts establish the macro-state of the system.

We now examine the system using refined microscopic instruments capable of determining at any moment the energy possessed by each particle, and we find that over a period of time, although the total energy of the system remains constant, the energy distributes itself among the five particles in different ways. At one moment one particle possesses 5 joules and four none, at another two particles possess 2 joules each, a third 1 joule and two none, and so on. In fact, over a period of time, we are able to identify seven ways in which the total energy of the system is distributed over the particles present:

1 (5),   and 4 (0)
1 (4), 1 (1) and 3 (0)
1 (3), 2 (1) and 2 (0)
1 (2), 3 (1) and 1 (0)
1 (3), 1 (2) and 3 (0)
2 (2), 1 (1) and 2 (0)
5 (1)

All of these distributions are micro-states available to the system as a whole, and as long as we restrict ourselves to macroscopic tools capable only of determining the total number of particles present and the total energy possessed by the system these micro-states are indistinguishable. We see, therefore, that to what we have called the macro-state of the system there corresponds a number of accessible micro-states, identifiable only when we are able to examine the system particle by particle. We assign the symbol W to the number of micro-states available to a particular macro-state, but delay for the moment giving the number a name.

Further consideration shows that the W value of a system, such as the model we have studied, depends not only on the total number of particles present and the total quantity of energy available for distribution but also on what we may call the "local rules" imposed. The first of these relates to the fact that we described the five particles as *identical*, and so implied that no one particle can be distinguished from any other. Let us suppose for the moment that instead we had described each particle as individually *labelled* by the letters A, B, C, D and E. Instead of there being only one identifiable micro-state

1 (5), 4 (0),

there would have been five:

A (5)   B C D E (0)
B (5)   A C D E (0)
C (5)   A B D E (0)
D (5)   A B C E (0)
E (5)   A B C D (0)

and instead of there being only one micro-state

1 (4), 1 (1) and 3 (0)

there would have been twenty

A (4) B (1) C D E (0)
A (4) C (1) B D E (0) and so on.

In fact, the W value of the system which we have shown to be seven when we suppose the particles to be individually indistinguishable rises to a hundred and twenty-six if we suppose that one particle can always be distinguished from any other. The significance of our argument will be seen in a later section.

The second point which we wish to make at this stage is to observe how much greater would the W value have been had the particles in the system been permitted to acquire energy in fractions of joules instead of in whole numbers. We note, however, that since Quantum Theory states that any particle can acquire energy only in whole numbers of quanta, the number of micro-states accessible to a system in a particular macro-state can never be infinite. To every macro-state there corresponds, depending on the conditions to which the system is subject, a finite and definite number of accessible micro-states.

Model 2

We now wish to relate the W value of a system in a particular macro-state to the *chance* that that macro-state be attained. We demonstrate this

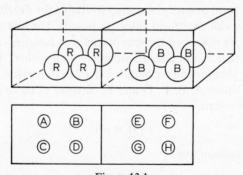

Figure 13,1.

relationship by considering a second model. This consists of a rectangular box containing eight balls, four red and four black. The floor of the box is slightly recessed to provide eight cups lettered A to H, so that when the model comes to rest after any internal disturbance one ball settles in each cup. The four red balls are individually indistinguishable, as are the four blacks, but the red balls weigh more than the black. (We can therefore always find out how many red balls and how many blacks there are on the left-hand side and how many on the right merely by weighing the left-hand side against the right.) By this means we are able to identify the following macro-states of the system:

macro-state 1—4 red on the left, 4 black on the right

macro-state 2—3 red and 1 black on the left, 3 black and 1 red on the right

macro-state 3—2 red and 2 black on the left, 2 black and 2 red on the right

macro-state 4—1 red and 3 black on the left, 1 black and 3 red on the right

macro-state 5—4 black on the left, 4 red on the right.

We shake the container and then permit the balls to come to rest. What is the most likely macro-state in which the systems will be found? In other words, if we shake the box a large number of times how many times will we expect to find the system in macro-state 1, how many times in macro-state 2 and so on?

Since no red (or black) ball is distinguishable from any other of the same colour, there is only one identifiable arrangement of balls which corresponds to macro-state 1, i.e. to macro-state 1 there corresponds only one micro-state:

$$W_1 = 1.$$

Macro-state 2 corresponds, however, to sixteen "micro-states", any one of the four positions on the left-hand side can be occupied by a black ball, and to each of these corresponds four positions on the right which may be occupied by a red, i.e.

$$W_2 = 16.$$

Macro-state 3 corresponds to thirty-six "microscopic" arrangements; there are six positions in which two red balls may be found on the left-hand side (in positions AB, AC, CD, BD, AD, and BC) and to each of these corresponds six positions in which two red balls may be found on the right, i.e.

$$W_3 = 36.$$

Macro-state 4 is the analogue of macro-state 2, so that

$$W_4 = 16,$$

and macro-state 5 is the analogue of macro-state 1, so that

$$W_5 = 1.$$

We see, therefore, that there are seventy ways in which four indistinguishable red balls and four indistinguishable black balls can be distributed in the container. After shaking the container *the balls are just as likely to be arranged in one way as in any other*. It follows that there is only one chance in seventy that the system be found in macro-state 1, sixteen chances in seventy that the system be found in macro-state 2, thirty-six chances that it be found in macro-state 3, sixteen in macro-state 4 and one in macro-state 5.

We denote the *chance* that the system be found in a particular macro-state by the symbol ω, and note that

$$\omega_1 = \tfrac{1}{70}$$

$$\omega_2 = \tfrac{16}{70}$$

$$\omega_3 = \tfrac{36}{70} \text{ and so on.}$$

Inspection shows that ω_i, the chance that the system be found in the ith macro-state, is proportional to W_i, and further that

$$\omega_i = \frac{W_i}{\sum_i W_i}.$$

We now assume that what we have demonstrated by means of model 2 is applicable to any isolated system. We suppose that an unstable isolated system can assume various different macro-states, to the first of which corresponds W_1 micro-arrangements, to the second W_2, and so on. Which will it choose? Since the chance that any particular macro-state is chosen is proportional to its W value, it follows that it is most likely that the final state achieved is that to which corresponds the greatest value of W. In other words, we suppose that *a spontaneous change in an isolated system is accompanied by an increase in W, and that the equilibrium state which the system will eventually reach is that to which corresponds the maximum value of W*.

It will have been noted that the argument upon which this conclusion is based depends on an assumption made when studying the second model. We assumed that *the system is just as likely to be found in one micro-state as in any other*. The formal statement that IN AN ISOLATED SYSTEM ALL POSSIBLE MICRO-STATES ARE EQUALLY ACCESSIBLE, is the basic assumption made in Statistical Thermodynamics. There is no "proof" that it is correct; it must be regarded, like the laws of classical thermodynamics, as a postulate which we accept because it enables us to predict results which are confirmed by experiment.

Since the W value of an isolated system in a particular macro-state is proportional to the chance that the system attains that state rather than any other, it is appropriate that the name given to the W value is one which carries with it the idea of chance; it is, in fact, called THE THERMO-DYNAMIC PROBABILITY of the system. We note that, like all thermodynamic properties, it is a state function and is independent of the previous history of the system.

The Relationship between the Entropy of a System and its Thermodynamic Probability

Earlier it was inferred that *a spontaneous change in an isolated system is accompanied by an increase in W, and that the equilibrium state which the system will eventually reach is that to which corresponds the maximum value of W.* Classical thermodynamics, however, teaches that a *spontaneous change in an isolated system leads to an increase in entropy, and that the equilibrium state is that at which the entropy of the system is at a maximum.* Clearly if our inference is correct, the thermodynamic probability and the entropy of a system must be closely related. We may suppose that one is a function of the other and write:

$$S = f(W).$$

We now require to deduce the type of function involved.

Consider two independent systems A and B situated side by side: the number of micro-states corresponding to the thermodynamic state of the first being W_A and the number corresponding to the thermodynamic state of the second W_B. What is the number of possible micro-states accessible to the two systems combined? To each of the W_A micro-states accessible to the first there are W_B possible micro-states accessible to the second; so that the number of possible micro-states accessible to the combined system is the product of the two, i.e.

$$W = W_A \times W_B.$$

Entropy is, however, an extensive property, and the entropy of the combined system the sum of the entropies of the individual parts, i.e.

$$S = S_A + S_B.$$

Clearly the simplest way in which we can reconcile these equations is to suggest that:

$$S_A = k \log_e W_A$$
$$S_B = k \log_e W_B$$

so that $\qquad S = S_A + S_B = k \log_e (W_A \times W_B)$

where k is some constant the value of which is the same for each system.

We infer therefore that the entropy of any system is a logarithmic function of its thermodynamic probability; the two quantities being connected by the equation

$$S = k \log_e W. \qquad \qquad \text{(13,1)}$$

Equation (13,1) implies that the *absolute* value of the entropy of a system can be calculated if the absolute value of its thermodynamic probability can be computed. Unfortunately, we have no means by which the absolute value of W can be obtained, and can determine only some of its parts.

Just as we have seen that the W value of a system is the product of the W values of the parts of a system, so also is the W value the product of various factors attributable to different reasons.

Let us suppose that the absolute W value of a particular system is due to only two causes, one the translational motion of the particles concerned and the other their electronic configuration, that the two causes are independent of each other, and that the first results in W_{trans} different translational micro-states being accessible to the system and the second W_{elec}. To each of the W_{trans} micro-states there exist W_{elec} states due to different electronic configurations, so that the total W value of the system is the product of the two, i.e.

$$W = W_{trans} \times W_{elec}.$$

It follows in the same way that if there are many independent factors which contribute to the total number of micro-states accessible to the system, the total W value is the product of the independent factors concerned, i.e.

$$W = W' \times W'' \times W''' \ldots$$

Let us now suppose that we can divide the factors concerned into two groups: those which are temperature-dependent and which result from the acquisition of energy in various ways as the temperature changes from absolute zero to that with which we are concerned, and which operate therefore at all temperatures except absolute zero: and those which are independent of temperature and the energy acquired, and which are therefore the same at all temperatures including absolute zero. We designate the product of the first W^{temp} and those of the second W^0.

The entropy of the system at temperature T will be given by the equation

$$S^T = k \log_e (W^{temp} \times W^0)$$

and its entropy at absolute zero by the equation

$$S^0 = k \log_e W^0.$$

As will be seen in the following pages, *the value of* W^{temp} *can be computed with certainty, but we have no means of assessing the value of* W^0. In other words, we have no means by which the absolute values of S^0 and S^T can be calculated, but can calculate $S^T - S^0$ since

$$S^T - S^0 = k \log_e W^{temp}.$$

Since we are unable to determine the *real* value of S^0 we are free to assign it any conventional value we please. We choose the conventional value

$$S^0 = 0$$

for all substances, which is the same as assigning the conventional value

$$W^0 = 1$$

so that in using the equation

$$S_{stat} = k \log_e W$$

the values of W we shall compute are really W^{temp} and the entropy values[1] obtained are relative to the arbitrary conventional value $S^0 = 0$.

In order that we may better understand why the value W^0 cannot be computed some discussion will be given of some of the phenomena which may contribute to it. One is the possible presence of isotopes in the system under consideration, the second the multiplicity of micro-states available within the nuclei and the third nuclear spin. The first is quite easily explained. A sample of chlorine prepared in the usual way contains about 75% of atoms of mass number 35 and about 25% of atoms of mass number 37, and is therefore a mixture of three molecular species $^{35}Cl^{35}Cl$, $^{37}Cl^{37}Cl$ and $^{35}Cl^{37}Cl$. The total entropy of such a mixture includes therefore not only the entropies of the individual species but also the entropy of mixing. The entropy of mixing may be calculated as may that which results from nuclear spin, but there is no point in doing so because we know nothing about the multiplicity of micro-states within the nucleus. In any case, the *real* value of W^0 is of no practical significance as far as we are concerned. This can be seen by considering a process in which a

---

[1] It is pointed out that this convention is not quite the same as that adopted in Chapter 12. There we assigned the arbitrary value zero to the entropy of a perfect crystalline body at $0°$ K, but showed that the entropy of bodies which are not perfect crystals at this temperature are positive and finite. The statistical value of the entropy at elevated temperatures is calculated relative to the value $S^0 = 0$ *for all substances*. It follows that in some cases the two conventions prove to be the same, but that in other cases they do not. This subject is discussed further in the next chapter.

system changes from state 1 (in which the *absolute* value of its entropy is S_1 and the *absolute* value of its probability equal to W_1) to state 2 (in which the *absolute* value of its entropy is S_2 and the *absolute* value of its probability equal to W_2).

As before, we express the absolute W values in terms of the temperature-dependent factors and the factors independent of temperature, so that

$$W_1 = W_1{}^{\text{temp}} \times W^0$$

and

$$W_2 = W_2{}^{\text{temp}} \times W^0.$$

It follows that the change in entropy is given by the equations

$$\Delta S = S_2 - S_1 = k \log_e \frac{W_2}{W_1}$$

$$= k \log_e \frac{W_2{}^{\text{temp}} \times W^0}{W_1{}^{\text{temp}} \times W^0}$$

$$= k \log_e \frac{W_2{}^{\text{temp}}}{W_1{}^{\text{temp}}}, \quad . \quad . \quad . \quad . \quad (13,2)$$

so that the fact that we cannot assign a real value to W^0 is of no significance, since in thermodynamics we are concerned only with changes in entropy and not with absolute values.

Before proceeding it is useful to observe that if the W value of a system is small, so that the constituent particles are able to assume relatively few spacial configurations, the *degree of order* within the system is relatively high. If, on the other hand, the W value is large, the particles are able to assume many spacial configurations, so that the degree of order is small. Since we have shown that an increase in entropy in an isolated system is equivalent to an increase in W, *an increase in entropy is associated with an increase in internal disorder of the system concerned.*

The Determination of the Value of k

The value of k is determined by considering a process in which a system consisting of one mole (i.e. N molecules) of ideal gas expands adiabatically against no resistance from an initial state at which its pressure is p_1 and its volume V_1 to a final state at which its pressure is p_2 and its volume V_2. We note that since the heat absorbed and the work performed by the gas are both zero, there is no change in internal energy, so that the final and initial temperatures of the gas are the same.

If two volumes V_1 and V_2 are equally accessible to a gas, the chance that at some particular moment a single molecule may be found in one rather than the other is obviously equal to the ratio $\frac{V_1}{V_2}$, and the chance that all N molecules lie in V_1 rather than V_2 must be $\left(\frac{V_1}{V_2}\right)^N$, so that if we denote the chance that all N molecules lie in volume V_1 by the symbol ω_1, and the chance that they lie in volume V_2 by the symbol ω_2, we may write

$$\frac{\omega_1}{\omega_2} = \left(\frac{V_1}{V_2}\right)^N.$$

We know, however, that for an isolated system the ω value is proportional to the thermodynamic probability, so that we may write

$$\frac{W_1}{W_2} = \left(\frac{V_1}{V_2}\right)^N \quad \text{and} \quad \log_e \frac{W_2}{W_1} = N \log_e \frac{V_2}{V_1}.$$

It follows from (13,2) that

$$\Delta S = kN \log_e \frac{V_2}{V_1}. \quad \ldots \quad \ldots \quad (13,3)$$

The change in entropy brought about by the expansion of one mole of ideal gas from state p_1V_1T to state p_2V_2T was, however, calculated in Chapter 8. There it was shown that

$$\Delta S = R \log_e \frac{V_2}{V_1}. \quad \ldots \quad \ldots \quad (13,4)$$

It follows that

$$kN = R$$

or that

$$\boxed{k = \frac{R}{N}} \quad \ldots \quad \ldots \quad (13,5)$$

The constant k is known as BOLTZMANN'S CONSTANT; its value is $1\cdot3804 \times 10^{-16}$ erg deg^{-1}.

We summarise the most important conclusions so far inferred:

1. To any single thermodynamic state of a system there corresponds a definite number of possible micro-states. This number is called the thermodynamic probability and is given the symbol W.

2. If all micro-states are equally accessible to the system the chance that a system assumes a particular thermodynamic state is proportional to the W value of that state.

3. During a natural spontaneous change in an isolated system the W value increases, and the equilibrium state is that to which corresponds the maximum value of W.

4. The entropy S and the thermodynamic probability[1] W are connected by the equation

$$S = k \log_e W \text{ in which the value of } k \text{ is } \frac{R}{N}.$$

The Application of Statistics to Systems of Various Types

The conclusions reached so far may in principle be applied to a system of any sort, but their development is very much simpler and the results obtained much more precise when applied to gases than when applied to systems containing solids and liquids. This is because a gas, or at least a gas approaching ideal behaviour, is an assembly of *independent* particles, so that the behaviour of any one can be studied without reference to the remainder, and because *the total energy of the system can be represented as the sum of the energies possessed by the particles concerned.* If, on the other hand, a system consists of an assembly of particles which are not independent, not only is it difficult to study the behaviour of any one without interference from the rest, but any expression for the total energy must include potential energy terms which relate to the forces between each particle and its neighbours. These terms are difficult to assess. The force of this argument will be appreciated more fully if we consider in greater detail an isolated system consisting of one mole (i.e. N molecules) of an ideal gas in some equilibrium state.

Owing to intermolecular collisions the energy of each molecule will change from time to time, but we may suppose that at some particular moment

$$n_0 \text{ molecules possess energy } \varepsilon_0$$

n_1	,,	,,	,,	ε_1
.	,,	,,	,,	.
.	,,	,,	,,	.
.	,,	,,	,,	.
n_i	,,	,,	,,	ε_i
.	,,	,,	,,	.
.	,,	,,	,,	.
.	,,	,,	,,	.

where the smallest quantity of energy possessed by any molecule is designated by the symbol ε_0, the next largest quantity by the symbol ε_1 and so on.

---

[1] We have established the fact that to any thermodynamic state of a system there corresponds a large number of possible micro-states, but so far have failed to give any idea of just how large a number is involved. This we can now do. We shall show in the next chapter that the entropy of one mole of ideal gas at 25° C and 1 atmosphere pressure is something of the order 40 cal deg^{-1}. Substituting this, and the value of k in equation (13,1) it follows that $\log_e W$ is about 10^{24}.

Obviously, the total number of molecules present is given by the equation

$$N = \sum_i n_i \qquad \text{(13,6)}$$

and because the particles are independent, so that intermolecular forces are zero, the internal energy of the system is given by the equation

$$U = \sum_i n_i \varepsilon_i. \qquad \text{(13,7)}$$

We shall see later that it is not difficult to calculate the W value for such a system as this and so obtain its entropy from equation (13,1), and the remaining molar thermodynamic properties of the system can be calculated with ease, since for an ideal gas $H = U + RT$ and A and G can be obtained from the equations

$$A = U - TS$$

and $$G = H - TS.$$

If, on the other hand, we study a system of dependent particles, any attempt to assign a particular quantity of energy to a particular particle would be wrong, so that equation (13,7) would be without meaning. It is true that if the particles are arranged in a fixed and definite pattern as in a perfect crystal, it is possible to attribute approximately independent energies, not to the molecules or atoms composing the crystal lattice, but to the normal modes of its vibration, and to derive expressions for the thermodynamic properties for the whole, but the solution of these expressions requires so many assumptions and approximations, which are legitimate only under certain conditions, that their use is limited. The best-known achievements in this direction are the Einstein and Debye expressions for the molar thermal capacity of a crystalline solid. Both expressions show that at high temperatures the value of C_v should approach $3R$, and that the value of C_v should reach zero as absolute zero is approached, but the values at intermediate temperatures do not agree closely with experimental results. The application of Statistical Thermodynamics to substances such as liquids is far less advanced. The reason for this is that it is much more difficult to devise a suitable molecular model for a liquid than it is for a gas or a crystalline solid, since a liquid is neither an assembly of independent particles nor a system in which the particles are arranged in a completely ordered pattern. The student is referred to the work by Fowler and Guggenheim[1] for an account of the progress made.

[1] Fowler and Guggenheim, *Statistical Thermodynamics* (1960), Chapter VIII.

Since the simplified form of statistics which will be described in this book can be applied only to a system of independent particles, in other words to an ideal gas, the student may question its utility. In fact, its utility is little impaired by the restrictions imposed. Once we have calculated statistically the thermodynamic properties of a substance as an ideal gas at some particular temperature and pressure, we can calculate the correction factors to be applied to account for non-ideal behaviour by means of one of the equations of state, and the change in thermodynamic properties when the substance passes to some other state can be calculated in the usual way. Thus, the statistical value for the molar entropy of steam at 1 atmosphere pressure, and at 25° C is 45·1 cal deg^{-1}, the vapour pressure of water at 25° C 23·76 mm mercury and its molar latent heat of evaporation 10,499 cal, so that the entropy of liquid water at 25° C can be calculated from the statistical value for steam by adding the increase in entropy due to the expansion of the steam from 760 to 23·76 mm pressure and subtracting the entropy of evaporation, i.e.

$$S_{0_{\text{water}}} = 45 \cdot 1 + R \log_e \frac{760}{23 \cdot 76} - \frac{10,499}{298 \cdot 15}$$

$$= 16 \cdot 7 \text{ cal deg}^{-1}.$$

The Statistical Criteria for Equilibrium in Gaseous Systems

It has been shown that the total number of molecules and the internal energy of a gaseous system are given by the equations

$$N = \sum_i n_i \qquad \qquad \qquad (13,6)$$

and

$$U = \sum_i n_i \varepsilon_i. \qquad \qquad \qquad (13,7)$$

We must now suppose that the number of molecules possessing energy ε_0 may fluctuate between n_0 and $n_0 \pm dn_0$, the number possessing energy ε_1 between n_1 and $n_1 \pm dn_1$ and so on. Since, however, such fluctuations can result in no change either in the total number of molecules present or in the internal energy of an isolated system we can write

$$\sum_i dn_i = 0 \qquad \qquad \qquad (13,8)$$

and

$$\sum_i \varepsilon_i dn_i = 0. \qquad \qquad \qquad (13,9)$$

We have also inferred that the W value of the system is a maximum at equilibrium, so that at equilibrium

$$dW = 0. \qquad \qquad \qquad (13,10)$$

It happens, for reasons which will become apparent later in the text, that it is more convenient to consider $\log_e W$ than W itself. The statistical criteria for equilibrium can therefore be written

$$\sum_i dn_i = 0 \qquad \cdots \cdots \quad (13,8)$$

$$\sum_i \varepsilon_i dn_i = 0 \qquad \cdots \cdots \quad (13,9)$$

$$\text{and} \quad d \log_e W = 0 \qquad \cdots \cdots \quad (13,11)$$

The Distinguishability of Micro-states

Later we shall show how the thermodynamic properties of a system at equilibrium may be calculated once the value W is known. We must therefore be able to *count* the number of possible micro-states available to the system at equilibrium.

The actual counting is done by statistical methods, and is comparatively easy once it has been established, in the case of any particular system, what does or does not constitute an accessible and distinct micro-state. This question is decided by the local rules governing the existence of the system itself.

What we mean by local rules can best be illustrated by considering one mole of gas in some equilibrium state defined by its volume and internal energy. At any particular moment we may suppose that

n_0 molecules possess energy ε_0

n_1 molecules possess energy ε_1 and so on.

Quite obviously, if the number of molecules possessing energy ε_0 change, a new micro-state is established; but what happens if one of the n_0 molecules and one of the n_1 molecules merely *exchange* their respective amounts of energy? Is or is not a new micro-state set up? *Clearly, a new micro-state is established only if the molecules concerned are individually distinguishable.*

Another question we need to answer is this: Is the state of an individual particle determined only by its *total* energy, that is to say when an individual particle possesses a definite quantity of energy, are several different states available to it or only one? We defer the answer to this question until a later paragraph.

The first attempts to determine the number of possible micro-states accessible to a system were made in the nineteenth century and the progress made was due mainly to Maxwell and Boltzmann. Implicit in their form of statistics are two assumptions:

(i) that the discrete particles comprising the system are distinguishable; and

(ii) that the state of each particle is determined completely by its total energy.

A system for which these assumptions are valid is called a Maxwell–Boltzmann system. The calculation of W for such a system at equilibrium is particularly simple:

Consider such a system containing N like particles, then if at a particular moment

n_0 particles possess energy ε_0

n_1 ,, ,, ,, ε_1

. ,, ,, ,, .

. ,, ,, ,, .

. ,, ,, ,, .

n_i ,, ,, ,, ε_i

. ,, ,, ,, .

. ,, ,, ,, .

the number of possible micro-states accessible to the system is the number of ways in which N distinguishable objects can be assigned to distinct groups, so that there are n_0 objects in one group, n_1 in another and so on. This number is

$$\frac{N!}{n_0! n_1! \ldots n_i! \ldots}$$

so that we write

$$W = \frac{N!}{\prod_i n_i!}. \qquad \ldots \ldots \quad (13,12)[1]$$

This equation forms the basis of classical statistical mechanics. When this value for W is substituted into equation (13,11) the criteria for equilibrium become

$$\sum_i dn_i = 0 \qquad \ldots \ldots \quad (13,8)$$

$$\sum_i \varepsilon_i dn_i = 0 \qquad \ldots \ldots \quad (13,9)$$

$$d \log_e \frac{N!}{\prod_i n_i!} = 0. \qquad \ldots \ldots \quad (13,13)$$

[1] The symbol $\prod_i n_i!$ means the product of terms $n_0! n_1! \ldots n_i! \ldots$

When these equations are applied to a gaseous system it proves very simple to obtain expressions from which its thermodynamic properties can be calculated, and the application of these equations to a simple system such as a monatomic gas leads to the prediction of some thermodynamic quantities (such as the principal molar thermal capacities) which are precisely the same as the experimental values. *Unfortunately, this agreement is limited; the most important discrepancy occurring in the value predicted for the entropy of the system, which is found to be much higher than the experimental value.*

Since the calculated entropy proves to be larger than the experimental value, it is clear that the W value of a gaseous system calculated by Maxwell–Boltzmann statistics is too high. A possible reason for this comes to mind when we remember the conclusions reached when we studied the first model. We showed then that the number of micro-states corresponding to each macro-state is very much greater if the particles concerned can be distinguished one from another than if they are individually indistinguishable. We suppose, therefore, that the reason why Maxwell–Boltzmann statistics give the wrong result for a gaseous system is that the individual particles in a gas cannot be distinguished one from another. This conclusion is confirmed by the fact that when we apply to a gaseous system a form of statistics based on the indistinguishability of like particles, values of the thermodynamic properties are predicted which agree closely with the experimental values.[1]

Degeneracy

We must also inquire whether or not the state of an atom or molecule is determined completely by its total energy. Consider a diatomic molecule in a quantity of gas at moderate temperature. Its total energy may be thought of as being contributed in separate parts, namely its translation energy, its rotational energy, its vibrational energy and its electronic energy, the last term including the kinetic energies of the electrons due to their movement relative to the nuclei and the potential energy due to their configuration, and possibly other parts which are undefined. We may therefore (with some reservations which will be discussed later in the chapter) write

$$\varepsilon = \varepsilon_{trans} + \varepsilon_{rot} + \varepsilon_{vib} + \varepsilon_{elec} \ldots$$

[1] It is pointed out that if we were to attempt to calculate the thermodynamic properties of a crystal, it would be correct to proceed as though its individual particles were distinguishable. In a crystal each particle occupies a particular *site*; accordingly, the interchange of two like particles in different energy states leads to two recognisably different micro-states for the crystal as a whole, for the particle sites in a crystal are distinguishable even if the particles are not, whereas the mention of a particular site in relation to the molecules in a gas is meaningless because no molecule is bound to it, the entire volume of the system being accessible to them all.

Clearly, the same total energy ε may relate to many different states distinguished only by the relative sizes of the parts named. In fact, we have simplified the picture overmuch. The translational energy itself may be regarded as due to three separate contributions defined as soon as we relate the motion of the molecule to some convenient co-ordinate system. Thus, if we resolve the velocity along three mutually perpendicular Cartesian axes X, Y and Z

$$\varepsilon_{\text{trans}} = \tfrac{1}{2}mC^2 = \tfrac{1}{2}mC_X^2 + \tfrac{1}{2}mC_Y^2 + \tfrac{1}{2}mC_Z^2$$

and it follows that $\varepsilon_{\text{trans}}$ itself may relate to many different states distinguished only by the relative sizes of these three parts, and limited in number only by any quantum restriction on the velocity components.

We should now state the above in somewhat more precise language. It is convenient to introduce the word *level*, and instead of saying that a particle possesses energy ε_0, ε_1, ε_2 . . ., etc., to say that the particle is in energy level ε_0, ε_1, ε_2 . . ., etc. The number of different states corresponding to the same total energy ε_i, that is the number of distinguishable ways in which the particle can possess this energy is called the *degeneracy* of the energy level. We denote it by the symbol g_i. (From the standpoint of wave mechanics, the degeneracy of an energy level arises when there are g_i distinct proper values satisfying the wave equation of the molecule in that particular level.) *It is clear that the degeneracy of a particular total energy level will be a very large number if the energy differences between possible translational, rotational, vibrational and electronic levels are small compared with the total amount of energy available for distribution between them.*

Fermi–Dirac and Bose–Einstein Statistics

Two statistics have been developed during this century based on the indistinguishability of gas molecules, and taking into account the degeneracy of each discrete energy level. One was developed by Fermi and Dirac, and the other by Bose and Einstein. To understand the fundamental difference between them requires a greater knowledge of wave mechanics than is assumed in this book, but a distinction which is of some practical utility as far as we are concerned is that Fermi–Dirac statistics apply to those systems in which any particular quantum state can be inhabited only by one particle at a time (this restriction is clearly linked with the Pauli Exclusion Principle), while Bose–Einstein statistics apply to those systems in which no restriction governs the number of particles occupying any particular quantum state.

These statistics are somewhat difficult to handle, but since we are concerned only in calculating the W value and ultimately the values of the molar thermodynamic properties of a gas, we shall see that we can, with full justification, make certain simplifications which render them no more difficult to handle than classical statistics.

As before, we consider a system consisting of N discrete indistinguishable molecules of the same kind. We designate the energy levels accessible to them ε_0, ε_1, ε_2, ... ε_i ..., and the degeneracy of each level g_0, g_1, g_2, ... g_i ..., and we suppose that at equilibrium n_0 molecules occupy level ε_0, n_1 occupy level ε_1, ... n_i occupy level ε_i ... and so on.

The system can therefore be represented by the scheme

Energy levels	ε_0, ε_1, ε_2, ... ε_i ...
Degeneracy of each energy level	g_0, g_1, g_2, ... g_i ...
Population numbers at each energy level	n_0, n_1, n_2, ... n_i ...

We first calculate the total number of micro-states available to the system as a whole on the assumption that the system is governed by Fermi–Dirac statistics, i.e. that each of the g_i quantum states available to the particle at energy level ε_i can be occupied by one particle only. The number of ways of assigning n_i indistinguishable objects to g_i distinguishable states under these conditions is given in Theorem 11, page xvi. The number is

$$\frac{g_i!}{n_i!(g_i - n_i)!}.$$

The number of ways therefore in which the complete system may be assembled is the product of these values for all levels, i.e.

$$W_{FD} = \prod_i \frac{g_i!}{n_i!(g_i - n_i)!}. \qquad \qquad (13,14)$$

It happens to be convenient to expand this result into the form

$$W_{FD} = \prod_i \frac{g_i(g_i - 1)(g_i - 2) \ldots (g_i - n_i + 1)}{n_i!} \qquad (13,15)$$

We now calculate the number of micro-states available to the system as a whole on the assumption that the system is governed by Bose–Einstein statistics. Here we are concerned with the problem of assigning n_i indistinguishable objects to g_i distinguishable states, where there is no restriction as to the number of objects in any one. The answer to this problem is given in Theorem 12, page xvi. The number of ways it can be done is

$$\frac{(g_i + n_i - 1)!}{(g_i - 1)!n_i!}.$$

The number of ways in which the complete system may be assembled is the product of the values for all energy levels, i.e.

$$W_{BE} = \prod_i \frac{(g_i + n_i - 1)!}{(g_i - 1)! n_i!}, \quad \cdots \cdots \quad (13,16)$$

and we expand this equation into the form

$$W_{BE} = \prod \frac{(g_i + n_i - 1)(g_i + n_i - 2) \ldots (g_i + 1)g_i}{n_i!}. \quad (13,17)$$

Earlier in this chapter we pointed out that the degeneracy of any energy level is a very large number as long as the differences between the various accessible translational, rotational, vibrational and electronic energy levels are small compared with the total energy available for distribution between them. The actual number can be calculated, and it is found that for a gas molecule at all but the lowest temperatures the degeneracy of each level is very much greater than the number of molecules likely to be found at each level, that is to say, at all energy levels the g values are very much greater than the corresponding values of n. Under these circumstances it is immaterial whether we apply Fermi–Dirac statistics or Bose–Einstein to the system, as it is unnecessary to inquire whether a particular quantum state is *permitted* to be occupied by only one or by any number of particles, because if the number of available quantum states greatly exceeds the number of molecules available to fill them, chance will ensure that each available quantum state is occupied by one particle at the most.

Under these circumstances equations (13,15) and (13,17) can be simplified. Consider equation (13,15) first: since all the values of g are very much greater than the corresponding values of n, each term in the numerator approximates to g_i, and since there are n_i terms we see that

$$W_{FD} \text{ is always less than but approaches } \prod_i \frac{g_i^{n_i}}{n_i!}.$$

From equation (13,17) it is evident that under the same conditions each term in the numerator approximates to g_i, and since there are again n_i terms, it follows that

$$W_{BE} \text{ is always greater than but approaches } \prod_i \frac{g_i^{n_i}}{n_i!}.$$

As long therefore as it is permissible to assume that the degeneracy of each energy level greatly exceeds the number of molecules available to occupy it, we may accept that the total number of micro-states available to the system as a whole is given by the equation

$$W = \prod_i \frac{g_i^{n_i}}{n_i!} \quad \cdots \cdots \cdots \quad (13,18)$$

As was stated earlier in the argument, this assumption can be made confidently as long as the gas is at all but the lowest temperatures. It must therefore be remembered that the equations which we shall derive from (13,18) are not applicable to systems at very low temperatures (i.e. at temperatures only one or two degrees above absolute zero).

Expressions for the Thermodynamic Properties of an Ideal Gas

At this point it is convenient to summarise some of the results we have obtained.

1. We have explained how a system of independent particles may be represented by the tabular scheme shown on page 253.
2. We have shown that the internal energy and entropy of such a system may be represented by equations

$$U = \sum_i n_i \varepsilon_i$$

$$S = k \log_e W$$

and that at all but extremely low temperatures the W value is given by the equation

$$W = \prod \frac{g_i^{n_i}}{n_i!}.$$

It follows therefore that for such a system

$$U = \sum_i n_i \varepsilon_i \qquad \quad \ldots \ldots \quad (13,7)$$

$$\text{and} \quad S = k \sum_i \log_e \frac{g_i^{n_i}}{n_i!} \quad \ldots \ldots \quad (13,19)$$

Clearly, once we have calculated U and S the remaining thermodynamic properties of a gas can be obtained easily, since we know that (considering molar quantities)

$$H = U + RT$$

$$A = U - TS$$

and

$$G = H - TS.$$

The value of ε_i and g_i for a particular molecule may be obtained theoretically or from spectrographic measurements. In order to complete the calculation we require to determine the values n_i or to eliminate the terms n_i from equations (13,7) and (13,19). We choose the latter method, and show how the term n_i may be expressed in terms of g_i and ε_i.

We consider a system containing N like independent particles, and suppose as before, that each energy level ε_i is g_i-fold degenerate, and is populated by n_i particles. We assume that conditions are such that equation (13,18) holds.

The conditions at equilibrium are

$$\sum_i dn_i = 0 \qquad \ldots \quad \ldots \quad (13,8)$$

$$\sum_i \varepsilon_i dn_i = 0 \qquad \ldots \quad \ldots \quad (13,9)$$

$$d \log_e W = 0. \qquad \ldots \quad \ldots \quad (13,11)$$

From (13,18)

$$\log_e W = \sum_i (n_i \log_e g_i - \log_e n_i!).$$

To proceed we make use of Stirling's Approximation Theorem, which states that if N is a very large number

$$\log_e N! \simeq N \log_e N - N,$$

hence $$\log_e W = \sum_i (n_i \log_e g_i - n_i \log_e n_i + n_i),$$

and $$d \log_e W = \sum_i (\log_e g_i dn_i - \log_e n_i dn_i - n_i d \log_e n_i + dn_i),$$

but $$n_i d \log_e n_i = dn_i,$$

so that $$d \log_e W = \sum_i \log_e \frac{g_i}{n_i} dn_i. \qquad \ldots \quad \ldots \quad (13,20)$$

The distribution of particles over the various energy levels at equilibrium is therefore governed by the simultaneous conditions

$$\sum_i dn_i = 0 \qquad \ldots \quad \ldots \quad (13,8)$$

$$\sum_i \varepsilon_i dn_i = 0 \qquad \ldots \quad \ldots \quad (13,9)$$

and $$\sum_i \log_e \frac{g_i}{n_i} dn_i = 0. \qquad \ldots \quad \ldots \quad (13,20)$$

We now wish to combine these three equations so as to express the conditions at equilibrium in a single expression. It is of course not permissible merely to add the equations as they stand, not only because this would not be the most general way of combining them but because the dimensions of the sums on the left-hand side of each are not the same, those in (13,8) and (13,20) are dimensionless, whereas those in (13,9) have the dimensions of energy. They are therefore combined using the Method of Undetermined Multipliers. This consists of multiplying (13,8) by some arbitrary dimensionless parameter α, (13,9) by an arbitrary parameter $-\beta$ which has the dimensions of inverse energy and adding the result so as to give the equation

$$\sum_i (\log_e \frac{g_i}{n_i} + \alpha - \beta\varepsilon_i)dn_i = 0. \qquad (13,21)$$

Since the quantities $dn_0, dn_1 \ldots dn_i \ldots$ may be real and finite, each term in (13,21) is only satisfied if the quantity enclosed in the bracket is zero, i.e.

$$\log_e \frac{g_i}{n_i} + \alpha - \beta\varepsilon_i = 0.$$

Hence

$$\log_e \frac{n_i}{g_i} = \alpha - \beta\varepsilon_i$$

or

$$\frac{n_i}{g_i} = e^{\alpha-\beta\epsilon_i}. \qquad (13,22)$$

Putting

$$e^\alpha = a$$

we obtain the equation

$$n_i = ag_ie^{-\beta i}$$

Since

$$N = \sum_i n_i = a\sum_i g_ie^{-\beta\epsilon_i} \qquad (13,23)$$

$$a = \frac{N}{\sum\limits_i g_ie^{-\beta\epsilon_i}}$$

Hence

$$\boxed{\frac{n_i}{N} = \frac{g_ie^{-\beta\epsilon_i}}{\sum\limits_i g_ie^{-\beta\epsilon_i}}.} \qquad (13,24)$$

This equation, known usually as the *Distribution Law* gives the distribution of particles over the various energy levels available to them.[1] The

---

[1] The Distribution Laws applicable to true Fermi–Dirac and Bose–Einstein systems may be deduced in the same way as that given above. In these cases we have to start from (13,14) and (13,16) instead of (13,18).

Equation (13,14) leads to the equation

$$\frac{n_i}{g_i - n_i} = e^{\alpha-\beta\epsilon_i} \qquad (13,25)$$

in the case of Fermi–Dirac, and equation (13,16) leads to the equation

$$\frac{n_i}{g_i + n_i} = e^{\alpha-\beta\epsilon_i} \qquad (13,26)$$

in the case of Bose–Einstein.

We note that if g_i is very much greater than n_i, these equations both reduce to (13,22).

greatest importance of the Distribution Law as far as we are concerned is that it permits us to express the population numbers n_i in terms of ε_i and g_i.

The Nature of the Parameter β

Consider a system divided into two parts, each of which is in a constant volume container in thermal equilibrium with the other but both insulated from the surroundings, so that the only property necessarily common to the two parts is temperature. We denote the quantities relating to the species of the first part by ε_i, g_i, n_i, and those relating to the species in the second part by ε_j, g_j, n_j.

Since the total number of micro-states accessible to the complete system equals the product of the number of micro-states permissible to each part, the conditions governing the equilibrium state are

$$d \log_e W_i W_j = 0 \quad \ldots \quad \ldots \quad (13,11)$$

$$\left. \begin{aligned} \sum_i dn_i &= 0 \\ \text{and} \quad \sum_j dn_j &= 0 \end{aligned} \right\} \quad \ldots \quad \ldots \quad (13,8)$$

But the conditions

$$\left. \begin{aligned} \sum_i \varepsilon_i dn_i &= 0 \\ \text{and} \quad \sum_j \varepsilon_j dn_j &= 0 \end{aligned} \right\} \quad \ldots \quad \ldots \quad (13,9)$$

do not hold. The two parts are in thermal equilibrium and energy may pass from one to the other, so that (13,9) must be replaced by the condition

$$\sum_{ij} (\varepsilon_i dn_i + \varepsilon_j dn_j) = 0. \quad \ldots \quad \ldots \quad (13,27)$$

The criteria for equilibrium are therefore (13,8), (13,11) and (13,27), and so, if we combine them in the same general way as we did above, we see that although we require to assign different parameters α' and α'' to the two equations (13,8), we require only one parameter $-\beta$ for (13,27). Clearly, therefore, β must be related to the only property common to the two parts of the system, i.e. temperature, and must be independent of any other property not necessarily shared by them. It will be remembered, too, that β has the dimensions of inverse energy. These conditions are satisfied by the equation

$$\beta = \frac{1}{kT} \quad \ldots \quad \ldots \quad \ldots \quad (13,28)$$

where k is the Boltzmann Constant $\frac{R}{N}$. We shall not prove this equation at this stage but shall accept it, use it where convenient, and reserve its general proof to a more convenient point in the next chapter.

The Absolute Partition Function

The quantity $\sum_i g_i e^{-\beta \epsilon_i}$ first introduced in equation (13,23) is known as the ABSOLUTE PARTITION FUNCTION OF THE PARTICLE. Next to the W number it is the most important quantity in statistical theory. It is assigned the symbol f_{abs} so that we may write

$$f_{abs} = \sum_i g_i e^{-\beta \epsilon_i}. \qquad (13,29)$$

This expression can be expanded so as to contain one term for each *energy level*, i.e.

$$f_{abs} = g_0 e^{-\beta \epsilon_0} + g_1 e^{-\beta \epsilon_1} \ldots g_i e^{-\beta \epsilon_i} \ldots \qquad (13,30)$$

or expanded farther so as to contain a separate term for each *accessible state*. i.e.

$$f_{abs} = (e^{-\beta \epsilon_0} + e^{-\beta \epsilon_0} \ldots)_{g_0 \text{ terms}} + (e^{-\beta \epsilon_1} + e^{-\beta \epsilon_1} \ldots)_{g_1 \text{ terms}}$$
$$\ldots + (e^{-\beta \epsilon_i} + e^{-\beta \epsilon_i} \ldots)_{g_i \text{ terms}} \ldots \qquad (13,31)$$

In other words, the partition function can be defined in terms of g_i if the summation takes place over the various possible energy levels, or without reference to g_i if it takes place over the various possible permitted states, i.e.

$$f_{abs} = \sum_{\text{levels}} g_i e^{-\beta \epsilon_i} = \sum_{\text{states}} e^{-\beta \epsilon_i}. \qquad (13,32)$$

This explains why the quantity f_{abs} is sometimes called the *state sum*.

The physical significance of the partition function can perhaps best be appreciated by considering equation (13,30), when it can be seen to list the various possible energy levels, but to multiply each level by a weighting factor (g_0, $g_1 \ldots g_i \ldots$) to show its relative importance in providing different accessible states.

It follows from (13,24) and (13,29) that the Distribution Law may be written in the form

$$\frac{n_i}{N} = \frac{g_i e^{-\beta \epsilon_i}}{f_{abs}} \qquad (13,33)$$

so that in principle the value of n_i in terms of g_i, ϵ_i and f_{abs} may be substituted in equations (13,7) and (13,19) and the resulting expressions for U and S evaluated. In fact, as will be seen in the next chapter, much simpler expressions for U and S in terms of the partition function can be obtained indirectly.

Factorisation of the Absolute Partition Function

The quantity ε_i used in the above represents any one of the total energy levels available to the particle. The particles in which we are particularly interested are gas molecules, and the total energy of such a molecule is contributed to by its translational energy, its energy of rotation, vibrational energies and that energy related to its electronic motion.

We shall for the moment assume that the total energy of a molecule can be resolved into *precise* components, one component due solely to translational motion, one component due solely to rotation and so on, i.e.

$$\varepsilon = \varepsilon_{\text{trans}} + \varepsilon_{\text{rot}} + \varepsilon_{\text{vib}} + \varepsilon_{\text{elec}}. \qquad . \quad . \quad . \quad (13,34)$$

This means that there are available in the molecule sets of translational energy levels, a typical member of which we can call ε_j, sets of rotational levels ε_k, sets of vibrational levels ε_l and sets of electronic levels ε_m, and that the set of total energy levels we have so far called ε_i is really the sum of typical values

$$\varepsilon_j + \varepsilon_k + \varepsilon_l + \varepsilon_m.$$

Since any value of j can occur with any value of k, l or m

$$g_i = g_{j,\,k,\,l,\,m} = g_j \times g_k \times g_l \times g_m. \quad . \quad . \quad . \quad (13,35)$$

The total partition function f_{abs} can therefore be written

$$f_{\text{abs}} = \sum_i g_i e^{-\beta \epsilon_i} = \sum g_{j,\,k,\,l,\,m}\, e^{-\beta(\epsilon_j + \epsilon_k + \epsilon_1 + \epsilon_m)}$$

$$= \left(\sum_j g_j e^{-\beta \epsilon_j}\right)\left(\sum_k g_k e^{-\beta \epsilon_k}\right)\left(\sum_l g_l e^{-\beta \epsilon_1}\right)\left(\sum_m g_m e^{-\beta \epsilon_m}\right).$$

The term in the first bracket is the absolute translational partition function, that in the second is the absolute rotational partition function and so on. We can therefore write

$$f_{\text{abs}} = f_{\text{trans}_{\text{abs}}} \times f_{\text{rot}_{\text{abs}}} \times f_{\text{vib}_{\text{abs}}} \times f_{\text{elec}_{\text{abs}}}. \quad . \quad . \quad (13,36)$$

In the next chapter we shall show how these individual factors can be determined in the case of simple molecules, and how from these values the thermodynamic properties of gases may be calculated.

It is, however, necessary to inquire whether we were really justified in our original assumption that it is possible to resolve the total energy of a molecule into *precise* components. There appears, in fact, to be no doubt at all that the translational energy of a molecule is completely independent of the other forms, so that we can write

$$\varepsilon = \varepsilon_{\text{trans}} + \varepsilon_{rve} \quad . \quad . \quad . \quad . \quad . \quad (13,37)$$

where ε_{rve} represents a composite term related to the other three, but whether or not this term can be precisely resolved into its separate components, and whether therefore the total absolute partition function can be factorised as we have shown above requires further discussion.

The nature of the problem can be seen by considering a diatomic molecule. Its rotational energy depends on the moment of inertia of the molecule and this depends on the distance between the two atomic nuclei concerned. Molecular vibrations will, however, lead to continual change in that distance, so that clearly the vibrational energy will affect the rotational energy and vice versa. It is obviously reasonable, too, to suspect that the mode of vibration may affect the quantum states in which the electrons exist.

Since it appears that the *precise* resolution of the total energy according to (13,34) and factorisation of the total absolute partition function according to (13,36) may not really be possible, the question which arises is whether any inaccuracies introduced by this possibly faulty factorisation are large enough to be significant. This question can, of course, only be answered by the factual evidence we have available. The thermodynamic properties of various gases have been determined exactly (by a laborious method which does not entail factorisation of the total partition function) and imprecisely by determining the individual partition functions in turn. The results show that the inaccuracies introduced in the second method are so small as to be insignificant if the gas molecules are simple, but are significant if the molecules are complicated. We shall therefore permit factorisation according to (13,36) because we are concerned only with the calculation of the thermodynamic properties of simple gases, for which the method is accurate enough.

In some cases the problem is simplified by the fact that all terms are not always significant. For example, in the case of a monatomic gas it is quite obvious that vibrational energies do not exist; further, we shall (as will be demonstrated in the next chapter) find that the quantity of energy required to bring about the rotation of a single atom is so large compared with that normally exchanged by intermolecular collisions that rotation will occur only at extremely high temperatures. At moderate temperatures therefore equation (13,36) reduces to

$$f_{\text{abs}} = f_{\text{trans}_{\text{abs}}} \times f_{\text{elec}_{\text{abs}}}. \quad . \quad . \quad . \quad (13,38)$$

In the case of diatomic molecules rotation occurs at all but extremely low temperatures, but vibrational energies are rarely significant until extremely high temperatures are reached.

We finally observe that if the total absolute partition function of a particular molecule can be factorised without significant inaccuracy, any one single factor may be used to solve a particular problem to which it is applicable, without taking into account the others.

EXERCISES 13

13,1. A chemical engineer intends to produce hydrogen by making use of the reaction

$$CO + H_2O_{(g)} \longrightarrow CO_2 + H_2.$$

He pumps a mixture containing equi-molar quantities of carbon monoxide and steam into a reaction vessel of 1000 litre capacity at 8 atmospheres pressure and at 819° K. To his dismay he observes that no reaction takes place, and on investigation finds that all the carbon monoxide has congregated in one-half of the reaction vessel and all the steam in the other half, the temperature remaining the same.

Calculate the chance that this unhappy event might in fact occur, and calculate the change in entropy which would result if it did.

13,2. As pointed out in the footnote on page 251, the *sites* in a crystalline solid are distinguishable even though the particles occupying them are indistinguishable. Maxwell–Boltzmann statistics are applicable to such a system. Use equation (13,12) to show that when one mole of an ideal solid solution is formed from n_1 moles of one substance and $(1 - n_1)$ moles of a second the entropy of mixing equals

$$-R(x_1 \log_e x_1 + x_2 \log_e x_2)$$

where x_1 and x_2 are the mole fractions of the two components.

13,3. It was pointed out on page 244 that increase in entropy is equivalent to an increase in disorder. It therefore follows that the Second Law of Thermodynamics is contained in the statement that *No spontaneous change in an isolated system can result in a decrease in disorder.*

It should also be apparent that the increase in disorder resulting from the acquisition of a given quantity of heat by a body at high temperature is less than that which would result if the body were at a lower temperature.

Show that these statements lead directly to the Second Law as enunciated by Clausius, i.e. that heat will not pass spontaneously from one body to another at higher temperature.

13,4. Explain why the W value of a system capable of being divided into separate parts can never be a prime number.

13,5. Discuss the evidence offered by Statistical Thermodynamics regarding the distinguishability or indistinguishability of gas molecules.

CHAPTER 14

THE CALCULATION OF THE THERMODYNAMIC PROPERTIES OF GASES BY STATISTICAL MEANS

The student is reminded that the statistics developed in the last chapter were derived for systems of independent particles under such conditions that the degeneracy of each energy level is very much greater than the corresponding energy level population numbers. These circumstances are precisely those that describe an ideal gas at all temperatures except those close to zero. In this chapter we shall calculate the values of the thermodynamic properties of gases at 25° C and 1 atmosphere pressure. Since the values obtained will be those for an ideal gas we must, if we wish to compare them with those of the real gas obtained as the result of calorimetric measurements, either correct our statistical values for the actual non-ideal behaviour of the gas, or correct the calorimetric measurements for ideal behaviour.

We shall again represent a system of independent particles by the scheme:

Energy levels—

$$\varepsilon_0, \varepsilon_1, \varepsilon_2, \ldots \varepsilon_i \ldots$$

Degeneracy of each energy level—

$$g_0, g_1, g_2, \ldots g_i \ldots$$

Number of molecules occupying each energy level—

$$n_0, n_1, n_2, \ldots n_i \ldots$$

Such a system is described by the following relationships:

1. The total number of molecules in the system is given by the equation

$$N = \sum_i n_i. \qquad \ldots \ldots \quad (13,3)$$

We shall, in fact, always consider systems containing one mole of gas, so that N is the Avogadro Number.

2. The internal energy of the system is given by the equation

$$U = \sum_i n_i \varepsilon_i. \qquad \ldots \ldots \quad (13,4)$$

3. The entropy of the system is given by the equation

$$S = k \log_e W \qquad \ldots \ldots \quad (13,1)$$

where

$$W = \prod_i \frac{g_i{}^{n_i}}{n_i!}. \qquad \ldots \ldots \quad (13,17)$$

In order to proceed farther we make use of the total absolute partition function of the molecule:

$$f_{\text{abs}} = \sum_{\text{levels}} g_i e^{-\beta \varepsilon_i}. \qquad \ldots \ldots \quad (13,30)$$

As explained in the last chapter, the real use of the partition function is to eliminate the numbers n_i from the expressions for the internal energy and entropy.

At this stage it is convenient to make use of the equation

$$\beta = \frac{1}{kT} \qquad \ldots \ldots \ldots \quad (13,29)$$

which we shall prove later.

We write

$$f_{\text{abs}} = \sum_{\text{levels}} g_i e^{-\frac{\varepsilon_i}{kT}}$$

and remembering that the partition function is a function of temperature and volume, write

$$\left(\frac{\partial f_{\text{abs}}}{\partial T} \right)_v = \sum \frac{\varepsilon_i}{kT^2} g_i e^{-\frac{\varepsilon_i}{kT}}$$

Hence

$$\frac{kT^2}{f_{\text{abs}}} \left(\frac{\partial f_{\text{abs}}}{\partial T} \right)_v = \sum \frac{\varepsilon_i g_i e^{-\frac{\varepsilon_i}{kT}}}{f_{\text{abs}}}$$

i.e.

$$kT^2 \left(\frac{\partial \log_e f_{\text{abs}}}{\partial T} \right)_v = \sum \frac{\varepsilon_i g_i e^{-\frac{\varepsilon_i}{kT}}}{f_{\text{abs}}}.$$

But from (13,24), (13,29) and (13,30) it follows that

$$\frac{g_i e^{-\frac{\varepsilon_i}{kT}}}{f_{\text{abs}}} = \frac{n_i}{N}$$

so that

$$NkT^2 \left(\frac{\partial \log_e f_{\text{abs}}}{\partial T} \right)_v = \sum \varepsilon_i n_i = U. \qquad \ldots \quad (14,1)$$

Since $Nk = R$, the internal energy of one mole of ideal gas at temperature T is given by the equation

$$U = RT^2\left(\frac{\partial \log_e f_{abs}}{\partial T}\right)_v. \qquad \cdots \quad (14,2)$$

This equation would permit us to calculate the *absolute* value of the internal energy of the gas if we knew the *absolute* values of the energy levels $\varepsilon_0, \varepsilon_1 \ldots \varepsilon_i$ which figure in the expression for the partition function. Unfortunately, we neither know nor have any means by which the absolute values of the energy levels may be determined. What we usually mean when we speak of the energy possessed by a body in a particular state is the difference between the energy it possesses in that state and that which it would possess in some standard state which we arbitrarily and conventionally "define" as being of zero energy, just as when we speak of a mountain as being 15,000 feet high we really mean that its summit is 15,000 feet above sea-level. The fact that we cannot assign absolute values to the energy levels $\varepsilon_0, \varepsilon_1, \varepsilon_2, \ldots \varepsilon_i$ of a particle, and so can evaluate neither the absolute value of f nor the absolute value of the internal energy is not, however, of any real importance, because it will be remembered from previous chapters that we are never interested in the absolute value of a thermodynamic property of this sort, but only in the change in value of the property as the result of a thermodynamic process.

The statistical picture of what happens when a system cools is that more and more particles drop out of the higher energy levels hitherto accessible to them and crowd into the lower levels. We suppose that at absolute zero all particles occupy the lowest possible energy level ε_0, so that in fact the energy of a system containing N particles at absolute zero is $N\varepsilon_0$. The molar zero point energy is usually depicted by the symbol E_0^0. We now proceed to show that although the absolute value of the internal energy cannot be determined, the quantity $U - E_0^0$ can be determined with ease.

The absolute partition function of the molecule is given by the expression

$$f_{abs} = g_0 e^{-\frac{\varepsilon_0}{kT}} + g_1 e^{-\frac{\varepsilon_1}{kT}} + g_2 e^{-\frac{\varepsilon_2}{kT}} \ldots g_i e^{-\frac{\varepsilon_i}{kT}} \ldots$$

We now factorise out the quantity $e^{-\frac{\varepsilon_0}{kT}}$. The above expression therefore becomes

$$f_{abs} = e^{-\frac{\varepsilon_0}{kT}}\{g_0 + g_1 e^{-\frac{\varepsilon_1-\varepsilon_0}{kT}} + g_2 e^{-\frac{\varepsilon_2-\varepsilon_0}{kT}} \ldots g_i e^{-\frac{\varepsilon_i-\varepsilon_0}{kT}} \ldots\}.$$

We describe the expression in brackets as the *rational* partition function of the particle, and so write

$$f_{abs} = e^{-\frac{\varepsilon_0}{kT}} f_{rational}. \qquad \cdots \quad (14,3)$$

It follows that

$$\log_e f_{\text{abs}} = -\frac{\varepsilon_0}{kT} + \log_e f_{\text{rational}}$$

and

$$\left(\frac{\partial \log_e f_{\text{abs}}}{\partial T}\right)_v = \frac{\varepsilon_0}{kT^2} + \left(\frac{\partial \log_e f_{\text{rational}}}{\partial T}\right)_v$$

so that, from (14,2)

$$U = RT^2 \frac{\varepsilon_0}{kT^2} + RT^2 \left(\frac{\partial \log_e f_{\text{rational}}}{\partial T}\right)_v.$$

Since $R/k = N$ and since $N\varepsilon_0 = E_0^0$ we write

$$U - E_0^0 = RT^2 \left(\frac{\partial \log_e f_{\text{rational}}}{\partial T}\right)_v. \qquad . \quad . \quad . \quad (14,4)$$

In the last chapter we showed that it is possible to factorise the total absolute partition function into partition functions which relate to the translational, rotational, vibrational and electronic energies of the molecule:

$$f_{\text{abs}} = f_{\text{trans(abs)}} \times f_{\text{rot(abs)}} \times f_{\text{vib(abs)}} \times f_{\text{elec(abs)}}. \qquad (13,36)$$

The rational partition function can be factorised in precisely the same way. The rational translational partition function and the absolute translational partition function are in fact the same, simply because it is quite possible for a molecule to possess zero translational energy at any temperature. The same applies to the rotational partition function. The rational and absolute vibrational and electronic partition functions are, however, very different.

To a first approximation a diatomic molecule may be treated as an harmonic oscillator for which the vibrational energy takes the form

$$\varepsilon_{\text{vib}} = (v + \tfrac{1}{2})hc\omega$$

where ω is the reciprocal wavelength expressed in cm^{-1}, and where v is the vibrational quantum number which can assume any integral value from zero to infinity. Vibrational energy levels happen to be non-degenerate, so that the absolute vibrational partition function is given by the expression

$$f_{\text{vib(absolute)}} = e^{-\frac{hc\omega}{2kT}} + e^{-\frac{3hc\omega}{2kT}} + e^{-\frac{5hc\omega}{2kT}} \ldots$$

while the rational vibrational partition function is given by the expression

$$f_{\text{vib(rational)}} = 1 + e^{-\frac{hc\omega}{kT}} + e^{-\frac{2hc\omega}{kT}} \ldots$$

$$= \frac{1}{1 - e^{-\frac{hc\omega}{kT}}}.$$

If we used the expression for the absolute vibrational partition function we should obtain the absolute value of the vibrational contribution to the internal energy, whereas, by using the rational partition function, we include the vibrational zero point energy in the term E_0^0.

Because the lowest translational and rotational energy levels are in any case zero, and because the lowest vibrational energy level is known, the student might wonder why the rational partition function has been introduced. The reason why it is essential to introduce it is clear as soon as we consider the electronic partition function. The absolute electronic partition function is given by the expression

$$f_{\text{elec(absolute)}} = g_0 e^{-\frac{\epsilon_0}{kT}} + g_1 e^{-\frac{\epsilon_1}{kT}} + g_2 e^{-\frac{\epsilon_2}{kT}} \ldots$$

where ϵ_0 is the lowest electronic energy level, ϵ_1 the next and so on. The absolute values of ϵ_0, ϵ_1, ϵ_2 . . . *cannot be obtained*. All that it is possible to do is to calculate their values *relative to some reference state to which we assign zero energy by convention*. In fact, the student will be aware that in the original Bohr Theory of the hydrogen atom, the energy of an electron was calculated *relative to its energy an infinite distance from the nucleus*, but there is no more reason why this procedure should give a *real* value for ϵ_0, ϵ_1, ϵ_2, . . . than any other. Atomic spectra measurements are no help, all that they provide are the differences between the various energy levels, the quantities $\epsilon_1 - \epsilon_0$, $\epsilon_2 - \epsilon_1$ and so on.

The *only* way out of the impasse is to factorise out $e^{-\frac{\epsilon_0}{kT}}$ from the expression for the absolute electronic partition function to obtain the expression

$$f_{\text{elec(rational)}} = g_0 + g_1 e^{-\frac{\epsilon_1 - \epsilon_0}{kT}} + g_2 e^{-\frac{\epsilon_2 - \epsilon_0}{kT}} \ldots$$

which expression can be evaluated with ease. The *actual* contribution of the electronic ground state energy is then, like the vibrational zero point energy, included in the term E_0^0.

From now on the rational partition function will be used in all calculations. It will be denoted by the symbol f and the suffix rational rarely included: i.e. we write

$$U - E_0^0 = RT^2 \left(\frac{\partial \log_e f}{\partial T} \right)_v. \qquad \cdots \qquad (14,4)$$

We shall denote rational energy levels, that is those calculated relative to the energy level of the particle in the ground state by the symbol $\Delta \epsilon_i$, which will have the meaning $\epsilon_i - \epsilon_0$. We note therefore that for the whole system

$$U - E_0^0 = \sum n_i \Delta \epsilon_i. \qquad \cdots \qquad (14,5)$$

We now require only to restate the Distribution Law in terms of the rational partition function and rational energy levels. In the last chapter the law was expressed in the form

$$\frac{n_i}{N} = \frac{g_i e^{-\beta \epsilon_i}}{f_{abs}}. \qquad \qquad \text{(13,35)}$$

Since

$$\beta = \frac{1}{kT}$$

$$\frac{n_i}{N} = \frac{g_i e^{-\frac{\epsilon_i}{kT}}}{f_{abs}}.$$

If top and bottom of the right-hand side be divided by $e^{-\frac{\epsilon_0}{kT}}$ we obtain

$$\frac{n_i}{N} = \frac{g_i e^{-\frac{\Delta \epsilon_i}{kT}}}{f_{rational}}. \qquad \qquad \text{(14,6)}$$

Expressions for the enthalpy and molar thermal capacities of a gaseous system follow directly from equation (14,4).

The Enthalpy

$$H = U + pV$$

and for an ideal gas $pV = RT.$

Hence $H = U + RT$, and from (14,4) it follows that

$$H - E_0^0 = RT^2 \left(\frac{\partial \log_e f}{\partial T} \right)_v + RT. \qquad \cdots \quad \text{(14,7)}$$

The Molar Thermal Capacity at Constant Volume

$$C_v = \left(\frac{\partial U}{\partial T} \right)_v = \left(\frac{\partial (U - E_0^0)}{\partial T} \right)_v$$

$$= 2RT \left(\frac{\partial \log_e f}{\partial T} \right)_v + RT^2 \frac{\partial}{\partial T} \left(\frac{\partial \log_e f}{\partial T} \right)_v.$$

This may be rearranged to give

$$C_v = -R \frac{\partial}{\partial T} \left(\frac{\partial \log_e f}{\partial \left(\frac{1}{T} \right)} \right)_v. \qquad \cdots \quad \text{(14,8)}$$

The Molar Thermal Capacity at Constant Pressure

$$C_p = C_v + R$$

Hence

$$C_p = R - R\frac{\partial}{\partial T}\left(\frac{\partial \log_e f}{\partial \left(\frac{1}{T}\right)}\right)_v \quad \dots \dots \quad (14,9)$$

The Entropy

We start with the expressions

$$S = k \log_e W \quad \dots \dots \quad (13,1)$$

and

$$W = \prod_i \frac{g_i{}^{n_i}}{n_i!}, \quad \dots \dots \quad (13,17)$$

and, as before make use of the partition function to eliminate the terms n_i. It follows from these equations that

$$\frac{S}{k} = \sum_i (n_i \log_e g_i - \log_e n_i!).$$

The Stirling Approximation formula states that

$$\log_e n_i! \simeq n_i \log_e n_i - n_i$$

so that

$$\frac{S}{k} = \sum (n_i \log_e \frac{g_i}{n_i} + n_i).$$

From (14,6) it follows that

$$\frac{n_i}{g_i} = \frac{N}{f}e^{-\beta \Delta \epsilon}$$

and

$$\log_e \frac{g_i}{n_i} = \log_e \frac{f}{N} + \beta \Delta \epsilon_i.$$

⌈At this point we pause in the main argument and prove formally that

$$\beta = \frac{1}{kT}$$

which relationship, it will be remembered, was assumed in the last chapter. From the last equation it follows that

$$\frac{S}{k} = \sum_i \left\{ n_i \left(\log_e \frac{f}{N} + \beta \Delta \epsilon_i \right) + n_i \right\}$$

so that

$$S = kN \log_e \frac{f}{N} + \beta k(U - E_0^0) + kN.$$

Hence $\qquad \left(\dfrac{\partial S}{\partial U}\right)_{v,\,T} = \beta k.$

But classical thermodynamics shows that

$$dU = TdS - pdV$$

so that $\qquad \left(\dfrac{\partial S}{\partial U}\right)_{v,\,T} = \dfrac{1}{T},$

It follows that $\qquad \beta = \dfrac{1}{kT}.$

Making use of this relationship we obtain the expression

$$S = kN \log_e \frac{f}{N} + \frac{U - E_0^0}{T} + Nk. \qquad . \quad . \quad . \quad (14,10)$$

Since $Nk = R$, it follows that (14,10) may be written

$$S = R \log_e \frac{f}{N} + \frac{U - E_0^0}{T} + R \qquad . \quad . \quad . \quad . \quad (14,11)$$

or $\qquad S = R \log_e \frac{f}{N} + RT \left(\dfrac{\partial \log_e f}{\partial T}\right)_v + R. . \quad . \quad . \quad (14,12)$

The Helmholtz Available Work Function

$$A = U - TS$$

so that $\qquad A = U - RT \log_e \dfrac{f}{N} - U + E_0^0 - RT$

i.e. $\qquad A - E_0^0 = -RT \log_e \dfrac{f}{N} - RT. \qquad . \quad . \quad . \quad . \quad (14,13)$

The Gibbs Free Energy

$$G = A + pV$$

and for one mole of ideal gas $pV = RT$

so that $\qquad G - E_0^0 = -RT \log_e \dfrac{f}{N}. \qquad . \quad . \quad . \quad (14,14)$

We repeat the most important equations so far derived in this chapter:

$$U - E_0^0 = RT^2\left(\frac{\partial \log_e f}{\partial T}\right)_v \quad \cdots \cdots \quad (14,4)$$

$$H - E_0^0 = RT^2\left(\frac{\partial \log_e f}{\partial T}\right)_v + RT \quad \cdots \cdots \quad (14,6)$$

$$C_v = -R\frac{\partial}{\partial T}\left(\frac{\partial \log_e f}{\partial\left(\frac{1}{T}\right)}\right)_v \quad \cdots \cdots \quad (14,7)$$

$$C_p = R - R\frac{\partial}{\partial T}\left(\frac{\partial \log_e f}{\partial\left(\frac{1}{T}\right)}\right)_v \quad \cdots \cdots \quad (14,8)$$

$$S = R \log_e \frac{f}{N} + \frac{U - E_0^0}{T} + R \quad \cdots \cdots \quad (14,11)$$

$$A - E_0^0 = -RT \log_e \frac{f}{N} - RT \quad \cdots \cdots \quad (14,13)$$

$$G - E_0^0 = -RT \log_e \frac{f}{N}. \quad \cdots \cdots \quad (14,14)$$

An Alternative Approach to Statistical Thermodynamics

This is probably the most convenient place to explain that the method used in this book to obtain expressions for the molar thermodynamic properties of a gas in terms of statistical quantities is not the only one possible. The method we have used depends essentially on the study of a single molecule and results, as we have seen, in equations in which the molar properties are expressed in terms of the rational partition function of the molecule itself. The alternative approach would have been to have considered not the energy levels accessible to the molecule but the *energy levels accessible to the system as a whole* and their corresponding degeneracies. We should then have constructed not the rational partition function of the molecule but the *rational partition function of the system*. This quantity is usually given the symbol Q. The expressions for the molar thermodynamic properties of the system in terms of Q are similar to, but not identical with, the expressions derived above. The most important of them are

$$U - E_0^0 = kT^2\left(\frac{\partial \log_e Q}{\partial T}\right)_v,$$

$$S = k \log_e Q + kT\left(\frac{\partial \log_e Q}{\partial T}\right)_v,$$

$$A - E_0^0 = -kT \log_e Q,$$

and $\qquad\qquad G - E_0^0 = -kT \log_e Q + RT.$

Since it can be shown that for a system of independent indistinguishable particles Q and f are connected by the equation[1]

$$Q = \frac{1}{N!} f^N$$

it is easy to see that these expressions are equivalent to those given in equations (14,4), (14,11), (14,13) and (14,14). The student should take care when consulting any reference book on this subject to find out which type of partition function is described before using any formula in which it is used.

The Evaluation of the Partition Function of a Molecule and the Molar Thermodynamic Properties of Gases at 298·15° K and 1 Atmosphere Pressure

The quantity f which appears in the equations derived above is the complete rational partition function for the independent molecule. We have already explained that so long as the translational, rotational, vibrational and electronic energies of the molecule are mutually independent, so that the total energy can be considered as the sum of four independent terms, the total partition function may be factorised according to the equation

$$f = f_{\text{trans}} \times f_{\text{rot}} \times f_{\text{vib}} \times f_{\text{elec}}.$$

We shall find it necessary to evaluate the four factors separately: two procedures are then open to us, we can either multiply them together to obtain f, or, since we always use the term $\log_e f$ rather than f itself, and since

$$\log_e f = \log_e f_{\text{trans}} + \log_e f_{\text{rot}} + \log_e f_{\text{vib}} + \log_e f_{\text{elec}} \qquad (14,15)$$

we can use each separately and evaluate separately that portion of the thermodynamic function related to the translational motion, that portion due to rotation and so on. We happen to find the latter procedure the more convenient. Therefore we expand the expressions for $U - E_0^0$ and S (the remainder are of course derivative from them) into the forms:

---

[1] The denominator $N!$ accounts for the indistinguishability of the particles concerned. If the particles were individually distinguishable the relationship between Q and f would simply be $Q = f^N$.

$$U - E_0^0 = U_{\text{trans}} + U_{\text{rot}} + U_{\text{vib}} + U_{\text{elec}} - E_0^0$$

$$= RT^2\left(\frac{\partial \log_e f_{\text{trans}}}{\partial T}\right)_v + RT^2\frac{d \log_e f_{\text{rot}}}{dT}$$

$$+ RT^2\frac{d \log_e f_{\text{vib}}}{dT} + RT^2\frac{d \log_e f_{\text{elec}}}{dT}, \quad . \quad . \quad (14,16)$$

and $\quad S = S_{\text{trans}} + S_{\text{rot}} + S_{\text{vib}} + S_{\text{elec}}$

$$= R \log_e \frac{f_{\text{trans}}}{N} + R \log_e f_{\text{rot}} + R \log_e f_{\text{vib}} + R \log_e f_{\text{elec}}$$

$$+ \frac{U - E_0^0}{T} + R. \quad . \quad . \quad . \quad . \quad . \quad . \quad (14,17)$$

The rotational, vibrational and electronic contributions are independent of volume, so where appropriate we have written complete rather than partial differentials in (14,16) and we have included the factor N in the translational term in (14,17).

We are now in a position to evaluate each term. We shall proceed by showing how the rational translational, rotational, vibrational and electronic partition functions may be evaluated for a gaseous molecule, and then select those terms which are significant in the case of monatomic, diatomic and some simple polyatomic gases.

The Evaluation of f_{trans}

The velocity of an independent particle may be resolved into three vectors C_x, C_y and C_z, parallel to three mutually perpendicular axes X, Y and Z, so that

$$C^2 = C_x^2 + C_y^2 + C_z^2.$$

The translational energy may similarly be resolved to give

$$\tfrac{1}{2}mC^2 = \tfrac{1}{2}mC_x^2 + \tfrac{1}{2}mC_y^2 + \tfrac{1}{2}mC_z^2$$

and the translational partition function may therefore similarly be factorised into three orthogonal components:

$$f_{\text{trans}} = f_x \times f_y \times f_z. \quad . \quad . \quad . \quad (14,18)$$

We consider now a particle mass m contained in a rectangular box, the length of the sides (parallel to the axes X, Y and Z) being x, y and z, and of total volume V. The component of its translational energy in direction X is ε_x, that in direction Y is ε_y, and that in direction Z is ε_z.

$$\varepsilon_x = \tfrac{1}{2}mC_x^2 = \frac{1}{2m}(mC_x)^2.$$

Modern atomic theory relates the momentum of a particle to an associated wavelength by the de Broglie relationship, which states that the product of the momentum and the wavelength equals Planck's constant.

The component of the momentum in direction X is therefore related to an associated wavelength λ by the equation

$$mC_x = \frac{h}{\lambda}.$$

When the particle is contained in a box of rigid sides, the associated wave motion must be such that its amplitude is zero at the sides, so that the distance between the sides must be an integral number of half-wavelengths,

i.e.
$$x = \frac{n\lambda}{2}$$

so that
$$mC_x = \frac{hn}{2x},$$

and
$$\varepsilon_x = \frac{1}{2m}\left(\frac{hn}{2x}\right)^2 = \frac{h^2n^2}{8mx^2}. \quad . \quad . \quad . \quad (14,19)$$

This equation means that however the particle moves within the box, the component of its translational energy along the X axis is given by the expression $\frac{h^2n^2}{8mx^2}$, where n can assume any integral number from zero to infinity. It follows that

$$f_x = \sum_{n=0}^{n=\infty} e^{-\frac{\varepsilon_x}{kT}} = \sum_{n=0}^{n=\infty} e^{-\frac{h^2n^2}{8mx^2kT}} \quad . \quad . \quad (14,20)$$

i.e.
$$f_x = \sum_{n=0}^{n=\infty} e^{-an^2}$$

where
$$a = \frac{h^2}{8mx^2kT}.$$

We now require to estimate the value of a. If we consider an atom of hydrogen ($m = 1 \cdot 6 \times 10^{-24}$ gm) contained between two walls 1 cm apart at 300° K, and insert the values of h (6·624 × 10^{-27} erg seconds) and k (1·38 × 10^{-16} erg deg^{-1}), we find that a is a dimensionless quantity of order 10^{-16}, and it is clear that a will be even smaller for other atoms or molecules in any container of reasonable size.

The first term in the expansion

$$\sum_{n=0}^{n=\infty} e^{-an^2} = e^0 + e^{-a} + e^{-4a} + e^{-9a} \ldots$$

will be unity, because it corresponds to the value $n = 0$, but because a is extremely small it follows that the second term is only infinitesimally smaller than the first, the third only infinitesimally smaller than the second and so on. The value of the summation will be given therefore by the sum of the areas of the rectangles shown on Figure 14,1, the area of the first rectangle representing the first term ($n = 0$), the area of the second representing the second term ($n = 1$) and so on. The sum of the areas of all the rectangles is extremely close to the area under the dotted

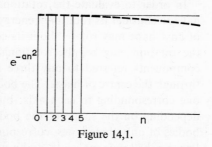

Figure 14,1.

line[1] which is given by the integral $\int_{n=0}^{n=\infty} e^{-an^2}$.

All that we have done is to show that because a is very much smaller than one, the summation

$\sum_{n=0}^{n=\infty} e^{-an^2} dn$ may be replaced by the integral $\int_{n=0}^{n=\infty} e^{-an^2} dn$.

The value of this integral is $\frac{1}{2}\left(\frac{\pi}{a}\right)^{\frac{1}{2}}$, so that we can write

$$f_x = \frac{1}{2}\left(\frac{\pi}{a}\right)^{\frac{1}{2}}$$

$$= \left(\frac{2\pi mkT}{h^2}\right)^{\frac{1}{2}} x. \qquad \ldots \ldots \quad (14,21)$$

Similar expressions can be written for f_y and f_z, so that it follows from (14,18) that the translational partition function for an independent particle in a rectangular box sides x, y and z, and of total volume V is given by the expression

$$f_{\text{trans}} = \left(\frac{2\pi mkT}{h^2}\right)^{\frac{3}{2}} x\,y\,z$$

i.e.

$$\boxed{f_{\text{trans}} = \left(\frac{2\pi mkT}{h^2}\right)^{\frac{3}{2}} V.} \qquad \ldots \ldots \quad (14,22)$$

This result is valid whatever the shape of the container. We note also that this expression applies to any gas molecule, irrespective of its atomicity.

[1] The dotted line actually falls only infinitesimally below the horizontal "full" line until n approaches the value $a^{-\frac{1}{2}}$, i.e. 10^8.

The Evaluation of f_{rot}

In order to evaluate the rotational partition function of a particle we have to consider its rotational energy, and its moments of inertia. A body of any shape may rotate about its centre of mass. However complicated the rotation may be, the rotational energy may be resolved into three components referred to any three mutually perpendicular axes passing through the centre of mass. The body will have three moments of inertia, one corresponding to each axis; but two or all three may be the same, depending on the shape of the body. It is sufficient for us to consider bodies of only three types, corresponding to a single atom, a diatomic or linear polyatomic molecule, and a non-linear polyatomic molecule.

Since almost all the mass of a single atom is concentrated in the nucleus, the rotation of a single atom corresponds fairly closely to that of a uniform sphere. The moment of inertia of a uniform sphere of mass m and radius r is the same whichever axis is considered, and is given by the equation

$$I = \tfrac{2}{5}mr^2.$$

It is of interest to evaluate this quality for an atom such as helium. The mass of the helium atom is about $6\cdot6 \times 10^{-24}$ gm and the radius of the nucleus something of the order 10^{-13} cm, so that the moment of inertia is about 3×10^{-50} gm-cm^2.

The second body we need consider is that corresponding to a diatomic or linear polyatomic molecule. We consider a linear triatomic molecule

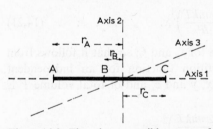

Figure 14,2. The three possible axes of rotation of a linear triatomic molecule ABC.

ABC. Rotation is possible about three axes, one passing through the line of centres, and the second and third passing through the centre of mass of the molecule but at right angles to each other. These three axes are shown in Figure 14,2. We may suppose that the three atoms of masses m_A, m_B and m_C are situated r_A, r_B and r_C from the centre of mass of the molecule.

The moment of inertia about axis 1, I_1, is obviously similar to that of the single atom described above. The moments of inertia about axes 2 and 3 are clearly equal, and are given by the equation

$$I_2 = I_3 = m_A r_A^2 + m_B r_B^2 + m_C r_C^2.$$

We can use this equation to estimate the moment of inertia of the hydrogen molecule. Since $m_A = m_B = 1\cdot66 \times 10^{-24}$ gm, and $r_A = r_B = 10^{-8}$ cm

I_2 and I_3 are about 3×10^{-40} gm-cm². We note from this that the moment of inertia of a linear molecule about an axis perpendicular to the line of centres is about 10^{10} greater than the moment of inertia of the molecule about the line of centres itself.

Figure 14,3 illustrates the rotation of a non-linear molecule DEF. It is sufficient for us to note that wherever we choose to place the three axes all *three* moments of inertia will approximate in size to the two moments of inertia of the linear molecule I_2 and I_3.

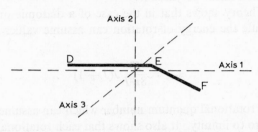

Figure 14,3. The three axes of rotation of a non-linear molecule DEF.

We summarise the results we have so far obtained:

1. The three moments of inertia of a monatomic molecule are the same, and are of the order 10^{-50} gm-cm².
2. One moment of inertia of a diatomic or linear polyatomic molecule is of the order 10^{-50} gm-cm², whereas the other two are equal and of the order 10^{-40} gm-cm².
3. All three moments of inertia of a non-linear polyatomic molecule are of the order 10^{-40} gm-cm².

As we shall show below, the energy required to set a body rotating about an axis or to excite it from one rotational energy level to a higher is inversely proportional to the moment of inertia concerned, and in fact the energy required to rotate a monatomic molecule or to rotate a diatomic or linear polyatomic molecule about an axis passing through the line of centres (corresponding to a moment of inertia about 10^{-50} gm-cm²) proves to be something of the order 10^{-5} erg, while that required to rotate a diatomic or polyatomic molecule about an axis corresponding to a moment of inertia of about 10^{-40} gm-cm² is only of the order 10^{-15} erg. We have not yet calculated the average translational energy of a molecule at temperature T, but when we do we shall find it of the order kT, which at $300°$ K is about 4×10^{-14} erg. This figure represents the sort of energy which we could reasonably expect one molecule to acquire from another as the result of intermolecular collisions. We see therefore that while we could expect rotation of a diatomic or polyatomic molecule to occur about an axis corresponding to a moment of inertia of about 10^{-40} gm-cm^2, it is extremely unlikely that rotation would occur at all in the case of a monatomic molecule or of a diatomic or linear polyatomic molecule about the axis passing through the line of centres. In other words, we need never consider the rotation of a monatomic molecule,[1] but must take into account rotation about two axes in the case of a diatomic or linear polyatomic molecule, and rotation about three axes in the case of a non-linear polyatomic.

Quantum Theory shows that in the case of a diatomic or linear polyatomic molecule the energy of rotation can assume values given by the equation

$$\varepsilon_{rot} = \frac{h^2}{8\pi^2 I} J(J+1) \quad . \quad . \quad . \quad . \quad (14,23)$$

where J is the rotational quantum number which can assume any integral value from zero to infinity. It also shows that each rotational energy level is $(2J+1)$fold-degenerate.

It follows that the rotational partition function for such molecules is given by the equation

$$f_{rot} = \sum_{J=0}^{J=\infty} (2J+1)e^{-\frac{h^2 J(J+1)}{8\pi^2 I k T}} . \quad . \quad . \quad . \quad (14,24)$$

There remains one small correction to make. If a diatomic molecule is homonuclear (i.e. if its two constituent atoms are identical) or if a linear polyatomic molecule is symmetrical (like $O = C = O$), so that the two ends of the molecule are indistinguishable, two otherwise distinct orientations are indistinguishable: this has the effect of dividing the number of possible micro-states by two. We account for this by including a term σ in our expression for the rotational partition function; σ is called the *symmetry factor* of the molecule and has the value unity for a heteronuclear diatomic molecule or for an unsymmetrical linear polyatomic, but the value two for a homonuclear diatomic or symmetrical linear polyatomic.

The final expression for the rotational partition function is therefore

$$f_{rot} = \sum_{J=0}^{J=\infty} \frac{2J+1}{\sigma} e^{-\frac{h^2 J(J+1)}{8\pi^2 I k T}} . \quad . \quad . \quad . \quad (14,25)$$

---

[1] This is, of course, the basis of the statement made earlier in this book that the rotational energy of a monatomic gas is zero: we see that this statement is true because the smallest quantity of rotational energy it could possess other than zero is so large that it is highly improbable that the atom could ever acquire it.

For temperatures at which the rotational quanta are very much smaller than kT it is permissible to replace this summation by an integral,[1] and to write

$$f_{rot} = \int_0^\infty \frac{2J+1}{\sigma} e^{-\frac{h^2}{8\pi^2 I k T} J(J+1)} dJ. \quad \ldots \quad (14,26)$$

Further, the high quantum numbers will make the greatest contribution to the integral, so that we can neglect the figure 1 in comparison with J and write

$$f_{rot} \simeq \int_0^\infty \frac{2J}{\sigma} e^{-\frac{h^2}{8\pi^2 I k T} J^2} dJ \quad \ldots \quad (14,27)$$

or

$$f_{rot} \simeq \int_0^\infty \frac{2J}{\sigma} e^{-aJ^2} dJ$$

where

$$a = \frac{h^2}{8\pi^2 I k T}.$$

$$\int_0^\infty J e^{-aJ^2} dJ = \frac{1}{2a}$$

so that for temperatures at which the rotational quanta are very much smaller than kT

$$\boxed{f_{rot} \simeq \frac{8\pi^2 I k T}{\sigma h^2}} \quad \ldots \quad (14,28)$$

A similar argument leads to the following expression for the rotational partition function for a non-linear polyatomic molecule:

$$f_{rot} \simeq \frac{8\pi^2 (8\pi^3 I_1 I_2 I_3)^{\frac{1}{2}}}{h^3} (kT) \quad \ldots \quad (14,29)$$

where I_1, I_2 and I_3 are the three principal moments of inertia about any three mutually perpendicular axes.

The Characteristic Temperature of Rotation

We have seen that the rotational energy of a diatomic molecule can assume values given by (14,23)

$$\varepsilon_{rot} = \frac{h^2}{8\pi^2 I} J(J+1).$$

[1] The argument is similar to that given on page 275.

Clearly the energy required to excite a molecule from J to $J + 1$ is

$$\frac{h^2}{8\pi^2 I}\{(J + 1)(J + 2) - J(J + 1)\}$$

i.e.
$$\frac{h^2}{8\pi^2 I}2(J + 1).$$

The smallest energy quantum involved is that required to excite the molecule from the ground state $J = 0$ (in which the molecule is not rotating) to $J = 1$, and this is

$$\frac{h^2}{4\pi^2 I}.$$

We also know that the quantity of energy acquired by a molecule as the result of intermolecular collisions rarely exceeds kT. The temperature T^1 at which

$$kT^1 = \frac{h^2}{4\pi^2 I} \qquad . \quad . \quad . \quad . \quad . \quad (14,30)$$

is called the *characteristic temperature of rotation* of the molecule. Below this temperature rotation of any sort is unlikely. For the hydrogen molecule it is about $170° K$, and for all other molecules much less. The effect of this on such properties as the molar thermal capacity of a gas will be mentioned later.

The Evaluation of f_{vib}

To a first approximation a diatomic molecule may be treated as an harmonic oscillator, for which the vibrational energy takes the form

$$\varepsilon_{vib} = (v + \tfrac{1}{2})hc\omega \qquad . \quad . \quad . \quad . \quad (14,31)$$

where ω is the reciprocal wavelength expressed in cm^{-1}, c is the velocity of light in cm per second, and v is the vibrational quantum number which can assume any value from zero to infinity. At very low temperatures the value of v is zero, but even at absolute zero the molecule vibrates with energy $\tfrac{1}{2}hc\omega$ erg or $\tfrac{1}{2}Nhc\omega$ erg mole^{-1}. At some higher temperature a quantum of energy $hc\omega$ is absorbed; at some higher temperature still a second quantum is absorbed, and so on.

The value of the zero point energy $\tfrac{1}{2}Nhc\omega$ erg mole^{-1} is not, in fact, of any importance as far as we are concerned, because it is included in the quantity E_o^0 which has appeared in our expressions for U, H, A and G, so that the energy levels which we need consider in order to evaluate the rational vibrational partition function and so calculate $U - E_o^0$ and so on are merely 0, $hc\omega$, $2hc\omega$ . . . and so on.

The vibrational energy levels are in fact non-degenerate so we can write

$$f_{vib} = e^0 + e^{-\frac{hc\omega}{kT}} + e^{-\frac{2hc\omega}{kT}} \ldots$$

i.e.
$$\boxed{f_{vib} = \frac{1}{1 - e^{-\frac{hc\omega}{kT}}}.} \qquad \ldots \ldots \quad (14,32)$$

For the nitrogen molecule the quantity $hc\omega$ proves to be about 48×10^{-14} erg, i.e. about twelve times greater than the quantity kT at $300°$ K. Clearly, in this case intermolecular collisions at this temperature are most unlikely to produce energy quanta large enough to raise the molecule from the ground to the first excited vibrational state. In fact, kT becomes equal to $hc\omega$ only at about $3600°$ K; we might expect, therefore, that it would be unlikely that the molecule be found in anything but the ground vibrational level at any temperature lower than this.

From (14,32) it follows that at all temperatures at which $kT \ll hc\omega$, the value of the vibrational partition function is very close to one. Whether or not for any particular molecule f_{vib} departs appreciably from unity at the temperature in which we are interested is, in fact, most conveniently decided by evaluating its so-called "characteristic temperature of vibration". This is the temperature T' at which

$$kT' = hc\omega.$$

For oxygen $\qquad\qquad T' = 2270°$ K

for carbon monoxide $\qquad T' = 3120°$ K

and for HCl $\qquad\qquad T' = 4300°$ K

As long as T' is very much greater than $300°$ K it is clear that no account need be taken of molecular vibrations in evaluating the standard thermodynamic properties of the gases concerned.

The Evaluation of f_{elec}

For simplicity we will consider first the hydrogen atom. The electron therein can occupy any one of a series of energy levels $\varepsilon_0, \varepsilon_1, \varepsilon_2, \ldots$, the ground state ε_0 being 2-fold degenerate, because the electron can possess either clockwise or anti-clockwise spin, the first excited state ε_1 being 8-fold degenerate, the second being 18-fold degenerate and so on. The absolute electronic partition function is therefore given by the equation

$$f_{elec(abs)} = 2e^{-\frac{\varepsilon_0}{kT}} + 8e^{-\frac{\varepsilon_1}{kT}} + 18e^{-\frac{\varepsilon_2}{kT}} \ldots \quad \ldots \quad (14,33)$$

As has been explained earlier, there is no way whatsoever of assigning absolute values to the energy levels ε_0, ε_1, ε_2, . . ., but the difference between any two levels can be calculated from Quantum Theory or determined experimentally from atomic spectra.

The student will remember that according to the Bohr Theory of the hydrogen atom, the energy of the electron *relative to its energy an infinite distance from the nucleus* is given by the expression

$$\varepsilon_{n-1} = -\frac{2\pi^2 e^4 m}{h^2 n^2} \quad . \quad . \quad . \quad . \quad . \quad (14,34)$$

where e and m are the values of the electronic charge and mass: so that when the electron is in the ground state its relative energy is -218×10^{-13} erg, when in the first excited state it is -54×10^{-13} erg, when in the second excited state it is -24×10^{-13} erg and so on. It follows that

$$\Delta\varepsilon_1 = \varepsilon_1 - \varepsilon_0 = +164 \times 10^{-13} \text{ erg,}$$

and $\qquad\qquad \Delta\varepsilon_2 = \varepsilon_2 - \varepsilon_0 = +194 \times 10^{-13} \text{ erg,}$

which values are precisely those obtained from measurements of atomic spectra. The rational electronic partition function of the hydrogen atom is therefore given by the expression

$$f_{\text{elec}} = 2e^0 + 8e^{-\frac{164 \times 10^{-13}}{kT}} + 18e^{-\frac{194 \times 10^{-13}}{kT}} \ldots \quad (14,35)$$

At 25° C (298·15° K) the value of kT is $1·38 \times 10^{-16} \times 298·15$ erg, i.e. about $0·4 \times 10^{-13}$ erg, so that it is clear that the values of the second and later terms are completely negligible compared with the first. In other words, the chance of a hydrogen atom existing in any excited state at 25° C is extremely small. It is suggested that the student evaluates the second and third terms at higher temperatures. He will find that their values become appreciable only above 20,000° K. We confidently assign therefore the value 2 to the rational electronic partition function for the hydrogen atom at all temperatures at which we are likely to require it.

We now consider monatomic gases other than atomic hydrogen. The problem resolves into two questions. What are the degeneracies of each energy level, and to what extent can we afford to neglect all energy levels except that of the ground state? A full discussion of these questions is out of place in this book; all that it is possible to do here is to discuss certain simple cases and to indicate the result.

It will be remembered that the figure 2 first arose in the expression for the electronic partition function for the hydrogen atom because the hydrogen atom ground state is 2-fold degenerate, the electron can have clockwise or anti-clockwise spin. The same fact applies to the ground state of those metals containing in the ground state one electron only in their outermost orbitals; such metals include Li, Na, K, Rb, Cs, Cu, Ag and Au. In these cases also, the energy required to excite the electron to a higher energy level is so great compared with kT that their contribution to the value f_{elec} is negligible at moderate values of T. The value of f_{elec} for these atoms is therefore 2.

We now consider the inert gases. When the atom of any one is in the ground state each electronic energy level is completely full; the ground state is therefore non-degenerate. Again, the energy required to excite an electron to a higher level is so great compared with kT that none but the ground state need be considered. f_{elec} therefore assumes the value 1.

The alkaline earth metals and Zn, Cd and Hg contain two electrons in their outermost orbitals in the ground state. These electrons are both in the s state, and since the energy required to excite them to the p state or higher is so great, no degeneracy is possible at moderate temperatures. The value of f_{elec} for these elements is therefore, as in the case of the inert gases, 1.

The energies necessary to excite a normal covalent molecule are usually very much greater even than those required to excite a hydrogen atom, so that the chance that the molecule exists in anything but ground state at any but the most elevated temperatures is so small as to be virtually impossible. Since all but the ground state of the molecule is uninhabited, and since we may, as we have done before, assign zero electronic energy to the ground state, the electronic partition function is given by the expression

$$f_{elec} = ge^0 = g. \qquad \ldots \ldots \quad (14,36)$$

In most covalent molecules each electronic energy level is completely full, so that no degeneracy is possible. In most cases, therefore, the value of f_{elec} is 1. (The only exceptions among common stable diatomic molecules are oxygen and nitric oxide: the former being 3-fold degenerate and the latter 4-fold: the electronic contribution to the thermodynamic properties of these gases is therefore significant.)

We are now in a position to calculate the molar thermodynamic properties of gases from the values of the various rational partition functions for the molecule.

A Monatomic Gas

We have seen that in the case of a monatomic gas only translational and electronic energies are significant. It therefore follows that equation (14,16) may be simplified to give

$$U - E_0^0 = U_{\text{trans}} + U_{\text{elec}} - E_0^0$$

$$= RT^2\left(\frac{\partial \log_e f_{\text{trans}}}{\partial T}\right)_v + RT^2\frac{d \log_e f_{\text{elec}}}{dT}. \quad (14,37)$$

From (14,22)

$$\log_e f_{\text{trans}} = \frac{3}{2}\log_e T + \log_e\left\{\frac{(2\pi mk)^{\frac{3}{2}}}{h^3}V\right\} \quad . \quad . \quad (14,38)$$

so that

$$\left(\frac{\partial \log_e f_{\text{trans}}}{\partial T}\right)_v = \frac{3}{2T}. \quad . \quad . \quad . \quad . \quad (14,39)$$

We have seen that for all common monatomic gases f_{elec} is either one or two, so that

$$\frac{d \log_e f_{\text{elec}}}{dT} = 0. \quad . \quad . \quad . \quad . \quad . \quad (14,40)$$

Hence

$$U - E_0^0 = \frac{3}{2}RT, \quad . \quad . \quad . \quad . \quad . \quad (14,41)^1$$

$$H - E_0^0 = U - E_0^0 + RT$$

$$= \frac{5}{2}RT, \quad . \quad . \quad . \quad . \quad . \quad (14,42)$$

$$C_v = \left(\frac{\partial U}{\partial T}\right)_v = \frac{3}{2}R, \quad . \quad . \quad . \quad (14,43)$$

and

$$C_p = C_v + R = \frac{5}{2}R. \quad . \quad . \quad . \quad (14,44)$$

Equation (14,17) simplifies to

$$S = S_{\text{trans}} + S_{\text{elec}}$$

$$= R \log_e\frac{f_{\text{trans}}}{N} + R \log_e f_{\text{elec}} + \frac{U - E_0^0}{T} + R. \quad (14,45)$$

We make use of (14,38) and (14,41) and obtain

$$S = \frac{3}{2}R \log_e T + R \log_e\left\{\frac{(2\pi mk)^{\frac{3}{2}}V}{Nh^3}\right\} + \frac{5}{2}R + R \log_e f_{\text{elec}}. \quad (14,46)$$

Remembering that $\frac{3}{2}R = C_v$

[1] Hence the average translational energy per molecule is $\frac{3}{2}kT$.

we may write

$$S = C_v \log_e T + R \log_e V + R \log_e \left\{ \frac{(2\pi mk)^{\frac{3}{2}}}{Nh^3} \right\}$$
$$+ \tfrac{5}{2}R + R \log_e f_{\text{elec}}. \quad (14,47)$$

It is of interest to refer to equation (8,9)

$$dS = \frac{C_v dT}{T} + R \frac{dV}{V}$$

the general integral of which is

$$S = C_v \log_e T + R \log_e V + I,$$

where I is the integration constant. It is clear that this constant equals the last three terms in (14,47).

We usually find it more convenient to express the entropy of a gas in terms of its pressure rather than its volume. We can do this by substituting $\frac{NkT}{p}$ for V in (14,46) and also substitute $\frac{M}{N}$ for m, where M is the molecular weight. This gives

$$S = \frac{5}{2}R \log_e T - R \log_e p + \frac{3}{2}R \log_e M + R \log_e \frac{(2\pi)^{\frac{3}{2}}k^{\frac{5}{2}}}{N^{\frac{3}{2}}h^3}$$
$$+ R \log_e f_{\text{elec}} + \tfrac{5}{2}R. \quad (14,48)$$

The fourth and sixth terms contain only universal constants and can be evaluated. If the pressure is expressed in dynes-cm^{-2}, the value of k which must be used in $1\cdot3804 \times 10^{-16}$ erg deg^{-1}. Using the following values of the remaining constants:

$$R = 1\cdot987 \text{ cal deg}^{-1}$$
$$h = 6\cdot625 \times 10^{-27} \text{ erg seconds}$$
$$N = 6\cdot025 \times 10^{23}$$
$$\pi = 3\cdot142$$

these terms amount to $25\cdot165$ cal deg^{-1}, so that we may write

$$S = \tfrac{5}{2}R \log_e T - R \log_e p + \tfrac{3}{2}R \log_e M + 25\cdot165 + R \log_e f_{\text{elec}}. \quad (14,49)$$

If the pressure is expressed in atmospheres we must subtract $R \log_e (1\cdot013 \times 10^6)$ from the right-hand side to obtain

$$S = \tfrac{5}{2}R \log_e T - R \log_e p + \tfrac{3}{2}R \log_e M - 2\cdot316 + R \log_e f_{\text{elec}}. \quad (14,50)$$

The "standard" molar entropy of a monatomic gas at $298 \cdot 15°$ K and 1 atmosphere pressure is therefore given by the equation

$$S = \tfrac{3}{2}R \log_e M + 25 \cdot 990 + R \log_e f_{\text{elec}}. \quad . \quad . \quad (14,51)$$

For those gases for which f_{elec} is unity, $R \log_e f_{\text{elec}}$ is zero, and for those for which f_{elec} is two, $R \log_e f_{\text{elec}}$ is $1 \cdot 38$ cal deg^{-1}. The student should verify that for those elements for which f_{elec} is 1,

$$A - E_0^0 = 5 \cdot 296T - \tfrac{5}{2}RT \log_e T + RT \log_e p - \tfrac{3}{2}RT \log_e M \quad (14,52)$$

and

$$G - E_0^0 = 7 \cdot 283T - \tfrac{5}{2}RT \log_e T + RT \log_e p - \tfrac{3}{2}RT \log_e M \quad (14,53)$$

and that for those elements for which $f_{\text{elec}} = 2$,

$$A - E_0^0 = 3 \cdot 916T - \tfrac{5}{2}RT \log_e T + RT \log_e p - \tfrac{3}{2}RT \log_e M \quad (14,54)$$

and

$$G - E_0^0 = 5 \cdot 903T - \tfrac{5}{2}RT \log_e T + RT \log_e p - \tfrac{3}{2}RT \log_e M. \quad (14,55)$$

A Diatomic Gas

From (14,16)

$$U - E_0^0 = U_{\text{trans}} + U_{\text{rot}} + U_{\text{vib}} + U_{\text{elec}} - E_0^0$$

$$= RT^2 \left(\frac{\partial \log_e f_{\text{trans}}}{\partial T} \right)_v + RT^2 \frac{d \log_e f_{\text{rot}}}{dT} + RT^2 \frac{d \log_e f_{\text{vib}}}{dT}$$

$$+ RT^2 \frac{d \log_e f_{\text{elec}}}{dT}.$$

The translational contribution is the same as that for a monatomic gas, i.e. $\tfrac{3}{2}RT$.

From (14,28)

$$f_{\text{rot}} \simeq \frac{8\pi^2 I k T}{\sigma h^2}$$

so that

$$\log_e f_{\text{rot}} \simeq \log_e T + \log_e \frac{8\pi^2 I k}{\sigma h^2} \quad . \quad . \quad . \quad . \quad (14,56)$$

and

$$\frac{d \log_e f_{\text{rot}}}{dT} = \frac{1}{T}. \quad . \quad . \quad . \quad . \quad . \quad (14,57)$$

To a first approximation

$$f_{\text{vib}} = \frac{1}{1 - e^{-\frac{hc\omega}{kT}}} \quad . \quad . \quad . \quad . \quad (14,32)$$

and at temperatures less than the characteristic temperature of vibration, i.e. when $hc\omega \ggg kT$; f_{vib} will not differ significantly from unity, and

$$\frac{d\log_e f_{vib}}{dT} = 0. \quad . \quad . \quad . \quad . \quad . \quad (14,58)$$

We know also that

$$\frac{d\log_e f_{elec}}{dT} = 0. \quad . \quad . \quad . \quad . \quad (14,59)$$

It follows that

$$U - E_o^0 = \tfrac{3}{2}RT + RT = \tfrac{5}{2}RT, \quad . \quad . \quad . \quad (14,60)$$

$$H - E_o^0 = \tfrac{7}{2}RT, \quad . \quad . \quad . \quad . \quad . \quad (14,61)$$

$$C_v = \left(\frac{\partial U}{\partial T}\right)_v = \frac{5}{2}R, \quad . \quad . \quad . \quad . \quad (14,62)$$

and

$$C_p = C_v + R = \tfrac{7}{2}R. \quad . \quad . \quad . \quad . \quad (14,63)$$

The student is here reminded that below the characteristic temperature of rotation, the rotational contribution to the energy of a molecule becomes insignificant. Above this temperature we expect the value of C_v, for example, to be $\frac{5}{2}R$ for a diatomic gas, but below this temperature we expect it to become $\frac{3}{2}R$. The only case in which the characteristic temperature of rotation is sufficiently high for the change in C_v or C_p to be actually observed is that of hydrogen; and it has been found experimentally that the value of C_v does indeed change from the value $\frac{5}{2}R$ to $\frac{3}{2}R$ as the temperature falls below the characteristic temperature of rotation.

Expressions for the molar entropy of a diatomic gas can be derived from (14,17)

$$S = R \log_e \frac{f_{trans}}{N} + R \log_e f_{rot} + R \log_e f_{vib} + R \log_e f_{elec}$$
$$+ \frac{U - E_o^0}{T} + R.$$

For those gases for which we may assume $f_{vib} = 1$, it follows from (14,22) and (14,28) that

$$S = R \log_e \left\{ \frac{(2\pi mkT)^{\frac{3}{2}}V}{Nh^3} \right\} + R \log_e \frac{8\pi^2 IkT}{\sigma h^2} + R \log_e f_{elec} + \frac{5}{2}R + R.$$

Substituting $\dfrac{NkT}{p}$ for V and $\dfrac{M}{N}$ for m, and expressing p in atmospheres, we obtain the equation

$$S = \tfrac{7}{2}R \log_e T - R \log_e p + \tfrac{3}{2}R \log_e M + R \log_e I - R \log_e \sigma$$
$$+ R \log_e f_{elec} + 175\cdot35, \quad (14,64)$$

and at $298 \cdot 15°$ K and 1 atmosphere pressure we obtain for the standard molar entropy the expression

$$S = \tfrac{3}{2}R \log_e M + R \log_e I - R \log_e \sigma + R \log_e f_{\text{elec}} + 214 \cdot 97. \quad (14,65)$$

As explained before, the symmetry factor σ is one for a heteronuclear molecule and two for a homonuclear. The value $R \log_e f_{\text{elec}}$ is zero for all common stable diatomic molecules except oxygen, for which $f_{\text{elec}} = 3$, and nitric oxide for which $f_{\text{elec}} = 4$.

Review of Results

We are now in a position to test the whole theory of Statistical Thermodynamics by comparing the values of the thermodynamic properties predicted with those obtained by direct measurement. In so doing we note that explicit expressions have been obtained only for the properties of monatomic and diatomic gases at "moderate" temperatures.

We first examine the principal molar thermal capacities. Statistical theory predicts the values $C_v = \tfrac{3}{2}R$, and $C_p = \tfrac{5}{2}R$ for a monatomic gas and the values $C_v = \tfrac{5}{2}R$, and $C_p = \tfrac{7}{2}R$ for a diatomic gas. These values are of course precisely those established by experiment. It must, however, be pointed out that this agreement is encouraging rather than conclusive, and provides evidence for the general correctness of the *form* of the equations concerned rather than for the accuracy of their detailed content. This statement requires amplification.

The predicted values of C_v and C_p derive essentially from the equations

$$U - E_0^0 = RT^2 \left\{ \frac{\partial \log_e f_{\text{trans}}}{\partial T} \right\}_v + RT^2 \frac{d \log_e f_{\text{rot}}}{dT} \cdots , \cdot \quad (14,16)$$

$$f_{\text{trans}} = \left(\frac{2\pi mkT}{h^2} \right)^{\frac{3}{2}} V, \quad \cdot \quad \cdot \quad \cdot \quad \cdot \quad \cdot \quad \cdot \quad \cdot \quad (14,22)$$

and in the case of a diatomic gas from the equation

$$f_{\text{rot}} = \frac{8\pi^2 IkT}{\sigma h^2}. \quad \cdot \quad \cdot \quad \cdot \quad \cdot \quad \cdot \quad (14,28)$$

Because of the mathematical *form* of equation (14,16), the correct value for $U - E_0^0$ and hence for C_v and C_p requires only that the expression for f_{trans} contains a term $T^{\frac{3}{2}}$ and that f_{rot} is proportional to T. In other words, the accuracy of the other terms in the expressions for f_{trans} and f_{rot} are not tested at all.

A test of quite a different sort is obtained by the comparison of the predicted entropy values of a gas with those obtained by direct calori-

metric measurements, simply because, as will be seen from equation
(14,17) the expression for S contains such terms as $R \log_e \dfrac{f_{\text{trans}}}{N}$, $R \log_e f_{\text{rot}}$
and so on. Agreement here provides evidence not only for the correctness
of the general form of the equations but for their detailed content. Table
14,I provides the values of the molecular weights of various monatomic
and diatomic gases, the moments of inertia of the latter and the values of
the standard molar entropies at 298·15° K and 1 atmosphere pressure,
calculated according to the statistical formulae derived above; the
references a, b and c denoting the equations used in the calculation. The
value S_{cal} given in the last column is the experimental value obtained as
described in Chapter 8 from measurements of specific heats, latent heats
and so on, and including a necessary correction for deviations from ideal
behaviour.

TABLE 14,I

		M	$I \times 10^{40}$ gm-cm^2	S_{stat}	S_{cal}
He	a	4·00	—	30·13	30·4
Ne	a	20·18	—	34·95	35·0
Ar	a	39·94	—	36·98	36·8
HCl	b	36·47	2·765	44·64	44·5
HBr	b	80·92	3·35	47·48	47·6
N$_2$	b	28·02	13·8	45·78	45·9
O$_2$	c	32·00	19·34	49·03	49·1

Results marked a were calculated from equation (14,51); results marked b were
calculated from equation (14,65); result marked c was calculated from equation (14,65),
but includes a term $R \log_e 3$ on account of the electronic degeneracy of the oxygen
molecule.

The agreement between the figures given in the fifth and sixth columns
is remarkable, particularly when one considers the diversity of methods
used to obtain them. Those in the fifth column were obtained by *counting*
the number of micro-states accessible to an assembly of N molecules of
gas at 25° C due to temperature dependent factors, and requires no
knowledge of the behaviour of the assembly under any other condition,
and those in the sixth were obtained from thermal measurements which
require no knowledge of the intimate structure of the material in any
state. The agreement between these figures makes it clear that in considering only translational, rotational, vibrational and electronic energies in
the calculation of the statistical results we have included all factors which
contribute to the increase in entropy of these gases from absolute zero to
25° C. Had some factor been neglected, the value of S_{stat} would have
been smaller than that of S_{cal}. *Such a result as this is never found.*

We are now in a position to consider again the conventions on which the quantities S_{cal} and S_{stat} are based. As has been explained in earlier sections, neither value is an absolute one. The value S_{cal}^{298} equals $\sum \frac{q}{T}$ between $0°$ K and $25°$ C, and is based on the conventional assignment of the value $S^0 = 0$ to all perfect crystalline bodies, whereas the value S_{stat}^{298} is really $k \log_e W^T$, where W^T is the ratio of the *true* W value of the system at $25°$ C and the *true* value W^0 at absolute zero, so that S_{stat}^{298} is the value of the entropy at $25°$ C relative to the conventional value $S^0 = 0$ *for all substances*. These conventions are not necessarily the same, but it is clear that they are the same for the substances listed in Table 14,I. In other words, the substances listed in Table 14,I would at absolute zero exhibit the properties of perfect crystalline bodies required by the Third Law. It follows that agreement between S_{stat} and S_{cal} would not be expected in the case of those substances which form amorphous solids, imperfect crystals or supercooled liquids as absolute zero is approached. In such cases it would be expected that S_{stat}^{298} is greater than S_{cal}^{298}.

Such a result is obtained in the case of carbon monoxide, nitrous oxide, water vapour and hydrogen, for which substances the values of S_{stat} and S_{cal} at $25°$ C are given in Table 14,II.

TABLE 14,II.

(Values in cal deg^{-1} mole^{-1}.)

	S_{stat}	S_{cal}	$S_{stat} - S_{cal}$
CO	47·30	46·2	1·1
N$_2$O	52·58	51·4	1·18
H$_2$O$_{(g)}$	45·11	44·3	0·81
H$_2$	31·21	29·7	1·51

The reason for the difference must be sought. The explanation in the case of carbon monoxide is particularly simple. The sizes of the carbon and oxygen atoms are sufficiently close that energetically a "mixed" crystal in which some CO molecules face right and some face left is just as likely as one in which all the molecules face right or all face left. One crystal might contain molecules arranged

CO CO OC OC CO
CO OC CO OC OC
.   .   .   .   .
.   .   .   .   .
.   .   .   .   .

and another

$$
\begin{array}{ccccc}
\text{CO} & \text{CO} & \text{CO} & \text{CO} & \text{CO} \\
\text{CO} & \text{CO} & \text{CO} & \text{CO} & \text{CO} \\
\end{array}
$$

Each molecule can therefore assume two possible positions. The number of possible micro-states accessible to a system containing N such molecules is therefore 2^N, and the entropy corresponding to this equals

$$k \log_e 2^N = R \log_e 2$$

i.e. $1 \cdot 38$ cal deg^{-1} mole^{-1}.

The fact that the actual difference between the statistical and calorimetric value is $1 \cdot 1$ suggests that the distribution within the crystal is ordered to some degree.

The explanation in the case of nitrous oxide is precisely the same. The molecule is linear, some molecules face right $N\equiv N\!=\!O$, and some face left, $O\!=\!N\equiv N$.

The explanation in the case of ice is rather more complicated. A structure which explains the entropy difference was proposed by Pauling;[1] it leads to a term $k \log_e (\frac{3}{2})^N$, i.e. $0 \cdot 806$ cal deg^{-1} mole^{-1}, in close agreement with the experimental difference $0 \cdot 81$.

The entropy difference in the case of hydrogen is due to the *ortho–para* effect and will not be discussed here.

It is of considerable interest that differences of the same order as those discussed above are found between the statistical and calorimetric values of the entropy of organic molecules such as methyl alcohol ($1 \cdot 75$), ethane ($1 \cdot 55$), ethyl alcohol ($3 \cdot 2$) and so on. The statistical value is calculated on the assumption that free internal rotation of one part of the molecule with respect to the other is possible about any single bond. This assumption is apparently incorrect. If rotation is restricted, the number of micro-states accessible to the system will be decreased. In other words, we would find that the value S_{stat}^{298} calculated on the assumption of free rotation is too high.

We must now discuss the values of S^{298} which must be used in calculations based on the Third Law. The use of the Third Law in calculations such as those described in Chapter 12, requires that the entropies of the substances concerned are the same at absolute zero. This is presumably

[1] L. Pauling, *J. Amer. Chem. Soc.*, 1935, **57**, 2680.

true for those substances listed in Table 14,I, and for all others for which S_{stat} and S_{cal} are the same within the limits of experimental error, and it is obviously immaterial which value is used.[1] The value S_{cal} cannot, however, be used for substances such as carbon monoxide, because our earlier argument would suggest that for such reactions as

$$CO + \tfrac{1}{2}O_2 \longrightarrow CO_2$$

ΔS^0 is $-1 \cdot 1$ rather than zero, but it is clear that if S_{stat} is used instead, the discrepancy disappears. The same applies to nitrous oxide, water and hydrogen. The reverse is true in the case of organic molecules such as methyl and ethyl alcohols and ethane. Since it is suggested that the statistical value is too high because of the unwarranted assumption of free internal rotation, it would follow that values of S_{cal} should be used.

Statistical Thermodynamic Data Available in the Literature

In recent years a great deal of information has become available as the result of spectrographic measurements and their interpretation by the statistical methods discussed. The volume SELECTED VALUES OF PRO-PERTIES OF HYDROCARBONS AND RELATED COMPOUNDS published by the National Bureau of Standards in Circular C461 is typical of those publications in which this information is given. This particular volume contains data from absolute zero to 1500° K in respect of nitrogen, hydrogen, water, carbon, carbon monoxide, carbon dioxide and the hydrocarbons. In all cases except carbon the values presented are those for an ideal gas at 1 atmosphere pressure. Values are given for

the RELATIVE ENTHALPY FUNCTION $\dfrac{H_0 - E_0^0}{T}$

the FREE ENERGY FUNCTION $-\dfrac{G_0 - E_0^0}{T}$

and the ENTROPY $\qquad S_{stat}$

together with values of the standard enthalpy of formation ΔH_{0_f}, the standard free energy of formation ΔG_{0_f}, and the logarithm of the equilibrium constant for formation $\log_{10} K_f$, and such information as heats of combustion, and enthalpies, entropies and free energies of evaporation at 25° C. Specimens of the data provided are shown in Table 14,III.

We have not previously mentioned the relative enthalpy function and the free energy function. The reason why these quantities are listed

---

[1] Because of the experimental difficulties in the determination of S_{cal}, the value of S_{stat} is probably the more accurate.

rather than the functions $H_0 - E_0^0$ and $G_0 - E_0^0$ is that they are the more convenient functions to tabulate over a large temperature range. The reason for this will be clear by inspecting an equation such as (14,53)

TABLE 14,III

Temperature	298·15° K	600° K	1000° K	1500° K
$\dfrac{H_0 - E_0^0}{T}$ cal deg^{-1} mole^{-1}				
H_2	6·7877	6·8810	6·9658	7·1295
H_2O	7·934	8·122	8·580	9·251
CO	6·9514	7·0159	7·2565	7·5725
CO_2	7·5064	8·8707	10·222	11·336
C_2H_2	8·021	10·212	12·090	13·694
C_6H_6	11·41	20·48	30·16	38·24
$-\dfrac{G_0 - E_0^0}{T}$ cal deg^{-1} mole^{-1}				
H_2	24·423	29·203	32·738	35·590
H_2O	37·172	42·768	47·018	50·622
CO	40·350	45·222	48·860	51·864
CO_2	43·555	49·239	54·109	58·481
C_2H_2	39·976	46·313	52·005	57·231
C_6H_6	52·93	63·70	76·57	90·45
S_0 cal deg^{-1} mole^{-1}				
H_2	31·211	36·084	39·704	42·720
H_2O	45·106	50·890	55·598	59·873
CO	47·301	52·238	56·116	59·436
CO_2	51·061	58·110	64·331	69·817
C_2H_2	47·997	56·525	64·095	70·925
C_6H_6	64·46	84·17	106·73	128·68
ΔH_{0f} kcal mole^{-1}				
H_2	0	0	0	0
H_2O	−57·7979	−58·499	−59·239	−59·811
CO	−26·4157	−26·330	−26·768	−27·545
CO_2	−94·0518	−94·123	−94·318	−94·555
C_2H_2	19·820	16·711	14·818	14·39
C_6H_6	54·194	53·931	53·304	52·548
ΔG_{0f} kcal mole^{-1}				
H_2	0	0	0	0
H_2O	−54·6351	−51·154	−46·036	−39·296
CO	−32·8079	−39·358	−47·942	−58·370
CO_2	−94·2598	−94·444	−94·610	−94·707
C_2H_2	50·000	45·835	40·604	34·410
C_6H_6	30·989	43·663	62·270	86·11
$\log_{10} K_f$				
H_2	—	—	—	—
H_2O	40·047	18·632	10·061	5·725
CO	24·048	14·336	10·478	8·504
CO_2	69·091	34·401	20·677	13·799
C_2H_2	−36·649	−16·695	−8·874	−5·013
C_6H_6	−22·714	−15·904	−13·609	−12·546

L

which holds for a monatomic gas, when it will be seen that the value of function $-\dfrac{G - E_0^0}{T}$ is not very sensitive to changes in temperature, so that its value can be tabulated at fairly large temperature intervals, and its value at intermediate temperatures obtained by graphical interpolation without undue inaccuracy.

We illustrate the use of these data by calculating by various means the free energy change at 600° K for the reaction

$$CO + H_2O \longrightarrow CO_2 + H_2.$$

By inspection it is clear that for any substance

$$G_0^T = T\left(\frac{G_0 - E_0^0}{T}\right) + E_0^0,$$

so that the standard free energy change at temperature T for a reaction

$$A \longrightarrow B$$

is given by the expression

$$\Delta G_0^T = T\Delta \frac{G_0 - E_0^0}{T} + \Delta E_0^0$$

$$= -T\left\{\left(-\frac{G_0 - E_0^0}{T}\right)_B - \left(-\frac{G_0 - E_0^0}{T}\right)_A\right\} + \Delta E_0^0 A \longrightarrow B.$$

Substituting the values of the free energy function $-\dfrac{G_0 - E_0^0}{T}$ for CO_2, H_2, CO and H_2O we obtain

$$\Delta G_0^{600} = -600\{49 \cdot 239 + 29 \cdot 203 - 45 \cdot 222 - 42 \cdot 768\} + \Delta E_0^0$$

$$= 5728 + \Delta E_0^0 \text{ cal.}$$

It remains to determine ΔE_0^0.

By inspection it is clear that for any substance

$$E_0^0 = H_0^T - T\left(\frac{H_0 - E_0^0}{T}\right)$$

and that for any reaction

$$\Delta E_0^0 = \Delta H_0^T - T\Delta\left(\frac{H_0 - E_0^0}{T}\right)$$

so that ΔE_o^0 can be calculated if we know the heat of reaction ΔH_o^T at any *convenient* temperature and the values of the requisite enthalpy functions at the same temperature. Thus at 25° C

$$\Delta H_o^{298} = \sum \Delta H_{o_f}^{298}(CO_2 + H_2 - CO - H_2O)$$

$$= -94 \cdot 0518 + 0 + 26 \cdot 4157 + 57 \cdot 7979 \text{ kcal}$$

$$= -9 \cdot 8382 \text{ kcal},$$

and $\quad \Delta\left(\dfrac{H_o - E_o^0}{T}\right)^{298} = 7 \cdot 5064 + 6 \cdot 7877 - 6 \cdot 9514 - 7 \cdot 934$

$$= -0 \cdot 5913 \text{ cal deg}^{-1}.$$

It follows that

$$\Delta E_o^0 = -9838 \cdot 2 - 298 \cdot 15 \times (-0 \cdot 5913)$$

$$= -9660 \text{ cal}$$

Hence $\qquad \Delta G_o^{600} = -3932 \text{ cal}.$

This result can of course be more simply obtained from the values of the free energy of formation of the species:

$$\Delta G_o^{600} = \sum \Delta G_{o_f}^{600}(CO_2 + H_2 - CO - H_2O)$$

$$= -94 \cdot 444 + 0 + 39 \cdot 358 + 51 \cdot 154$$

$$= -3 \cdot 932 \text{ kcal}.$$

The value of the equilibrium constant for this reaction is given by the expression

$$\log_{10} K = -\frac{\Delta G}{2 \cdot 303 RT}$$

so that $\qquad \log_{10} K = \dfrac{3932}{2 \cdot 303 \times 1 \cdot 987 \times 600}$

$$= 1 \cdot 433.$$

This again can be obtained more easily since

$$\log_{10} K = \sum \log_{10} K_f.$$

From the values given

$$\log_{10} K = 34 \cdot 401 + 0 - 14 \cdot 336 - 18 \cdot 632$$

$$= 1 \cdot 433.$$

EXERCISES 14

14,1. The energies of the electron in the first and second . . . excited states in the hydrogen atom *relative to the ground state* are 164×10^{-13} erg, 194×10^{-13} erg . . . and the degeneracies of the ground state, first and second . . . excited states are 2, 8, 18. . . .

The value of k is $1\cdot38 \times 10^{-16}$ erg deg^{-1}. Calculate the percentage of hydrogen atoms in the first excited state at $12,000°$ K and $20,000°$ K.

14,2. Since for a system capable of performing only expansion work

$$p = - \left(\frac{\partial A}{\partial V} \right)_T$$

equation (14,13) may be used to obtain an expression for the pressure of an ideal gas in terms of the partition function of the molecule. Obtain this and show that it leads to the more familiar expression

$$pV = RT.$$

14,3. You are presented with specimens of a pure solid A, a pure solid B and a solid solution of A in B (mole fraction of A = mole fraction of B = $0\cdot5$). You carry out specific heat measurements on all three substances from $25°$ C to a temperature as close as possible to absolute zero and find no evidence of crystalline modifications. You use the results to calculate the molar entropies of A and B and the entropy of one mole of the solid solution.

Do you expect to find that $S_{cal\,(solid\;solution)}$ is the same as $\frac{1}{2}(S_{cal_A} + S_{cal_B})$ or not?

If not, what difference would you expect to find?

14,4. It was stated on page 272 that the molar partition function for a system of independent indistinguishable particles is connected to the molecular partition function by the equation

$$Q = \frac{1}{N!} f^N.$$

Use this equation to show that the expressions given for the molar properties of such a system in terms of Q are in fact equivalent to those in terms of f. (Make use of Stirling's Approximation formula.)

14,5. (*a*) Experiment shows that $21\cdot4\%$ of hydrogen iodide is decomposed into hydrogen and iodine at $721°$ K at a total pressure of 1 atmosphere.

Calculate the equilibrium constant for the reaction.

(*b*) Calculate the same constant by thermodynamic means given that at $300°$ K

$$2HI_{(g)} \longrightarrow H_{2(g)} + I_{2(g)}, \quad \Delta H_0^{300} = +2\cdot48 \text{ kcal,}$$

and that the values of the relative enthalpy and free energy function evaluated from spectroscopic data are:

	$H_0 - E_o^0$ cal mole^{-1} at 300° K	$-\dfrac{G_0 - E_o^0}{T}$ cal deg^{-1} mole^{-1} at 721° K
H$_2$	2024	30·46
I$_2$	2418	61·55
HI	2069	48·52

14,6. Explain why an absolute measure of the entropy of a substance is unobtainable.

14,7. You are required to calculate the entropy change for the reaction

$$2CO + 4H_2 \longrightarrow C_2H_5OH + H_2O$$

at 1 atmosphere pressure and at 200° C. Values of S_{stat}^{473} *and* values of S_{cal}, i.e. $\displaystyle\sum_{T=0}^{T=473} \dfrac{q}{T}$ are available for all four substances. State which value you choose for each reactant and give reasons for your choice.

14,8. The American JANAF Tables of Thermochemical data list the values

$$-\frac{G_0 - H_o^{298}}{T} \quad \text{and} \quad H_0 - H_o^{298}$$

at various temperatures instead of the more usual functions

$$-\frac{G_0 - E_o^0}{T} \quad \text{and} \quad \frac{H_0 - E_o^0}{T}.$$

The JANAF values for CO, H$_2$O, CO$_2$ and H$_2$ at 600° K are:

	$-\dfrac{G_0 - H_o^{298}}{T}$ cal deg^{-1} mole^{-1}	$H_0 - H_o^{298}$ kcal mole^{-1}
CO	48·591	2·137
H$_2$O	46·710	2·509
CO$_2$	52·981	3·087
H$_2$	32·573	2·106

ΔH^{298} for the reaction

$$CO + H_2O_{(g)} \longrightarrow CO_2 + H_2$$

is $-9\cdot8382$ kcal.

Show that the JANAF Tables lead to the same value of ΔG_0^{600} as that given on page 295.

14,9. Calculate the quantity $\Delta H_{S,\,p}$ for the reaction

$$C_{(graphite)} + \tfrac{1}{2}O_2 \longrightarrow CO$$

in which the graphite and oxygen are initially at 300° K and at 1 atmosphere pressure.

You are provided with the following data:

(i) The enthalpy of formation of carbon monoxide at constant temperature and pressure at 300° K is −26,200 cal.

(ii) The value of C_p for carbon monoxide may be taken as $6·4 + 2·0 \times 10^{-3}T$ cal deg^{-1} over the temperature range required.

(iii) The value for $H − E_0^0$ for graphite is 252 cal mole^{-1} at 300° K, that of oxygen 2070 cal mole^{-1} and that for carbon monoxide 2075 cal mole^{-1} at the same temperature. The value of $H − E_0^0$ for carbon monoxide at any lower temperature may be calculated from equation (14,61).

(iv) The molar entropies of graphite and oxygen at 300° K and 1 atmosphere pressure are 1·4 cal deg^{-1} and 49·0 cal deg^{-1} respectively, and the statistical value for carbon monoxide is 47·3 cal deg^{-1} under the same conditions. It may be assumed that equation (14,64) holds in the case of carbon monoxide over the entire temperature range required.

(Hint: It is suggested that Exercises 9,3 and 9,4 and their solutions are studied before this exercise is attempted. Part of the exercise can be done in two ways: one requires the information given in (i), (ii) and (iv) above, and in this case it is suggested that the student reads the section in Chapter 6 on maximum flame temperatures, and the other requires the information given in (i), (iii) and (iv) and depends entirely on the techniques described in the present chapter. It is suggested that the student carries out both procedures.)

14,10. The residual molar entropy at 0° K of NO appears to be $\frac{1}{2}Nk \log_e 2$, and that of CH$_3$D appears to be $Nk \log_e 4$. How do you justify these figures?

PART IV

APPLICATION OF THERMODYNAMICS
TO SPECIAL SYSTEMS

CHAPTER 15

PHASE RELATIONS AND THE THERMO-DYNAMICS OF SOLUTIONS

The most important fact that bears upon the behaviour of a multi-phase system at equilibrium is that principle which is in this book called THE FIRST STATEMENT OF CHEMICAL POTENTIALS, the statement that the chemical potential of a component present in more than one phase in an equilibrium system is the same in each phase. One consequence of this statement is that information on the behaviour of a component in one phase can often be obtained by measurements carried out in another. For example, much information on a binary liquid system is obtained from measurements of the partial pressures of the vapours in equilibrium with it, and much information on the behaviour of a non-volatile solute from measurements of the vapour pressure of the solvent. Any distinction between a study of phase relations and that of the behaviour of solutions is therefore not only artificial but misleading: phase relations and the behaviour of solutions are therefore considered together.

The most important thermodynamic quantity with which we shall be concerned is the chemical potential of a component, but at times we shall require to consider other partial molar quantities, the partial molar volume $\bar{v}$, the partial molar enthalpy $\bar{h}$ and the partial molar entropy $\bar{s}$. These quantities were defined in Chapter 11,

$$\mu_i = \left(\frac{\partial G}{\partial n_i}\right)_{p,\,T,\,n_1,\,\ldots\,n_{i-1},\,n_{i+1},\,\ldots}$$

$$\bar{v}_i = \left(\frac{\partial V}{\partial n_i}\right)_{p,\,T,\,n_1,\,\ldots\,n_{i-1},\,n_{i+1},\,\ldots}$$

$$\bar{h}_i = \left(\frac{\partial H}{\partial n_i}\right)_{p,\,T,\,n_1,\,\ldots\,n_{i-1},\,n_{i+1},\,\ldots}$$

$$\bar{s}_i = \left(\frac{\partial S}{\partial n_i}\right)_{p,\,T,\,n_1,\,\ldots\,n_{i-1},\,n_{i+1},\,\ldots}$$

where G, V, H and S are the values of the free energy, volume, enthalpy and entropy of a solution containing n_1, n_2, $\ldots$ n_i, $\ldots$ moles of components 1, 2, ... i, ... at temperature T and pressure p. The partial molar quantities are connected by the equations

$$\left(\frac{\partial \mu_i}{\partial p}\right)_{T,\, n_1, \ldots n_i, \ldots} = \bar{v} \quad \ldots \quad \ldots \quad (11,34)$$

$$\left\{\frac{\partial\left(\dfrac{\mu_i}{T}\right)}{\partial T}\right\}_{p,\, n_1, \ldots n_i, \ldots} = -\frac{\bar{h}_i}{T^2} \quad \ldots \quad \ldots \quad (11,31)$$

$$\left(\frac{\partial \mu_i}{\partial T}\right)_{p,\, n_1, \ldots n_i, \ldots} = -\bar{s}_i \quad \ldots \quad \ldots \quad (11,28)$$

and $$\mu_i = \bar{h}_i - T\bar{s}_i. \quad \ldots \quad \ldots \quad (11,30)$$

It will be noticed that the partial molar quantities μ, $\bar{v}$, $\bar{h}$ and $\bar{s}$ are all derivatives of the corresponding extensive property *under the same conditions*, i.e. at constant p, T, n_1, ... This permits the following generalised treatment.

If X represents any of the extensive properties G, V, H and S, we can write

$$X = f(p,\, T,\, n_1,\, n_2,\, \ldots n_i,\, \ldots)$$

so that

$$dX = \left(\frac{\partial X}{\partial p}\right)_{T,\, n_1, \ldots} dp + \left(\frac{\partial X}{\partial T}\right)_{p,\, n_1, \ldots} dT + \left(\frac{\partial X}{\partial n_1}\right)_{T,\, p,\, n_2, \ldots} dn_1, \ldots$$
$$+ \left(\frac{\partial X}{\partial n_i}\right)_{T,\, p,\, n_1, \ldots} dn_i, \ldots$$

Expressing the partial molar quantities by $\bar{x}_1$, ..., we see that the variation in X due to composition changes at constant temperature and pressure is given by the equation:

$$dX = \bar{x}_1 dn_1 \ldots + \bar{x}_i dn_i, \ldots \quad \ldots \quad \ldots \quad (15,1)$$

which on integration gives

$$X = n_1 \bar{x}_1 \ldots + n_i \bar{x}_i, \ldots \quad \ldots \quad \ldots \quad (15,2)$$

General differentiation of (15,2) yields

$$dX = n_1 d\bar{x}_1 + \bar{x}_1 dn_1 \ldots + n_i d\bar{x}_i + \bar{x}_i dn_i \ldots$$

and by comparison with (15,1) we see that

$$n_1 d\bar{x}_1 \ldots + n_i d\bar{x}_i \ldots = 0. \quad \ldots \quad \ldots \quad (15,3)$$

From (15,2) we see that

$$G = n_1\mu_1 \ldots + n_i\mu_i \ldots \qquad \ldots \ldots \quad (15,4)$$

$$V = n_1\bar{v}_1 \ldots + n_i\bar{v}_i \ldots \qquad \ldots \ldots \quad (15,5)$$

$$H = n_1\bar{h}_1 \ldots + n_i\bar{h}_i \ldots \qquad \ldots \ldots \quad (15,6)$$

$$S = n_1\bar{s}_1 \ldots + n_i\bar{s}_i \ldots \qquad \ldots \ldots \quad (15,7)$$

and from (15,3) we see that for systems at constant temperature and pressure

$$n_1 d\mu_1 \ldots + n_i d\mu_i \ldots = 0 \quad \ldots \ldots \quad (15,8)$$

$$n_1 d\bar{v}_1 \ldots + n_i d\bar{v}_i \ldots = 0 \quad \ldots \ldots \quad (15,9)$$

$$n_1 d\bar{h}_1 \ldots + n_i d\bar{h}_i \ldots = 0 \quad \ldots \ldots \quad (15,10)$$

$$n_1 d\bar{s}_1 \ldots + n_i d\bar{s}_i \ldots = 0. \quad \ldots \ldots \quad (15,11)$$

These last equations are generally known as the Gibbs–Duhem Equations.

A more general form of (15,8) containing terms accounting for additional variations in T and p was derived in Chapter 11 (see equation (11,27)).

IDEAL AND REAL SOLUTIONS

In Chapter 11 a component of a solution was said to be of ideal behaviour if it obeyed Raoult's Law; that is to say, if p_i its partial pressure, x_i its mole fraction and p_i^0 the vapour pressure it would exert at the same temperature as a pure substance, are connected by the equation

$$p_i = x_i p_i^0 \qquad \ldots \ldots \quad (15,12)$$

and a solution was defined as ideal if all its components behaved ideally.

This criterion can be put into a form which is particularly useful in the case of a solution containing a simple non-volatile solute. Consider a solution containing n_i moles of solvent and n_s moles of solute, i.e. of mole fractions x_i and x_s:

$$p_i^0 - p_i = p_i^0 - x_i p_i^0 = p_i^0(1 - x_i) = p_i^0 x_s$$

so that

$$x_s = \frac{n_s}{n_i + n_s} = \frac{p_i^0 - p_i}{p_i^0}$$

and

$$\frac{n_s}{n_i} = \frac{p_i^0 - p_i}{p_i}. \qquad \ldots \ldots \quad (15,13)$$

If the solution consists of w_s gm of solute of molecular weight M_s and w_i gm of solvent of molecular weight M_i, it follows that

$$\frac{w_s M_i}{M_s w_i} = \frac{p_i^0 - p_i}{p_i}. \qquad \cdots \qquad (15,14)$$

This provides a method for the determination of the molecular weight of one component if that of the other is known.

We showed that the chemical potential of components that obey Raoult's Law can be expressed by the equation

$$\mu_i = \mu_{o_x} + RT \log_e x_i \qquad \cdots \qquad (15,15)$$

where μ_{o_x} is the chemical potential of the component in the pure state ($x = 1$), or by equations of type

$$\mu_i = \mu_{o_c} + RT \log_e C_i \qquad \cdots \qquad (15,16)$$

or
$$\mu_i = \mu_{o_m} + RT \log_e m_i \qquad \cdots \qquad (15,17)$$

where μ_{o_c} and μ_{o_m} are the chemical potentials of the component at unit molarity and unit molality. An alternative but precisely equivalent definition of an ideal solution to that using criterion (15,12) is therefore one in which the chemical potentials of all the components obey equations (15,15), (15,16) or (15,17).

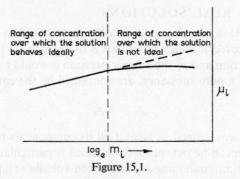

Figure 15,1.

It should be noted that the fact that a solution is ideal at one particular composition, or over a particular composition range does not necessarily mean that the solution is ideal over the entire composition range possible. It very often happens that a solution of a single component i is ideal at very low concentrations, but non-ideal at high. In this case the graph of μ_i against $\log_e m_i$, for example, is as shown in Figure 15,1.

A third criterion can be developed for a solution which is ideal over the whole concentration range.

If equation (15,15) is differentiated with respect to pressure we obtain

$$\left(\frac{\partial \mu_i}{\partial p}\right)_{T,\,n_i,\,\ldots} = \bar{v}_i = \left(\frac{\partial \mu_{0_x}}{\partial p}\right)_T.$$

Since μ_{0_x} is independent of composition, so also is its derivative, so that over the concentration range for which the solution is ideal the partial molar volume of each component is independent of composition. In the case of solutions which are ideal over the entire composition range extending to $x_i = 1$, $\bar{v}_i$ must be the same as V_i, the molar volume of the pure component, so that the volume of a solution containing n_1 moles of one component and n_2 moles of a second . . ., is given by the equation

$$V = n_1 V_1 + n_2 V_2 \ldots \qquad \qquad (15,18)$$

Such mixtures can therefore be prepared at constant temperature and pressure without volume change.

If equation (15,15) is written in the form

$$\frac{\mu_i}{T} = \frac{\mu_{0_x}}{T} + R \log_e x_i,$$

and differentiated with respect to temperature, we obtain

$$\left\{\frac{\partial\left(\frac{\mu_i}{T}\right)}{\partial T}\right\}_{p,\,n_i,\,..} = -\frac{\bar{h}_i}{T^2} = \left\{\frac{\partial\left(\frac{\mu_{0x}}{T}\right)}{\partial T}\right\}_{p,\,n_i,\,\ldots}$$

Since the right-hand term is independent of composition, $\bar{h}_i$ must, for solutions which are ideal over the whole concentration range extending to $x_i = 1$, be the same as H_i, the molar enthalpy of the pure component, so that the enthalpy of a solution containing n_1 moles of one component and n_2 moles of a second . . ., is given by the equation

$$H = n_1 H_1 + n_2 H_2 \ldots \qquad \qquad (15,19)$$

Such mixtures can therefore be prepared at constant temperature and pressure without heat effect.

The Entropy and Free Energy of Mixing

In direct contrast to what we have just done we differentiate equation (15,15) with respect to temperature at constant pressure, and make use of equation (11,28) to obtain the equation

$$\bar{s}_i = \bar{s}_{0_i} - R \log_e x_i.$$

For a solution which is ideal over the whole concentration range, $\bar{s}_{0_i}$ is the same as S_i, the molar entropy of the pure component at the same temperature and pressure.

Let us imagine therefore that we allow n_1 moles of one component to mix with n_2 moles of a second ... The entropy before mixing equals $n_1 S_1 + n_2 S_2 \ldots$, and the entropy after mixing equals

$$(n_1 S_1 - n_1 R \log_e x_1) + (n_2 S_2 - n_2 R \log_e x_2) \ldots,$$

so that the entropy of mixing is given by the equation

$$\Delta S_{\text{mixing}} = -n_1 R \log_e x_1 - n_2 R \log_e x_2 \ldots \ldots \quad (15,20)$$

This equation is precisely the same as equation (12,8), which refers to the entropy of mixing of ideal gases under the same condition.

Since we know from (15,19) that the enthalpy of mixing of an ideal solution is zero, the free energy of mixing

$$\Delta G_{\text{mixing}} = \Delta H_{\text{mixing}} - T \Delta S_{\text{mixing}}$$

must be given by the equation

$$\Delta G_{\text{mixing}} = nRT \log_e x_1 + n_2 RT \log_e x_2 \ldots \ldots \quad (15,21)$$

We note that this quantity is negative, as would be expected.

Equations (15,12) to (15,21) refer to ideal solutions. They may be applied to non-ideal solutions only if the mole fractions and concentration terms are replaced by activity terms. It must be remarked that solutions which obey these equations over the whole concentration range available to a particular system are rare, but that all solutions approach ideal behaviour when the mole fraction of one component approaches unity and that of the other components approach zero; in other words, when the solution approaches infinite dilution.

We are now in a position to consider the application of thermodynamics to various physical phenomena. Neither the list of phenomena discussed nor the treatment given to each is intended to be exhaustive; the principal object of this treatment is to demonstrate the thermodynamic basis of some of the principles of physical chemistry. Solutions of electrolytes (which present peculiar problems of their own) are studied in the next chapter.

THE PHASE RULE

Consider a system in equilibrium at temperature T and pressure p consisting of P phases and C distinct chemical species which may be present in arbitrary quantities,[1] and which are capable of taking part in R independent reactions.[2] The so-called *Phase Rule*, originally deduced by Gibbs, determines the number of *intensive* properties that can be varied arbitrarily.

Before deducing the Phase Rule, it is probably helpful to mention the sort of question to which it provides the answer:

(a) A system consists of a single chemical species present as both a liquid and a vapour in equilibrium. Is it possible to keep its temperature constant, but to increase the pressure without the vapour phase disappearing?

(b) A system consists of a saturated solution in equilibrium with one component in the solid state. Is it possible to maintain the solution at the same concentration by changing arbitrarily both the temperature and the pressure?

(c) Is it possible for ice water and water vapour to exist in equilibrium at any temperature as long as the pressure is "suitably" adjusted?

The answer to these questions will be discussed after the Phase Rule has been derived.

We determine the number of intensive properties that may be varied arbitrarily by considering first the number of such properties which are required to define a system which is not in equilibrium, and subtracting those which are automatically defined by the various criteria of equilibrium. We already know that the pressure, temperature and the mole fraction of a single component in a single phase automatically defines its chemical potential, partial molar enthalpy, entropy and volume. It follows that the maximum possible number of intensive properties which *might* be varied arbitrarily in the system under consideration are the temperature, the pressure and the mole fraction of each component in each phase; so that if for the present we suppose that every component is present in every phase, the maximum possible number appears to be $CP + 2$. Since, however, the sum of the mole fractions of all components in each

---

[1] The significance of this restriction will be discussed later.

[2] A system consisting of C, CO, CO_2 and O_2 is capable of four reactions

$$C + CO_2 \longrightarrow CO \quad (1)$$
$$C + O_2 \longrightarrow CO_2 \quad (2)$$
$$C + \tfrac{1}{2}O_2 \longrightarrow CO \quad (3)$$
$$CO + \tfrac{1}{2}O_2 \longrightarrow CO_2 \quad (4)$$

(and four reactions in the reverse direction).

Only two of these reactions (say (2) and (3)) are independent; (1) can be expressed as $2(3)-(2)$ and (4) can be expressed as $(2)-(3)$.

phase must equal unity, it follows that if $C - 1$ mole fractions are arbitrarily chosen, that of the Cth is automatically decided. We must therefore reduce the number to $(C - 1)P + 2$.

We now have to decide how many of these are in fact truly independent, and how many are rendered dependent by the various criteria of equilibrium. We first apply the First Statement of Chemical Potentials which states that the chemical potential of any single component must be the same in each phase. Since at any temperature and pressure the chemical potential of a particular component is defined by its mole fraction, so must its mole fraction be defined by its chemical potential. In other words, if the mole fraction of a single component in a single phase is arbitrarily chosen, that in all other phases is automatically defined. This means that the number $(C - 1)P + 2$ must be reduced by $C(P - 1)$.

We must now consider the R independent reactions. For each reaction the Fourth Statement of Chemical Potentials imposes the restriction that at equilibrium the sums of the chemical potentials of the reacting species on both sides of the chemical equation must be the same, so that in a reaction

$$X + Y \rightleftharpoons Z$$

knowledge of the chemical potentials of X and Y at equilibrium determines that of Z. Each independent reaction must therefore reduce the number of arbitrary variations by one.

The number of intensive properties that can be varied arbitrarily is therefore given by

$$(C - 1)P + 2 - C(P - 1) - R$$

i.e. by $C + 2 - R - P$.

This number is usually given the symbol F, so that the Phase Rule is expressed by the equation

$$F = C + 2 - R - P. \quad . \quad . \quad . \quad . \quad (15,22)$$

We must now decide whether any change in this equation must be made if one[1] particular component is absent from any one phase.

The number of variables corresponding to $CP + 2$ is now

$$\{C(P - 1) + C - 1\} + 2.$$

One mole fraction in each phase is determined by that of the remainder, irrespective of whether there are C or $C - 1$ components in that particular phase, so that the maximum number of variables reduces to

$$\{C(P - 1) + C - 1\} - P + 2.$$

[1] The argument is the same if more than one component is absent from more than one phase.

The First Statement of Chemical Potentials leads to the reduction of this number by $(C-1)(P-1)$ to account for the $C-1$ components present in all phases, and by $P-2$ to account for the component present in only $P-1$ phases. The number of independent reactions is not effected, so that the number of intensive properties that can be varied arbitrarily is given by

$$\{C(P-1)+C-1\}-P+2-(C-1)(P-1)-(P-2)-R$$

i.e. by
$$C+2-R-P.$$

We again arrive at the equation
$$F = C + 2 - R - P. \qquad . \quad . \quad . \quad . \quad (15,22)$$

The principal difficulty in use of the Phase Rule is the identification of C, the number of distinct chemical species, and R the number of independent reactions. In some cases, such as that of a system containing carbon dioxide, calcium carbonate and calcium oxide, no difficulty exists. The reaction which takes place between the three species is the same whether it be written

$$CaCO_3 \rightleftharpoons CaO + CO_2$$

or
$$CaO + CO_2 \rightleftharpoons CaCO_3.$$

The value of C is clearly three, and that of R is one.

The sort of difficulty we have in mind is perhaps best illustrated by considering a system consisting of liquid water and steam at some particular temperature and pressure. Water vapour has the molecular formula H_2O, but liquid water is believed to consist of a mixture of the monomer H_2O and polymers $(H_2O)_2$, $(H_2O)_3$ and so on. How do we select the number of distinct chemical species? The answer is that *where ambiguity exists, the selection of the "correct" value of C is unimportant as long as the appropriate value of R is considered at the same time.* Let us calculate the value of F for the system by choosing various values of C in turn.

We first choose to regard the system as containing only one molecular species H_2O. Since R is then obviously zero, and since $P=2$, $F=1$. We now choose to regard the liquid phase as a mixture of two species H_2O and $(H_2O)_2$, so that $C=2$. One chemical reaction is possible

$$2H_2O \rightleftharpoons (H_2O)_2$$

so that
$$R = 1.$$

It again follows that
$$F = 1.$$

If we regard the liquid phase as a mixture of three species H_2O, $(H_2O)_2$ and $(H_2O)_3$, so that $C = 3$, we find that two independent reactions are possible

$$2H_2O \rightleftharpoons (H_2O)_2$$

$$(H_2O)_3 \rightleftharpoons (H_2O)_2 + H_2O$$

so that again $F = 1$.

It is obvious that the reason why we have this freedom of choice is that in equation (15,22) C appears in conjunction with $-R$. The Phase Rule is in fact sometimes defined without reference to the number of independent reactions which may take place. In this case the system is defined in terms of C', the number of *independent* components. Since components are independent only if no reaction can take place between them, it is obvious that

$$C' = C - R.$$

In the argument just pursued, the ionisation of water was ignored. It must now be considered. For ease of argument we will suppose that liquid water consists of only one uncharged species H_2O and that it ionises according to the equation

$$2H_2O \rightleftharpoons H_3O^+ + OH^-.$$

The system contains three distinct components with only one reaction between them, so that the value of F calculated from (15,22) appears to be two, which result is at variance with our earlier conclusion.

The answer to this is, that by considering ionisation we are removing the system from the conditions under which equation (15,22) was derived. Equation (15,22) was derived for a system containing C distinct chemical species *which may be present in arbitrary quantities*. An equilibrium system containing charged particles is subject to the restriction of electroneutrality. This means that in the system under consideration the number of hydrogen ions must be the same as that of hydroxyl ions. We are thus imposing a further restriction on the system, which must result in the reduction of the number of properties that may be varied arbitrarily, by one. Equation (15,22) must therefore be replaced by the equation

$$F = C + 2 - R - P - \rho \quad . \quad . \quad . \quad . \quad (15,23)$$

where ρ accounts for the electroneutrality restriction.

We illustrate the use of (15,23) by considering a system composed of water and acetic acid. As far as the Phase Rule is concerned it is immaterial whether (*a*) we consider the system to contain two components

(H_2O and HAc) and consider that no significant reaction takes place between them; in which case we choose the values

$$C = 2, \ R = 0, \ \rho = 0$$

or whether (*b*) we take into account two reactions

$$2H_2O \rightleftharpoons H_3O^+ + OH^-$$

and

$$H_2O + HAc \rightleftharpoons H_3O^+ + Ac^-$$

and the electroneutrality restriction that the number of hydrogen ions must equal the sum of the number of hydroxyl and acetate ions; in which case we choose the values

$$C = 5, \ R = 2, \ \rho = 1.$$

It is of interest to consider the form that the Phase Rule must assume when applied to an osmotic system. Such a system is characterised by the fact that at equilibrium two phases, the solution and pure solvent are at different pressures. Both equations (15,22) and (15,23) were derived on the assumption that the pressure and temperature of the system concerned are the same throughout. It is these two variables that account for the figure 2 in both equations. It would appear at first sight that when applied to an osmotic system the figure 2 should be replaced by 3 to account for the extra variable. This is not, however, correct, because (as we shall see later in this chapter) although the pressure of one phase may be arbitrarily chosen, the difference in pressure between the two phases is defined by the temperature and the composition of the solution.

It is instructive to apply the Phase Rule to the questions posed earlier in this section. (15,22) may be applied to all.

(*a*) To increase the pressure on the system but keep its temperature constant means that we require to *choose* the values of both T and p. In other words we *require* that

$$F = 2.$$

Since $C = 1$ and $R = 0$, F can be 2 only if $P = 1$. It follows that if the pressure on the system is increased but the temperature kept constant, one phase must disappear. We observe that the Phase Rule does not say *which* phase will remain. The fact that it is the vapour phase which disappears follows from Le Chatelier's Principle.

(b) $C = 2, P = 2, R = 0.$

Hence $F = 2$.

The requirement to maintain the saturated solution at the same concentration by changing both the temperature and the pressure in an arbitrary manner implies that we wish to *choose* the value of three intensive properties, the mole fraction of one component in the binary solution, the pressure and the temperature. Since $F = 2$, we see that two properties only are independent. The concentration of solution can remain the same at a different temperature only if the pressure changes to some definite value about which we have no choice.

(c) Here $C = 1, P = 3, R = 0.$

Hence $F = 0.$

The system is invariant, the three phases can co-exist only at a particular temperature and particular pressure, about which we have no choice. The condition under which ice, water and water vapour can exist in equilibrium is known as the *Triple Point* and is found by experiment to be at $+0.0098°$ C and a pressure of 4·58 mm of mercury.

The three questions we have just discussed illustrate the sort of information which the Phase Rule provides. It is particularly valuable in establishing the relationship between one crystalline form of a substance and another, and probably its greatest contribution is to metallurgy. For information on these matters the student is referred to the monographs mentioned below.[1]

THE CLAUSIUS–CLAPEYRON EQUATION

The Clausius–Clapeyron equation was derived in Chapter 10, using one of Maxwell's Relations. It is instructive to give an alternative derivation.

Consider a pure substance existing in two phases α and β in equilibrium at temperature T and pressure p. It follows from the First Statement of Chemical Potentials that

$$\mu_\alpha = \mu_\beta.$$

We now change the temperature by an amount dT. Since the system consists of a single component system existing in two phases, it follows from the Phase Rule that an arbitrary change in one intensive property

[1] Bowden, *The Phase Rule and Phase Reactions* (Macmillan, 1945). Rhines, *Phase Diagrams in Metallurgy* (McGraw-Hill).

must be accompanied by automatic changes in the others, so that the pressure changes to $p + dp$, and the chemical potentials to $\mu_\alpha + d\mu_\alpha$ and $\mu_\beta + d\mu_\beta$.

It must also follow that if the system remains in equilibrium

$$\mu_\alpha + d\mu_\alpha = \mu_\beta + d\mu_\beta$$

so that $\qquad\qquad\qquad d\mu_\alpha = d\mu_\beta.$

μ_α and μ_β may be expressed as functions of temperature and pressure, so that we may write

$$\left(\frac{\partial\mu_\alpha}{\partial T}\right)_p dT + \left(\frac{\partial\mu_\alpha}{\partial p}\right)_T dp = \left(\frac{\partial\mu_\beta}{\partial T}\right)_p dT + \left(\frac{\partial\mu_\beta}{\partial p}\right)_T dp,$$

and from (11,28) and (11,34)

$$-S_\alpha dT + V_\alpha dp = -S_\beta dT + V_\beta dp,$$

where S_α and V_α are the molar entropy and volume of the component in phase α, S_β and V_β the same quantities in the second phase.[1]

It follows that

$$\frac{dT}{dp} = \frac{V_\beta - V_\alpha}{S_\beta - S_\alpha}.$$

If L is the molar latent heat of transformation from phase α to phase β

$$S_\beta - S_\alpha = \frac{L}{T},$$

so that $\qquad\qquad\qquad \dfrac{dT}{dp} = \dfrac{T(V_\beta - V_\alpha)}{L} \quad . \quad . \quad . \quad . \quad (15,24)$

which is the general form of the Clausius–Clapeyron equation.

It will be remembered that in the case of equilibrium between liquid and vapour phases at temperatures well below the critical temperature, it may be argued that the molar volume of the liquid phase is very small compared with that of the vapour, and that if we make the additional assumption that the vapour behaves as an ideal gas, we may write

$$\frac{d\log_e p}{dT} = \frac{L_e}{RT^2} \quad . \quad . \quad . \quad . \quad . \quad (15,25)$$

so obtaining an expression for the variation of vapour pressure of a liquid with temperature. A similar argument holds for the equilibrium between a solid and its vapour, and results in the equation

$$\frac{d\log_e p'}{dT} = \frac{L_s}{RT^2} \quad . \quad . \quad . \quad . \quad (15,26)$$

[1] We write S and V rather than the partial molar quantities $\bar{s}$ and $\bar{v}$ because we are considering a pure substance.

where p' is the vapour pressure of the solid and L_s is the molar latent heat of sublimation.

Equations (15,25) and (15,26) may be integrated over a temperature range small enough for us to assume constancy of values L_e and L_s, to give the equation

$$\log_e p = -\frac{L}{RT} + b \quad . \quad . \quad . \quad . \quad (15,27)$$

so that measurement of the vapour pressure at two temperatures is sufficient to determine the corresponding value of the latent heat, or conversely, knowledge of the latent heat and the vapour pressure at one temperature is sufficient to enable the vapour pressure at any other temperature to be determined.

An interesting application of equation (15,25) is its use to estimate the boiling point of a metal. If the vapour pressure of the liquid metal at two convenient temperatures is measured, the value of L_e can be calculated. At the boiling point of the metal its vapour pressure is 1 atmosphere, and the temperature at which this is obtained can be estimated from the equation

$$\int_{p=p}^{p=1} d\log_e p = \int_{T=T}^{T=T_b} \frac{L_e}{RT^2} dT$$

i.e.

$$\log_e \frac{1}{p} = \frac{L_e}{R}\left(\frac{1}{T} - \frac{1}{T_b}\right). \quad . \quad . \quad . \quad (15,28)$$

This equation assumes that the latent heat of evaporation remains constant over the temperature range T to T_b. Since this assumption is not correct, the value obtained for T_b will be approximate only. A more accurate result may be obtained by using Kirchhoff's Law to obtain an expression for L_e as a function of temperature.

ENTROPIES OF EVAPORATION AND FUSION

Some information on the constitution of a pure liquid can be obtained from the value of its entropy of evaporation at its boiling point, and on the constitution of a pure solid from the value of its entropy of fusion. In this context it is useful to invest an entropy change with the physical significance derived from Statistical Thermodynamics. It will be remembered that the entropy of a system may be expressed by the equation

$$S = k \log_e W \quad . \quad . \quad . \quad . \quad . \quad (13,1)$$

and the change in entropy when the system proceeds from one state to another by the equation

$$\Delta S = S_2 - S_1 = k \log_e \frac{W_2}{W_1} \quad . \quad . \quad . \quad (13,2)$$

where the symbol W is used to denote the number of micro-states accessible to the system as a whole. We have also seen that the W value of a system is associated with its internal disorder. If the W value is small, the particles in the system are able to assume relatively few spacial configurations, so that the degree of order in the system is relatively high. It follows that the increase in entropy of a system during some change of state is proportional to the increase in internal disorder of the particles concerned. In a crystalline solid, the independent particles, whether molecules, atoms or ions, are arranged in a definite pattern within the crystal lattice, so that the degree of order is high and the entropy low. In a liquid the independent particles enjoy much greater freedom of movement, so that the degree of disorder is greater than that in the solid state. The evaporation of a liquid is accompanied by an even greater increase in disorder, so that we would expect both entropies of fusion and evaporation to be positive, and in general entropies of evaporation to be greater than those of fusion.

Entropies of Boiling,[1] Trouton's Law

It was discovered in the 19th century that the evaporation of many liquids conform to three empirical generalisations. The first, generally known as Trouton's Law, states that the numerical value of the quotient obtained by dividing the molar latent heat of evaporation expressed in calories by its boiling point expressed in °K lies between 20 and 23. Since the entropy of boiling is given by the equation

$$\Delta S_b = \frac{L_e}{T_b}$$

Trouton's Law is equivalent to the statement that the molar entropy of boiling of many liquids lies between 20 and 23 cal deg^{-1}.

The second generalisation put forward originally by van der Waals connects the vapour pressure of a liquid and its critical temperature and pressure by the equation

$$\log_{10} \frac{p}{p_c} = k\left(1 - \frac{T_c}{T}\right)$$

where k is a dimensionless constant approximately equal to 3. It was found also that for liquids which obey this equation the ratio of the boiling point to the critical temperature is approximately 0·6.

---

[1] Whereas in earlier sections we have used the symbol ΔS_e to denote the entropy of evaporation of a liquid at *any* temperature, we here used the symbol ΔS_b to denote the entropy of boiling, i.e. the specific value of ΔS_e at the boiling point (that temperature at which the vapour pressure of the liquid equals 1 atmosphere). The boiling point, as in earlier sections, is denoted by the symbol T_b.

The third generalisation relates to the integrated form of the Clausius–Clapeyron equation

$$\log_e p = -\frac{L_e}{RT} + b \quad . \quad . \quad . \quad . \quad . \quad . \quad (15,27)$$

which may be written in the form

$$p = ae^{-\frac{L_e}{RT}}.$$

where $a = $ anti-log b.

It was found that over a large temperature range including the boiling point a is the same for many liquids and has the value $2 \cdot 7 \times 10^4$ atmospheres. The liquids to which the three generalisations apply are the same, and the three laws are in fact equivalent. For the derivation of Trouton's Law from the other two the student is referred to the solutions of Exercises 15,3 and 15,4. The first predicts that the entropy of boiling will be 23 cal deg^{-1} and the second 20 cal deg^{-1}. Since the three generalisations are equivalent we shall consider in detail only the first.

The degree to which Trouton's Law is obeyed is shown by the values given in Table 15,I.

TABLE 15,I
Molar Latent Heats and Entropies of Boiling

Substance	Boiling point, °K	L_e cal mole^{-1}	ΔS_b cal deg^{-1} mole^{-1}
Hydrogen	20·4	214	10·4
Helium	4·29	22	5·1
n-Butane	273	5,351	19·6
Diethyl ether	307	6,466	21·1
Benzene	353	7,497	21·2
Carbon disulphide	319	6,490	20·4
Chloroform	334	6,970	20·8
Carbon tetrachloride	350	7,140	20·4
Mercury	630	14,200	22·6
Sodium	1155	23,300	20·2
Zinc	1180	27,730	23·5
Water	373	9,700	26·0
Methyl alcohol	338	8,380	24·8
Ethyl alcohol	351	9,448	26·9

The reason for the wide disparity between the values of ΔS_b for hydrogen and helium and those of other substances cannot be discussed here. Those substances listed in the second group, i.e. those from n-butane to zinc are seen to obey Trouton's Law. They are typical of that class of liquids which are called *normal*. Water, methyl alcohol and ethyl alcohol, which it will be seen, do not obey Trouton's Law, are typical of that class of liquids which is called *associated*. The difference between these two classes of liquids can best be established by considering the condensation of a gas. A gas condenses to what is called a *normal liquid* if two conditions are satisfied:

   (i) if the number of discrete particles existing in the liquid is the same as that which was present in the gas from which the liquid derives; and

  (ii) if the process of condensation results in little change in the rotational, vibrational and electronic energies of the molecules concerned, so that the rotational, vibrational and electronic behaviour of each molecule is not seriously disturbed by the close proximity of its neighbours.

It follows that the rotational, vibrational and electronic partition functions of the molecule in the liquid phase are much the same as those in the gas, so that the main difference between a normal liquid and the gas from which it derives lies in the difference in the translational energies of the particles concerned. The entropy of boiling of such a liquid is therefore represented almost completely by the difference in the translational partition functions in the two phases concerned.

On the other hand, the condensation of a gas to what is called an associated liquid leads to molecular interactions, so that the rotational, vibrational and sometimes the electronic behaviour of the molecules are seriously affected. In some cases the identity of the molecules may change, double or multiple molecules being formed. In other cases the interactions may extend throughout the whole liquid, so that the identity of the original molecules may be completely lost. In all cases not only will the partition functions of the particles be modified, but the *number* of discrete particles composing the system will be less than that in the gas from which the liquid derived. It follows that we would expect the entropy of an associated liquid to be smaller, and the entropy of boiling of an associated liquid to be greater than the values we would expect if the liquid were normal.

While it is possible, as we have shown, to explain qualitatively the departure of entropies of boiling of associated liquids from those of normal liquids, it has not yet appeared possible to account *quantitatively* for the value of the entropy of boiling of normal liquids or (which is the same thing) to account for the value $k = 3$ in the van der Waals equation, or for the value $a = 2·7 \times 10^4$ atm. in the equation

$$p = ae^{-\frac{L_e}{RT}}.$$

Since, in effect, a normal liquid is defined as one in which rotational, vibrational and electronic contributions to the entropy are much the same as those values in the gas at the same temperature, the entropy of boiling of a normal liquid is much the same as the increase in translational entropy brought about. We would expect to find therefore that in no case is the molar translational entropy of the gas at 1 atmosphere pressure and at its boiling point smaller than the entropy of boiling. The first quantity may be calculated by means of the equation

$$S_{\text{trans}} = \tfrac{5}{2}R \log_e T + \tfrac{3}{2}R \log_e M - 2·316$$

and yields the value 37·5 cal deg^{-1} for n-butane for which ΔS_b is 19·6, and the value 33·0 for ethylene for which ΔS_b is 19·1. Little more of value can be established. This is because the application of Statistical Thermodynamics to liquids is far less advanced than its application to gases or to crystalline solids. The reason for this is that it is much more difficult to devise a suitable molecular model for the liquid than it is in the case of the gas or solid. In the case of the gas the behaviour of a single molecule can, as we saw in Chapters 13 and 14, be studied without interference from the others in the system; and in the case of the crystal the particles concerned are arranged in a completely ordered pattern. In the case of a liquid neither condition applies. For an account of the progress which has so far been made the student is referred to Fowler and Guggenheim.[1]

We move on to surer ground when we consider the evaporation of a liquid at temperatures approaching the critical temperature. Since at the critical temperature the latent heat of evaporation vanishes for both normal and associated liquids, it follows that the entropy of the liquid and that of its vapour must be the same. This would suggest that associated liquids become normal as the critical temperature is approached.

The principle use of Trouton's Law is in indicating whether a particular liquid is normal or associated at and around its boiling point. It is of some use in other ways. If a liquid is assumed to be normal, the law permits an estimation of its latent heat of evaporation, if its boiling point is known, or alternatively it permits a very approximate estimation of its boiling point from the value of the latent heat. This has been of some use in the case of metals and of those liquids which decompose before the boiling point is reached, because the latent heat can be estimated by means

[1] Fowler and Guggenheim, *Statistical Thermodynamics* (1960), Chapter VIII.

of the Clausius–Clapeyron equation from vapour pressure measurements at lower temperatures.

Entropies of Fusion

Entropies of fusion differ much more widely from substance to substance than do entropies of boiling, and depend to a considerable degree on molecular shape. In the case of elements or those compounds the molecules of which are approximately spherical in shape free rotation in the solid state might be expected. It should therefore follow that fusion would result in little change in the rotational partition function of the particle. For substances in which little change in rotational, vibrational and electronic partition functions would be expected, and which melt to form normal liquids, it is possible from Statistical Thermodynamics to predict that the entropy of fusion will be equal to, or slightly greater than R, i.e. 2 cal deg^{-1} mole^{-1}. This prediction is confirmed by experimental values in many cases. For example, the molar entropy of fusion of copper is 2 cal deg^{-1}, that of silver 2·2, mercury 2·4, tertiary butyl chloride 2·0, cyclohexane 2·3 and so on.

On the other hand, the entropies of fusion of solids in which free rotation is not possible are very much greater. The effect is particularly noticeable in the case of long-chain organic compounds. In the solid state the long-chain molecules are locked securely in position, so that the W value of the system is small. In the liquid state the molecules can contort to assume a large number of shapes, so that the W value is high. In such cases entropy values as much as 30 cal deg^{-1} have been recorded. In general, entropies of fusion of solids which melt to form associated liquids are smaller than those which would be expected if fusion to a normal liquid were possible. Thus that of water is 5·3 cal deg^{-1} mole^{-1}, while that of benzene is 8·3. This, too, would be expected in view of the fact that the entropies of associated liquids are smaller than those of normal liquids. An extreme case of an associated liquid is that of an anisotropic liquid, sometimes called a liquid crystal. In such cases fusion leads to relatively little change in the molecular arrangement of the molecules, and hence to little change in the W value for the system. It would be expected therefore that the entropies of fusion for such compounds are small.

SOLUTIONS CONTAINING AN INVOLATILE SOLUTE

We are here concerned with a two-component system, one component of which is called the solvent and the other the solute. The object of this section is to compare some of the properties of the solution with those of the pure solvent.

Consider a system containing n_1 moles of solvent and n_2 moles of solute, and denote the mole fractions of the two components by the symbols x_1 and x_2. The properties of the solvent *in solution* are denoted by the suffix 1, and those of the pure solvent by the suffix 1 and by the super-fix 0, so that, for example, the vapour pressure of water in an aqueous solution is denoted by p_1 and that of pure water by p_1^0.

We first consider very dilute solutions so that the mole fraction of the solvent is very close to unity and that of the solute very close to zero. Under these circumstances the solution may be assumed to be ideal. It follows from (15,12) that at any temperature $p_1 = x_1 p_1^0$, so that at any temperature the vapour pressure of the solution is lower than that of the pure solvent. The most interesting result of this is its effect on the boiling point and freezing point of the solution, and the information that can be obtained therefrom on the state of the solute.

The boiling point of a liquid is defined as that temperature at which the vapour pressure of the liquid is precisely 1 atmosphere. We denote the boiling point of the solution by T_1 and that of the pure solvent by T_1^0. It follows from (15,25) that if we assume that the latent heat of evaporation of the solvent in solution is the same as that in the pure state, and that it is independent of temperature over the range T_1^0 to T_1, the boiling point of the solution is given by the equation

$$\int_{p_1}^{p_1^0} d \log_e p_1 = \int_{T_1^0}^{T_1} \frac{L_e}{RT^2} dT \quad \quad \cdots \quad \cdots \quad (15,29)$$

i.e. $$\log_e \frac{p_1^0}{p_1} = \frac{L_e}{R} \left\{ \frac{T_1 - T_1^0}{T_1 T_1^0} \right\}.$$

Since $p_1^0 > p_1$, it follows that $T_1 > T_1^0$, i.e. that the boiling point of a solution is higher than that of the pure solvent.

It follows from (15,12) that

$$\log_e \frac{p_1^0}{p_1} = -\log_e x_1 = -\log_e (1 - x_2) = \frac{L_e}{R} \left\{ \frac{T_1 - T_1^0}{T_1 T_1^0} \right\}.$$

When x_2 is very small, the following approximations may be made:

$$-\log_e (1 - x_2) \simeq x_2 \simeq \frac{n_2}{n_1}$$

and

$$T_1 T_1^0 \simeq T_1^{02}.$$

Denoting $T_1 - T_1^0$ by ΔT, we obtain the equation

$$\frac{n_2}{n_1} \simeq \frac{L_e \Delta T}{RT_1^{02}}.$$

It follows that if the solution contains w_1 gm of solvent of molecular weight M_1, and w_2 gm of solute of molecular weight M_2,

$$\frac{L_e \Delta T}{RT_1^{02}} \simeq \frac{w_2 M_1}{w_1 M_2}. \qquad \qquad \cdots \cdots \quad (15,30)$$

This equation permits the determination of the molecular weight of solute from the elevation of boiling point.

Equation (15,30) may be rewritten in the form

$$\Delta T \simeq \frac{RT_1^{02} M_1}{w_1 L_e} \frac{w_2}{M_2}.$$

If w_1 is 1000 gm, the quantity $\frac{w_2}{M_2}$ becomes the molality of the solute m_2, and the quantity $\frac{RT_1^{02} M_1}{1000 L_e}$, which is a constant for a given solvent is known as the molal boiling point constant K_b.

Since $\Delta T = K_b m_2$, it follows that for dilute solutions the elevation of boiling point is proportional to the molality of the solution, and that K_b is numerically equal to the elevation of boiling point of a 1-molal solution. The value of K_b for water is 0·52, for benzene 2·62 and for carbon tetrachloride 5·0.

We now consider the effect of solute on the freezing point of the solvent. We consider first two systems, one consisting of ice and the second consisting of liquid water, both in equilibrium with water vapour. The variation of vapour pressure of ice with temperature is given by equation (15,26)

$$\frac{d \log_e p_{ice}}{dT} = \frac{L_s}{RT^2} \qquad \cdots \cdots \quad (15,26)$$

and that of water by equation (15,25)

$$\frac{d \log_e p_1^0}{dT} = \frac{L_e}{RT^2}. \qquad \cdots \cdots \quad (15,25)$$

Since the change in enthalpy, when a solid transforms into a vapour at the same pressure, is the same whether the process takes place in one stage (i.e. sublimation) or in two stages (i.e. fusion followed by evaporation), it follows that the latent heats of sublimation and fusion of the solid and the latent heat of evaporation of the supercooled liquid at the same temperature are connected by the equation

$$L_s = L_f + L_e, \qquad \cdots \cdots \quad (15,31)$$

so that at the same temperature

$$L_s > L_e,$$

and therefore
$$\frac{d \log_e p_{\text{ice}}}{dT} > \frac{d \log_e p_1^0}{dT}.$$

In other words, the slope of the vapour pressure curve against temperature is greater in the case of ice than in the case of water at all temperatures.

The vapour pressure curves of ice, water and supercooled water are shown in Figure 15,2.

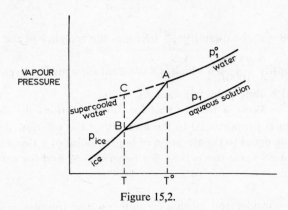

Figure 15,2.

The curves intercept at point A, which is the triple point of water. The triple point is so close to the freezing point of water (i.e. the temperature at which water is in equilibrium with ice under an external pressure of 1 atmosphere), that it is sufficient to regard T^0, the temperature corresponding to point A, as the freezing point of water in the present argument.

Since the vapour pressure of a solution is lower than that of the pure solvent at all temperatures, the vapour pressure curve of an aqueous solution must lie below that of pure water, as shown in Figure 15,2. The interception of this curve with that of ice gives the freezing point of the solution. We observe that the freezing point of a solution is lower than that of the pure solvent.

It follows from (15,25), (15,26) and (15,31) that, denoting the vapour pressure of supercooled water at temperature T by p_1^0 and that of ice at the same temperature by p_{ice},

$$\frac{d \log_e \frac{p_{\text{ice}}}{p_1^0}}{dT} = \frac{L_s - L_e}{RT^2} = \frac{L_f}{RT^2}. \quad . \quad . \quad . \quad (15,32)$$

Since at the freezing point of the solution the vapour pressure of ice equals that of the solution, the ratio p_{ice}/p_1^0 must at this point be the same as p_1/p_1^0, and since for an ideal solution

$$p_1 = x_1 p_1^0,$$

it follows that

$$\frac{d \log_e x_1}{dT} = \frac{L_f}{RT^2} \quad \cdots \cdots \cdots \quad (15,33)$$

so that

$$\log_e x_1 = -\frac{L_f}{RT} + I.$$

When

$$x_1 = 1, \, T = T^0$$

so that

$$I = \frac{L_f}{RT^0}$$

and therefore

$$\log_e x_1 = \frac{L_f}{R}\left\{\frac{1}{T^0} - \frac{1}{T}\right\} \quad \cdots \cdots \quad (15,34)$$

The mole fraction of the solute is related to that of the solvent by the equation

$$x_1 = (1 - x_2)$$

and for a very dilute solution it is permissible to write

$$\log_e (1 - x_2) = -x_2$$

and

$$TT^0 \simeq T^{02},$$

so that expressing $T^0 - T$ by ΔT, we obtain the equation

$$x_2 = \frac{L_f \Delta T}{RT^{02}}. \quad \cdots \cdots \cdots \quad (15,35)$$

As before this may be written

$$\frac{L_f \Delta T}{RT^{02}} = \frac{w_2 M_1}{w_1 M_2}$$

or

$$\Delta T = \frac{RT^{02} M_1}{w_1 L_f} \cdot \frac{w_2}{M_2}.$$

If w_1 is 1000 gm the quantity $\dfrac{w_2}{M_2}$ becomes m_2, the molality of the solute.

The quantity $\dfrac{RT^{02} M_1}{1000 L_f}$ is given the symbol K_f and is known as the molal freezing-point constant for the solvent.

Since

$$\Delta T = K_f m_2$$

it follows that for dilute solutions, the depression of freezing point is proportional to the molality of the solution.

The value of K_f for water is 1·858, for benzene 5·12 and for camphor 40. The magnitude of the last value has led to the wide use of camphor as a solvent in the Rast method for the determination of molecular weights of organic materials.

BINARY LIQUID SYSTEMS

We consider first a mixture of two liquids A and B which is ideal throughout the whole composition range. It follows that throughout the whole composition range the partial pressures of A and B at any particular temperature are given by the equations

$$p_A = x_A p_A^0$$

$$p_B = x_B p_B^0.$$

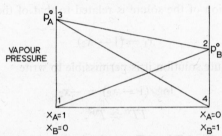

Figure 15,3. The partial pressures of the two components of an ideal mixture.

The variation of p_A and p_B with composition are shown by the lines 1–2 and 4–3, while line 3–2 shows the variation of total vapour pressure of the mixture.

Let us consider the composition of the vapour phase in equilibrium with a liquid mixture in which

$$x_A = x_B = 0·5.$$

If we suppose that $$p_A^0 > p_B^0$$

it is clear that $$p_A > p_B$$

so that the mole fraction of A in the vapour phase is greater than 0·5 and that of B is less than 0·5. In other words, the vapour is relatively richer in the component whose addition to the liquid phase results in an increase in total vapour pressure. This generalisation is known as Konowaloff's Rule.

It follows from this that if the composition of both vapour and liquid phases be plotted against boiling point (i.e. the temperature at which the total vapour pressure of the mixture equals 1 atmosphere), the curves will be of the form shown in Figure 15,4, so that, for example, at temperature T a liquid mixture of composition i is in equilibrium with a vapour phase of composition j. Boiling under a fractionating column will tend therefore to produce a vapour phase rich in component A, and a liquid phase rich in B. The practical significance of the *shape* of the curves shown in Figure 15,4 is that the ideal mixture can be separated completely by fractional distillation.

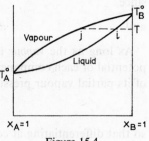

Figure 15,4.

Solutions which deviate from ideal behaviour fall into four categories as shown in Figure 15,5. Systems (i) and (iii) are said to show positive deviations from ideal behaviour, signifying that each partial pressure is greater than the theoretical value for an ideal solution, and systems (ii) and (iv) are said to show negative deviations.[1] The difference between the behaviour of systems (i) and (iii) and that between systems (ii) and (iv) appears at first sight to be one only of degree, but the fact that the total

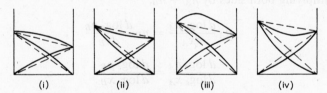

Figure 15,5. The partial pressure curves of non-ideal solutions.

vapour pressure curve in (iii) shows a maximum, and that in (iv) a minimum, while those in (i) and (ii) do not, is of considerable practical significance. In order to appreciate this we proceed as follows. The Gibbs–Duhem equation for a system of two components A and B at constant temperature and pressure takes the form

$$n_A d\mu_A = -n_B d\mu_B,$$

so that, dividing both sides by $n_A + n_B$, we obtain

$$x_A d\mu_A = -x_B d\mu_B.$$

[1] Why do no systems exist in which one component shows positive deviations and the second negative?

M

Therefore $\qquad x_A \dfrac{d\mu_A}{dx_A} = -x_B \dfrac{d\mu_B}{dx_A} = x_B \dfrac{d\mu_B}{dx_B}$

since $\qquad\qquad\qquad x_A = 1 - x_B$

and $\qquad\qquad\qquad dx_A = -dx_B.$

As long as the *vapour* approximates to ideal behaviour, the chemical potential of each component in the liquid phase can be expressed in terms of its partial vapour pressure by the equation

$$\mu = \mu_0 + RT \log_e p$$

so that differentiating at constant temperature

$$\frac{d\mu_A}{dx_A} = RT \frac{d \log_e p_A}{dx_A}$$

and $\qquad\qquad \dfrac{d\mu_B}{dx_B} = RT \dfrac{d \log_e p_B}{dx_B}.$

It follows that

$$x_A \frac{d \log_e p_A}{dx_A} = x_B \frac{d \log_e p_B}{dx_B} \qquad . \quad . \quad . \quad (15,36)$$

or, multiplying both sides by $n_A + n_B$,

$$n_A \frac{d \log_e p_A}{dx_A} = n_B \frac{d \log_e p_B}{dx_B} \qquad . \quad . \quad . \quad (15,37)$$

or $\qquad\qquad \dfrac{d \log_e p_A}{d \log_e x_A} = \dfrac{d \log_e p_B}{d \log_e x_B}. \qquad . \quad . \quad . \quad (15,38)$

These three equations are different forms of the *Duhem–Margules* equation. It is much used in the investigation of the behaviour of binary liquid systems. We shall use it only to investigate the significance of the maxima and minima in the vapour pressure curves of systems shown in Figure 15,5.

Remembering that $\qquad dx_A = -dx_B$

(15,36) is written in the form

$$\frac{x_A dp_A}{p_A dx_A} + \frac{x_B dp_B}{p_B dx_A} = 0.$$

The vapour pressure of the solution equals $p_A + p_B$, and at a maximum or minimum

$$\frac{dp}{dx_A} = 0$$

i.e. at the maxima and minima

$$\frac{dp}{dx_A} = \frac{dp_A}{dx_A} + \frac{dp_B}{dx_A} = \frac{dp_A}{dx_A} - \frac{x_A p_B}{x_B p_A}\frac{dp_A}{dx_A}$$

$$= \frac{dp_A}{dx_A}\left\{1 - \frac{x_A p_B}{x_B p_A}\right\} = 0.$$

Since $\dfrac{dp_A}{dx_A}$ cannot equal zero

$$\frac{x_A p_B}{x_B p_A} = 1$$

i.e.

$$\frac{p_A}{x_A} = \frac{p_B}{x_B}$$

so that at the maxima and minima points in Figures 15,5 *the composition of the vapour phase is the same as that of the liquid mixture with which it is in equilibrium.*

The composition to which corresponds a maximum combined vapour pressure must have a lower boiling point than a mixture of any other composition, and a composition to which corresponds a minimum combined vapour pressure must have a higher boiling point than a mixture of any other composition. It follows from this and from the

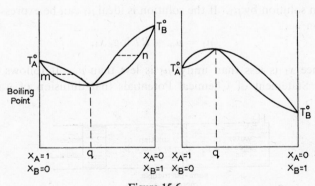

Figure 15,6.

previous argument that the boiling-point–composition curves for systems of types (iii) and (iv) are of the forms shown in Figure 15,6. The significance of this is, that whereas systems the vapour pressure curves of which correspond to (i) and (ii) in Figure 15,5, and which do not show maxima and minima, may, like ideal solutions, be separated into pure components by fractional distillation, fractional distillation of a mixture of type (iii)—say a mixture of composition *n* in Figure 15,6—will result only in separation into two fractions, one consisting of pure B and the other consisting of the constant boiling mixture of composition q. Similarly, fractional distillation of a mixture of composition m will give a fraction consisting of pure A and a fraction of composition q. Precisely the same result will be obtained in the case of a system of type (iv), so that systems of types (iii) and (iv) cannot be separated completely by fractional distillation. Systems corresponding to type (iii) are common, one of the most important examples being a mixture of ethyl alcohol and water. The most important example of type (iv) is a mixture of hydrochloric acid and water; the composition of the constant boiling mixture obtained when such a mixture is distilled at atmospheric pressure containing 20·222% HCl by weight.

OSMOSIS AND OSMOTIC PRESSURE

Consider a system separated into two parts. The left-hand side consists of pure water and the right-hand side consists of an aqueous solution in which the mole fraction of the water is given by x_1, and that of the solute by x_2. We now suppose that the two parts of the system are separated by a membrane permeable to water but impermeable to solute molecules, but that both parts of the system are at the same temperature and pressure. The chemical potential of the pure water is denoted by μ_0, and that of the water in solution by μ_1. If the solution is ideal μ_1 can be expressed by the equation

$$\mu_1 = \mu_0 + RT \log_e x_1,$$

and since x_1 is less than unity, μ_1 is less than μ_0. It follows from the Second Statement of Chemical Potentials that diffusion of water from

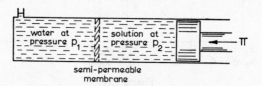

semi-permeable
membrane

Figure 15,7. An osmotic system in equilibrium.

the left-hand side to the right will be spontaneous. This process is known as OSMOSIS. It is an experimental fact that osmosis may be prevented by subjecting the solution to an excess pressure Π, known as the OSMOTIC PRESSURE of the solution.

Figure 15,7 shows such a system in which the solution subjected to external pressure Π is in equilibrium with water. It is clear that the two parts of the system are at different pressures, the water at pressure p_1 and the solution at pressure p_2, and that

$$\Pi = p_2 - p_1. \quad \quad \quad \quad (15,39)$$

It follows from the First Statement of Chemical Potentials that at equilibrium the chemical potential of water is the same in both parts of the system; in other words, the chemical potential of pure water at p_1 equals that in solution at p_2

i.e. $$\mu^0_{H_2O \text{ at } p_1} = \mu_{1 H_2O \text{ at } p_2}. \quad \quad \quad (15,40)$$

If the solution is ideal, this equation can be written

$$\mu^0_{H_2O \text{ at } p_1} = \mu^0_{H_2O \text{ at } p_2} + RT \log_e x_1. \quad (15,41)$$

Since x_1 must be less than unity, the term $RT \log_e x_1$ is negative, so that the standard chemical potential of water at p_2 must be greater than that at p_1.

The chemical potential of a liquid is related to the pressure to which it is subjected by the equation

$$\mu^0_{p_2} - \mu^0_{p_1} = \bar{V}(p_2 - p_1) \quad \quad \quad (11,42)$$

where $\bar{V}$ is the molar volume. It follows that for osmotic equilibrium p_2 must be greater than p_1. It is therefore evident from (15,39) that the osmotic pressure of a solution is always positive.

What has been deduced for an aqueous solution holds for a solution in other media. The osmotic pressure of a solution is therefore formally defined as the difference between two pressures p_2 and p_1, the values of which are such that the chemical potential of the solvent in solution at p_2 equals that of the pure solvent at p_1, the temperature being the same in both cases.

A theory of osmosis put forward originally by van't Hoff traced the osmotic pressure of a solution to the imagined bombardment of the semi-permeable membrane by solute molecules. This theory (in its entirety at least,) is now known to be incorrect. The osmotic pressure of a solution is not a *real* pressure actually experienced by a solution; it is an excess pressure which must be applied to a solution to place it in equilibrium with the pure solvent. As Guggenheim[1] points out: "It is in fact analogous to the freezing point of a solution, which has no relation to the actual temperature, but is the temperature to which it must be brought to reach a certain equilibrium state."

[1] E. A. Guggenheim, *Thermodynamics* (North Holland Publishing Coy., 1957), page 236.

It will be remembered that the van't Hoff theory gained support from the fact that it predicted the relationship between the osmotic pressure of a solution and its concentration,

$$\Pi = CRT, \quad \ldots \ldots \ldots \quad (15,42)$$

and that this equation was found to describe fairly accurately the osmotic pressure of very dilute solutions of non-electrolytes in water. It will be remembered, too, that the fact that a correction had to be applied to this equation amending it to

$$\Pi = iCRT \quad \ldots \ldots \ldots \quad (15,43)$$

in the case of very dilute solutions of electrolytes played an important part in the acceptance of the Arrhenius Theory of Electrolytic Dissociation. We have stated that the van't Hoff theory of osmosis is incorrect. We now proceed to show that notwithstanding this, the osmotic pressure of a solution of a non-electrolyte can be described by equation (15,42), as long as the solution *is* very dilute. These are, of course, the conditions under which it was found to apply.

Consider a solution of n_2 moles of solute in n_1 moles of water, so that the mole fraction of the water is

$$x_1 = \frac{n_1}{n_1 + n_2}$$

and that of the solute

$$x_2 = \frac{n_2}{n_1 + n_2}.$$

We then have

$$\mu_{O_{H_2O}\ at\ p_1} = \mu_{O_{H_2O}\ at\ p_2} + RT \log_e x_1 \quad . \quad . \quad . \quad (15,41)$$

$$\mu_{O_{H_2O}\ at\ p_2} - \mu_{O_{H_2O}\ at\ p_1} = \bar{V}(p_2 - p_1) \quad . \quad . \quad . \quad (11,42)$$

and
$$\Pi = p_2 - p_1, \quad . \quad . \quad . \quad . \quad . \quad (15,39)$$

so that
$$\Pi \bar{V} = -RT \log_e x_1 = -RT \log_e (1 - x_2). \quad . \quad . \quad (15,44)$$

If the solution is very dilute, so that x_2 is very much smaller than unity

$$-\log_e (1 - x_2) \simeq x_2 \simeq \frac{n_2}{n_1}$$

so that
$$\Pi = \frac{RT n_2}{n_1 \bar{V}}. \quad . \quad . \quad . \quad . \quad . \quad (15,45)$$

Since $n_1 \bar{V}$ is the total volume of solvent, $\dfrac{n_2}{n_1 \bar{V}}$ equals the molar concentration of solute. We therefore reach the van't Hoff equation

$$\Pi = CRT$$

and observe that although the thesis upon which the van't Hoff theory of osmosis rests may lack reality, the van't Hoff equation is true as long as the solution is both ideal and very dilute. These are precisely the conditions under which the equation was found to be supported by experiment.

The fact that the osmotic pressure of a solution of a strong electrolyte is greater than that of a non-electrolyte of the same molality is due of course to the ionisation of the solute in the first case. The ions produced must be treated as independent species, so that the mole fraction of water in a solution containing one mole of potassium chloride per 1000 gm of solvent is

$$\frac{1000/18}{1000/18 + 1 + 1}$$

whereas in a solution containing one mole of non-electrolyte per 1000 gm of solvent it is

$$\frac{1000/18}{1000/18 + 1}.$$

We lastly observe that the osmotic pressure of an ideal solution may be expressed in terms of the partial pressure of the solvent. Since

$$p_1 = x_1 p_1^0 \qquad \cdots \quad \cdots \quad \cdots \quad (15,12)$$

it follows from (15,44) that

$$\Pi = -\frac{RT}{V} \log_e \frac{p_1}{p_1^0}. \qquad \cdots \quad \cdots \quad (15,46)$$

THE NERNST DISTRIBUTION LAW

Consider a two-phase liquid system consisting of two immiscible or slightly miscible components α and β. If a third component soluble in both liquids is added, it is distributed between the two liquids so that its chemical potential is the same in each phase;

i.e. $$\mu^\alpha = \mu^\beta.$$

The chemical potentials are expressed in terms of their equilibrium molar concentrations by equations

$$\mu^\alpha = \mu_0^\alpha + RT \log_e C^\alpha$$

and $$\mu^\beta = \mu_0^\beta + RT \log_e C^\beta.$$

It follows that

$$\frac{C^\alpha}{C^\beta} = e^{\frac{\mu_0^\beta - \mu_0^\alpha}{RT}},$$

so that at constant temperature we may write

$$\frac{C^\alpha}{C^\beta} = D \quad \cdot \quad \cdot \quad \cdot \quad \cdot \quad \cdot \quad \cdot \quad (15,47)$$

where D is the *Distribution Constant*.

The above result is true only if the solution is ideal, and if the molecular species of the solute is the same in each phase. For non-ideal solutions the concentration terms in equation (15,47) must be replaced by activities. The second condition is the more interesting.

Consider a solute A distributed between two solvents α and β, and suppose that it exists as the monomer A in solvent α, but that in solvent β, A is partially associated to form a polymer A_n. The species in solvent β is subject to the chemical equilibrium

$$nA \rightleftharpoons A_n.$$

If the molar concentration of the species in solvent β is C^β calculated as the monomer, and if a is its degree of association, the concentration of the monomer at equilibrium is $C^\beta(1 - a)$ and that of the polymer $\dfrac{C^\beta a}{n}$.

It follows from the Law of Mass Action that at equilibrium

$$\frac{C^\beta a/n}{\{C^\beta(1 - a)\}^n} = K$$

so that

$$C^\beta(1 - a) = \left\{\frac{C^\beta a}{nK}\right\}^{\frac{1}{n}}. \quad \cdot \quad \cdot \quad \cdot \quad \cdot \quad (15,48)$$

The distribution condition

$$\mu^\alpha = \mu^\beta$$

applies only to the species common to both phases, so that at equilibrium

$$\mu_0^\alpha + RT \log_e C^\alpha = \mu_0^\beta + RT \log_e \left\{\frac{C^\beta a}{nK}\right\}^{\frac{1}{n}}$$

i.e.

$$\frac{\left\{\dfrac{C^\beta a}{nK}\right\}^{\frac{1}{n}}}{C^\alpha} = D. \quad \cdot \quad \cdot \quad \cdot \quad \cdot \quad \cdot \quad \cdot \quad (15,49)$$

If association in solvent β is almost complete, so that

$$a \simeq 1,$$

this equation reduces to the form

$$\frac{C^{\beta^{\frac{1}{n}}}}{C^\alpha} = D'. \quad \cdots \cdots \quad (15,50)$$

The concentrations of benzoic acid distributed between water and benzene are found to obey an equation of this sort. The equilibrium concentrations in water C^α, and in benzene C^β, quoted by Glasstone[1] are shown below:

C^α	0·00329	0·00579	0·00749	0·0114
C^β	0·0156	0·0495	0·0835	0·195
C^β/C^α	4·76	8·55	11·24	17·24
$\dfrac{C^{\beta^{\frac{1}{2}}}}{C^\alpha}$	38·02	38·17	38·61	38·76

The fact that the values C^β/C^α show no constancy, but that the values $\dfrac{C^{\beta^{\frac{1}{2}}}}{C^\alpha}$ are approximately the same over a considerable concentration range indicates that in benzene benzoic acid exists almost completely as the dimer. The Distribution Law is particularly useful in the detection of polymerisations of this sort.

THE SOLUBILITY OF ONE SUBSTANCE IN ANOTHER

It is not within the province of thermodynamics to explain why a substance is readily soluble in one solvent, but almost insoluble in another, but it is interesting to discuss the difference in thermodynamic terms. Consider the case in which the molecular species of a substance Y is the same in the crystalline state as in solution, and select two solvents A and B such that the solubility of Y in A is very much greater than that in B. In both instances we consider equilibrium between solid Y and a saturated solution of Y in A or B, denoting the molal concentration of Y in A at saturation by the symbol $m_{(A)}$ and that of Y in B at saturation by the symbol $m_{(B)}$.

It follows from the First Statement of Chemical Potentials that the chemical potential of the solid must be the same as that of the species in solution, so that we may write

$$\mu_{Y(s)} = \mu_{0Y(A)} + RT \log_e \gamma_{(A)} m_{(A)}$$

and

$$\mu_{Y(s)} = \mu_{0Y(B)} + RT \log_e \gamma_{(B)} m_{(B)}$$

[1] Glasstone, *Textbook of Physical Chemistry* (Macmillan).

where $\mu_{0Y(A)}$ is the standard chemical potential of Y in solvent A (i.e. is the chemical potential of Y under such (possibly hypothetical) conditions that the molality is unity), the symbol $\mu_{0Y(B)}$ has the same significance, and $\gamma_{(A)}$ and $\gamma_{(B)}$ are the activity coefficients of Y in solvents A and B.

It follows that

$$\mu_{0Y(A)} + RT \log_e \gamma_{(A)} m_{(A)} = \mu_{0Y(B)} + RT \log_e \gamma_{(B)} m_{(B)}$$

so that

$$RT \log_e \frac{m_{(A)}}{m_{(B)}} = \mu_{0Y(B)} - \mu_{0Y(A)} + RT \log_e \frac{\gamma_{(B)}}{\gamma_{(A)}}.$$

We have supposed that the solubility of Y in A is very much greater than that in B, i.e. that

$$m_{(A)} \gg m_{(B)}.$$

It must therefore follow, either—

(i) that if the activity coefficients of Y in A and B are much the same, $\mu_{0Y(B)}$ is much greater than $\mu_{0Y(A)}$; or

(ii) that if $\mu_{0Y(B)}$ and $\mu_{0Y(A)}$ are much the same, the activity coefficient of Y in (B) must be greater than that in (A).

It would be possible to decide between these two possibilities if sufficient data were available. It could be decided in the case of silver chloride in water and say, ethyl alcohol for example, if the solubility and thermo-dynamic solubility product of silver chloride in ethyl alcohol were known with the same accuracy as these quantities are known in water. An interesting case which can be discussed fully is that of a pair of conjugate solutions. Water and benzene are, for example, relatively immiscible, and if water and benzene are shaken together the system separates into two layers: layer (i) consisting of a saturated solution of benzene in water, and layer (ii) of a saturated solution of water in benzene. If we denote benzene in (i) by the symbol $b(i)$ and in (ii) by the symbol $b(ii)$, we may write:

$$\mu_{b(i)} = \mu_{b(ii)}$$

i.e. $$\mu_{0b} + RT \log_e \gamma_{b(i)} x_{B(i)} = \mu_{0b} + RT \log_e \gamma_{b(ii)} x_{b(ii)}$$

where $x_{b(i)}$ and $x_{b(ii)}$ are the mole fractions of benzene in the two layers, $\gamma_{b(i)}$ and $\gamma_{b(ii)}$ their activity coefficients, and $\mu_{0(b)}$ the chemical potential of pure benzene at the same temperature and pressure. It therefore follows that

$$\gamma_{b(i)} x_{b(i)} = \gamma_{b(ii)} x_{b(ii)}.$$

At 25° C it is found that layer (i) contains 99·9% water and layer (ii) contains 0·07%, so that

$$x_{b(i)} = \frac{\frac{0·1}{78}}{\frac{99·9}{18} + \frac{0·1}{78}} = 0·00023$$

and

$$x_{b(ii)} = \frac{\frac{99·93}{78}}{\frac{99·93}{78} + \frac{0·07}{18}} = 0·999.$$

If we suppose that $\gamma_{b(ii)}$ is very close to unity, it follows that

$$\gamma_{b(i)} \simeq \frac{x_{b(ii)}}{x_{b(i)}} = \frac{0·999}{0·00023} = 4344.$$

The same reasoning shows that $\gamma_{w(ii)}$, i.e. the activity coefficient of water in benzene is about 360.

Precisely the same results are obtained by considering the partial vapour pressures of the two solutions. The same vapour phase is in equilibrium with both solutions, so that the vapour pressure exerted by the benzene in water solution is the same as that exerted by the benzene in solution (ii).

EXERCISES 15

15,1. A system consists of a single chemical species present as both a liquid and vapour in a cylinder fitted with a frictionless piston. Use the Phase Rule and any other information available to decide the effect of reducing the temperature of the system but keeping the external pressure applied to the piston the same.

Explain how the result is modified if the system consists of two chemical species, one present as liquid and vapour and the second present only in the vapour phase.

15,2. An equilibrium system consists of P phases and C chemical species. Each of P-2 phases contains C components, but the remaining two phases contain only one component each.

How many intensive properties may be arbitrarily determined?

15,3. For many unassociated liquids the ratio of the boiling point to the critical temperature is approximately equal to 0·6. For such liquids an empirical relationship is found to exist between the vapour pressure of the liquid and its critical temperature and pressure. This relationship first suggested by van't Hoff is

$$\log_{10} \frac{p}{p_c} = k\left(1 - \frac{T_c}{T}\right)$$

where the constant k has the value 3. This equation can be put in the form

$$\log_e p_R = 2 \cdot 3k \left(1 - \frac{1}{T_R} \right)$$

where p_R and T_R are the reduced pressure and temperature.

Use one form of the Clausius–Clapeyron equation to show that these facts predict a value for the entropy of boiling of approximately 23 cal deg^{-1} mole^{-1}.

15,4. Show that for those liquids which obey the equation

$$p = ae^{-\frac{Le}{RT}}$$

where p is the vapour pressure and a has the value $2 \cdot 7 \times 10^4$ atm. that the entropy of boiling is apqroximately 20 cal deg^{-1} mole^{-1}.

15,5. A solution consists of 117 gm of sodium chloride in 1000 gm water. What is the mole fraction of the water?

15,6. The "mean molecular weight" of air is approximately 28·8. Calculate the quantity of water vapour present per lb of air saturated with water vapour at 60° F and at 1 atmosphere pressure. The saturation vapour pressure of water at 60° F is 0·256 lbf in^{-2} (1 atm. = 14·7 lbf in^{-2}).

15,7. Konowaloff's Rule states that the vapour phase of a binary liquid system is richer than the liquid in the component, increase of which in the liquid phase would lead to an increase in the total vapour pressure of the mixture. Show that this rule may be deduced from the Duhem–Margules equation. (The reasoning is similar to that used on page 326.)

15,8. Show that the average heat of solution of a solute over the temperature range T_1 to T_2 may be determined from the solubilities at T_1 and T_2 and is given by the equation

$$\Delta H = R \left\{ \frac{T_1 T_2}{T_2 - T_1} \right\} \log_e \frac{C_{T_2}}{C_{T_1}}.$$

15,9. The vapour pressure of molten sodium at 500° K is $1 \cdot 52 \times 10^{-3}$ mm Hg and that at 700° K 1·12 mm. Estimate the average molar latent heat of evaporation over these temperatures, and the boiling point of sodium at 1 atmosphere pressure.

What is the boiling point if sodium obeys Trouton's Law?

15,10. A 2-molal solution of glucose in water is separated from pure water by a semi-permeable membrane. The system is at 300° K and under a pressure of 1 atmosphere throughout. Calculate the driving force (i.e. the affinity) tending to impel the water through the membrane in the initial moments.

15,11.

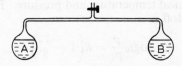

A solution containing initially one mole of a non-volatile solute in 200 gm of water is placed in bulb A in the apparatus shown above. Bulb B contains pure water. All air is removed from the system. Bulb A is maintained at 32° C and bulb B at 30° C.

At what molality will be the solution in A after the system has been left undisturbed for several hours? It may be assumed that the solution is ideal. The vapour pressure of water at 30° C is 31·792 mm Hg and at 32° C is 35·630 mm.

15,12. Analysis shows that benzoic acid distributes itself between water and benzene to give solutions of the following molarities:

C_{water}	0·00329	0·00579	0·00749	0·0114
$C_{benzene}$	0·0156	0·0495	0·0835	0·195

Assuming that benzoic acid exists in aqueous solution as the monomer, and that ionisation is negligible, what information can be deduced about the state of benzoic acid in benzene?

15,13. Discuss the relationship between composition and partial vapour pressures of two completely miscible liquids. What bearing has the relationship upon the possibility of separating two such liquids by fractional distillation?

15,14. Propyl alcohol and water are miscible in all proportions. The vapour pressure curve passes through a maximum corresponding to a mixture containing about 80% of propyl alcohol. The corresponding curve for formic acid passes through a minimum at 75% of formic acid. Compare the behaviour on distillation of aqueous solutions containing 50% of formic acid and propyl alcohol respectively.

CHAPTER 16

THE APPLICATION OF THERMODYNAMICS TO SOLUTIONS OF ELECTROLYTES

There would appear to be no reason why the concept of chemical potentials should not be applied to systems in which some or all of the reacting species are ions, just as surely as it has been applied to systems containing electrically-neutral atoms or molecules. Systems containing ions do, however, present special features. They are subject to the special restriction of electro-neutrality, so that in a solution containing, for example, hydrogen, ferrous, ferric, hydroxyl and chloride ions, the number of ions of each species cannot be decided arbitrarily and independently, but are controlled by the equation

$$n_{H^+} + 2n_{Fe^{++}} + 3n_{Fe^{+++}} = n_{OH^-} + n_{Cl^-}.$$

On the other hand, the ions must be considered *independent* as far as their contribution to the colligative properties of the system is concerned. A strong electrolyte such as sodium chloride is completely ionised, so that in a system in which one mole of salt is dissolved in twenty moles of water, the system must be assumed to contain one mole of sodium ions, one mole of chloride ions and twenty moles of water, so that the mole fraction of water is $\frac{20}{22}$ and not $\frac{20}{21}$. It follows that the osmotic pressure of such a solution, its vapour pressure depression, boiling-point elevation and so on, will be approximately twice that of a solution of an unionised solute at the same concentration. It is evident that such measurements on a solution containing an electrolyte which is only partially ionised can be used to determine the degree of ionisation.

It must also be remarked that a solution containing charged particles will be subject to very much stronger forces of inter-molecular attraction than will a system containing only electrically-neutral particles, so that it must be expected that the behaviour of such solutions will be far from ideal except when the concentration is *extremely* small, so that activity terms must be used instead of stoichiometric concentrations in all calculations.

One of the most important deductions of Chapter 11 is that when a reaction

$$aA + bB \ldots \rightleftharpoons cC + dD \ldots$$

338

has reached equilibrium, the equilibrium chemical potentials of the reacting species are related by the equation

$$a\mu_{A_{eq}} + b\mu_{B_{eq}} \ldots = c\mu_{C_{eq}} + d\mu_{D_{eq}} \ldots \quad . \quad (11,73)$$

This equation is now applied to the ionisation of a weak electrolyte, i.e. to an electrolyte the ionisation of which is not complete.

The Ionisation of a Weak Electrolyte

If an electrolyte such as acetic acid is dissolved in water, ionisation takes place to a limited degree

$$HAc \rightleftharpoons H^+ + Ac^-.$$

We assume that equation (11,73) applies to such an equilibrium and write

$$\mu_{HAc_{eq}} = \mu_{H^+_{eq}} + \mu_{Ac^-_{eq}}. \quad . \quad . \quad . \quad (16,1)$$

We also assume that, as in the case of the neutral atom or molecule, the chemical potential of a single ion species in a real solution is dependent on the activity of the ion, and write

$$\mu_{ion} = \mu_{0_{ion}} + RT \log_e a_{ion}. \quad . \quad . \quad . \quad (16,2)$$

It happens to be customary to express concentrations of electrolytes in terms of molalities, i.e. the number of moles of solute per 1000 gm of solvent. This system will be used throughout this chapter, and it will be understood that when we use such symbols as a_{H^+} or γ_{H^+} we mean the activity or activity coefficient referred to the molal measure of concentration.

Expressing the equilibrium chemical potentials of acetic acid, the hydrogen and acetate ions in terms of activities, substituting in (16,1) and rearranging we obtain the equation

$$\mu_{0_{HAc}} - (\mu_{0_{H^+}} + \mu_{0_{Ac^-}}) = RT \log_e \frac{a_{H^+_{eq}} \times a_{Ac^-_{eq}}}{a_{HAc_{eq}}}. \quad (16,3)$$

The terms on the left-hand side are the standard chemical potentials of the species at unit activity, so that the value of the left-hand side is independent of concentration. It follows that at constant temperature

$$\frac{a_{H^+_{eq}} \times a_{Ac^-_{eq}}}{a_{HAc_{eq}}} = K(T). \quad . \quad . \quad . \quad (16,4)$$

The constant K is known as the Ionisation Constant of the electrolyte. It can be expressed in terms of the equilibrium molalities and the activity coefficients $\left(\gamma = \dfrac{a}{m}\right)$ by the equation

$$\frac{m_{H^+_{eq}} \times m_{Ac^-_{eq}}}{m_{HAc_{eq}}} \times \frac{\gamma_{H^+_{eq}} \times \gamma_{Ac^-_{eq}}}{\gamma_{HAc_{eq}}} = K(T). \quad . \quad . \quad (16,5)$$

Probably the most important ionisation constant is that of water. Water ionises according to the equation

$$H_2O \rightleftharpoons H^+ + OH^- \text{ (see footnote 1)}$$

and is governed by the equation

$$\frac{a_{H^+} \times a_{OH^-}}{a_{H_2O}} = K.$$

Water is such a weak electrolyte that the activity of the unionised molecules is virtually independent of the degree of ionisation. It is customary therefore to combine the constant quantity a_{H_2O} with the constant K and write

$$a_{H^+} \times a_{OH^-} = K_w. \qquad \ldots \ldots \quad (16,6)$$

The constant K_w is known as the *Ionic Product of Water*.

It will have been noted that the equations so far deduced contain either the *sum* of the chemical potentials of the ionic species, or the *product* of their activities or activity coefficients. These sums or products, as the case may be, can be determined with ease, but it happens that the chemical potential, activity or activity coefficient of a single ion species cannot be determined. We therefore find it convenient to define quantities which we call the mean chemical potential, the mean ionic activity and the mean ionic activity coefficient of the electrolyte.

The *mean chemical potential* of the electrolyte $\mu_{\pm}$ is the *arithmetic* mean of the chemical potentials of the single ion species, i.e. for a uni-univalent electrolyte such as acetic acid

$$\mu_{\pm} = \tfrac{1}{2}\{\mu_{H^+} + \mu_{Ac^-}\}. \qquad \ldots \ldots \quad (16,7)$$

From (16,1) it follows that

$$2\mu_{\pm HAc} = \mu_{HAc}. \qquad \ldots \ldots \quad (16,8)$$

The mean ionic activity and mean ionic activity coefficient is defined as the *geometric* mean of those quantities referring to the individual ionic species, i.e.

$$a^2_{\pm HAc} = a_{H^+} \times a_{Ac^-}, \qquad \ldots \ldots \quad (16,9)$$

$$\gamma^2_{\pm HAc} = \gamma_{H^+} \times \gamma_{Ac^-}. \qquad \ldots \ldots \quad (16,10)$$

The most important characteristic of solutions of that group of substances known as *strong electrolytes* is that ionisation is complete. It is

---

[1] In all the above equations we have described the hydrogen ion by the symbol H^+. In fact, the student will be aware that in solution the proton invariably coordinates to a donor ion or molecule to form a stable complex. In aqueous solution the hydrogen ion is probably the complex H_3O^+.

therefore doubtful whether such expressions as the chemical potential, the activity and the activity coefficient of sodium chloride (as such) in water has any meaning or reality, and in fact the only meaning of the term "concentration of a sodium chloride in water" is that it is a quantity which relates to the amounts of salt and water which were brought together. Here again the mean chemical potentials, mean ionic activities and mean ionic activity coefficients are the only quantities of real significance.

We now require to define these mean ionic quantities in the general case of an electrolyte which dissociates into ν_+ cations each of charge z_+, and ν_- anions each of charge z_-. The mean chemical potential is defined by the equation

$$\mu_\pm = \frac{\nu_+\mu_+ + \nu_-\mu_-}{\nu_+ + \nu_-}, \qquad \qquad (16,11)$$

and the mean ionic activity and mean ionic activity coefficient by the equations

$$a_\pm^{(\nu_+ + \nu_-)} = a_+^{\nu_+} \times a_-^{\nu_-} \qquad \cdots \qquad (16,12)$$

$$\gamma_\pm^{(\nu_+ + \nu_-)} = \gamma_+^{\nu_+} \times \gamma_-^{\nu_-}. \qquad \cdots \qquad (16,13)$$

We note that the principle of electrical neutrality dictates that

$$z_+\nu_+ + z_-\nu_- = 0. \qquad \cdots \qquad (16,14)$$

The Solubility Product of an Electrolyte

Consider an ionic compound AB in equilibrium with its saturated solution in any solvent. In Chapter 11 we showed that if a component is present in more than one phase in a system at equilibrium, the chemical potential of the component is the same in each phase.

Hence, if the compound is completely ionised in solution,

$$\mu_{AB(s)} = \mu_{A^+ \text{solution}} + \mu_{B^- \text{solution}}. \qquad \cdots \qquad (16,15)$$

We apply (16,2) and rearrange to obtain

$$\mu_{AB(s)} - (\mu_{0A^+ \text{solution}} + \mu_{0B^- \text{solution}}) = RT \log_e a_{A^+} \times a_{B^-} \qquad (16,16)$$

where a_{A^+} and a_{B^-} denote the saturation activities of the ions. All terms on the left-hand side are independent of concentration (or indeed of the presence of other species), so that it follows that at constant temperature,

$$a_{A^+} \times a_{B^-} = K_s. \qquad \cdots \qquad (16,17)$$

The constant K_s is known as the *Solubility Product* of the electrolyte. It can be expressed in terms of the ionic molalities and the mean ionic activity coefficient in the form

$$(m_{A^+} \times m_{B^-})\gamma_{\pm AB}^2 = K_s. \qquad \cdots \qquad (16,18)$$

In the case of a very insoluble salt such as silver chloride in water, the solution will approximate to ideality, so that the mean ionic activity coefficient will be very close to unity, and the equation reduce to

$$m_{A^+} \times m_{B^-} \backsimeq K_s. \quad \ldots \quad (16,19)$$

Here again it can be shown that in the case of an electrolyte which dissociates into ν_+ cations and ν_- anions

$$m_+^{\nu_+} \times m_-^{\nu_-} \times \gamma_\pm^{(\nu_+ + \nu_-)} = K_s. \quad \ldots \quad (16,20)$$

The Ionic Strength of a Solution

When considering solutions in which more than one electrolyte is dissolved we shall make use of a quantity I, introduced originally by Lewis and Randall,[1] and known as the Ionic Strength.

$$I = \tfrac{1}{2}\sum_i C_i z_i^2 \quad \ldots \quad (16,21)$$

where C_i is the concentration of each ion species of charge z_i. The ionic strength of a solution containing 0·1 moles of $CaCl_2$ and 0·3 moles of NaCl is

$$I = \frac{0 \cdot 1 \times 4 + 0 \cdot 2 + 0 \cdot 3 + 0 \cdot 3}{2} = 0 \cdot 6.$$

It should be noted that for a uni-univalent electrolyte, the ionic strength is the same as the concentration.

The Debye–Hückel Theory of Strong Electrolytes

At all but *extremely* low concentrations, solutions of electrolytes are far from ideal. It is not the function of thermodynamics to predict whether a particular solution will or will not depart from ideality, or to trace the reasons for any deviation. It may, however, be observed that the departure from ideality is largely due to the long-range electrostatic forces operating between the ions in the solution. The first successful attempts to account for the value of the activity coefficient of an electrolyte in solution (which may of course be regarded as a quantitative measure of the departure of the solution from ideality), in terms of these long-range forces were made by Debye and Hückel.[2] This theory leads to the following expression for the mean ionic activity coefficient of a multivalent electrolyte in a dilute solution of ionic strength I:

$$-\log_{10} \gamma_+ = |\, z_+ z_- \,|\; A I^{\frac{1}{2}} \frac{1}{1 + B \mathring{a} I^{\frac{1}{2}}} \quad \ldots \quad (16,22)$$

[1] Lewis and Randall, *J. Am. Chem. Soc.*, 1921, **43**, 1112.
[2] Debye and Hückel, *Phys. Zeit.*, 1924, **24**, 185.

where A and B are parameters and $\overset{\circ}{a}$ is the distance of closest approach of the ions concerned. If the solution is *extremely* dilute, the last term in the denominator may be neglected, and the expression reduced to the form

$$-\log_{10} \gamma_+ = |z_+ z_-| A I^{\frac{1}{2}}. \qquad . \quad . \quad . \quad (16,23)$$

As we shall demonstrate in the next chapter, it is possible to use electrochemical cells to obtain experimental values of mean ionic activity coefficients with great accuracy. In such cases graphs of $\log_e \gamma_+$ against the square root of the ionic strength tend to approximate, at the lowest ionic strength, to straight lines, the slope of which is just that predicted by the limiting Debye–Hückel equation.

Donnan Membrane Equilibrium

Consider a system consisting initially of a solution of sodium chloride separated from an equal volume of a solution of a salt ACl by a membrane permeable to sodium and chloride ions but impermeable to the ion A^+.

If the initial concentrations of sodium chloride and the salt ACl are C_1 and C_2, the initial state of the system may be represented by the scheme

$$
\begin{array}{c|c}
1 & 2 \\
Na^+ = C_1 & A^+ = C_2 \\
Cl^- = C_1 & Cl^- = C_2.
\end{array}
$$

If the sodium and chloride ions were independent in every sense, it would be expected that they would separately diffuse from one solution to the other until the activity, and hence the chemical potential, of each species is the same in both. The principle of electrical neutrality requires, however, that diffusion of sodium ions in any one direction is accompanied by the diffusion in the same direction of the equivalent number of chloride ions. The final equilibrium state is determined, therefore, not by the conditions that the chemical potentials of the sodium and chloride ions are *separately* the same on both sides, but that the sum of the chemical potentials of the two ions shall be the same.

Let us suppose, therefore, that a quantity of sodium chloride diffuses from side 1 to side 2, so that at equilibrium the concentrations of the various species are given by the scheme

$$
\begin{array}{c|c}
1 & 2 \\
Na^+ = C_1 - y & A^+ = C_2 \\
Cl^- = C_1 - y & Na^+ = y \\
& Cl^- = C_2 + y.
\end{array}
$$

At equilibrium

$$\mu_{0Na^+} + RT \log_e a_{Na^+_{(1)}} + \mu_{0Cl^-} + RT \log_e a_{Cl^-_{(1)}}$$
$$= \mu_{0Na^+} + RT \log_e a_{Na^+_{(2)}} + \mu_{0Cl^-} + RT \log_e a_{Cl^-_{(2)}}$$

so that $\qquad\qquad a_{Na^+_{(1)}} \times a_{Cl^-_{(1)}} = a_{Na^+_{(2)}} \times a_{Cl^-_{(2)}}.$

This equation becomes

$$(C_1 - y)^2 \gamma_{Na^+_{(1)}} \gamma_{Cl^-_{(1)}} = y(C_2 + y) \gamma_{Na^+_{(2)}} \gamma_{Cl^-_{(2)}}.$$

The product of the activity coefficients on both sides will be approximately the same, so that we may write

$$(C_1 - y)^2 \simeq y(C_2 + y)$$

and $\qquad\qquad \dfrac{y}{C_1} \simeq \dfrac{C_1}{2C_1 + C_2}.$ . . . . . (16,24)

This equation, first derived by Donnan in 1911, shows that the percentage sodium chloride which diffuses from one side to the other, $\dfrac{y}{C_1}$, is the smaller the larger be the concentration of the salt ACl. The prediction has been verified by experiment. The Donnan membrane equilibrium equation has been of considerable use in the study of lyophylic colloids and biological systems.

The Thermodynamic Properties of Ions in Solution

The application of thermodynamics to an ionic reaction in solution requires a knowledge of the thermodynamic properties of the electrolyte in the same condition. In particular, it is evident that the use of the Third Law to calculate equilibrium constants for such a reaction requires knowledge of the entropy of the electrolyte in solution, and of a method whereby it may be apportioned between the various ions concerned. It has already been pointed out that the behaviour of solutions containing charged particles is far from ideal. It follows that if it is required to carry out calculations on such solutions with any degree of accuracy, activity coefficients must be known.

The determination of all such quantities as these is most easily and accurately achieved from measurements carried out on electro-chemical cells. The methods used will be discussed in the next two chapters.

CHAPTER 17

THE THERMODYNAMICS OF ELECTRO-CHEMICAL CELLS

One of the oldest and best-known chemical cells is illustrated in Figure 17,1. It consists of two solutions, one of zinc sulphate and the other of copper sulphate, separated by a small porous disc or capilliary tube filled with one of the solutions, and two metal rods, one of zinc partly immersed in the solution of zinc sulphate, and the other of copper, partly immersed in the second solution. This particular cell is called the Daniell Cell.

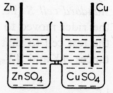

Figure 17,1. The Daniell Cell.

If the two metal rods, which are called *electrodes*, are connected by a voltmeter, it is found that the copper electrode is at a higher potential than the zinc, and if the voltmeter is replaced by a galvanometer a current flows through it from the copper to the zinc. The production of current in such a cell is occasioned by a chemical reaction: that which takes place in the Daniell cell being

$$Zn + CuSO_4 \longrightarrow ZnSO_4 + Cu.$$

Since both the copper sulphate and zinc sulphate are strong electrolytes, this equation can be written more simply in the form

$$Zn + Cu^{++} \longrightarrow Zn^{++} + Cu.$$

It is an experimental fact that the rate at which the reaction takes place is proportional to the current produced, and that if all external connection between the electrodes is broken, the reaction ceases. It is also an experimental fact that the potential difference established between the electrodes is uncertain, and not precisely reproducible, *if measured when the reaction is actually taking place.* Only if measured when no current is flowing through the cell does the potential difference rise to a maximum value which is precise and reproducible. This precise value of the potential difference between the electrodes is called the ELECTROMOTIVE FORCE of the cell, or its e.m.f., and is given the symbol **E**.

The e.m.f. of a cell is quite easily measured. It is done by balancing it against a known fall of potential between two points in an auxiliary circuit. The method is illustrated by Figure 17,2. The auxiliary circuit consists of a cell or battery D, of e.m.f. greater than that of the cell under test, connected to a uniform wire AB of high resistance. The test cell C

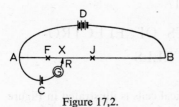

Figure 17,2.

is connected to A, and through a galvanometer G to a contact rider R, the connections CA and CGR being of negligible resistance.

The rider is moved along the wire to a point X at which no current flows through the galvanometer. Clearly at this point, the e.m.f. of the cell is precisely balanced by the drop in potential along AX. The test cell is then replaced by a *standard cell S* (i.e. a cell the e.m.f. of which is precisely known), and the rider moved to the next balance point X_s. The ratio of the e.m.f. of the test cell to that of the standard cell is the same as the ratio of distances AX and AX_s,

i.e.
$$\mathbf{E} = \frac{AX}{AX_s} \times \mathbf{E}_s.$$

This method, due originally to Poggendorff, is essentially that upon which the extremely accurate modern potentiometers are based.

The significance of the e.m.f. of the cell is established by the following argument. When the contact rider R is positioned to the left of the balance point X, at some point F, the test cell produces current in the direction $CAFGC$, and the cell reaction

$$\mathrm{Zn} + \mathrm{Cu}^{++} \longrightarrow \mathrm{Zn}^{++} + \mathrm{Cu}$$

takes place.

Let us imagine that the cell reaction proceeds to an extent $d\xi$. It follows from Faraday's Laws of Electrolysis that when a reaction proceeds to a definite extent, a definite quantity of electricity is concerned. We denote the quantity of electricity transported through the cell when the reaction proceeds to an extent $d\xi$, by the symbol dQ. The only form of work performed by the reagents concerned happens in this case to be electrical work and is given by the product of the quantity of electricity transported, dQ, and the potential difference between the points A and F. It is clear that the closer be the point F to the balance point X, the greater is the potential difference between A and F and the greater is the quantity of work performed by the cell.

If we now position the rider to the right of balance point X, i.e. at some point J, we find that the current flows through the test cell in the reverse direction, and that as a result the reaction which takes place in the cell is the reverse of that which was encountered before, i.e. the reaction which now takes place is

$$Zn^{++} + Cu \longrightarrow Zn + Cu^{++}.$$

It follows that the quantity of electrical work performed by the cell when the reaction

$$Zn + Cu^{++} \longrightarrow Zn^{++} + Cu$$

proceeds to an extent $d\xi$ is the maximum possible when the rider is positioned at the balance point X, and that therefore the maximum electrical work will be given by the expression $\mathbf{E}dQ$. It follows also that the conditions which operate when the rider is at the balance point are those under which the cell reaction proceeds reversibly.

We shall represent the Daniell cell in future discussions by the device

$$\overset{-}{Zn} \mid ZnSO_{4(aq)} \overset{\|}{\vdots} CuSO_{4(aq)} \mid \overset{+}{Cu}$$

where we use the full vertical line to denote the phase boundary between the electrode and the solution; and the double broken verticals to denote the liquid junction between the different solutions concerned. We denote the electrode which developes the higher potential by the $+$ sign and that which developes the lower potential by the $-$ sign, and place the former on the right, so that each electrode material is on the same side as that on which it appears in the chemical equation for the spontaneous reaction.

Although the Daniell cell is a convenient one with which to introduce the subject of galvanic cells, its complete analysis by thermodynamic methods proves to be difficult. We find it simpler at this stage to consider a cell which we represent by the scheme

$$H_2\ Pt \mid HCl_{(aq)}, \quad AgCl_{(sat)} \mid Ag.$$

This cell contains a single solution, that of HCl saturated with silver chloride. The electrode on the left is the so-called HYDROGEN ELECTRODE. It consists of a piece of platinum foil coated with platinum black, over which hydrogen bubbles. The hydrogen molecules absorbed by the platinum black establish equilibrium with the hydrogen ions in solution. The second electrode is silver: the atoms therein establish equilibrium with the silver ions in solution from the silver chloride. The current established is occasioned by the reaction

$$H_2 + 2Ag^+ \longrightarrow 2H^+ + 2Ag.$$

We now consider the reaction proceeding reversibly to an extent $d\xi$, resulting in the disappearance of $d\xi$ moles of hydrogen gas and $2d\xi$ moles of silver ion, and the formation of $2d\xi$ moles each of hydrogen ions and silver, and the passage of a quantity of electricity dQ.

As shown above, the electrical work performed equals $\mathbf{E}dQ$, but this particular reaction involves the disappearance of gaseous hydrogen, and so, a decrease in volume of the system. The total work involves therefore both electrical work and expansion work.

It is customary to operate cells under conditions of constant temperature and pressure, and it will be remembered that under these conditions, the maximum work performed by the system *other than the expansion work involved* equals the decrease in free energy. It is therefore immaterial whether or not a change in volume results. If when the reaction proceeds to an extent $d\xi$, so that a quantity of electricity dQ passes through the cell, the decrease in free energy is given by the equation

$$-dG = \mathbf{E}dQ. \qquad \qquad (17,1)$$

In Chapter 11 we showed[1] that if the reaction

$$a\mathrm{A} + b\mathrm{B} \longrightarrow c\mathrm{C} + d\mathrm{D}$$

proceeds to an extent $d\xi$ at constant temperature and pressure, the affinity of the reaction and the decrease in free energy may be expressed in terms of the chemical potentials of the reactants by the expression

$$\mathbf{A}d\xi = -dG_{T,\,p} = (a\mu_\mathrm{A} + b\mu_\mathrm{B} - c\mu_\mathrm{C} - d\mu_\mathrm{D})d\xi.$$

We may apply this expression to the cell reaction in which we are interested, to obtain

$$\mathbf{A}d\xi = -dG_{T,\,p} = (\mu_{\mathrm{H}_2} + 2\mu_{\mathrm{Ag}^+} - 2\mu_{\mathrm{H}^+} - 2\mu_{\mathrm{Ag}})d\xi. \qquad (17,2)$$

We require now only to obtain the connection between $d\xi$ and dQ.

It follows from Faraday's Laws of Electrolysis that the conversion of one mole of a z-valent element M into the ions M^{z+} involves the transfer of z Faradays of electricity. The Faraday, to which we assign the symbol F, equals 96,487 coulombs. If therefore the reaction

$$z\mathrm{A} + \mathrm{B}^{z+} \longrightarrow z\mathrm{A}^{1+} + \mathrm{B}$$

proceeds to an extent $d\xi$, the quantity of electricity transferred is $zFd\xi$ coulombs. This is the quantity dQ.

It will be noted that in the case of the reaction with which we are concerned, and which we have chosen to represent by the equation[2]

$$\mathrm{H}_2 + 2\mathrm{Ag}^+ \longrightarrow 2\mathrm{H}^+ + 2\mathrm{Ag}$$

---

[1] See equations (11,5) and (11,65).
[2] We could equally well have written the equation in the form

$$\tfrac{1}{2}\mathrm{H}_2 + \mathrm{Ag}^+ \longrightarrow \mathrm{H}^+ + \mathrm{Ag}$$

in which case z would have acquired the value one.

z acquires the value two. We will, however, retain the symbol z so that it is not lost sight of.

Substituting $dQ = zFd\xi$ (17,3) into (17,1) we obtain

$$-dG = zFd\xi, \qquad \cdots \cdots \quad (17,4)$$

and since we know that $\qquad \mathbf{A}d\xi = -dG_{T,\,p}$

we can write $\qquad\qquad \mathbf{A} = z\mathbf{E}F. \qquad \cdots \cdots \quad (17,5)$

It is evident therefore that the affinity of a reaction taking place in a galvanic cell may be evaluated simply by determining the value of the e.m.f. established.[1]

In Chapter 11 we showed that the value of the chemical potential of a gaseous reactant is a function of its partial pressure (or more precisely of its fugacity), and that that of a reactant in solution is a function of its concentration (or activity). It follows from (17,2) that the e.m.f. of the cell is a function not only of the reaction on which the cell depends, but also of the concentration of the reactants. Let us now imagine that we have assembled such a cell as that described above in a thermostat at temperature T, and that the quantities of chemicals assembled are so large that when reaction proceeds from $\xi = 0$ to $\xi = 1$, i.e. to such an extent that one mole of hydrogen passes into solution and 2 gm atoms of silver are deposited, only a negligible change in concentration of the solution results. Since the concentration terms remain the same, the affinity of reaction and the e.m.f. remain constant throughout, so that it is possible to obtain a measure of the molar decrease in free energy for the cell reaction at the particular concentration concerned, by integrating equation (17,4) between the limits $\xi = 0$ and $\xi = 1$. This gives the equation

$$-\Delta G = z\mathbf{E}F. \qquad \cdots \cdots \quad (17,6)$$

We now proceed to express the affinity of reaction, the molar decrease in free energy and the electromotive force of the cell in terms of the concentrations of the reactants. We express the partial pressure of hydrogen in atmospheres, and the concentration of components in solution in molalities, so that it will be understood that when we use such symbols as a or γ we mean the activity or activity coefficient referred to the molal measure of concentration.

It follows from (17,2), (17,5) and (17,6) that

$$z\mathbf{E}F = \mathbf{A} = -\Delta G = \mu_{H_2} + 2\mu_{Ag^+} - 2\mu_{H^+} - 2\mu_{Ag}. \quad (17,7)$$

---

[1] The student is reminded that if $\mathbf{E}$ is expressed in volts and F in coulombs, the affinity of reaction and the decrease in free energy is evaluated in joules.

We now express μ_{H_2} in terms of the partial pressure[1]

$$\mu_{H_2} = \mu_{0_{H_2}} + RT \log_e p_{H_2}, \qquad . \quad . \quad . \quad (17,37)$$

and following (16,2) write

$$\mu_{Ag^+} = \mu_{0_{Ag^+}} + RT \log_e a_{Ag^+}$$

and

$$\mu_{H^+} = \mu_{0_{H^+}} + RT \log_e a_{H^+},$$

where the terms μ_0 represent the standard chemical potential of the ion at unit activity.

We note that, as explained in Chapter 11, the chemical potential of a pure solid is independent of the quantity present. This is the same as adopting the pure solid state as the standard state. We may therefore write

$$\mu_{Ag} = \mu_{0_{Ag}}.$$

Substituting into (17,7) and rearranging, we obtain

$$z\mathbf{E}F = \mathbf{A} = -\Delta G = (\mu_{0_{H_2}} + 2\mu_{0_{Ag^+}} - 2\mu_{0_{H^+}} - 2\mu_{0_{Ag}})$$
$$+ RT \log_e \frac{p_{H_2} \times a_{Ag^+}^2}{a_{H^+}^2}. \quad (17,8)$$

The quantities in the bracket are independent of concentration. By inspection, it is clear that they represent the decrease in molar free energy when the reaction takes place under such circumstances that the hydrogen is at a partial pressure of 1 atmosphere and the silver and hydrogen ions are both at unit activity. We represent this quantity by the symbol $-\Delta G_0'$ and write

$$z\mathbf{E}F = \mathbf{A} = -\Delta G = -\Delta G_0' + RT \log_e \frac{p_{H_2} \times a_{Ag^+}^2}{a_{H^+}^2}. \quad (17,9)$$

The activity of the silver ions in solution is governed by the solubility product of silver chloride, and from (16,17) can be written

$$a_{Ag^+} = \frac{K_s}{a_{Cl^-}}.$$

We also remember from (16,9) that

$$a_{H^+} \times a_{Cl^-} = a^2_{\pm HCl},$$

so that, after substitution into (17,9) and rearranging, we obtain

$$z\mathbf{E}F = \mathbf{A} = -\Delta G = -\Delta G_0' + 2RT \log_e K_s + RT \log_e p_{H_2}$$
$$- 4RT \log_e a_{\pm HCl}. \quad (17,10)$$

[1] The behaviour of hydrogen at low pressures approaches ideality so closely that it is unnecessary to consider the fugacity of the gas.

The first two terms on the right-hand side are independent of concentration, so they may be combined to give $-\Delta G_0$. We finally obtain, therefore, the equation

$$z\mathbf{E}F = \mathbf{A} = -\Delta G = -\Delta G_0 + RT \log_e p_{H_2} - 4RT \log_e a_{\pm HCl}. \quad (17,11)$$

It is usual in operating a cell containing a hydrogen electrode, either to ensure that the hydrogen bubbles over the platinum electrode at a partial pressure of precisely 1 atmosphere, when the second term on the right-hand side of (17,11) disappears, or to use hydrogen at some partial pressure other than 1 atmosphere, but record readings of the e.m.f. corrected to 1 atmosphere.[1] For the remainder of this chapter we shall assume (except where otherwise stated) that this has been done, so that (17,11) simplifies to:

$$z\mathbf{E}F = \mathbf{A} = -\Delta G = -\Delta G_0 - 4RT \log_e a_{\pm HCl}. \quad (17,12)$$

It is evident that the quantity $-\Delta G_0$ is the standard molar decrease in free energy for the reaction

$$H_2 + 2Ag^+ \longrightarrow 2H^+ + 2Ag$$

taking place in the cell

$$H_2 \ Pt \mid HCl, \quad AgCl_{(sat)} \mid Ag$$

when the hydrochloric acid is at such concentration that its mean ionic activity is unity.

From (17,12) we may write

$$\mathbf{E} = -\frac{\Delta G_0}{zF} - \frac{4RT}{zF} \log_e a_{\pm HCl}$$

and denote the quantity $-\dfrac{\Delta G_0}{zF}$ by the symbol $\mathbf{E}_0$

i.e. $$\mathbf{E} = \mathbf{E}_0 - \frac{4RT}{zF} \log_e a_{\pm HCl}. \quad . \quad . \quad . \quad . \quad (17,13)$$

The quantity $\mathbf{E}_0$ is called the STANDARD ELECTROMOTIVE FORCE of the cell. We note that it is the e.m.f. of the cell under such conditions that both the partial pressure of the hydrogen (in atmospheres) and the mean ionic activity of the hydrochloric acid are unity.

---

[1] If $\mathbf{E}'$ is the e.m.f. at partial pressure p atmospheres, the e.m.f. corrected to 1 atmosphere is given by the equation

$$\mathbf{E} = \mathbf{E}' - \frac{RT}{2F} \log_e p_{H_2}.$$

The Measurement of the Standard Electromotive Force of the Cell

The determination of the standard electromotive force of a cell happens to be of extreme importance. The method we describe for the hydrogen, silver, silver chloride cell is the same in principle as that which may be used for any cell.

We rewrite equation (17,13), including the fact that in this case the value of z is two, and expressing the mean ionic activity of the hydrochloric acid as the product of its molality and mean ionic activity coefficient,

$$\mathbf{E} = \mathbf{E_0} - \frac{2RT}{F} \log_e m_{HCl}\, \gamma_{\pm HCl}.$$

The difficulty which exists is that for every measurement of the e.m.f. for a particular concentration of hydrochloric acid, there are two unknown quantities, $\mathbf{E_0}$ and the mean ionic activity coefficient. The difficulty is surmounted as follows:

The equation is rearranged to give

$$\mathbf{E} + \frac{2RT}{F} \log_e m_{HCl} = \mathbf{E_0} - \frac{2RT}{F} \log_e \gamma_{\pm HCl}. \qquad (17,14)$$

The expression on the left-hand side of this equation contains only quantities which may be directly measured, and we note that since the mean ionic activity coefficient of an electrolyte tends towards unity at infinite dilution, the left-hand side tends towards $\mathbf{E_0}$ as m approaches zero. It follows from (16,23) (remembering that for a uni-univalent electrolyte the ionic strength is the same as the concentration), that a plot of the left-hand side against $m^{\frac{1}{2}}$ yields a straight line at low concentrations. Extrapolation of this straight line to $m = 0$ yields $\mathbf{E_0}$. This method was first devised by Lewis and Randall.[1]

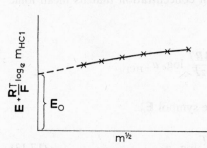

Figure 17,3. The determination of $\mathbf{E_0}$ by the method of Lewis and Randall.

The student is advised to illustrate the method by the solution of Exercise 17,1 given at the end of this chapter.

The Lewis and Randall method is perhaps not capable of giving results of the highest degree of accuracy, because as is shown in Figure 17,3, the graph of $\mathbf{E} + \frac{2RT}{F} \log_e m_{HCl}$ against $m^{\frac{1}{2}}$ shows a slight curvature except

[1] Lewis and Randall, *J. Am. Chem. Soc.*, 1921, **43**, 1112.

at extremely small concentrations, and at such concentrations the actual measurements of the e.m.f. of the cell are somewhat uncertain. A more accurate, but much more laborious, method was devised by Brown and MacInnes,[1] for details of which the student is referred to the origina paper. The Brown and MacInnes procedure has been widely used, but the worth of the simpler method due to Lewis and Randall should not be under-rated. Thus the author[2] found that in a cell of this type, the values of E_0 obtained by the Brown and MacInnes method differed from those obtained by the Lewis and Randall extrapolation only by about 0·1 mv (i.e. by about one part in two thousand).

The accepted "best result" for the standard electromotive force of the cell under consideration is 0·2225 volt. This particular cell has been used very widely, particularly by Harned and his co-workers.[3] We shall, later in this chapter, give some examples of its use in the determination of thermodynamic quantities. At present we merely note that once E_0 has been determined, its value may be placed in equation (17,14) and the mean ionic activity coefficient for hydrochloric acid calculated for any molality.

SINGLE ELECTRODE POTENTIALS

We continue to consider the hydrogen, silver, silver chloride cell, and again choose to consider a cell in which the hydrogen is at a partial pressure of precisely 1 atmosphere. We now make use of equation (17,9) which, on putting $p_{H_2} = 1$, can be written in the form

$$E = -\frac{\Delta G'_0}{zF} + \frac{RT}{zF} \log_e \frac{a^2_{Ag^+}}{a^2_{H^+}} \qquad . \quad . \quad (17,15)$$

We now represent the quantity $-\dfrac{\Delta G'_0}{zF}$ by E'_0 (see footnote 4) and replace

z by its numerical value two in the second expression to obtain the simple equation

$$E = E'_0 + \frac{RT}{F} \log_e \frac{a_{Ag^+}}{a_{H^+}}. \qquad . \quad . \quad . \quad (17,16)$$

---

[1] Brown and MacInnes, *J. Am. Chem. Soc.*, 1935, **57**, 1356.

[2] Everdell, *J. Chem. Soc.*, 1949, 483, 2289.

[3] Harned and Owen, *Physical Chemistry of Electrolytic Solutions* (Reinhold Publishing Corporation, 1943).

[4] The reader should note that the quantity E'_0 is NOT the same as the quantity E_0 which figures in (17,13). E_0 is the e.m.f. of the cell when the mean ionic activity of the hydrochloric acid is unity, whereas E'_0 is the e.m.f. of the cell under hypothetical conditions such that the activities of the silver ion and hydrogen ion are equal. The two quantities are, of course, related; the reader should verify that

$$E'_0 = E_0 - \frac{RT}{F} \log_e K_{s\,AgCl}.$$

The student is now reminded that although the reaction on which the cell depends is represented by the equation

$$\tfrac{1}{2}H_2 + Ag^+ \longrightarrow H^+ + Ag$$

the chemical reaction appears to occur as two separate events:

(i) a "half-molecule" of hydrogen giving up an electron at the hydrogen electrode, and passing into solution as a hydrogen ion

$$\tfrac{1}{2}H_2 \longrightarrow H^+ + \bar{e}$$

and

(ii) a silver ion acquiring an electron at the other electrode to become a silver atom

$$Ag^+ + \bar{e} \longrightarrow Ag.$$

It is therefore reasonable to suppose that the e.m.f. of the cell is made up of two parts, one of which may be called E_H, and which we might suppose to represent the difference in potential between the hydrogen electrode and the solution, and which depends on half-reaction (i), and the other which may be called E_{Ag}, which we might suppose to represent the difference in potential between the silver electrode and the solution, and which depends on half-reaction (ii). The question which then arises is whether we write

$$E = E_{Ag} - E_H \quad \text{or} \quad E = E_H - E_{Ag}.$$

There is no evidence that one procedure is wrong and the other right, and it is unfortunate that different procedures have been adopted by different workers. That which has been adopted by most British and European scientists, and which is adopted in this book is to treat as positive the electrode *to which the electrons flow in the outer circuit*, in other words, to write

$$E = E_{Ag} - E_H.$$

The opposite convention has been adopted by most American scientists. When equation (17,16) is expanded according to the European convention it becomes

$$E = \left\{ E_{o_{Ag/Ag^+}} + \frac{RT}{F} \log_e a_{Ag^+} \right\} - \left\{ E_{o_{H_2/H^+}} + \frac{RT}{F} \log_e a_{H^+} \right\} \quad (17,17)$$

where the E_0' term in (17,16) has been put equal to

$$E_{o_{Ag/Ag^+}} - E_{o_{H_2/H^+}},$$

but when expanded according to the American convention it becomes

$$E = \left\{ E_{o_{H_2/H^+}} - \frac{RT}{F} \log_e a_{H^+} \right\} - \left\{ E_{o_{Ag/Ag^+}} - \frac{RT}{F} \log_e a_{Ag^+} \right\} \quad (17,18)$$

where the E_0' term has been put equal to

$$E_{o_{H_2/H^+}} - E_{o_{Ag/Ag^+}}.$$

The quantity in the first bracket of (17,17) and the second bracket of (17,18) is called the electrode potential of the silver electrode, and the term $E_{o_{Ag/Ag^+}}$ is called the *standard electrode potential* of silver, and we suppose it to represent the difference in potential between the silver electrode and the solution when the latter contains silver ions at unit activity. The quantity in the second bracket of (17,17) and the first bracket in (17,18) is called the electrode potential of the hydrogen electrode, and the term $E_{o_{H_2/H^+}}$ is called the *standard electrode potential* of hydrogen, and we suppose it to represent the difference in potential between the electrode and the solution when it contains hydrogen ions at unit activity. It would certainly be of great interest to know the *absolute* value of such quantities as single electrode potentials and standard electrode potentials, but unfortunately it does not appear possible either to determine them experimentally or to calculate their value theoretically.[1] We do, however, find it convenient to assign them *conventional* values, which have no absolute significance, but which are of great practical use.

The convention we adopt is to assign the value zero to the standard electrode potential of hydrogen at all temperatures, that is to say, we conventionally assign the value zero to the potential difference established between the hydrogen (platinum) electrode and the hydrogen ions in solution when the latter are at unit activity.

This immediately raises a second problem. We stated earlier that it is quite impossible to determine the activity of a single ion species, and we may well ask therefore how we know when the hydrogen ions in solution are at unit activity and when they are not. The answer is that we do not; we are again concerned with a conventional quantity. The Debye–Hückel Theory of Strong Electrolytes predicts that the activity coefficients of ions of equal and opposite charge are the same in a particular solution; so that in a solution of hydrochloric acid in water

$$\gamma_{H^+} = \gamma_{Cl^-}.$$

We have already defined the mean ionic activity coefficient by the equation

$$\gamma_{\pm_{HCl}}^2 = \gamma_{H^+} \times \gamma_{Cl^-},$$

so that it follows that the Debye–Hückel Theory predicts that

$$\gamma_{H^+} = \gamma_{Cl^-} = \gamma_{\pm_{HCl}}.$$

---

[1] There has been much argument on this question. The reader is referred to Latimer, *Oxidation Potentials* (Prentice-Hall, 1952).

The mean ionic activity coefficient can be determined, and we have no doubt at all about what is meant therefore by a solution of hydrochloric acid, the mean ionic activity of which is unity. By conventionally assigning the value zero to the standard electrode potential of hydrogen we are assigning the value zero to the potential difference established between a hydrogen electrode and a solution of hydrochloric acid of such concentration that the mean ionic activity is unity.

If we now consider the cell

$$H_2 \ Pt \ \underset{1 \ atm}{|} \ HCl_{(a_{\pm} = 1)} AgCl_{(sat)} \ | \ Ag$$

we see that by adopting the convention we have chosen, the second bracket in (17,17) disappears and we are left with the equation

$$E = E_{0 \ Ag/Ag^+} + \frac{RT}{F} \log_e a_{Ag^+}. \qquad . \qquad . \qquad . \qquad (17,19)$$

We know, too, that the e.m.f. of the cell when the mean ionic activity of hydrochloric acid is unity is the Standard Electromotive Force of the cell, and that its value is 0·2225 volt.

It follows that

$$E_{0 \ Ag/Ag^+} + \frac{RT}{F} \log_e a_{Ag^+} = 0 \cdot 2225 \text{ volt,}$$

but since

$$a_{Ag^+} \times a_{Cl^-} = K_s$$

$$E_{0 \ Ag/Ag^+} + \frac{RT}{F} \log_e K_s - \frac{RT}{F} \log_e a_{Cl^-} = 0 \cdot 2225 \text{ volt.}$$

At 25° C the value of the solubility product of silver chloride is $1 \cdot 77 \times 10^{-10}$, and since it follows from our previous assumption that when $\gamma_{\pm \ HCl} = 1$, $\gamma_{Cl^-} = 1$, the last term disappears for a solution of hydrochloric acid of such concentration that $a_{\pm} = 1$, so that $E_{0 \ Ag/Ag^+}$ may be evaluated to give the result

$$E_{0 \ Ag/Ag^+} = 0 \cdot 799 \text{ volt.}$$

We emphasise again that this value has no absolute significance, but represents the standard electrode potential of silver *relative to that of the standard hydrogen electrode*.

CELLS WITH LIQUID–LIQUID JUNCTIONS

Earlier in this chapter it was said that the thermodynamic analysis of the Daniell cell proves to be difficult. We are now in a position to return this cell, and find out the nature of the difficulties involved. We consider the cell

$$Zn \ | \ ZnSO_{4aq} \ \vdots \ CuSO_{4aq} \ | \ Cu$$

We permit the cell reaction

$$Zn + Cu^{++} \longrightarrow Zn^{++} + Cu$$

to proceed to an extent $d\xi$, and write

$$\mathbf{A}d\xi = -dG_{T,\,p} = (\mu_{Zn} + \mu_{Cu^{++}} - \mu_{Zn^{++}} - \mu_{Cu})d\xi,$$

and as before show that

$$\mathbf{A} = z\mathbf{E}F, \quad \ldots \ldots \quad (17,5)$$

and note that in this case z acquires the value 2, and that

$$z\mathbf{E}F = \mathbf{A} = (\mu_{0_{Zn}} + \mu_{0_{Cu^{++}}} - \mu_{0_{Zn^{++}}} - \mu_{0_{Cu}}) + RT \log_e \frac{a_{Cu^{++}}}{a_{Zn^{++}}}$$

so that
$$\mathbf{E} = \mathbf{E}_0 + \frac{RT}{2F} \log_e \frac{a_{Cu^{++}}}{a_{Zn^{++}}} \quad \ldots \quad (17,20)$$

where $\mathbf{E}_0$ is the Standard Electromotive Force of the cell, i.e. the e.m.f. of the cell when the copper sulphate and zinc sulphate solutions are of such concentrations that $a_{Cu^{++}} = a_{Zn^{++}}$.

As before we can, if we wish, divide the total e.m.f. into two portions, one relating to the copper electrode, and the other to the zinc, and write

$$\mathbf{E} = \left\{ \mathbf{E}_{0_{Cu}} + \frac{RT}{2F} \log_e a_{Cu^{++}} \right\} - \left\{ \mathbf{E}_{0_{Zn}} + \frac{RT}{2F} \log_e a_{Zn^{++}} \right\} \quad (17,21)$$

where the terms $\mathbf{E}_{0_{Cu}}$ and $\mathbf{E}_{0_{Zn}}$ are the standard electrode potentials of copper and zinc.

We now raise a difficult question. The Daniell cell differs from the hydrogen–silver–silver chloride cell which we considered earlier, in that in the Daniell cell there is an abrupt change in composition of the solutions at the liquid–liquid junction; so that in fact the two solutions are really two different liquid phases, across which a potential difference will exist. This potential difference is called the liquid junction potential, to which we assign the symbol $\mathbf{E}_j$.

This means that the real e.m.f. of the Daniell cell is not given by equations (17,20) and (17,21) but by equations

$$\mathbf{E} = \mathbf{E}_j + \mathbf{E}_0 + \frac{RT}{2F} \log_e \frac{a_{Cu^{++}}}{a_{Zn^{++}}} \quad \ldots \quad (17,22)$$

and

$$\mathbf{E} = \mathbf{E}_j + \left(\mathbf{E}_{0_{Cu}} + \frac{RT}{2F} \log_e a_{Cu^{++}} \right) - \left(\mathbf{E}_{0_{Zn}} + \frac{RT}{2F} \log_e a_{Zn^{++}} \right). \quad (17,23)$$

N

There is, unfortunately, no method by which the liquid junction potential can be eliminated completely, or computed exactly, so that there is no way in which we can accurately determine the quantity

$$\left(\mathbf{E}_{o_{Cu/Cu^{++}}} + \frac{RT}{2F} \log_e a_{Cu^{++}} \right) - \left(\mathbf{E}_{o_{Zn/Zn^{++}}} + \frac{RT}{2F} \log_e a_{Zn^{++}} \right).$$

Notwithstanding this, it happens that we can determine the quantity $(\mathbf{E}_{o_{Cu/Cu^{++}}} - \mathbf{E}_{o_{Zn/Zn^{++}}})$ with complete assurance. This can be done by using the Lewis and Randall method previously described. We re-arrange (17,23) into the form

$$\mathbf{E} - \frac{RT}{2F} \log_e \frac{m_{Cu^{++}}}{m_{Zn^{++}}}$$

$$= (\mathbf{E}_{o_{Cu/Cu^{++}}} - \mathbf{E}_{o_{Zn/Zn^{++}}}) + \mathbf{E}_j + \frac{RT}{2F} \log_e \frac{\gamma_{Cu^{++}}}{\gamma_{Zn^{++}}}. \quad (17,24)$$

We now set up a Daniell cell in which the copper and zinc ions are of equal molality m, and plot the value of the left-hand side against $m^{\frac{1}{2}}$. We extrapolate the straight line obtained for dilute solutions to zero concentration. As the solutions approach zero concentration, not only do the values of the activity coefficients approach unity but also the solutions become more closely identical, so that the liquid junction potential approaches zero. It follows that the extrapolated value of the left-hand side at zero concentration gives $(\mathbf{E}_{o_{Cu/Cu^{++}}} - \mathbf{E}_{o_{Zn/Zn^{++}}})$.

It should be noted that although we have determined $\mathbf{E}_{o_{Cu}} - \mathbf{E}_{o_{Zn}}$ with complete assurance, we are still in no position to determine the activity of the copper or zinc ions, or even to determine the ratio of their activities. It is clear from (17,23) that the difficulty lies in the liquid junction potential. In fact, the inability either to eliminate completely or compute the liquid junction potential, and our inability to measure single ionic activities is really one and the same. If we knew the value of the liquid junction potential, we could use a cell of the sort we have described to determine single ionic activities; if we knew the latter, we could compute liquid junction potentials.

The Establishment of a Scale of Standard Electrode Potentials

From measurements[1] made on the cell

$$\text{Zn} \mid \text{ZnCl}_2 \mathbin{\vdots} \text{HCl} \mid \text{Pt H}_2$$

which depends on the reaction

$$\text{Zn} + 2\text{H}^+ \longrightarrow \text{Zn}^{++} + \text{H}_2$$

---

[1] All measurements discussed in this section refer to 25° C.

and by using the Lewis and Randall extrapolation method, the value of

$$E_{o_{H_2/H^+}} - E_{o_{Zn/Zn^{++}}}$$

can be determined. It is 0·763 volt. As has been discussed before, it is impossible to determine the *absolute* value of a single electrode potential or standard electrode potential, but by adopting the convention in which we assign the value zero to the standard electrode potential of hydrogen, it follows that on this same convention

$$E_{o_{Zn/Zn^{++}}} = -0·763 \text{ volt.}$$

From the Daniell cell it is found that

$$E_{o_{Cu/Cu^{++}}} - E_{o_{Zn/Zn^{++}}} = 1·100 \text{ volt.}$$

It therefore follows that

$$E_{o_{Cu/Cu^{++}}} = +0·337 \text{ volt.}$$

From the cell

$$Cu \mid CuSO_4 \vdots AgNO_3 \mid Ag$$

it is found that

$$E_{o_{Ag/Ag^+}} - E_{o_{Cu/Cu^{++}}} = 0·462 \text{ volt,}$$

hence

$$E_{o_{Ag/Ag^+}} = +0·799 \text{ volt.}$$

The standard electrode potential of many of the elements can be determined in this way. In some cases, such as the alkali metals, more complicated methods have to be adopted. For details of these the student is referred to standard texts on electrochemistry.[1]

A selection of values at 25° C taken from Latimer's *Oxidation Potentials* (Prentice-Hall, New York, 1952) is given in Table 17,I.

TABLE 17,I

$E_{o_{Li/Li^+}}$	−3·045 volt	$E_{o_{Co/Co^{++}}}$	−0·283 volt
$E_{o_{K/K^+}}$	−2·925 volt	$E_{o_{Ni/Ni^{++}}}$	−0·250 volt
$E_{o_{Ba/Ba^{++}}}$	−2·90 volt	$E_{o_{H_2/H^+}}$	0·000 volt
$E_{o_{Na/Na^+}}$	−2·714 volt	$E_{o_{Cu/Cu^{++}}}$	+0·337 volt
$E_{o_{Mn/Mn^{++}}}$	−1·18 volt	$E_{o_{Hg/Hg_2^{++}}}$	+0·789 volt
$E_{o_{Zn/Zn^{++}}}$	−0·763 volt	$E_{o_{Ag/Ag^+}}$	+0·799 volt
$E_{o_{Fe/Fe^{++}}}$	−0·440 volt		

The standard electromotive force of a cell made up of any two electrodes represented in the table is the algebraic difference between the individual electrode potentials. Thus for the cell

$$Ni \mid Ni_{aq}^{++} \vdots Cu_{aq}^{++} \mid Cu$$

[1] For example: MacInnes, *The Principles of Electrochemistry*, 1939.

the standard electromotive force is $0.337-(-0.250)$, i.e. 0.587 volt. The actual value of the e.m.f. of the cell will differ slightly from this value, and will depend on the liquid junction potential and the concentration of the solutions concerned.

The order of elements listed in Table 17,I is often called the ELECTRO-MOTIVE SERIES. It is sometimes stated that a metal higher in the list displaces one lower down from its salts. This statement is not always true, first, because the standard electrode potentials listed therein are those in *aqueous* solution and their relative values may differ in non-aqueous solution, and secondly, because the activities of the ions concerned may influence the result. What is really true is that metal A will displace metal B from an *aqueous* solution containing both A^{+z} and B^{+z} ions if

$$\left(\mathbf{E}_{0_A} + \frac{RT}{zF} \log_e a_{A^{+z}} \right) < \left(\mathbf{E}_{0_B} + \frac{RT}{zF} \log_e a_{B^{+z}} \right)$$

where the values of $\mathbf{E}_0$ are those given in Table 17,I. The same will be true in the case of a non-aqueous solution, but requires knowledge of the values of $\mathbf{E}_0$ in the particular solvent concerned.

The student is reminded that in assigning numerical values to the standard electrode potentials we have followed the British and European sign convention. Had the alternative convention been used, the potentials would have acquired the opposite sign, thus the standard electrode potential of manganese would have been written $+1.18$ volt and that of silver -0.799 volt.

We have already shown that the standard electromotive force of the cell

$$\text{H}_2 \text{ Pt} \mid \text{HCl}_{a_{\pm}=1} \qquad \text{AgCl}_{(\text{sat})} \mid \text{Ag}$$

is 0.2225 volt, and that this cell may be regarded as the combination of a hydrogen electrode in equilibrium with hydrogen ions at unit activity, and a silver electrode in equilibrium with silver ions the activity of which is governed by the equilibrium between silver chloride and chloride ions of unit activity. Since by convention the hydrogen electrode potential is zero, it follows that

$$\mathbf{E}_{0 \, \text{Ag}/\text{Ag}^+} + \frac{RT}{F} \log_e K_s = 0.2225 \text{ volt.}$$

This quantity is called the standard electrode potential of the silver–silver chloride electrode, and is given by the symbol

$$\mathbf{E}_{0 \, \text{Ag}/\text{AgCl}/\text{Cl}^-}.$$

Another electrode which works on the same principle as the silver–silver chloride electrode is the CALOMEL ELECTRODE, which consists of mercury in contact with a solution of any chloride saturated with mercurous chloride. The electrode potential of the calomel electrode may be shown to be a function of the chloride ion activity as follows:

$$\mathbf{E} = \mathbf{E}_{0_{Hg/Hg_2^{++}}} + \frac{RT}{2F} \log_e a_{Hg_2^{++}},$$

but

$$a_{Hg_2^{++}} \times a_{Cl^-}^2 = K_s,$$

therefore

$$\mathbf{E} = \mathbf{E}_{0_{Hg/Hg_2^{++}}} + \frac{RT}{2F} \log_e K_s - \frac{RT}{F} \log_e a_{Cl^-}$$

$$= \mathbf{E}_{0_{Hg/Hg_2Cl_2/Cl^-}} - \frac{RT}{F} \log_e a_{Cl^-},$$

where $\mathbf{E}_{0_{Hg/Hg_2Cl_2/Cl^-}}$ is the standard electrode potential of the calomel electrode. Its value is $+0.268$ volt. The calomel electrode is widely used as a reference electrode and is usually assembled in aqueous potassium chloride at one of two concentrations, normal or decinormal. The electrode potential of the first is 0.2801 volt at $25°$ C, and that of the second is 0.3338 volt.

Another electrode of the same type is the lead–lead sulphate electrode which is reversible to sulphate ions:

$$\mathbf{E}_{0_{Pb/PbSO_4/SO_4^{--}}} = -0.3505 \text{ volt,}$$

while another is the mercury–mercurous sulphate electrode which again is reversible to sulphate ions. This electrode has in fact been used for many years in the Weston and Clark *standard cells*. These are cells which when once assembled establish an electromotive force which remains constant to a remarkable degree, and which can therefore be used as a primary standard for the calibration of others.

In the Weston cell, the electrodes are mercury and a 12.13% amalgam of cadmium in mercury. The solution connecting the electrodes is a saturated solution of hydrated cadmium sulphate in contact with excess crystals of the salt. The compartment of the cell in contact with the mercury electrode is saturated with mercurous sulphate. The cell depends on the reaction

$$Cd + Hg_2^{++} \longrightarrow Cd^{++} + 2Hg.$$

Its e.m.f. is 1.0183 volt at $20°$ C, and its temperature coefficient is -0.00004 volt deg^{-1}.

The two electrodes in the Clark cell consist of mercury and a 10%

amalgam of zinc in mercury. The electrolyte is a saturated solution of hydrated zinc sulphate containing excess crystals of the salt, and the compartment of the cell in contact with the mercury electrode is saturated with mercurous sulphate. The cell reaction is

$$Zn + Hg_2^{++} \longrightarrow Zn^{++} + 2Hg.$$

Its e.m.f. is 1·4324 volt at 20° C and its temperature coefficient is $-0 \cdot 00119$ volt deg^{-1}.

The Standard Electromotive Force of a Chemical Cell and the Equilibrium Constant for the Cell Reaction

If metal A is added to a solution of the salt of metal B the reaction

$$nA + B^{z+} \longrightarrow nA^{\frac{z}{n}+} + B$$

proceeds until equilibrium is reached. At equilibrium the affinity of reaction and the molar decrease in free energy are both zero, so that it follows from the Reaction Isotherm that

$$-\Delta G = -\Delta G_0 - RT \log_e \frac{\left(a_{A^{\frac{z}{n}+}}\right)_{eq}^n}{a_{B^{z+} eq}}.$$

and that at equilibrium when $-\Delta G = 0$,

$$-\Delta G_0 = RT \log_e \frac{\left(a_{A^{\frac{z}{n}+}}\right)_{eq}^n}{a_{B^{z+} eq}} = RT \log_e K,$$

where K is the equilibrium constant for the reaction concerned.

If the reactants are assembled in the cell represented by the scheme

$$A \mid A^{\frac{z}{n}+} \; \vdots \; B^{z+} \mid B$$

it has been shown that

$$-\Delta G_0 = z \mathbf{E}_0 F$$

and that

$$\mathbf{E}_0 = \mathbf{E}_{0B/B^{z+}} - \mathbf{E}_{0A/A^{\frac{z}{n}+}}.$$

It follows that

$$\mathbf{E}_{0B/B^{z+}} - \mathbf{E}_{0A/A^{\frac{z}{n}+}} = \frac{RT}{zF} \log_e K. \quad . \quad . \quad (17,25)$$

This equation can be used in some cases to determine the standard electrode potential of a metal, when for some reason a more direct way is impracticable. It was used by Noyes and Toabe[1] to determine the standard electrode potential of tin. These workers allowed finely divided tin to react with lead perchlorate in solution,

$$Sn_{(s)} + Pb(ClO_4)_2 \rightleftharpoons Pb_{(s)} + Sn(ClO_4)_2,$$

[1] J. Am. Chem. Soc., 1917, **39**, 1537.

and found that at equilibrium at 25° C the ratio $\dfrac{m_{Sn^{++}}}{m_{Pb^{++}}}$ equals 2·98. It may be assumed that the ionic activity coefficients of the two ions are not very different, so that 2·98 may be accepted as the value of the equilibrium constant.

Hence $\mathbf{E}_{0Pb/Pb^{++}} - \mathbf{E}_{0Sn/Sn^{++}} = \dfrac{RT}{2F} \log_e 2\cdot98.$

The value of the standard electrode potential of lead is known to be −0·126 volt. It follows from this equation that that of tin is −0·140 volt.

OXIDATION–REDUCTION POTENTIALS

All electro-chemical processes are essentially oxidation–reduction reactions. Thus the cell reaction

$$Zn + 2H^+ \longrightarrow Zn^{++} + H_2$$

may be regarded as the oxidation of zinc by hydrogen ions, or the reduction of hydrogen ions by zinc, or as two separate processes, the oxidation of zinc at one electrode accompanied by the reduction of hydrogen ions at the other.

The standard e.m.f. of the cell which depends on this reaction is 0·763 volt at 25° C, so that it follows from equation (17,5) that the standard affinity of the reaction equals

$$\frac{2 \times 0\cdot763 \times 96{,}487}{4\cdot184}, \text{ i.e. } 35{,}190 \text{ cal.}$$

This figure may be regarded as the tendency of zinc to act as a reducing agent (i.e. its tendency to be oxidised) *relative to that of hydrogen under the same standard conditions.*

Although, as was said earlier, all electro-chemical processes are essentially oxidation–reduction reactions, the term *oxidation–reduction potentials* is usually reserved to describe the electrode processes in cells of

type $H_2 \ Pt \ \Big| \ H^+ \ \vdots \ \begin{matrix} Fe^{++} \\ Fe^{++} \end{matrix} \ \Big| \ Pt.$

The right-hand side of this cell consists of an inert electrode, such as smooth platinum, immersed in a solution containing both ferric and ferrous ions. The cell depends on the reaction

$$\tfrac{1}{2}H_2 + Fe^{+++} \longrightarrow H^+ + Fe^{++}$$

and since

$$\mathbf{A} = -\Delta G = z\mathbf{E}F = \tfrac{1}{2}\mu_{H_2} + \mu_{Fe^{+++}} - \mu_{H^+} - \mu_{Fe^{++}} + z\mathbf{E}_jF$$

where $\mathbf{E}_j$ is the liquid junction potential, it follows that

$$\mathbf{E} = \frac{1}{zF}\{\tfrac{1}{2}\mu_{0_{H_2}} + \mu_{0_{Fe^{+++}}} - \mu_{0_{H^+}} - \mu_{0_{Fe^{++}}}\}$$
$$+ \frac{RT}{zF}\log_e \frac{p_{H_2}^{\frac{1}{2}}\, a_{Fe^{+++}}}{a_{H^+}\, a_{Fe^{++}}} + \mathbf{E}_j. \quad (17,26)$$

The value of z for the reaction as written is unity, so that when the partial pressure of hydrogen and the activity of the hydrogen ions in the solution on the left-hand side are both unity, the equation simplifies to the form

$$\mathbf{E} = \mathbf{E}_0 + \frac{RT}{F}\log_e \frac{a_{Fe^{+++}}}{a_{Fe^{++}}} + \mathbf{E}_j. \quad \cdot \quad \cdot \quad \cdot \quad (17,27)$$

The value of $\mathbf{E}_0$ can be determined by the same techniques as those used for other cells. It proves to be 0·772 volt at 25° C. The standard affinity of the reaction is thus 17,800 cal. This figure may be regarded as the tendency of ferric ions to act as an oxidising agent relative to that of hydrogen ions under the same standard conditions. The high value of the affinity of reaction indicates that the reaction proceeds strongly from left to right. This may be confirmed as follows. The e.m.f. of a cell in which the reactants have reached equilibrium is zero, so that (neglecting the liquid junction potential)

$$\mathbf{E}_0 = -\frac{RT}{F}\log_e \frac{p_{H_{2eq}}^{\frac{1}{2}}\, a_{Fe_{eq}^{+++}}}{a_{H_{eq}^+}\, a_{Fe_{eq}^{++}}}.$$

Under such conditions that $p_{H_{2eq}} = 1$ atmosphere, and $a_{H_{eq}^+} = 1$,

$$\frac{a_{Fe_{eq}^{+++}}}{a_{Fe_{eq}^{++}}} = 10^{-13}.$$

The standard oxidation–reduction potential of other systems of the same sort are

Cr^{++}, Cr^{+++}	−0·4 volt
Sn^{++}, Sn^{++++}	+0·15 volt
Co^{++}, Co^{+++}	+1·82 volt.

It follows from these figures that the ferric ion will oxidise chromous and stannous ions, but that the cobaltic ion will oxidise ferrous to ferric.

An oxidation–reduction electrode which has been much used in the determination of hydrogen ion activities is the QUINHYDRONE ELECTRODE. Quinhydrone is an addition compound formed from equimolecular

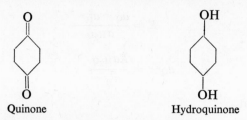

Quinone   Hydroquinone

quantities of quinone and hydroquinone. Hydroquinone is a weak dibasic acid which ionises according to the equation

so that, denoting the quinone molecule by Q, and the hydroquinone ion by Q^{--}, we see that the quinhydrone electrode

$$Pt \left| \begin{matrix} Q \\ Q^{--} \end{matrix} \right.$$

is similar in type to the ferrous–ferric electrode discussed above.

The cell $$H_2 \, Pt \left| HCl \, \begin{matrix} \vdots \end{matrix} \, \begin{matrix} H_2Q \\ Q \end{matrix} \right| Pt$$

will depend on the reaction

$$H_2 + Q \rightleftharpoons 2H^+ + Q^{--}$$

so that

$$\mathbf{E} = -\frac{\Delta G}{zF} = \frac{1}{zF}\{\mu_{H_2} + \mu_Q - 2\mu_{H^+} - \mu_{Q^{--}}\} + \mathbf{E}_j$$

$$= \frac{1}{zF}\{\mu_{0H_2} + \mu_{0Q} - 2\mu_{0H^+} - \mu_{0Q^{--}}\} + \frac{RT}{zF}\log_e \frac{p_{H_2}\, a_Q}{a^2_{H^+}\, a_{Q^{--}}} + \mathbf{E}_j. \quad (17,28)$$

If we arrange that the hydrogen is at unit pressure and the hydrochloric acid at unit mean ionic activity, and insert the value $z = 2$, this equation reduces to the form

$$\mathbf{E} = \mathbf{E}'_0 + \frac{RT}{2F}\log_e \frac{a_Q}{a_{Q^{--}}} + \mathbf{E}_j. \qquad . \qquad . \qquad (17,29)$$

The hydroquinone will be in equilibrium with the hydrogen ions in the solution *on the right-hand side of the cell*, and will be governed by the equation

$$H_2Q \rightleftharpoons Q^{--} + 2H^+,$$

so that
$$K = \frac{a_{Q^{--}} \, a_{H^+}^2}{a_{H_2Q}}$$

and
$$a_{Q^{--}} = \frac{K a_{H_2Q}}{a_{H^+}^2}.$$

It follows that

$$\mathbf{E} = \mathbf{E}_0' + \frac{RT}{2F} \log_e \frac{a_Q}{K a_{H_2Q}} + \frac{RT}{F} \log_e a_{H^+} + \mathbf{E}_j. \qquad (17,30)^1$$

As long as the solution on the right-hand side of the cell is not strongly alkaline, ionisation of the hydroquinone will be so small that the ratio a_Q/a_{H_2Q} will remain virtually constant, and we may write

$$\mathbf{E} = \mathbf{E}_0 + \frac{RT}{F} \log_e a_{H^+} + \mathbf{E}_j. \qquad . \quad . \quad . \quad (17,31)$$

If the quinone and hydroquinone added originally were in the form of quinhydrone, so that $m_Q = m_{H_2Q}$, the value of $\mathbf{E}_0$ proves to be 0·6994 volt.

The quinhydrone electrode has been much used for the determination of the p_H of a solution. For this purpose the test solution and quinhydrone electrode is coupled with any standard half-cell, such as a calomel electrode to give the cell

$$\text{Hg} \ \Big| \ \text{Hg}_2\text{Cl}_2, \text{KCl} \ \vdots \ \text{test solution} \ \frac{Q}{Q^{--}} \ \Big| \ \text{Pt.}$$

Since the p_H of a solution is defined by the equation

$$p_H = -\log_{10} a_{H^+},$$

it follows from (17,31) that the e.m.f. of the cell is given by the expression

$$\mathbf{E} = 0\cdot6994 - \frac{2\cdot303 RT}{F} p_H - \mathbf{E}_{cal} + \mathbf{E}_j. \qquad . \quad . \quad (17,32)$$

It is usual to reduce the liquid junction potential to a negligible quantity[2] by linking the two half-cells by a saturated KCl bridge; this enables the p_H of the test solution to be calculated once the e.m.f. of the cell is known.

---

[1] The student should note carefully that the term a_{H^+} in (17,30) is not the same as the term a_{H^+} in (17,28). That in (17,28) refers to the solution on the left-hand side of the cell, and that in (17,30) to the right-hand side.

[2] It is important to observe that $\mathbf{E}_j$ is not *completely* eliminated, or at least we do not *know* whether it is completely eliminated, so that the value of the p_H obtained is uncertain to a very small amount, so illustrating the earlier statement that the activity of a single ion species is unobtainable.

CONCENTRATION CELLS

Consider the cell

$$\text{H}_2 \ \text{Pt} \ | \ \text{HCl}_{m_1}\text{AgCl}_{(\text{sat})} \ | \ \text{Ag} - \text{Ag} \ | \ \text{AgCl}_{(\text{sat})}\text{HCl}_{m_2} \ | \ \text{Pt} \ \text{H}_2$$
$$\text{1 atm} \qquad\qquad\qquad\qquad\qquad\qquad\qquad\qquad\qquad \text{1 atm}$$

and let us imagine that when assembled the current flows through the cell from left to right. The cell reaction in the left-hand side compartment is

$$\text{H}_2 + 2\text{AgCl} \longrightarrow 2\text{H}^+ + 2\text{Cl}^- + 2\text{Ag}$$

and that in the right-hand side compartment the reverse.

The overall result of the cell reaction is that HCl is produced in the left-hand side and removed from the right-hand side.

An expression for the e.m.f. of the joint cell can be obtained in two ways:

(1) The e.m.f. of the left-hand side compartment is

$$\mathbf{E}_1 = \mathbf{E}_0 - \frac{2RT}{F} \log_e a^{\pm}{}_{\text{HCl}_{(1)}},$$

and that of the compartment on the right

$$\mathbf{E}_2 = -\mathbf{E}_0 + \frac{2RT}{F} \log_e a^{\pm}{}_{\text{HCl}_{(2)}}.$$

$$\mathbf{E} = \mathbf{E}_1 + \mathbf{E}_2 = \frac{2RT}{F} \log_e \frac{a^{\pm}{}_{\text{HCl}_{(2)}}}{a^{\pm}{}_{\text{HCl}_{(1)}}} \quad . \quad . \quad . \quad (17,33)$$

or

$$\mathbf{E} = \frac{2RT}{F} \log_e \frac{m_2 \, \gamma_{\pm 2}}{m_1 \, \gamma_{\pm 1}}. \quad . \quad . \quad . \quad (17,34)$$

(2) The total changes which result from the cell giving current in the direction shown are:

    (a) one mole of hydrogen absorbed at 1 atmosphere on the left-hand side;

    (b) two moles of HCl produced on the left-hand side;

    (c) two moles of Ag deposited on the left-hand side;

    (d) two moles of AgCl formed on the right-hand side;

    (e) two moles of HCl disappearing from the right-hand side; and

    (f) one mole of hydrogen gas evolved at 1 atmosphere on the right-hand side.

The only operations involving a change in free energy are (b) and (e); i.e.

the transfer of two moles of H^+ and Cl^- from a solution of HCl at m_2 to one at m_1.

$$\Delta G = 2(\mu_{H^+} + \mu_{Cl^-})_1 - 2(\mu_{H^+} + \mu_{Cl^-})_2$$

$$= 2\{\mu_{0\,H^+} + RT \log_e a_{H^+_{(1)}} + \mu_{0\,Cl^-} + RT \log_e a_{Cl^-_{(1)}}\}$$

$$- 2\{\mu_{0\,H^+} + RT \log_e a_{H^+_{(2)}} + \mu_{0\,Cl^-} + RT \log_e a_{Cl^-_{(2)}}\}.$$

i.e. $$\Delta G = 2RT \log_e \frac{a_{H^+_{(1)}} a_{Cl^-_{(1)}}}{a_{H^+_{(2)}} a_{Cl^-_{(2)}}}$$

$$= 4RT \log_e \frac{a_{\pm\,HCl_{(1)}}}{a_{\pm\,HCl_{(2)}}}.$$

When the cell proceeds to this extent two Faradays of electricity are transported through the cell, so that

$$-\Delta G = 2\mathbf{E}\mathbf{F}$$

i.e. $$\mathbf{E} = \frac{2RT}{F} \log_e \frac{a_{\pm\,HCl_{(2)}}}{a_{\pm\,HCl_{(1)}}}, \quad . \quad . \quad . \quad . \quad (17,33)$$

which is the same as before.

The above cell is called a *Concentration Cell without transport*, because no liquid junction is involved. The equations produced are therefore precise. There are interesting variations on concentration cells without transport; one is the cell

$$H_{2_{p_1}} Pt \mid HCl \mid Pt\, H_{2_{p_2}}.$$

Here the overall effect is the solution of hydrogen at one partial pressure and its dissolution at the other. The e.m.f. of such a cell gives information on the relative fugacities of the hydrogen at the two partial pressures. The student is referred to Exercise 17,3.

A second is the cell

$$ZnHg_{(1)} \mid ZnSO_4 \mid ZnHg_{(2)}$$

in which the two electrodes consist of zinc amalgam at different concentrations. The e.m.f. of this cell gives information regarding the relative activity coefficients of the zinc in the different amalgams.

Another is a method of determining the transition temperature of a metal existing in two crystalline modifications

$$M_{(1)} \mid M^+ \mid M_{(2)}.$$

Over that temperature range at which the natural spontaneous process is for crystalline modification 1 to convert into 2, the standard electrode potentials of the two modifications will differ, so that the cell will give current in such a direction that $M_{(1)}$ goes into solution and $M_{(2)}$ is deposited. At the transition temperature the standard electrode potentials will become equal and the e.m.f. of the cell will become zero.

Concentration Cells with Transport

Now consider the cell

$$H_2 \ Pt \ | \ HCl_{m_1} \ \| \ HCl_{m_2} \ | \ Pt \ H_2$$
$$1 \text{ atm} \qquad\qquad\qquad 1 \text{ atm}$$

where m_2 is greater than m_1.

This cell is much the same as the first concentration cell considered, except that the two Ag/AgCl electrodes have been removed and the two parts of the cell connected by a liquid junction.

We now imagine that the cell gives current so that one Faraday of Electricity passes through the cell (the current will flow through the cell from left to right). The following changes will take place:

(a) Half mole of hydrogen will pass into solution on the left-hand side to produce one mole (gm-ion) of hydrogen ions.

(b) t_+ moles of hydrogen ions will migrate across the liquid junction from m_1 to m_2, and $(1 - t_+)$ moles of chloride ions from m_2 to m_1, where t_+ is the transport number of the cation.

(c) One mole of hydrogen ions will pass out of solution on the right-hand side to give half mole of hydrogen.

The overall change is therefore the transfer of $(1 - t_+)$ moles of hydrogen ions and chloride ions from m_2 to m_1. Since $(1 - t_+) = t_-$, where t_- is the transport number of the anion, the change in free energy is given by the expressions

$$\Delta G = t_-\{(\mu_{H^+_{(1)}} + \mu_{Cl^-_{(1)}}) - (\mu_{H^+_{(2)}} + \mu_{Cl^-_{(2)}})\}$$

$$= t_- \, RT \log_e \frac{a_{H^+_{(1)}} \times a_{Cl^-_{(1)}}}{a_{H^+_{(2)}} \times a_{Cl^-_{(2)}}}$$

$$= 2t_- \, RT \log_e \frac{a_{\pm \, HCl_{(1)}}}{a_{\pm \, HCl_{(2)}}}.$$

Since $\Delta G = -\textbf{E}\textbf{F},$

it follows that

$$\textbf{E} = \frac{2t_- RT}{F} \log_e \frac{a_{\pm \, HCl_{(2)}}}{a_{\pm \, HCl_{(1)}}}. \qquad . \qquad . \qquad . \quad (17,35)$$

It should be noted that equation (17,35) can be used to determine the value of the transport numbers of the ions concerned.

Equation (17,35) is based on the assumption that the transport numbers of the ions concerned are independent of concentration. This is generally not correct. The variation of transport number with concentration can be taken into account in the following way: if the two solutions are of almost the same concentration, so that one is of activity $a_{\pm}$ and the other $(a + da)_{\pm}$, the e.m.f. between them will be given by the equation

$$d\mathbf{E} = \frac{2t_- RT}{F} \log_e \frac{a + da}{a}.$$

But

$$\log_e \frac{a + da}{a} = \log_e \left(1 + \frac{da}{a}\right)$$

$$\simeq \frac{da}{a} \simeq d \log_e a,$$

so that

$$\mathbf{E} = \frac{2RT}{F} \int_{a_{\pm (1)}}^{a_{\pm (2)}} t_- \, d \log_e a_{\pm}. \quad . \quad . \quad . \quad (17,36)$$

The importance of concentration cells lies in their use in the determination of activity coefficients. This matter will be discussed in the next chapter.

The Origin of the Liquid Junction Potential and an Approximate Expression for it

When two solutions of the same electrolyte at different concentrations are in contact, diffusion from the more concentrated to the more dilute solution will occur spontaneously. The rates of diffusion of the two ions may, however, differ (the rates will in fact be proportional to the transport numbers of the ions), so that if the cation be the faster (as in HCl), the dilute solution will tend to acquire a potential positive to that of the more concentrated solution. This difference in potential is the liquid junction potential.

An approximate expression for its value in the case of the cell we have studied can be obtained by making use of equation (17,35),

$$\mathbf{E} = 2t_- \frac{RT}{F} \log_e \frac{a_{\pm \text{HCl}_{(2)}}}{a_{\pm \text{HCl}_{(1)}}}. \quad . \quad . \quad . \quad (17,35)$$

and comparing it with an expression for the e.m.f. of the cell obtained by considering the electrode potentials and the liquid junction potential separately. The second expression is

$$\mathbf{E} = \left\{ \mathbf{E}_{0\,\mathrm{H_2}} + \frac{RT}{F} \log_e a_{\mathrm{H}^+_{(2)}} \right\} - \left\{ \mathbf{E}_{0\,\mathrm{H_2}} + \frac{RT}{F} \log_e a_{\mathrm{H}^+_{(1)}} \right\} + \mathbf{E}_j$$

$$= \frac{RT}{F} \log_e \frac{a_{\mathrm{H}^+_{(2)}}}{a_{\mathrm{H}^+_{(1)}}} + \mathbf{E}_j. \quad\ldots\ldots\ldots\ldots\ldots \quad (17,37)$$

Such an expression contains single ionic activities on which, as has been explained earlier, we have no information. If, however, we make the assumption that

$$a_{\mathrm{H}^+} = a_{\mathrm{Cl}^-} = a_{\pm\,\mathrm{HCl}}$$

equation (17,37) becomes

$$\mathbf{E} \eqsim \frac{RT}{F} \log_e \frac{a_{\pm\,\mathrm{HCl}_{(2)}}}{a_{\pm\,\mathrm{HCl}_{(1)}}} + \mathbf{E}_j, \quad\ldots\quad (17,38)$$

so that

$$\mathbf{E}_j \eqsim (2t_- - 1) \frac{RT}{F} \log_e \frac{a_{\pm\,\mathrm{HCl}_{(2)}}}{a_{\pm\,\mathrm{HCl}_{(1)}}}. \quad\ldots\quad (17,39)$$

We note that this equation predicts that the liquid junction potential becomes zero in the case of an electrolyte the transport numbers of the ions of which are equal (i.e. $t_+ = t_- = 0\cdot5$), which prediction is in accordance with the origin of the potential which we have cited.

We emphasise, however, that equation (17,39) is—

(a) based on the assumption that the transport numbers are independent of concentration; and

(b) depends on the assumption that $a_{\mathrm{H}^+} = a_{\mathrm{Cl}^-}$ for which we have no complete evidence. It is for this reason that the quasi-equality sign $\eqsim$ has been used in both equations.

More complicated expressions for the liquid junction potential have been deduced by Henderson and Planck. These expressions (which incidentally demonstrate why a saturated salt bridge of KCl will "almost" eliminate a liquid junction potential) will not, however, be discussed here.

THE USE OF ELECTRO–CHEMICAL CELLS FOR THE DETERMINATION OF THERMODYNAMIC QUANTITIES

Electro-chemical cells are of great importance to thermodynamics because of the ease with which e.m.f. measurements may be made to yield thermodynamic data relating to the reactions on which the cells depend.

The reaction which takes place in the cell

$$\mathrm{Pb} \mid \mathrm{PbCl_{2(sat)}}; \mathrm{HCl}_{m=1}; \mathrm{AgCl_{(sat)}} \mid \mathrm{Ag}$$

is

$$\tfrac{1}{2}\mathrm{Pb} + \mathrm{AgCl} \longrightarrow \tfrac{1}{2}\mathrm{PbCl_2} + \mathrm{Ag}.$$

Its e.m.f. at 25° C is 0·4900 volt and at and around this temperature

$$\left(\frac{\partial \mathbf{E}}{\partial T}\right)_p = -0 \cdot 000145 \text{ volt deg}^{-1}.$$

ΔG, ΔS and ΔH for the reaction may be calculated directly as follows:

$$\Delta G = -z\mathbf{E}F = -0 \cdot 4900 \times 96{,}487 \text{ joule}$$

$$= -11{,}300 \text{ cal.}$$

$$\Delta S = -\left(\frac{\partial(\Delta G)}{\partial T}\right)_p = zF\left(\frac{\partial \mathbf{E}}{\partial T}\right)_p$$

$$= -96{,}487 \times 0 \cdot 000145 \text{ joule deg}^{-1}$$

$$= -3 \cdot 344 \text{ cal deg}^{-1}$$

$$\Delta H = \Delta G + T\Delta S$$

$$= -12{,}296 \text{ cal.}$$

Since the chemical potential of a solid salt equals that of the salt in a saturated solution, the values of ΔG, ΔS and ΔH calculated above are the same as those for the reaction

$$\tfrac{1}{2}Pb + AgCl \longrightarrow \tfrac{1}{2}PbCl_2 + Ag$$

in the solid state.

The value for ΔH requires further discussion. The value obtained represents the heat absorbed by the system when the reaction takes place at constant pressure in a beaker or calorimeter; and should be the same as the value obtained by direct measurement (in fact, direct measurement yields the value $-12{,}085$ cal, which result is in excellent agreement with that calculated above), but bears no relation to the heat absorbed by the system when the reaction takes place in an electro-chemical cell. This is because the increase in enthalpy in a constant pressure process is equal to the heat absorbed only if the only work performed by the system is expansion work. When the reaction takes place in a cell, electrical work is performed and the relationship $\Delta H = q_p$ (4,18) no longer holds.[1]

The heat absorbed by the cell can, however, be calculated. Since the cell reaction is both reversible and isothermal,

$$q_p = T\Delta S = -996 \text{ cal,}$$

so that when the reaction takes place in the cell at 25° C to such an extent that a half mole of lead reacts with one mole of silver chloride a quantity

[1] If the student is not clear on this point, he should read again the argument upon which the derivation of equation (4,18) was based.

of work equal to 11,300 cal is performed and a quantity of heat equal to 996 cal passes to the surroundings.

The results of calculations based on e.m.f. measurements made on different cells may often be combined to give information relating to quite a different reaction. Thus the values of **E** and $(\partial \mathbf{E}/\partial T)_p$ for the cells

$$Pb \mid PbCl_{2(sat)}, \quad HCl, \quad AgCl_{(sat)} \mid Ag$$

and

$$Pb \mid PbI_{2(sat)}, \quad KI, \quad AgI_{(sat)} \mid Ag$$

may be used to evaluate ΔG, ΔS and ΔH for the reaction

$$PbI_{2(s)} + 2AgCl_{(s)} \longrightarrow PbCl_{2(s)} + 2AgI_{(s)}.$$

Much use has been made of cell reactions in thermodynamics, because of the ease with which quantities such as ΔG, ΔS and ΔH may be evaluated. The student is reminded of the part played by such results in the formulation and verification of the Third Law.

The Determination of the Ionisation Constant of Weak Electrolytes from e.m.f. Measurements

The hydrogen, silver–silver chloride cell was introduced earlier in this chapter in the form

$$H_2 \ Pt \mid HCl, \quad AgCl_{(sat)} \mid Ag.$$

The cell is, however, essentially the same if the HCl is replaced by a mixture of electrolytes, as long as one provides hydrogen ions (to establish equilibrium with the hydrogen electrode), and the other provides chloride ions (to establish equilibrium with the silver chloride).

Consider, for example, the case where the electrolyte is a mixture of a weak acid HA, the sodium salt of the acid and sodium chloride:

$$\underset{\text{1 atm}}{H_2} \ Pt \mid HA, \quad NaA, \quad NaCl, \quad AgCl_{(sat)} \mid Ag.$$

The cell reaction is

$$H_2 + 2Ag^+ \longrightarrow 2Ag + 2H^+$$

so that we may write:

$$z\mathbf{E}F = -\Delta G = (\mu_{0_{H_2}} + 2\mu_{0_{Ag^+}} - 2\mu_{0_{H^+}} - 2\mu_{0_{Ag}}) + RT \log_e \frac{a^2_{Ag^+}}{a^2_{H^+}}$$

$$= -\Delta G_0' + RT \log_e \frac{a^2_{Ag^+}}{a^2_{H^+}}.$$

But

$$a_{Ag^+} \times a_{Cl^-} = K_s$$

so that

$$zEF = -\Delta G = -\Delta G'_0 + 2RT \log_e K_s - 2RT \log_e a_{H^+} a_{Cl^-}$$
$$= -\Delta G_0 - 2RT \log_e a_{H^+} a_{Cl^-}.$$

Since for the reaction as written, $z = 2$,

$$E = E_0 - \frac{RT}{F} \log_e a_{H^+} a_{Cl^-}. \quad . \quad . \quad . \quad (17,40)$$

The important point to note is that the standard electrode potential E_0 is

$$\frac{1}{zF} \{\mu_{0\,H_2} + 2\mu_{0\,Ag^+} - 2\mu_{0\,H+} - 2\mu_{0\,Ag}\} + \frac{2RT}{zF} \log_e K_s$$

and is therefore precisely the same[1] as that for the simpler cell

$$H_2 \mid HCl \qquad AgCl_{(sat)} \mid Ag.$$

Its numerical value at 25° C is therefore the same (0·2225 volt), although its physical significance is somewhat different. The physical significance of E_0 for the cell

$$H_2\ Pt \mid HCl \qquad AgCl_{(sat)} \mid Ag$$

is that it is the e.m.f. of the cell under such conditions that the mean ionic activity of HCl is unity, whereas E_0 for the cell

$$H_2\ Pt \mid HA,\ NaA,\ NaCl,\ AgCl_{(sat)} \mid Ag$$

is the e.m.f. of the cell under such conditions that

$$a_{H^+} = a_{Cl^-} = 1$$

irrespective of the source of each ion.

The cell described is typical of the many varieties used by Harned and his co-workers and others, in the determination of ionisation constants. The method is quite general. In order to determine the ionisation constant of a weak acid HA, the cell shown below is set up:

$$H_2,\ Pt \mid HA_{m_1},\ NaA_{m_2},\ NaCl_{m_3},\ AgCl_{(sat)} \mid Ag.$$

We have seen that its e.m.f. is given by the expression

$$E = E_0 - \frac{RT}{F} \log_e a_{H^+} a_{Cl^-}. \quad . \quad . \quad . \quad (17,40)$$

The activity of hydrogen ions is governed by the reaction

$$HA \rightleftharpoons H^+ + A^-$$

for which
$$\frac{a_{H^+} a_{A^-}}{a_{HA}} = K.$$

[1] Compare the above with equations (17,8)–(17,13).

Equation (17,40) may therefore be written in the form

$$\mathbf{E} = \mathbf{E_0} - \frac{RT}{F} \log_e \frac{K a_{HA} a_{Cl^-}}{a_{A^-}} \qquad \cdots \qquad (17,41)$$

or $\qquad \mathbf{E} = \mathbf{E_0} - \frac{RT}{F} \log_e K - \frac{RT}{F} \log_e \frac{m_{HA} m_{Cl^-}}{m_{A^-}} \cdot \frac{\gamma_{HA} \gamma_{Cl^-}}{\gamma_{A^-}}. \quad (17,42)$

This equation is exact. If we assume that the acid HA is very weak, the equilibrium molality m_{HA} will be almost the same as the stoichiometric molality m_1, and m_{A^+} the same as m_2. Since m_{Cl^-} is the same as m_3, these values may be substituted into (17,42) and the equation rearranged to give

$$\mathbf{E} - \mathbf{E_0} + \frac{RT}{F} \log_e \frac{m_1 m_3}{m_2} = -\frac{RT}{F} \log_e K - \frac{RT}{F} \log_e \frac{\gamma_{HA} \gamma_{Cl^-}}{\gamma_{A^-}}. \quad (17,43)$$

Since the value of $\mathbf{E_0}$ is known (-0.2225 volt), measurement of $\mathbf{E}$ permits the evaluation of all terms of the left-hand side. The solution is now diluted and new values of m_1, m_2, m_3 and $\mathbf{E}$ obtained. The values of the left-hand side are now plotted against the square root of the ionic strength. Extrapolation to zero ionic strength at which the term $\frac{RT}{F} \log_e \frac{\gamma_{HA} \gamma_{Cl^-}}{\gamma_{A^-}}$ vanishes, gives the value of $-\frac{RT}{F} \log_e K$ as the intercept. The student is advised to illustrate the method by solving Exercise 17,4.

The method may be extended to give the separate ionisation constants of polybasic acids. Thus, the ionisation constant of the acid $H_2PO_4^-$ may be obtained from measurements made on the cell

$$H_2 \; Pt \; | \; NaH_2PO_4, \quad Na_2HPO_4, \quad NaCl, \quad AgCl_{(sat)} \; | \; Ag.$$

If the acid is not sufficiently weak to permit the assumptions made after (17,42), an approximate value of K is obtained as described above, the degree of ionisation of the acid HA in the presence of the salt NaA estimated, and the necessary corrections made to the terms m_{HA} and m_{A^-}. Such corrections are rarely significant.

The ionisation constant for water may be determined from measurements made on the cell

$$H_2 \; Pt \; | \; KOH_{m_1}, \quad KCl_{m_2}, \quad AgCl_{(sat)} \; | \; Ag.$$
$$\text{1 atm}$$

Again $\qquad\qquad \mathbf{E} = \mathbf{E_0} - \frac{RT}{F} \log_e a_{H^+} a_{Cl^-},$

and since $\qquad\qquad a_{H^+} \times a_{OH^-} = K_w,$

we proceed as before to obtain the equation

$$\mathbf{E} - \mathbf{E_0} + \frac{RT}{F} \log_e \frac{m_2}{m_1} = -\frac{RT}{F} \log_e K_w - \frac{RT}{F} \log_e \frac{\gamma_{Cl^-}}{\gamma_{OH^-}}. \quad (17,44)$$

Extrapolation of the left-hand side against the square root of the ionic strength gives $-\dfrac{RT}{F}\log_e K_w$ as the intercept at zero ionic strength. The value of K_w obtained by this method is $1 \cdot 0083 \times 10^{-14}$ at $25°$ C.

The ionisation constant of a weak base may be obtained in the same way. Consider a base B which ionises by the reaction

$$B + H_2O \rightleftharpoons BH^+ + OH^-$$

$$K_b = \frac{a_{BH^+} a_{OH^-}}{a_B}.$$

This equilibrium is linked to that between water and its ions, for which

$$K_w = a_{H^+} a_{OH^-}$$

so that

$$a_{H^+} = \frac{K_w a_{BH^+}}{K_b a_B}. \qquad \qquad \text{(17,45)}$$

The e.m.f. of the cell

$$H_2 \text{ Pt} \mid B_{m_1}, \quad BHCl_{m_2}, \quad AgCl_{(sat)} \mid Ag$$
$$\text{1 atm}$$

is given by the expression

$$E = E_0 - \frac{RT}{F}\log_e a_{H^+} a_{Cl^-},$$

so that, introducing the value of a_{H^+} from (17,45), expressing the various activities as the product of the molalities and the activity coefficients, and rearranging, we obtain the expression

$$E - E_0 + \frac{RT}{F}\log_e \frac{m_2^2}{m_1} = \frac{RT}{F}\log_e \frac{K_b}{K_w} - \frac{RT}{F}\log_e \frac{\gamma_{BH^+}\gamma_{Cl^-}}{\gamma_B}. \quad \text{(17,46)}$$

Extrapolation of the left-hand side against the square root of the ionic strength gives $\dfrac{RT}{F}\log_e \dfrac{K_b}{K_w}$ as the intercept at zero ionic strength. Since K_w is known, K_b can be evaluated directly.

The values of ionisation constants obtained by the method described above are probably more accurate than those obtained in any other way. Much of the work carried out in this field is described in great detail in the book, *The Physical Chemistry of Electrolytic Solutions*, by H. S. Harned and B. B. Owen (Reinhold Publishing Corporation, 1943).

It is pointed out that knowledge of an ionisation constant leads directly to the evaluation of the standard free energy of ionisation, and that knowledge of the ionisation constant at two temperatures permits the use of the van't Hoff equation to give the corresponding enthalpy change.

The Determination of the Solubility Product of a Slightly Soluble Salt from e.m.f. Measurements

Earlier in the chapter we showed that the standard electrode potential of the silver–silver chloride electrode and that of the silver–silver ion electrode are connected by the equation

$$\mathbf{E}_{0\,Ag/AgCl} = \mathbf{E}_{0\,Ag/Ag^+} + \frac{RT}{F} \log_e K_s \quad . \quad . \quad (17,47)$$

where K_s is the solubility product of silver chloride.

At that point in the argument the value of K_s was assumed, so as to permit the calculation of the standard electrode potential of silver from the known value for the silver–silver chloride electrode, but it is rather more useful to use the known value of $\mathbf{E}_{0\,Ag/Ag^+}$, which may be determined accurately by other means, to calculate the value of K_s. Precisely the same procedure may be adopted in order to calculate K_s for other silver salts, such as the bromide or iodide. Thus the standard electrode potential of the silver–silver bromide electrode at 25° C evaluated from measurements made on the cell

$$\text{H}_2 \text{ Pt} \mid \text{HBr,} \qquad \text{AgBr}_{(sat)} \mid \text{Ag}$$

is 0·0711 volt, so that the solubility product for silver bromide is given by the equation

$$\mathbf{E}_{0\,Ag/AgBr} - \mathbf{E}_{0\,Ag/Ag^+} = \frac{RT}{F} \log_e K_s \quad . \quad . \quad (17,48)$$

from which since $\mathbf{E}_{0\,Ag/Ag^+}$ is 0·799 volt it follows that

$$K_s = 4·9 \times 10^{-13}.$$

THE FREE ENERGY AND ENTHALPY OF FORMATION OF IONS AND IONIC ENTROPIES

Although we have seen that the change in free energy, enthalpy and entropy of an ionic reaction in solution can often be evaluated directly from e.m.f. measurements, many ionic reactions are not amenable to this treatment simply because it is impracticable to devise a suitable electrochemical cell. For the determination of such quantities for such reactions there is no alternative but to revert to the more general methods discussed in earlier chapters. In effect, these methods require knowledge either of free energies of formation of the ions concerned or of their enthalpies of formation and entropies. Before describing the methods by which these quantities may be determined one principle must be discussed.

All quantities which may be measured or calculated during study of a system containing one or more electrolytes are of the form

$$X_{M^+} - \frac{1}{z} X_{N^{z+}} \quad \ldots \ldots \quad \text{(i)}$$

or of the form

$$X_{M^+} + \frac{1}{z} X_{N^{z-}} \quad \ldots \ldots \quad \text{(ii)}$$

The first depends on a reaction of type

$$N + zM^+ \longrightarrow N^{z+} + zM$$

such as

$$Zn + 2H^+ \longrightarrow Zn^{++} + H_2$$

in which case such quantities as

$$\Delta G_{f_{Zn^{++}}} - 2\Delta G_{f_{H^+}}$$

may be obtained, and the second depends on some measurement made on the electrolyte as a whole and results in such quantities as

$$\Delta H_{f_{Ba^{++}}} + \Delta H_{f_{SO_4^{--}}}.$$

No measurements are possible which relate to a single ion species, so that any method by which the measured quantity (i) or (ii) is partitioned between the two ions concerned is necessarily conventional. Any set of conventions is permissible subject to the condition that it is both internally self-consistent, and consistent with any related conventions already adopted.

As far as we are concerned in the present context we require to adopt—

(i) a convention by which a measured free energy change may be partitioned between two ions, so as to permit one part to be called the free energy of formation of one ion and the second the free energy of formation of the second;

(ii) a convention whereby a measured enthalpy change may be similarly partitioned; and

(iii) a convention whereby a measured entropy change may be so divided.

These conventions are internally self-consistent if the conventional entropy of formation of an ion calculated from values based on conventions (i) and (ii) by the equation

$$\Delta S_f = \frac{\Delta H_f - \Delta G_f}{T}$$

is the same as that obtained using convention (iii).

These conventions must also be consistent with that adopted earlier in this chapter in partitioning the e.m.f. of a cell between the two electrodes concerned. The conventions chosen are explained in the following sections.

Free Energies of Formation of Ions

It follows from Table 17,I that the standard e.m.f. of the cell

$$H_2 Pt \mid H^+_{(aq)} \mid\mid Cu^{++}_{(aq)} \mid Cu$$

i.e. the e.m.f. of the cell under such conditions that the partial pressure of hydrogen, the activity of hydrogen ions and that of copper ions are all unity, is 0·337 volt at 25° C. The reaction on which the cell depends is

$$H_2 + Cu^{++}_{(aq)} \longrightarrow 2H^+_{(aq)} + Cu$$

so that the standard free energy change for the reaction, $-z\mathbf{E}_0 F$, i.e. $-2 \times 0·337 \times 96,487$ joules or $-15,540$ cal, is the standard free energy of formation of two moles of aqueous hydrogen ions from hydrogen minus the standard free energy of formation of one mole of aqueous copper ions from copper.

Just as it was recognised that there is no way by which the e.m.f. of the cell can be apportioned between the two electrode processes to give absolute values of single electrode potentials, so, as was explained above, there is no way by which the standard free energy for the whole reaction may be divided to give absolute values for the free energy changes for the individual reactions

$$\tfrac{1}{2}H_2 \longrightarrow H^+_{(aq)} + \bar{e}$$

or

$$Cu \longrightarrow Cu^{++}_{(aq)} + 2\bar{e}.$$

However, the convention by which the standard electrode potential of hydrogen is assigned the value of zero at all temperatures of interest is equivalent to *assigning the value zero to the standard free energy of formation of aqueous hydrogen ions at all temperatures*, so that the (conventional) standard free energy of formation of copper ions becomes 15,540 cal mole^{-1}

In other words, we define the (conventional) standard free energy of formation of an ion in terms of its standard electrode potential by the equation[1]

$$\Delta G_{0_f} = z\mathbf{E}_0 F. \quad . \quad . \quad . \quad . \quad . \quad (17,49)$$

It is clearly the standard free energy change for such a reaction as

$$Cu + 2H^+_{(aq)} \longrightarrow H_2 + Cu^{++}_{(aq)}.$$

[1] The student is reminded that the American convention for the sign of electrode potentials requires that the free energy of formation be defined by the equation $\Delta G_{0_f} = -z\mathbf{E}_0 F$.

Equation (17,49) provides the simplest method by which the standard free energy of formation of an ion may be determined. It sometimes happens, however, that it cannot be used directly, simply because the electrode concerned does not give reproducible results. An example of this is the Fe, Fe^{+++} system. The value of the standard free energy of formation of the ferric ion is obtained indirectly by measuring the standard electrode potential of the Fe, Fe^{++} system, and the oxidation-reduction potential of the Fe^{++}, Fe^{+++} electrode. The value of the first is -0.440 volt, so that the free energy change for the reaction

$$2H^+_{(aq)} + Fe \longrightarrow H_2 + Fe^{++}_{(aq)}$$

is $-2 \times 0.440 \times 96{,}487$ joules, i.e. $-20{,}300$ cal. The value of the second is 0.772 volt, so that the standard free energy change for the reaction

$$H^+_{(aq)} + Fe^{++}_{(aq)} \longrightarrow Fe^{+++}_{(aq)} + \tfrac{1}{2}H_2$$

is $0.772 \times 96{,}487$ joules, i.e. $17{,}800$ cal. It follows that the standard free energy change for the reaction

$$3H^+_{(aq)} + Fe \longrightarrow \tfrac{3}{2}H_2 + Fe^{+++}_{(aq)}$$

i.e. ΔG_{o_f} for the ferric ion, is -2500 cal.

Another method by which the free energy of formation of an ion in solution may be determined is by making use of the solubility product of a sparsely soluble salt. This method will be illustrated by the evaluation of the free energy of formation of the sulphate ion from the known solubility product of barium sulphate. From the First Statement of Chemical Potentials it follows that the chemical potential of solid barium sulphate equals the sum of the chemical potentials of the barium and sulphate ions in a saturated solution at the same temperature. So that

$$\mu_{(s)} = \mu_{o_{Ba^{++}}} + \mu_{o_{SO_4^{--}}} + RT \log_e a_{Ba^{++}_{(sat)}} a_{SO_4^{--}_{(sat)}}$$

$$= \mu_{o_{Ba^{++}}} + \mu_{o_{SO_4^{--}}} + RT \log_e K_s, \quad . \quad . \quad . \quad (17,50)$$

where the symbols μ_o refer to the chemical potential of the separate ion species at such concentration that they are each at unit activity, and K_s is the solubility product. It follows that the standard free energy of precipitation of barium sulphate, i.e. the increase in free energy when one mole of barium ions at unit activity and one mole of sulphate ions at unit activity form one mole of solid barium sulphate at the same temperature is given by the equation

$$\Delta G_{ppn} = RT \log_e K_s. \quad . \quad . \quad . \quad (17,51)$$

It also follows that since

$$\Delta G_{ppn} = G_{\text{BaSO}_4(s)} - \left\{ G_{0\text{Ba}^{++}_{(\text{aq})}} + G_{0\text{SO}_4^{--}_{(\text{aq})}} \right\}$$

$$\Delta G_{ppn} = \Delta G_{f\text{BaSO}_4(s)} - \left\{ \Delta G_{0f\text{Ba}^{++}_{(\text{aq})}} + \Delta G_{0f\text{SO}_4^{--}_{(\text{aq})}} \right\}$$

so that

$$\Delta G_{0f\text{Ba}^{++}_{(\text{aq})}} + \Delta G_{0f\text{SO}_4^{--}_{(\text{aq})}} = \Delta G_{f\text{BaSO}_4(s)} - RT \log_e K_s. \quad (17,52)$$

ΔG_f for crystalline barium sulphate can be determined by using the Third Law. It proves to be $-323,000$ cal at $25°$ C. The solubility of barium sulphate at this temperature is $9 \cdot 57 \times 10^{-6}$ molal, and its mean ionic activity coefficient[1] at saturation $0 \cdot 971$, so that the thermodynamic solubility product is $(9 \cdot 57 \times 10^{-6} \times 0 \cdot 971)$.[2] It follows that

$$\Delta G_{ppn} = RT \log_e K_s$$

$$= -13,740 \text{ cal,}$$

and that

$$\Delta G_{0f\text{Ba}^{++}_{(\text{aq})}} + \Delta G_{0f\text{SO}_4^{--}_{(\text{aq})}} = -309,260 \text{ cal.}$$

The standard free energy of formation of the barium ion can be determined from its standard electrode potential by using equation (17,49). It proves to be $-133,850$ cal, so that

$$\Delta G_{0f\text{SO}_4^{--}} = -175,410 \text{ cal.}$$

If the standard free energy of formation of an ion cannot be determined by one of the methods described above, it is necessary to calculate it from the enthalpy of formation and the ionic entropy by using the equation

$$\Delta G_{0f} = \Delta H_{0f} - T\Delta S_{0f}.$$

The methods by which ΔH_{0f} and $S_{0\text{M}^+}$ are determined will now be considered.

Enthalpies of Formation of Ions

It follows from the Gibbs–Helmholtz equation

$$\Delta G = \Delta H + T\left(\frac{\partial(\Delta G)}{\partial T}\right)_p$$

that the convention whereby the value zero is assigned to the standard free energy of formation of the aqueous hydrogen ion at all temperatures

---

[1] This figure is estimated from the Debye–Hückel Limiting Law.

is consistent with the convention that the value zero is assigned to its standard enthalpy of formation at all temperatures. The standard enthalpy of formation for other ions based on the convention may, in many cases, be obtained directly from measurements of heats of reaction. When one mole of aluminium is dissolved in dilute hydrochloric acid at 25° C and a pressure of 1 atmosphere; 126,300 cal is evolved. This is the heat of reaction for the process

$$Al + 3HCl_{(aq)} \longrightarrow Al^{+++}{}_{(aq)} + 3Cl^-{}_{(aq)} + \tfrac{3}{2}H_2,$$

i.e. for the process

$$Al + 3H^+{}_{(aq)} \longrightarrow Al^{+++}{}_{(aq)} + \tfrac{3}{2}H_2,$$

and since the enthalpies of formation of hydrogen ions and aluminium are zero by convention, the value

$$\Delta H_0 = -126,300 \text{ cal}$$

becomes the standard enthalpy of formation of the aluminium ion.

The value for the chloride ion may be obtained by combining this result with the heat of reaction at constant pressure for the process

$$Al + \tfrac{3}{2}Cl_2 \longrightarrow AlCl_{3(s)}, \ \Delta H_1$$

and with the heat of solution for the process

$$AlCl_{3(s)} + aq \longrightarrow Al^{+++}{}_{(aq)} + 3Cl^-{}_{(aq)}, \ \Delta H_2.$$

Clearly, $\Delta H_{o_{f_{Cl^-}}} = \tfrac{1}{3}(\Delta H_1 + \Delta H_2 - (-126,300)).$

The same principle may be extended to other ions. In those cases in which the standard free energy of formation of an ion at more than one temperature is obtainable readily from e.m.f. measurements, the standard enthalpy of formation may be obtained by means of the Gibbs–Helmholtz equation.

Standard Entropy of Ions

Since for any process

$$\left(\frac{\partial(\Delta G)}{\partial T}\right)_p = -\Delta S,$$

the convention whereby the value zero is assigned to the standard free energy of formation of the hydrogen ion at all temperatures of interest necessitates the assignment of zero to the standard entropy of formation of the hydrogen ion at all temperatures.

This convention is, however, not sufficient for our purpose, and we therefore adopt the *additional* convention by which we assign zero to the standard entropy itself at all temperatures.[1]

Some of the methods available for the determination of ionic entropies based on this convention are given below.

The standard electrode potential of silver is the standard electro-motive force of the cell

$$\text{H}_2 \quad \text{Pt} \mid \text{H}^+_{(aq)} \quad \vdots \quad \text{Ag}^+_{(aq)} \mid \text{Ag}$$
$$\text{1 atm.}$$

so that ΔG_0 for the reaction

$$\tfrac{1}{2}\text{H}_2 + \text{Ag}^+_{(aq)} \longrightarrow \text{H}^+_{(aq)} + \text{Ag}$$

is given by the equation

$$\Delta G_0 = -\mathbf{E}_0 F,$$

and ΔS_0 by the equation

$$\Delta S_0 = F\left(\frac{\partial \mathbf{E}_0}{\partial T}\right)_p.$$

Since the entropy change is given also by the equation

$$\Delta S_0 = S_{0\,\text{H}^+(aq)} + S_{\text{Ag}} - \tfrac{1}{2}S_{0\,\text{H}_2} - S_{0\,\text{Ag}^+(aq)}, \quad . \quad (17,53)$$

and since $S_{0\,\text{H}^+(aq)}$ is zero by convention, and S_{Ag} and $S_{0\,\text{H}_2}$ are known, the standard entropy of the silver ion may be evaluated.

The value of $\mathbf{E}_0$ for this reaction has been measured very accurately at temperatures around 25° C, and expressed as a function of temperature by Harned and Owen by the equation

$$\mathbf{E}_0 = 0.7991 - 9.88 \times 10^{-4}(t - 25) + 7.0 \times 10^{-7}(t - 25)^2, \quad (17,54)$$

where t is the temperature in degrees C. It follows that at 25° C

$$\left(\frac{\partial \mathbf{E}_0}{\partial T}\right)_p = -9.88 \times 10^{-4} \text{ volt deg}^{-1}.$$

Since S_{Ag} equals 10.2 and $S_{0\,\text{H}_2}$ equals 31.2 cal deg^{-1}, $S_{0\,\text{Ag}^+}$ is given by the equation

$$-\frac{96,487}{4.184} \times 9.88 \times 10^{-4} = 0 + 10.2 - 15.6 - S_{0\,\text{Ag}^+},$$

so that $S_{0\,\text{Ag}^+}$ proves to be 17.4 cal deg^{-1}.

[1] The implications of the two conventions considered together are discussed in a later section.

In principle, this method may be used if the standard electrode potential of any element is known at two or more temperatures around 25° C. It is obvious, however, that the method requires that the standard e.m.f.s be measured with the highest degree of accuracy, as an error of say 0·001 volt in one measurement would lead to an extremely large error in $\partial \mathbf{E}_0 / \partial T$.

The value of $S_{0\,Ag^+}$ may now be used in the determination of $S_{0\,Cl^-}$. As was shown earlier in the case of barium sulphate, the increase in free energy when one mole of a sparsely soluble salt is precipitated from a solution in which its ions are at unit activity is given by the equation

$$\Delta G_{ppn} = RT \log_e K_s. \qquad . \quad . \quad . \quad . \quad (17,51)$$

If the solubility product is known over a temperature range, ΔS_{ppn} may be calculated, since

$$\Delta S_{ppn} = - \left\{ \frac{\partial(\Delta G_{ppn})}{\partial T} \right\}_p . \quad . \quad . \quad . \quad (17,55)$$

It will be remembered that the solubility product of silver chloride is given by the equation

$$\frac{RT}{F} \log_e K_s = \mathbf{E}_{0\,Ag/AgCl} - \mathbf{E}_{0\,Ag/Ag^+},$$

so that

$$\Delta S_{ppn} = - \frac{F}{4 \cdot 184} \left\{ \frac{\partial \mathbf{E}_{0\,Ag/AgCl}}{\partial T} - \frac{\partial \mathbf{E}_{0\,Ag/Ag^+}}{\partial T} \right\}_p . \quad (17,56)$$

The standard electrode potential of the silver–silver chloride electrode has been measured at temperatures around 25° C by Harned and Owen, and shown to obey the equation

$$\mathbf{E}_{0\,Ag/AgCl} = 0 \cdot 23659 - 4 \cdot 8564 \times 10^{-4} t$$
$$- 3 \cdot 4205 \times 10^{-6} t^2 + 5 \cdot 869 \times 10^{-9} t^3. \quad (17,57)$$

The use of this and equation (17,54) leads to the value

$$\Delta S_{ppn} = -7 \cdot 91 \text{ cal deg}^{-1}.$$

Since

$$\Delta S_{ppn} = S_{AgCl_{(s)}} - S_{0\,Ag^+} + S_{0\,Cl^-},$$

and the entropy of solid silver chloride is known to be 22·97 cal deg^{-1} at 25° C, and we have shown that the value of $S_{0\,Ag^+}$ is 17·4 cal deg^{-1}, it follows that

$$S_{0\,Cl^-} = 13 \cdot 5 \text{ cal deg}^{-1}.$$

The standard entropy of the hydroxyl ion can be obtained from knowledge of the ionic product of water at two temperatures. Since

$$K_w = a_{H^+} a_{OH^-}$$

the standard free energy change for the reaction

$$H_2O_{(liq)} \longrightarrow H^+ + OH^-$$

is given by the equation

$$\Delta G_0 = -RT \log_e K_w.$$

If K_w is known at two or more temperatures, the standard entropy change for the reaction may be calculated, since

$$\Delta S_0 = -\left(\frac{\partial(\Delta G_0)}{\partial T}\right)_p.$$

The value obtained equals $S_{0_{H^+}} + S_{0_{OH^-}} - S_{0_{H_2O(liq)}}$. Since the first term is zero by convention and the last term is known, that of the second can be calculated. The value of $S_{0_{OH^-}}$ may, in turn, be used to obtain $S_{0_{Al^{+++}}}$ from values of the solubility product of aluminium hydroxide, . . ., and so on. By this means a table of standard ionic entropies may be built up. Values of ΔG_{0_f}, ΔH_{0_f} and S_0 for many ions are given in Table 17,II.

The use of the quantities listed in Table 17,II in the determination of free energy changes in ionic reactions in aqueous solution requires no

TABLE 17,II

Standard Free Energies and Enthalpies of Formation of Aqueous Ions (in kcal mole⁻¹) and Standard Ionic Entropies (in cal deg⁻¹ mole⁻¹) at 25° C

Ion	ΔG_{0_f}	ΔH_{0_f}	S_0
H⁺	0	0	0
Na⁺	−62·59	−57·28	14·4
K⁺	−67·46	−60·04	24·5
Mg⁺⁺	−108·99	−110·41	−28·2
Ca⁺⁺	−132·18	−129·77	−13·2
Al⁺⁺⁺	−115·5	−126·3	−75·0
Ag⁺	18·43	25·31	17·7
Cl⁻	−31·35	−40·023	13·2
Br⁻	−24·57	−28·9	19·3
I⁻	−12·35	−13·37	26·14
OH⁻	−37·59	−54·8	−2·5
SO₄⁻⁻	−177·34	−216·90	4·1
CO₃⁻⁻	−126·22	−161·63	−12·7
NO₃⁻	−26·43	−49·37	35·0

Details of how many of these figures have been obtained may be found in Latimer, *Oxidation Potentials* (Prentice-Hall, 2nd Edition, 1952).

explanation. One other important use is the calculation of the standard electrode potentials of those metals which for one reason or another cannot be measured directly. We shall illustrate this aspect by using the values of $S_{0_{Al^{+++}}}$ and $\Delta H_{0_{f_{Al^{+++}}}}$ to calculate the standard electrode potential of aluminium.

Direct measurement of the e.m.f. of the cell

$$\text{Al} \mid \text{Al}^{+++}_{(aq)} \; \vdots \; \text{H}^+_{(aq)} \mid \text{PtH}_2$$

fails to give reproducible results, so that the standard free energy change for the reaction on which the cell depends can only be calculated from the equation

$$\Delta G_0 = \Delta H_0 - T\Delta S_0.$$

The cell reaction is

$$\text{Al} + 3\text{H}^+_{(aq)} \longrightarrow \text{Al}^{+++}_{(aq)} + \tfrac{3}{2}\text{H}_2$$

and since the enthalpies of formation of aluminium and hydrogen are zero, and that of the hydrogen ion zero by convention

$$\Delta H_0 = \Delta H_{0_{f_{Al^{+++}}}}.$$

From Table 17,II this is seen to be $-126,300$ cal.

$$\Delta S_0 = S_{Al^{+++}_{(aq)}} + \tfrac{3}{2}S_{0_{H_2}} - S_{Al} - 3S_{0_{H^+_{(aq)}}}$$

$$= -75 \cdot 0 + \tfrac{3}{2} \times 31 \cdot 2 - 6 \cdot 7 - 0$$

$$= -34 \cdot 9 \text{ cal deg}^{-1},$$

so that $\Delta G_0 = -115,900$ cal.

The standard e.m.f. of the cell is therefore

$$\frac{115,900 \times 4 \cdot 184}{3 \times 96,487} \text{ volt, i.e. } 1 \cdot 67 \text{ volt.}$$

Since the standard e.m.f. of the cell equals

$$\mathbf{E}_{0_{H_2/H^+}} - \mathbf{E}_{0 \; Al/Al^{+++}}$$

the standard electrode potential of aluminium is $-1 \cdot 67$ volt.

Half-reactions and the Thermodynamic Properties of Electrons

It will have been noted that in the last section care was taken to discuss only the overall reaction upon which an electro-chemical cell depends. However, as has been pointed out earlier, although the measurements which may be made on a cell such as

$$\text{H}_2, \text{Pt} \mid \text{H}^+_{(aq)} \; \vdots \; \text{Cu}^{++}_{(aq)} \mid \text{Cu}$$

refer to the complete reaction

$$H_2 + Cu^{++}{}_{(aq)} \longrightarrow 2H^+{}_{(aq)} + Cu$$

the process is apparently the combination of two half-reactions, one

$$H_2 \longrightarrow 2H^+{}_{(aq)} + 2\bar{e}(e)$$

taking place at one electrode, and the second

$$Cu^{++} + 2\bar{e}(e) \longrightarrow Cu$$

taking place at the other. In both cases the symbol $\bar{e}(e)$ is used to denote the fact that the electron concerned is located on the electrode itself. Absolute measurements cannot be made which relate to half-reactions separately, but there is some interest in discussing them from the thermodynamic viewpoint.

The thermodynamic changes concerned in the reaction

$$\tfrac{1}{2}H_{2(g)} \longrightarrow H^+{}_{(aq)} + \bar{e}(e)$$

under standard conditions are given by the equations:

$$\Delta H_0 = \Delta H_{0_{f_{H^+{}_{(aq)}}}} + \Delta H_{f_{\bar{e}(e)}} - \tfrac{1}{2}\Delta H_{0_{f(H_2)}}, \quad . \quad . \quad (17,58)$$

$$\Delta G_0 = \Delta G_{0_{f_{H^+{}_{(aq)}}}} + \Delta G_{f_{\bar{e}(e)}} - \tfrac{1}{2}\Delta G_{0_{f(H_2)}}, \quad . \quad . \quad (17,59)$$

and

$$\Delta S_0 = \Delta S_{0_{f_{H^+{}_{(aq)}}}} + \Delta S_{f_{\bar{e}(e)}} - \tfrac{1}{2}\Delta S_{0_{f(H_2)}}. \quad . \quad . \quad (17,60)$$

In order to proceed it is necessary to assign absolute or conventional values to the quantities $\Delta H_{f_{\bar{e}(e)}}$, $\Delta G_{f_{\bar{e}(e)}}$ and $\Delta S_{f_{\bar{e}(e)}}$. *They are conventionally assigned the value zero at all temperatures of interest.* It follows that since the first and third terms on the right-hand side of each equation are also zero by convention, the values of ΔH_0, ΔG_0 and ΔS_0 must be zero also. Since the electrode potential of hydrogen obviously depends on the reaction under consideration, this last conclusion is consistent with the convention previously adopted in which the standard electrode potential of hydrogen was assigned the value zero.

The standard entropy change for the half-reaction can be expressed, not only by equation (17,60), but by the equation

$$\Delta S_0 = S_{0_{H^+{}_{(aq)}}} + S_{0_{\bar{e}(e)}} - \tfrac{1}{2}S_{0_{H_2}}, \quad . \quad . \quad (17,61)$$

and since we have already shown that resultant on the conventions already adopted $\Delta S_0 = 0$, and $S_{0_{H^+{}_{(aq)}}} = 0$, it follows that we must assign a value to the entropy of the electron such that at all temperatures

$$S_{0_{\bar{e}(e)}} = \tfrac{1}{2}S_{0_{H_2}}. \quad . \quad . \quad . \quad . \quad (17,62)$$

Since the standard molar entropy of hydrogen at 25° C is 31·211 cal deg^{-1}, that of the electron at the same temperature is 15·606 cal deg^{-1}. The question of the molar entropy of the electron is of no importance when considering reactions of the type

$$2H^+ + Zn \longrightarrow H_2 + Zn^{++}$$

because the electrons concerned do not appear in the equation. It is essential, however, that it should be included in calculations which are made on all half-reactions in which the electron figures. *In other words, it is necessary in such reactions to treat the electron as a chemical species as important as any other chemical species present.*

To illustrate this point we calculate the standard free energy of formation of the barium ion at 25° C from conventional values of its standard enthalpy of formation and the standard entropies of the species concerned, by considering the reaction

$$Ba \longrightarrow Ba^{++}_{(aq)} + 2\bar{e}(e).$$

The conventional value of the standard enthalpy of formation of the barium ion can be determined by one of the methods discussed above. It is known to be $-128,400$ cal. Since we have assigned the value zero to $\Delta H_{f\bar{e}(e)}$ at all temperatures of interest, the value $-128,400$ cal becomes the standard enthalpy change for the half-reaction concerned.

$$\Delta S_0 = S_{0Ba^{++}(aq)} + 2S_{0\bar{e}(e)} - S_{Ba}.$$

The conventional value of the standard molar entropy of the aqueous barium ion can be determined by one of the methods described earlier. It is known to be 2·3 cal deg^{-1}, and the molar entropy of barium at 25° C is known to be 15·1. It follows that the standard free energy of formation of the barium ion at 25° C is given by the equation

$$\Delta G_{0_f} = -128,400 - 298 \cdot 15 (2 \cdot 3 + 2 \times 15 \cdot 6 - 15 \cdot 1)$$

$$= -133,850 \text{ cal.}$$

This value may be compared with that obtained directly by using equation (17,49). The standard electrode potential of barium is $-2·90$ volt, and the value of ΔG_{0_f} calculated from it identical with that obtained above.

The Physical Significance of the Entropy Values of Electrolytes in Solution

The standard molar entropy of a strong electrolyte in water is given by the sum of the standard entropies of the separate ion species, so that that of sodium chloride is 14·4 + 13·2, i.e. 27·6 cal deg^{-1}; that of silver nitrate $17 \cdot 7 + 13 \cdot 2$, i.e. $30 \cdot 9$; that of magnesium sulphate $-28 \cdot 2 + 4 \cdot 1$, i.e. $-24 \cdot 1$; and that of aluminium sulphate $-2 \times 75 \cdot 0 + 3 \times 4 \cdot 1$, i.e. $-137 \cdot 1$ cal deg^{-1}. These values may be called "Third Law values", and may be used with complete assurance in such calculations as those discussed in Chapter 12. The entropy change for the reaction

$$3Mg + Al_2(SO_4)_{3(aq)} \longrightarrow 3MgSO_{4(aq)} + 2Al$$

carried out under standard conditions at $25°$ C may be cited as an example.

$$\Delta S_0 = 3S_{0_{MgSO_4(aq)}} + 2S_{Al} - 3S_{Mg} - S_{0_{Al_2(SO_4)_3(aq)}}.$$

The molar entropy of aluminium at $25°$ C is $6 \cdot 7$ cal deg^{-1}, and that of magnesium $7 \cdot 8$, so that

$$\Delta S_0 = -3 \times 24 \cdot 1 + 2 \times 6 \cdot 7 - 3 \times 7 \cdot 8 - (-137 \cdot 7)$$

$$= 55 \cdot 4 \text{ cal deg}^{-1}.$$

Since the value of the entropy of a single ion species in solution is a conventional one which depends on the assignment of zero to the standard entropy of the aqueous hydrogen ion at all temperatures, the fact that the standard entropies of some aqueous ions such as Mg^{++}, Al^{+++}, OH^- and CO_3^{--} are negative is without significance. However, it may not, at first sight, be understood how it comes about that the values of the entropy of some aqueous solutions of electrolytes as a whole (such as magnesium sulphate and aluminium sulphate) are negative, and how they may be accepted as "Third Law values" when the Third Law shows that a negative value for the entropy of a pure substance is incomprehensible. The physical significance of these negative values will now be explained.

The effect of a reaction such as that represented by the equation

$$3Mg + Al_2(SO_4)_{3(aq)} \longrightarrow 3MgSO_{4(aq)} + 2Al$$

is not limited to the reactants which actually appear in the chemical equation. The reaction brings about changes in the state of the solvent, and results in an entropy change thereof. *The values of the standard entropy of an electrolyte in aqueous solution include the entropy change in the water resultant on the solution of the electrolyte*, so that the value of ΔS_0 for the reaction under discussion includes not only the change in entropy of the reactants that appear in the equation but also that which results in the solvent as well. In fact what we have called the conventional standard molar entropy of an ion in solution is really a conventional standard partial molar entropy.

This point may be better understood if we consider in detail the

O

reaction in which a mole of an electrolyte such as magnesium sulphate dissolves in sufficient water to give a solution of unit activity. The reaction may be considered in two parts. The first consists purely of the change in condition of the electrolyte. The ions which were originally closely packed and rigidly held in the crystal lattice become widely separated and free (within limits) to move about the solution. This "part" of the reaction will, quite obviously, lead to a considerable increase in entropy. We designate this quantity $\Delta S_{(i)}$. The second "part" of the reaction concerns the interaction of the ions and solvent. The strong electrostatic field around each ion will cause the nearest water molecules to so orientate themselves as to reduce the field as far as possible. Water is a polar molecule in which the hydrogen atoms are slightly positively charged and the oxygen atoms negatively charged. We may suppose, therefore, that the water molecules nearest a positive ion will so orientate themselves that the oxygen atom is adjacent to the positive ion and the hydrogen atoms are pointed away. The water molecules nearest a negative ion will assume the opposite pattern. In some cases the interaction will be so strong that the water molecules may be thought actually to be attached to the ions. In this case we say that the ion is solvated. Whether or not this extreme situation is reached in any particular case is immaterial to the argument in hand. However strong or weak be the forces between the water and ions, the water molecules which previously enjoyed comparative freedom of movement within the liquid are now subject to a degree of order much greater than before. In the extreme case the water molecules immediately adjacent to the ions will be arranged to form a pattern, the rigidity of which approaches that which operates in the case of crystals of ice. Since the molecules concerned are no longer free to assume the number of micro-states previously accessible to them, it is clear that their entropy must decrease. We designate the change in entropy due to ion–solvent interaction $\Delta S_{(ii)}$.

It follows that the entropy change for the reaction

$$MgSO_{4(s)} + water \longrightarrow MgSO_{4(aq)}$$

is given by the equation

$$\Delta S = \Delta S_{(i)} + \Delta S_{(ii)}.$$

There is no method by which $\Delta S_{(i)}$ and $\Delta S_{(ii)}$ may be determined separately, but their sum may be determined with ease. The entropy of solid magnesium sulphate at 25° C is 21·9 cal deg^{-1} mole^{-1}, and that of magnesium sulphate in solution, *the value for which includes the decrease in entropy of the water concerned*, −24·1; so that

$$\Delta S = \Delta S_{(i)} + \Delta S_{(ii)} = -46·0 \text{ cal deg}^{-1}.$$

Although we have no means whereby $\Delta S_{(i)}$ and $\Delta S_{(ii)}$ may be separately determined, we have shown above that $\Delta S_{(i)}$ will always be positive and $\Delta S_{(ii)}$ invariably negative. The sign of ΔS will therefore be determined by the relative sizes of the two parts. The molar entropy of sodium chloride at $25°$ C is $17\cdot3$ and that of sodium chloride in solution $27\cdot6$, so that $\Delta S = \Delta S_{(i)} + \Delta S_{(ii)} = 10\cdot3$ cal deg^{-1}. In this case it is clear that $\Delta S_{(i)}$ is more important than $\Delta S_{(ii)}$, and therefore that the interaction between the ions and water molecules is relatively slight. On the other hand, the molar entropy of crystalline aluminium sulphate at $25°$ C is $57\cdot2$ cal deg^{-1} and that of aluminium sulphate in solution $-137\cdot7$, so that

$$\Delta S = \Delta S_{(i)} + \Delta S_{(ii)} = -194\cdot9 \text{ cal deg}^{-1}.$$

It is clear in this case that $\Delta S_{(ii)}$ is very much more important than $\Delta S_{(i)}$, and that the interaction between ions and water molecules is extreme. The relative values of ΔS for the solution of aluminium sulphate, magnesium sulphate and sodium chloride, i.e. $-194\cdot9$, $-46\cdot0$ and $+10\cdot3$, are, of course, just what we would expect, because quite clearly the interaction between ion and solvent will be stronger the bigger the charge on the ion concerned.

We are now in a position to return to the reaction

$$3Mg + Al_2(SO_4)_{(aq)} \longrightarrow 3MgSO_{4(aq)} + 2Al.$$

The change may be expressed in terms of the reactions

$$Mg + S + 2O_2 \longrightarrow MgSO_{4(s)} \quad . \quad . \quad . \quad . \quad \text{(iii)}$$

$$2Al + 3S + 6O_2 \longrightarrow Al_2(SO_4)_{3(s)} \quad . \quad . \quad . \quad . \quad \text{(iv)}$$

$$MgSO_{4(s)} + \text{water} \longrightarrow MgSO_{4(aq)}) \quad . \quad . \quad . \quad . \quad \text{(v)}$$

and $\qquad Al_2(SO_4)_{3(s)} + \text{water} \longrightarrow Al_2(SO_4)_{3(aq)}. \quad . \quad . \quad . \quad \text{(vi)}$

It follows that

$$\Delta S_0 = 3\Delta S_{(iii)} - \Delta S_{(iv)} + 3\Delta S_{(v)} - \Delta S_{(vi)}.$$

Since $\qquad \Delta S_{(iii)} = 21\cdot9 - 7\cdot8 - S_{(S+2O_2)}$

$$\Delta S_{(iv)} = 57\cdot2 - 2 \times 6\cdot7 - 3S_{(S+2O_2)}$$

$$\Delta S_{(v)} = -46\cdot0$$

and $\qquad \Delta S_{(vi)} = -194\cdot9,$

$\Delta S_0 = 55\cdot4$ cal deg^{-1}, which is, of course, the same value as that obtained before. The only advantage in considering the complete reaction in terms of others is that the inclusion of the change in entropy of the solvent is made clear.

Before leaving this subject it is perhaps worth considering again the reaction

$$Al_2(SO_4)_{3(s)} + \text{water} \longrightarrow Al_2(SO_4)_{3(aq)}$$

because of the magnitude of the decrease in entropy which results. It is not possible to carry out precise calculations of the sort we have in mind, because, quite apart from the other assumptions we have to make, mean activity coefficients of aqueous solutions of aluminium sulphate at high concentrations are not known, and we do not know therefore how many moles of water are required to dissolve one mole of aluminium sulphate to produce a solution at unit molal activity. If, however, we ignore the question of activity coefficients and assume that such a solution will be obtained by dissolving one mole of aluminium sulphate in 1000 gm of water, our conclusions will be imprecise, but no less interesting for that.

We have seen that for this reaction

$$\Delta S = \Delta S_{(i)} + \Delta S_{(ii)} = -194.9 \text{ cal deg}^{-1}.$$

Since $\Delta S_{(i)}$ is positive, the decrease in entropy due to ion–solvent interaction must be greater than 194.9 cal deg^{-1}. For the sake of argument let us call it 200 cal deg^{-1}. This quantity is made up of two parts, one which relates to the decrease of entropy of the ions due to solvation, and the other which relates to the decrease in entropy of the water concerned. We have no means of deciding the relative sizes of the two parts, so again, for the sake of argument, let us divide the total quantity into two equal parts, and apportion one to each. We arrive at the conclusion that the solution of one mole of aluminium sulphate in 1000 gm of water (55.5 moles) leads to the reduction in entropy of the water by 100 cal deg^{-1}, approximately 2 cal deg^{-1} per mole.

The molar entropy of water at 25° C is 16.7 cal deg^{-1}, and the hypothetical value for that of ice at that temperature (obtained by extrapolation from 0° C) is 9.9, so that the difference between the two is 6.8 cal deg^{-1}. We see that solution of aluminium sulphate in water leads to a decrease in entropy of the latter nearly one-third of that decrease which would accompany the conversion of water into ice; and it is quite likely that the assumptions we have made have been so conservative that the true value is very much greater than that obtained. Since it would appear impossible to reduce the entropy of water, by solution of an electrolyte, to a value *lower* than that of ice at the same temperature, since it is difficult to imagine the water molecules in a greater state of order than that in ice, our argument would suggest that a solution of aluminium sulphate containing more than about three moles of salt per 1000 gm of water is not possible. In fact, the maximum solubility of aluminium sulphate in water at 25° C is 27·4% by weight, which corresponds to a solution of molality 1·12.

One other interesting prediction can be made. Since the entropy of water in such a solution is much lower than that of pure water, the entropy of fusion of ice in equilibrium with a saturated solution of aluminium sulphate (and hence its latent heat of fusion) should be very much less than that of ice in equilibrium with pure water at the same temperature. It is possible that the determination of the latent heat of fusion of ice under these conditions would permit some of the assumptions made in this section to be improved.

EXERCISES 17

Note: At 25° C the value of $\dfrac{RT}{F}\log_e 10$ equals 0·05916 volt, so that

$$\frac{RT}{F}\log_e m = 0.05916 \log_{10} m.$$

17,1. Values for the e.m.f. of the cell

$$\text{H}_2 \text{ Pt } | \text{ HCl}_{(m)}, \text{ AgCl}_{(\text{sat})} | \text{ Ag at 25° C}$$
$$1 \text{ atm}$$

for various values of m are given in the following table:

E.m.f. (volts)	Molality m
0·5205	0·00321
0·5038	0·00449
0·4926	0·00562
0·4795	0·00731
0·4686	0·00914
0·4586	0·01119
0·4497	0·01341

Use these results to estimate the standard e.m.f. of the cell using the graphical method described on page 352.

17,2. Calculate the e.m.f. at 25° C of the cell

$$\text{Zn } | \text{ ZnSO}_{4(\text{aq})} \vdots \text{ CdSO}_{4(\text{aq})} | \text{ Cd}$$
$$m = 0.02 \qquad m = 0.01$$

given that the standard electrode potential of zinc is −0·763 volt, that of cobalt −0·402 volt, the mean ionic activity coefficient of zinc sulphate solution at $m = 0.02$ is 0·298 and that cadmium sulphate at $m = 0.01$ is 0·383.

The liquid junction potential may be ignored.

17,3. Consider the cell

$$\text{H}_2 \text{ Pt } | \text{ HCl}_{(m)} \text{ Hg}_2\text{Cl}_{2(\text{sat})} | \text{ Hg–Hg } | \text{ Hg}_2\text{Cl}_{2(\text{sat})} \text{ HCl}_{(m)} | \text{ Pt N}_2,\text{H}_2$$
$$1 \text{ atm} \qquad\qquad\qquad\qquad\qquad\qquad\qquad\qquad\qquad\qquad 1 \text{ atm}$$

The left-hand electrode is a hydrogen electrode in which the hydrogen is pure and at a pressure of exactly 1 atmosphere. The right-hand electrode has bubbling over it a mixture of nitrogen and hydrogen at a total pressure of 1 atmosphere. The nitrogen is completely inert.

At 25° C, when the partial pressure of hydrogen on the right-hand side was 0·0944 atmosphere, the cell gave an e.m.f. of 0·0303 volt.

(a) What is the overall chemical change which results when the cell gives current?

(b) Calculate the e.m.f. of the cell under the conditions stated assuming that the fugacity coefficient of gaseous hydrogen in the mixture is unity. What information on the real value of the fugacity coefficient can you obtain by comparing the value of the e.m.f. calculated with that given?

17,4. The e.m.f. of the cell

$$\begin{array}{c|ccc|c} H_2\ Pt & HAc & m_1 & AgCl_{(sat)} & Ag \\ 1\ atm & NaAc & m_2 & & \\ & NaCl & m_3 & & \end{array}$$

at 25° C, and at various values of m_1, m_2 and m_3 are given below:

E (volt)	$m_1 \times 10^3$	$m_2 \times 10^3$	$m_3 \times 10^3$
0·6398	4·78	4·60	4·90
0·6160	12·035	11·58	12·33
0·6017	21·01	20·22	21·52
0·5800	49·22	47·37	50·42

The value of the standard electrode potential for the cell

$$\begin{array}{c|c c|c} H_2\ Pt & HCl & AgCl_{(sat)} & Ag \\ 1\ atm & & & \end{array}$$

is 0·2225 volt.

Determine graphically the ionisation constant of acetic acid.

17,5. The standard electrode potential of cobalt at 25° C is −0·283 volt, and that of nickel is −0·250 volt. It follows that if cobalt is added to a solution of cobaltous and nickelous ions both at the same activity, the reaction

$$Co + Ni^{++} \longrightarrow Co^{++} + Ni$$

will take place.

Nickel will, however, precipitate cobalt from a solution of cobaltous and nickelous ions if the ratio of the activities of cobaltous to nickelous ions is sufficiently high. What is the minimum value of this ratio at 25° C?

17,6. The standard e.m.f. of the cell

$$\begin{array}{c|c:c|c} H_2\ Pt & H^+_{(aq)} & \begin{array}{c} Cr^{++} \\ Cr^{+++}_{(aq)} \end{array} & Pt \end{array}$$

at 25° C is −0·4 volt. Calculate the ratio of the activities of chromous and chromic ions in an equilibrium system in which the hydrogen ions are at unit activity and the hydrogen at 1 atmosphere pressure.

17,7. Given that the standard free energy of formation of crystalline lead sulphate is $-193\cdot4$ kcal, that of the lead ion $-5\cdot8$ kcal and that of the sulphate ion $-177\cdot3$ kcal at $25°$ C, calculate the solubility product of lead sulphate at the same temperature.

17,8. The standard electrode potential of the Ag | $AgN_{3(sat)}$, N_3^- electrode is $0\cdot292$ volt at $25°$ C.

Assuming that this electrode functions in the same way as the silver–silver chloride electrode, calculate the solubility product of silver azide.

17,9. Given that the standard molar entropy of zinc is $9\cdot95$ cal deg^{-1} and that of hydrogen is $31\cdot21$ cal deg^{-1} both at $25°$ C, and that the temperature coefficient of the standard electrode potential of zinc is $-1\cdot00 \times 10^{-4}$ volt deg^{-1}, calculate the standard molar entropy of the zinc ion at the same temperature.

17,10. You are required to obtain the values of ΔG, ΔH and ΔS at $25°$ C for the following reactions:

  (i) $Ag + Fe^{+++}{}_{(aq)} \longrightarrow Ag^+{}_{(aq)} + Fe^{++}{}_{(aq)}$
  (ii) $Zn + 2AgBr_{(s)} \longrightarrow ZnBr_{2(aq)} + 2Ag$
  (iii) $Pb(OH)_{2(s)} + H_{2(g)} \longrightarrow Pb + 2H_2O_{(liq)}$.

Devise electro-chemical cells by means of which these quantities may be obtained.

17,11. What are the chemical reactions which take place when the following electro-chemical cells give current?

  (i) $Ag \mid Ag_2O_{(sat)}$, $KOH_{(aq)} \mid Pt$, $H_{2(g)}$
  (ii) $Hg \mid Hg_2Cl_{2(sat)}$, $KCl_{(aq)} \vdots K_2SO_{4(aq)}$, $Hg_2SO_{4(sat)} \mid Hg$
  (iii) $Cl_{2(g)}$, $Pt \mid KCl_{(aq)} \vdots KBr_{(aq)} \mid Pt$, $Br_{2(g)}$.

Derive equations for the e.m.f. of these cells.

17,12. When granulated silver is placed in a solution of ferric nitrate the following reaction takes place

$$Ag + Fe^{+++} \rightleftharpoons Ag^+ + Fe^{++}.$$

If the solution is extremely dilute (so that activity coefficients may be neglected) it is found that the equilibrium concentrations of the ions are given by the expression

$$\frac{m_{Fe^{++}}m_{Ag^+}}{m_{Fe^{+++}}} = 0\cdot128 \text{ at } 25° \text{ C.}$$

Calculate the standard electrode potential of the cell

$$Ag \mid Ag^+ \vdots Fe^{++}, Fe^{+++} \mid Pt.$$

SOME METHODS FOR THE DETERMINATION OF FUGACITY COEFFICIENTS OF GASES AND OF ACTIVITY COEFFICIENTS OF THE COMPONENTS OF A SOLUTION

The term fugacity of a gas was introduced in Chapter 11 during the development of the concept of chemical potentials in non-ideal systems. The essential points of the presentation are repeated.

It was shown that the chemical potential of an ideal gas at pressure p may be represented by the equation

$$\mu = \mu_0 + RT \log_e p \quad \ldots \quad \ldots \quad (11,37)$$

where μ_0 is its chemical potential at 1 atmosphere.

Since this equation derives from the ideal gas equation

$$p\bar{V} = RT,$$

equation (11,37) may be considered as an equivalent criterion for ideal gas behaviour. In other words, a gas may be considered ideal if, at constant temperature, its chemical potential is linearly proportional to the logarithm of its pressure. Equation (11,37) is not precisely obeyed by a real gas except at moderately low pressures, but whatever the nature of the gas, its chemical potential can be represented by an equation

$$\mu = \mu_0^* + RT \log_e \gamma p \quad \ldots \quad \ldots \quad (11,41)$$

where γ is a dimensionless function of pressure and temperature, and μ_0^* is the value of its chemical potential under such conditions that the product γp is unity. The quantity γ is known as the fugacity coefficient of the gas and the product γp its fugacity.

The fugacity is given the symbol p^*, so that equation (11,41) may be written in the form

$$\mu = \mu_0^* + RT \log_e p^*. \quad \ldots \quad \ldots \quad (11,40)$$

Since the behaviour of any gas approaches ideality at extremely low pressures, the definition of these quantities is completed by the condition

$$\gamma = \frac{p^*}{p} \longrightarrow 1 \text{ as } p \longrightarrow 0.$$

It is clear that at any pressure the departure of γ from unity gives a measure of the departure of the gas from ideal behaviour.

From (11,40) it follows that

$$\left\{\frac{\partial \mu}{\partial \log_e p^*}\right\}_T = RT,$$

and since it follows from equation (11,34) that for any pure substance

$$\left(\frac{\partial \mu}{\partial p}\right)_T = \bar{V}$$

where $\bar{V}$ is the molar volume, we can write

$$RT d \log_e p^* = \bar{V} dp, \quad . \quad . \quad . \quad . \quad . \quad (18,1)$$

so that

$$\left\{\frac{\partial \log_e p^*}{\partial p}\right\}_T = \frac{\bar{V}}{RT}. \quad . \quad . \quad . \quad . \quad (18,2)$$

We now define a quantity j by the equation

$$\bar{V} = \frac{RT}{p} - j. \quad . \quad . \quad . \quad . \quad . \quad (18,3)$$

It is clear that the value of j at any pressure p and temperature T may be determined by direct measurement of the molar volume, and that under such conditions that the gas approaches ideal behaviour j approaches zero.

It follows from the last two equations that

$$d \log_e p^* = d \log_e p - \frac{j}{RT} dp,$$

so that

$$d \log_e \gamma = d \log_e \frac{p^*}{p} = -\frac{j}{RT} dp. \quad . \quad . \quad (18,4)$$

Integrating between limits $p = 0$ and $p = p$, and remembering that at $p = 0$, $\gamma = 1$, we obtain the final equation

$$\log_e \gamma = -\frac{1}{RT} \int_0^p j \, dp. \quad . \quad . \quad . \quad . \quad (18,5)$$

If $\bar{V}$ and j are expressed in litres, p in atmospheres and R in litre-atmospheres per degree, the quantity $\frac{j}{RT}$ has the dimensions of an inverse atmosphere, so that if the experimental values of $\frac{j}{RT}$ are plotted against the pressure from $p = 0$ to p, the area under the curve represents a dimensionless quantity which is the value of $-\log_e \gamma$ at pressure p. This method is capable of giving results of great accuracy.

In many cases results with this degree of accuracy are not required, and it is sufficient to estimate fugacity coefficients by a general method which will now be described.

It is an experimental fact that the so-called compressibility factor

$$\sigma = \frac{p\bar{V}}{RT}$$

has almost identical values for all gases if compared at the same reduced temperature T_R and the same reduced pressure[1] p_R, so that generalised

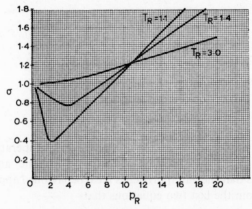

Figure 18,1. Generalised compressibility curves for gases at three reduced temperatures.

compressibility curves of σ against the reduced pressure p_R at different reduced temperatures can be constructed which apply to all gases. Examples of such curves[2] at $T_R = 1\cdot1$, $T_R = 1\cdot4$, $T_R = 3\cdot0$ are shown in Figure 18,1.

[1] The reduced temperature of a gas is the ratio of its actual temperature (in °K) to its critical temperature, i.e.

$$T_R = \frac{T}{T_c}.$$

The reduced pressure is the ratio of its actual pressure to its critical pressure, i.e.

$$p_R = \frac{p}{p_c}.$$

[2] For curves at other reduced temperatures see Lydersen, Greenkorn and Hougen, *Generalised Thermodynamic Properties of Pure Fluids* (Univ. Wisconsin, Eng. Expt. Sta., Rept. 4, 1955).

It follows from (18,3) that

$$\frac{j}{RT} = \frac{1}{p}\left\{1 - \frac{p\bar{V}}{RT}\right\} = \frac{1-\sigma}{p}, \qquad . \quad . \quad . \quad (18,6)$$

so that substituting in (18,5) and replacing the pressure terms by reduced pressures we obtain the equation

$$\log_e \gamma = \int_0^{p_R} \frac{\sigma - 1}{p_R} \, dp_R. \qquad . \quad . \quad . \quad (18,7)$$

Values of γ at a particular reduced temperature and particular reduced pressure can therefore be calculated graphically by obtaining values of σ from curves such as those shown in Figure 18,1, and plotting $\dfrac{\sigma - 1}{p_R}$

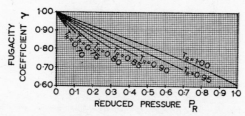

Figure 18,2. Fugacity coefficients of gases below the critical temperature.

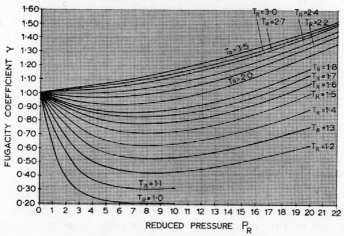

Figure 18,3. Fugacity coefficients of gases in the intermediate temperature range.

against p_R. This procedure may be repeated at different reduced temperatures to give charts in which γ is plotted against p_R for various values of T_R. Such curves[1] are shown in Figures 18,2, 18,3 and 18,4.

[1] These curves are reproduced by permission from R. H. Newton, *Ind. Eng. Chem.*, 1935, **27**, 302.

Let us suppose we wish to determine the fugacity coefficient for ammonia at 800° K and at 600 atmospheres pressure. The critical temperature for ammonia is 405° and the critical pressure 111 atmospheres, so that 800° K and 600 atmospheres pressure is the same as a reduced temperature of

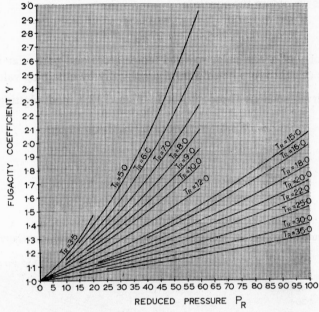

Figure 18,4. Fugacity coefficients of gases in the high temperature range.

$\frac{800}{405}$, i.e. $T_R = 2$, and a reduced pressure of $\frac{600}{111}$, i.e. $p_R = 5\cdot4$. From the curve corresponding to $T_R = 2$, it is seen that at a reduced pressure of $5\cdot4$, the fugacity coefficient is $0\cdot92$.

The Fugacity Coefficient for a Component in a Gas Mixture: the Lewis and Randall Rule

The precise determination of the fugacity coefficient for a component in a gas mixture requires knowledge of the partial molar volume of the component over the complete concentration range from zero to that mole fraction at which the value of γ is required.[1] The method has been discussed by Gillespie.[2] Usually the rather lengthy procedure involved is unnecessary, because it has been found that in many cases *the fugacity of a*

---

[1] In some cases simpler methods can be used. The student is referred to Exercise 17,3 for an example in which the fugacity coefficient of hydrogen in nitrogen may be determined from e.m.f. measurements.

[2] Gillespie, *J. Am. Chem. Soc.*, 1935, **47**, 305, 3106; 1936, **48**, 28.

component in a gas mixture equals the product of its mole fraction and the fugacity it would exhibit as a pure gas at the same temperature and same total pressure, i.e.

$$p_i^* = y_i p^*. \qquad \qquad \qquad (18,8)$$

In other words, it has been found that the degree of departure from ideality of a real gas is much the same, whether it is studied as a pure gas or as the component of a gas mixture. These findings were first put forward by Lewis and Randall[1] and are known as the Lewis and Randall Rule.

Since in an ideal mixture of ideal gases

$$p_i = y_i p \qquad \qquad \qquad (18,9)$$

it follows from (18,8) that

$$\frac{p_i^*}{p_i} = \frac{p^*}{p}$$

i.e. $$\gamma_i = \gamma, \qquad \qquad \qquad (18,10)$$

so that the fugacity coefficient of a component in a mixture is the same as that it would exhibit as a pure gas at the same temperature and same total pressure. The determination of the fugacity coefficient of a component in a mixture reduces therefore to that of the same gas in the pure state.

The Lewis and Randall Rule is not precisely obeyed by any gas mixture, but deviations from it are usually so small as to be unimportant. It is, in fact, as well to realise that the behaviour of most gases when studied either as pure substances or as components in mixtures, is so close to ideality at moderately low pressures (say 20 atmospheres or less), that inaccuracies which result from the use of partial pressures instead of partial fugacities are small. It is *essential* that fugacity coefficients are included only in calculations involving gases at pressures greater than these.

The Determination of the Activity Coefficient for the Components of a Solution

It will be remembered that the concept of activity was introduced in Chapter 11 in much the same way as was the concept of fugacity. It was shown there that whereas the chemical potential of a component in an ideal solution may be represented by an equation of form

$$\mu_i = \mu_0 + RT \log_e [i] \qquad \qquad (18,11)$$

[1] Lewis and Randall, *Thermodynamics* (McGraw-Hill, 1923).

where the symbol $[i]$ is used to denote any one of the methods by which the concentration of the component may be expressed; that of a component in a solution which is not ideal requires the inclusion of a "correction factor" to give the equation

$$\mu_i = \mu_0 + RT \log_e \gamma[i]. \quad . \quad . \quad . \quad (18,12)$$

The "correction factor" is known as the activity coefficient of the component, and the product $\gamma[i]$ its activity.

The actual form of equation (18,12) and the precise significance of the term μ_0 depends on the method by which the concentration of the component is expressed. In the case of that component which is usually called the solvent, its concentration is usually expressed by its mole fraction, so that equation (18,12) takes the form

$$\mu_i = \mu_{0_x} + RT \log_e \gamma_x x_i. \quad . \quad . \quad . \quad (18,13)$$

In this case the definition of the activity coefficient is completed by the condition that

$$\gamma_x \longrightarrow 1 \quad \text{as} \quad x_i \longrightarrow 1, \quad . \quad . \quad . \quad (18,14)$$

which is an expression of the experimental observation that the solution approaches ideality as the concentration of the solute approaches zero, and that of the solvent unity. In this case the term μ_{0_x} is the chemical potential of the solvent as a pure liquid at the same temperature and pressure.

In the case of that component which is usually called the solute it is more convenient to express its concentration in molality terms, so that equation (18,12) takes the form

$$\mu_i = \mu_{0_m} + RT \log_e \gamma_m m_i. \quad . \quad . \quad . \quad (18,15)$$

The definition of the activity coefficient is then completed by the condition

$$\gamma_m \longrightarrow 1 \quad \text{as} \quad m_i \longrightarrow 0. \quad . \quad . \quad . \quad (18,16)$$

In this case the term μ_{0_m} is the chemical potential of the solute in a (possibly hypothetical) solution in which its activity is unity.

Many methods are available by which activity coefficients may be determined. We propose here to discuss only simple solutions containing only two components, one of which we shall call the solvent and one the solute. We shall first discuss some of the methods by which the activity coefficient of the solvent may be determined, then show how the Gibbs–Duhem equation may be used to evaluate the activity coefficient of one component when that of the other is known, and lastly describe the procedures which may be used in those cases in which the solute is an electrolyte.

The Determination of the Activity Coefficients of a Solvent from Vapour-pressure Measurements

Consider a solution in which the mole fraction of the solvent is x_1. If the behaviour of the solvent is ideal its vapour pressure is given by the equation

$$p_1 = x_1 p_1^0 \quad \ldots \quad \ldots \quad (18,17)$$

where p_1^0 is the vapour pressure it would exert as a pure liquid at the same temperature and pressure.

If the behaviour of the solvent is not ideal, its actual vapour pressure is given by the equation

$$p_1' = a_1 p_1^0 \quad \ldots \quad \ldots \quad (18,18)$$

where a_1 is its activity and p_1^0 has the same significance as before.[1]

It follows that the activity coefficient of the solvent is given by the equation

$$\gamma = \frac{a_1}{x_1} = \frac{p_1'}{x_1 p_1^0}. \quad \ldots \quad \ldots \quad (18,19)$$

This method is illustrated by the following example: the water vapour pressure of a solution containing three moles of sucrose in 1000 gm of water at 30° C is 93·25% that of pure water at the same temperature, so that

$$\frac{p_1'}{p_1^0} = 0.9325.$$

Since

$$x_1 = \frac{\frac{1000}{18}}{\frac{1000}{18} + 3} = \frac{55 \cdot 51}{58 \cdot 51}$$

the activity coefficient of the water is 0·983.

The Determination of the Activity Coefficient of the Solvent from Freezing-point Determinations

It was shown in Chapter 15 that the molar latent heat of fusion of a solvent in an ideal solution is given by the equation

$$\frac{d \log_e x_1}{dT} = \frac{L_f}{RT^2}. \quad \ldots \quad \ldots \quad (15,33)$$

---

[1] Actually both p_1' and p_1^0 should be replaced by fugacities, but, as was seen earlier in this chapter, at low pressures the difference between partial pressures and partial fugacities is without practical significance.

The same relationship must hold for a non-ideal solution if we substitute a_1, the activity of the solvent on the mole fraction scale for x_1; so that,

$$\frac{d \log_e a_1}{dT} = \frac{L_f}{RT^2}. \qquad \ldots \ldots \quad (18,20)$$

The latent heat of fusion of the solvent will itself be a function of temperature, and since a latent heat of fusion at constant temperature is an enthalpy change, its variation with temperature will be governed by Kirchhoff's Law,

i.e. $$\left(\frac{\partial L_f}{\partial T}\right)_p = C_{p\text{(liq)}} - C_{p(s)} \qquad \ldots \quad (18,21)$$

where the suffix (s) denotes the solid.

Over relatively small temperature ranges the two molar thermal capacities may be regarded as independent of temperature, so that (18,21) may be integrated between the limits T, the freezing point of the solution, and T_0, the freezing point of the pure solvent, and L_f, the latent heat of the solvent in equilibrium with the solution, and L_{f_0}, the latent heat of the pure solvent, i.e.

$$\int_{L_f}^{L_{f_0}} dL_f = \int_T^{T_0} \Delta C_p dT \qquad \ldots \ldots \quad (18,22)$$

where $$\Delta C_p = C_{p\text{(liq)}} - C_{p(c)} \qquad \ldots \ldots \quad (18,23)$$

i.e. $$L_{f_0} - L_f = \Delta C_p(T_0 - T)$$

so that $$L_f = L_{f_0} - \Delta C_p(T_0 - T). \qquad \ldots \ldots \quad (18,24)$$

Substituting in (18,20) and expressing $T_0 - T$ by ΔT, it follows that

$$d \log_e a_1 = \frac{L_{f_0} - \Delta C_p \Delta T}{RT^2} dT.$$

Since $$T = T_0 - \Delta T$$

$$dT = -d(\Delta T)$$

so that $$d \log_e a_1 = -\frac{L_{f_0} - \Delta C_p \Delta T}{R(T_0 - \Delta T)^2} d(\Delta T)$$

$$= -\left\{\frac{(L_{f_0} - \Delta C_p \Delta T)}{RT_0^2}\left(1 - \frac{\Delta T}{T_0}\right)^{-2}\right\} d(\Delta T).$$

Expanding the last term and rearranging we see that

$$d \log_e a_1 = -\frac{1}{RT_0^2}\left[L_{f_0} + \left\{\frac{2L_{f_0}}{T_0} - \Delta C_p\right\}\Delta T \right.$$

$$\left. + \left\{\frac{3L_{f_0}}{T_0} - \frac{2\Delta C_p}{T_0}\right\}(\Delta T)^2 - \frac{3\Delta C_p}{T_0^2}(\Delta T)^3 \ldots\right] d(\Delta T). \quad (18,25)$$

This equation may be integrated between (a) those conditions in which the mole fraction and activity of the solvent are both unity, when $\Delta T = 0$, and (b) those conditions in which the mole fraction of the solvent is x_1, its activity a_1, its freezing point T and $\Delta T = T_0 - T$, so that

$$-\log_e a_1 = \frac{1}{RT_0^2}\left[L_{f_0}\Delta T + \left\{\frac{2L_{f_0}}{T_0} - \Delta C_p\right\}\frac{(\Delta T)^2}{2}\right.$$
$$\left. + \left\{\frac{3L_{f_0}}{T_0^2} - \frac{2\Delta C_p}{T_0}\right\}\frac{(\Delta T)^3}{3}\dots\right]. \quad (18,26)$$

Since x_1, the mole fraction of solvent in the solution is presumably known, the activity coefficient may be calculated. This method is illustrated by the following example:

The freezing point of a 2·0 molal solution of glycerol in water is $-3·932°$ C

$$x_1 = \frac{55·5}{57·5},$$

$$L_{f_0} = 1438 \text{ cal mole}^{-1},$$

$$T_0 = 273·2° \text{ K},$$

$$\Delta T = 3·932°,$$

$$C_{p_{\text{water}}} = 18 \text{ cal deg}^{-1},$$

$$C_{p_{\text{ice}}} = 9 \text{ cal deg}^{-1},$$

so that

$$-\log_e a_1 = \frac{1}{1·987 \times 273·2^2}\left[1438 \times 3·932 + \left\{\frac{2 \times 1438}{273} - 9\right\}\frac{3·932^2}{2}\right.$$
$$\left. + \left\{\frac{3 \times 1438}{273^2} - \frac{18}{273}\right\}\frac{3·932^3}{3}\dots\right]$$
$$= \frac{1}{1·987 \times 273·2^2}\{5654 + 12 + 0·1\dots\},$$

(all terms within the square brackets have been evaluated to demonstrate that it is rarely necessary to consider terms beyond $(\Delta T)^2$).

Hence $a_1 = 0·962.$

Since $\gamma = \dfrac{a_1}{x_1},$

it follows that $\gamma = 0·997.$

It should be noted that this is the value of the activity coefficient of water in the solution concerned *at the freezing point of the solution.*

The example given is instructive not only for its own sake but also because it demonstrates how close to ideality is the behaviour of water in a solution of this sort. No great inaccuracy is therefore incurred if the activity coefficient of the solvent in a dilute solution is taken as unity.

A method similar to that described above exists by which the activity coefficient of the solvent may be determined at its boiling point from the elevation of boiling point. This method derives from equation (15,29). It will not be described further, since the principles by which an expression for $\log_e a_1$ are obtained are essentially the same as those used above.

The Use of the Gibbs–Duhem Equation to Calculate the Activity Coefficient of One Component in a Binary Solution from that of the Other

If we consider a solution containing n_1 moles of component 1 and n_2 moles of component 2, then at constant temperature and pressure, the Gibbs–Duhem equation takes the form

$$n_1 d\mu_1 + n_2 d\mu_2 = 0.$$

Dividing by $n_1 + n_2$ this equation becomes

$$x_1 d\mu_1 + x_2 d\mu_2 = 0 \quad \ldots \ldots \quad (18,27)$$

where x_1 and x_2 are the respective mole fractions.

This equation holds for all binary solutions, whether ideal or not. The chemical potentials of the two components of a solution which is not ideal can be expressed by the equations

$$\mu_1 = \mu_{0_1} + RT \log_e a_1$$

and

$$\mu_2 = \mu_{0_2} + RT \log_e a_2,$$

so that at constant temperature and pressure

$$d\mu_1 = RTd \log_e a_1$$

and

$$d\mu_2 = RTd \log_e a_2.$$

Substituting these values into (18,27) we see that

$$x_1 d \log_e a_1 = -x_2 d \log_e a_2. \quad \ldots \ldots \quad (18,28)$$

Since

$$x_1 + x_2 = 1$$

$$dx_1 = -dx_2$$

$$x_1 \frac{dx_1}{x_1} = -x_2 \frac{dx_2}{x_2}$$

and

$$x_1 d \log_e x_1 = -x_2 d \log_e x_2. \quad \ldots \ldots \quad (18,29)$$

It follows from (18,28) and (18,29) that

$$x_1 d \log_e \frac{a_1}{x_1} = -x_2 d \log_e \frac{a_2}{x_2},$$

i.e.
$$x_1 d \log_e \gamma_1 = -x_2 d \log_e \gamma_2 \quad . \quad . \quad . \quad . \quad (18,30)$$

so that
$$d \log_e \gamma_1 = -\frac{x_2}{x_1} d \log_e \gamma_2. \quad . \quad . \quad . \quad (18,31)$$

This equation may be integrated between the conditions $x_2 = 0$, $x_1 = 1$, $\gamma_1 = 1$, $\gamma_2 = 1$, and the conditions x_2, x_1, γ_1, γ_2, so that

$$-\log_e \gamma_1 = \int_{x_2 = 0}^{x_2} \frac{x_2}{x_1} d \log_e \gamma_2. \quad . \quad . \quad . \quad (18,32)$$

If therefore the value $\frac{x_2}{x_1}$ be graphed against $\log_e \gamma_2$ from $x_2 = 0$, $\log_e \gamma_2 = 0$ to x_2, $\log_e \gamma_2$, the area under the curve is a dimensionless quantity equal to the negative logarithm of the activity coefficient of component 1 at mole fraction x_1. This procedure permits the calculation of the activity coefficient of the solvent if that of the solute is known over the concentration range $x_2 = 0$ to x_2.

In principle the same method can be used to obtain the activity coefficient of the solute from that of the solvent, since equation (18,30) can be written in the form

$$d \log_e \gamma_2 = -\frac{x_1}{x_2} d \log_e \gamma_1, \quad . \quad . \quad . \quad . \quad (18,33)$$

but a practical difficulty arises when plotting $\frac{x_1}{x_2}$ against $\log_e \gamma_1$. As x_2 approaches zero, $\frac{x_1}{x_2}$ approaches infinity, so that the area under the curve is difficult to estimate with great accuracy. The difficulty has been circumvented in various ways. Such methods which permit the calculation of the activity coefficients of the solute from freezing-point measurements of the solution, and which combine equations (18,25) and (18,28) are described by Lewis and Randall, and Glasstone.[1]

In principle the activity coefficient of both the solvent and solute can always be determined if the activity coefficients of the solvent and solute of another *reference solution* based on the same solvent are known over

---

[1] Lewis and Randall, *Thermodynamics* (McGraw-Hill, 1923). Glasstone, *Thermodynamics for Chemists* (Van Nostrand, 1958).

the appropriate concentration range. Let us suppose that the activity coefficients of both solute and solvent in a solution of glucose in water are known over a large concentration range, and that we wish to obtain the same information relating to a solution of glycerol in water. If two beakers each containing one of the solutions are placed in an evacuated container and maintained at constant temperature, solvent from one solution will distil into the second until the water-vapour pressures of each are the same. It follows from equation (18,18) that the activities of the water in both solutions are the same.[1] The solutions may now be analysed to determine the mole fraction of water in both cases. Since the activity coefficient of water in the reference solution is known, its activity and hence the activity coefficient of water in the second can be calculated.

This method is of greater use when applied to the determination of the activity coefficients of the solute, particularly when the solute is an electrolyte. In order to see how this is done we must first determine the form of the Gibbs–Duhem equation applicable to solutions of electrolytes.

Let us consider a solution containing n_1 moles of water and n_2 moles of a strong electrolyte M^+A^-. Then since the electrolyte may be assumed to be completely ionised, we may write equation (11,20) in the form

$$dG = -SdT + Vdp + \mu_1 dn_1 + \mu_+ dn_2 + \mu_- dn_2 \qquad (18,34)$$

where the symbol with the suffix $+$ refers to the cation, and that with the suffix $-$ to the anion.

Similarly, equation (11,26) becomes

$$dG = \mu_1 dn_1 + \mu_+ dn_2 + \mu_- dn_2 + n_1 d\mu_1 + n_2 d\mu_+ + n_2 d\mu_-. \qquad (18,35)$$

Comparison of these last equations shows that

$$-SdT + Vdp - n_1 d\mu_1 - n_2 d\mu_+ - n_2 d\mu_- = 0, \qquad (18,36)$$

so that under conditions of constant temperature and pressure

$$n_1 d\mu_1 + n_2 d\mu_+ + n_2 d\mu_- = 0. \qquad . \quad . \quad . \quad (18,37)$$

It was explained in Chapter 16 that the quantities μ_+ and μ_- cannot be determined individually, but that the mean chemical potential of the electrolyte, defined by the equation

$$\mu_\pm = \tfrac{1}{2}\{\mu_+ + \mu_-\}$$

is significant. It therefore follows that (18,37) may be written in the form

$$n_1 d\mu_1 + 2n_2 d\mu_\pm = 0. \qquad . \quad . \quad . \quad . \quad (18,38)$$

---

[1] Such solutions are called *isotonic*.

We now express the chemical potentials of the individual species by the equations

$$\mu_1 = \mu_{0_1} + RT \log_e a_1$$

$$\mu_+ = \mu_{0_+} + RT \log_e a_+$$

$$\mu_- = \mu_{0_-} + RT \log_e a_-$$

so that at constant temperature

$$d\mu_1 = RTd \log_e a_1$$

$$d\mu_+ = RTd \log_e a_+$$

$$d\mu_- = RTd \log_e a_-$$

and

$$2d\mu_\pm = RTd \log_e a_+a_-$$

$$= 2RTd \log_e a_\pm,$$

where $a_\pm$ is the mean ionic activity of the electrolyte. It follows that (18,38) may be written in the form[1]

$$n_1d \log_e a_1 + 2n_2d \log_e a_\pm = 0. \quad . \quad . \quad . \quad (18,39)$$

Since it is usual to express the concentration of electrolytes in terms of molalities, we substitute $1000/M_1$ for n_1 (where M_1 is the molecular weight of the solvent), and m for n_2, to obtain the equation

$$\frac{2mM_1}{1000}d \log_e a_\pm = -d \log_e a_1. \quad . \quad . \quad . \quad (18,40)$$

This equation corresponds to (18,31).

We now suppose that a solution of a binary electrolyte at molality m is found to be isotonic with a reference solution of another binary electrolyte at molality m_R, the mean ionic activity coefficients of which are known over the complete concentration range. We may write

$$\frac{2m_RM_1}{1000}d \log_e a_{\pm R} = -d \log_e a_1,$$

so that comparing this with equation (18,40) we can write

$$md \log_e a_\pm = m_Rd \log_e a_{\pm R} \quad . \quad . \quad . \quad . \quad (18,41)$$

or

$$md \log_e \gamma_\pm m = m_Rd \log_e \gamma_{\pm R}m_R.$$

Rearranging, we see that

$$d \log_e \gamma_\pm = d \log_e \gamma_{\pm R} + d \log_e \frac{m_R}{m} + \frac{\left(\dfrac{m_R}{m} - 1\right)}{\gamma_{\pm R}m_R}d(\gamma_{\pm R}m_R). \quad (18,42)$$

[1] It should be noted that the figure 2 in (18,39) arises from the fact that the electrolyte concerned dissociates into two ions. The student should derive the corresponding equation for an electrolyte dissociating into ν ions.

This equation may be integrated to give

$$\log_e \gamma_+ = \log_e \gamma_{\pm R} + \log_e \frac{m_R}{m} + \int_0^{m_R} \frac{\left(\dfrac{m_R}{m} - 1\right)}{\gamma_{\pm R} m_R} d(\gamma_{\pm R} m_R). \quad (18,43)$$

In order to evaluate this integral we require to know the value of the molality of the test solution isotonic with the reference solution at all values of m_R. Then, since we have supposed that $\gamma_{\pm R}$ is known at all concentrations from $m_R = 0$ to m_R, the integral may be evaluated graphically by plotting $\left(\dfrac{m_R}{m} - 1\right)/\gamma_{\pm R} m_R$ against the product $\gamma_{\pm R} m_R$. The value of $\gamma_\pm$ for the test solution at any value of m can then be obtained. This method appears to have been developed first by Robinson and Sinclair,[1] who used a potassium chloride solution as the reference solution (using the values of $\gamma_\pm$ obtained from e.m.f. measurements), and so determined the activity coefficients of lithium iodide, lithium chloride, sodium chloride, rubidium chloride and caesium chloride.

The Determination of the Mean Ionic Activity Coefficient of Electrolytes from Measurements made on Electro-chemical Cells

It was shown in Chapter 17 that the e.m.f. of the cell

$$\underset{\substack{1 \text{ atm}}}{H_2 \ Pt} \mid HCl_{(aq)} \qquad AgCl_{(sat)} \mid Ag$$

is given by the equation

$$\mathbf{E} + \frac{2RT}{F} \log_e m_{HCl} = \mathbf{E}_0 - \frac{2RT}{F} \log_e \gamma_{\pm HCl}, \quad (17,14)$$

and that the standard electrode potential can be obtained with considerable accuracy. It follows that if the e.m.f. of the cell is known at any value of m_{HCl}, the mean ionic activity coefficient of HCl may be evaluated. Some of the results obtained by this method by Harned and Ehlers[2] are shown below:

m	$\gamma_\pm$
0·003215	0·939
0·009138	0·908
0·02563	0·863
0·1238	0·788

This cell has been much used to determine the activity coefficients of HCl in non-aqueous and mixed solvents. Those in ethyl alcohol have been

[1] *J. Am. Chem. Soc.*, 1934, **56**, 1830.
[2] Harned and Ehlers, *Ibid.*, 1932, **54**, 1350.

obtained by Woolcock and Hartley,[1] those in methyl alcohol by Nonhebel and Hartley[2] and those in dioxane–water mixtures by Harned and Morrison.[3]

Application of the same principles as those discussed above permit the calculation of the mean ionic activity coefficients of zinc chloride from measurements made on the cell

$$\text{Zn} \mid \text{ZnCl}_{2(aq)} \qquad \text{AgCl}_{(sat)} \mid \text{Ag}$$

those of zinc sulphate from the cell

$$\text{Zn} \mid \text{ZnSO}_{4(aq)} \qquad \text{PbSO}_{4(sat)} \mid \text{Pb}$$

and so on.

Similar use has been made of concentration cells without transport, i.e. cells of the type

$$\text{H}_2 \ \text{Pt} \mid \text{HCl}_{m_1} \ \text{AgCl}_{(sat)} \mid \text{Ag–Ag} \mid \text{AgCl}_{(sat)} \ \text{HCl}_{m_2} \mid \text{Pt} \ \text{H}_2.$$
$$\text{1 atm} \hspace{11cm} \text{1 atm}$$

It follows from equation (17,33) that the e.m.f. of the cell may be expressed by the equation

$$\mathbf{E} = \frac{2RT}{F} \log_e \frac{m_2 \gamma_{\pm 2}}{m_1 \gamma_{\pm 1}},$$

so that knowledge of the activity coefficient at one concentration permits its calculation at another. Activity coefficients may also be determined from measurements made on cells with transport (see equation (17,36)), but this requires knowledge of the transport numbers of the ions concerned over the complete concentration range. The methods employed are described in great detail in monographs on Electrochemistry.[4]

We lastly consider the determination of the activity coefficient of one metal in another. The chemical potential of thallium in an amalgam in which its mole fraction is x_2 is given by the equation

$$\mu = \mu_0 + RT \log_e \gamma_2 x_2$$

where its activity coefficient is expressed on the mole fraction scale and μ_0 is the chemical potential of pure (liquid) thallium at the same temperature. Consider now an electro-chemical cell consisting of two

[1] Woolcock and Hartley, *Phil. Mag.*, 1928, (7) **5**, 1133.
[2] Nonhebel and Hartley, *ibid.*, 1925, (6) **50**, 729.
[3] Harned and Morrison, *J. Am. Chem. Soc.*, 1936, **58**, 1908.
[4] See Harned and Owen, *The Physical Chemistry of Electrolyte Solutions* (Reinhold, 1950).

thallium amalgams of different concentrations immersed in a solution of thallous salt,

$$\text{Tl amalgam } (x_2) \mid \text{Tl}^+ \text{ (aq)} \mid \text{Tl amalgam } (x_2').$$

If we suppose that x_2 is greater than x_2' the chemical potential of thallium will be greater in the electrode on the left-hand side, so that there will be a tendency for the thallium to go into solution on the left-hand side and to be deposited on the electrode on the right. The decrease in free energy when one mole of thallium is transferred is given by the expression

$$-\Delta G = \mu - \mu'$$

$$= RT \log_e \frac{\gamma_2 x_2}{\gamma_2' x_2'}.$$

so that the e.m.f. of the cell is given by the equation

$$\mathbf{E} = \frac{RT}{F} \log_e \frac{\gamma_2 x_2}{\gamma_2' x_2'}$$

so that
$$\log_e \gamma_2 = \left\{ \frac{EF}{RT} - \log_e x_2 \right\} + \log_e a_2'. \quad . \quad . \quad (18,44)$$

A series of cells is now constructed in which the concentration of thallium on the left-hand side is varied, while that on the right-hand side remains constant. The quantity $\left\{ \dfrac{EF}{RT} - \log_e x_2 \right\}$ is now plotted against x_2, and extrapolated to $x_2 = 0$, at which concentration $\log_e \gamma_2 = 0$. The extrapolated value of $\left(\dfrac{EF}{RT} - \log_e x_2 \right)$ gives $-\log_e a_2'$. When this is inserted in (18,44) the value of γ_2 at any concentration can be evaluated. This method has been discussed in great detail by Lewis and Randall[1] using the experimental results of Richards and Daniels.[2]

EXERCISES 18

18,1. At a particular temperature T^* a gas is found to obey the equation
$$p\bar{V} = RT^*(1 - 0.74 \ 10^{-3}p + 0.14 \ 10^{-5}p^2).$$
Calculate the value of the fugacity coefficient of the gas at a pressure of 100 atmospheres.

18,2. The critical temperature for the gas discussed in Exercise 18,1 is $154°$ K and its critical pressure is 49.7 atmospheres. Use one of the

[1] Lewis and Randall, *J. Am. Chem. Soc.*, 1921, **43**, 233.
[2] Richards and Daniels, *ibid.*, 1919, **41**, 1732.

fugacity charts and the value of the fugacity coefficient determined above
to estimate the value of T^*.

18,3. The critical temperature and pressure for the following gases are
as shown below

	T_c (°K)	p_c (atm)
H_2	33·2	12·8
N_2	126·0	33·6
HN_3	406·0	111·6

The value of the equilibrium constant

$$K = \frac{p_{NH_3}}{p_{N_2}^{\frac{1}{2}} p_{H_2}^{\frac{3}{2}}}$$

at 450° C is $7·25 \times 10^{-3}$ atm^{-1} at 100 atmospheres pressure and 12·94
atm^{-1} at 600 atmospheres pressure. These values would, of course, be
the same if the gases were ideal. Use the fugacity coefficient charts shown
in Figures 18,2, 18,3 and 18,4 to calculate the true equilibrium constant

$$K_{p^*} = \frac{p_{NH_3}^*}{p_{N_2}^{*\frac{1}{2}} p_{H_2}^{*\frac{3}{2}}}$$

at both pressures, and show that they are much more nearly equal. The
Lewis and Randall rule may be used. (We may presume that the fact that
the Lewis and Randall rule is not precisely true is the reason why the two
values of K_{p^*} are not identical.)

18,4. At 300° C the vapour pressure of mercury is 248·6 mm, but the
vapour pressure of mercury above a mercury–thallium amalgam in which
the mole fraction of each metal is 0·5 is 107·6 mm. What is the activity
coefficient of the mercury in the amalgam at this temperature?

18,5. The following values were obtained for the e.m.f. of a cell consisting of a hydrogen electrode and a silver–silver chloride electrode in
hydrochloric acid in a mixture of water and glucose containing 40%
glucose at 25° C. The symbol m denotes the molality of HCl.

E_{volt}	0·2997	0·3176	0·3362	0·3564	0·3760
m	0·1317	0·0900	0·06075	0·03929	0·02592
E_{volt}	0·3926	0·4088	0·4198	0·4536	
m	0·01828	0·01314	0·01044	0·00523	

(Everdell, *J. Chem. Soc.*, 1939, 483, 2289.)

Use this data to determine the value of the standard electrode potential
of the silver–silver chloride electrode in this medium at 25° C, using the
method of Lewis and Randall as described in Chapter 17 (see Figure 17,3)
and hence calculate the mean activity coefficients of HCl at molalities
0·1, 0·09 . . . 0·01. The latter values should be reported as $-\log_{10} \gamma_{\pm}$.

18,6. An electro-chemical cell is constructed consisting of a solution
of hydrochloric acid in which two hydrogen electrodes are immersed.
Pure hydrogen bubbles over one electrode at 128 atmospheres, and an

equimolar mixture of hydrogen and helium at 128 atmospheres bubbles over the second. The e.m.f. of the cell is measured at 60° C. What value for the e.m.f. would you expect to find? Values of the critical temperature and critical pressure for hydrogen will be found in Exercise 18,3.

18,7. Explain how you would set up an electro-chemical cell to determine the values of the activity coefficient of thallium in a series of amalgams at different concentrations. Then explain how the Gibbs–Duhem equation may be used to obtain from these values those of mercury in the same substances.

APPENDIX 1

ANSWERS AND DISCUSSION OF EXERCISES

CHAPTER 4

4,1. (a) $\Delta U = 0$, $\Delta H = V\Delta p$.

(b) $\Delta H = 0$, U decreases if an expansion has occurred and increases if the volume of the system has decreased.

4,3. 847 joules; 2497 cal.

CHAPTER 5

5,1. $1 \cdot 2 \times 10^{-2}$ moles.

5,2. (a) $w = q = 1382$ cal; (b) $w = q = 540$ cal.

5,3. $4 \cdot 2 \times 10^{12}$ erg.

5,4. $476°$ C.   5,5. 102.

5,6. $0 \cdot 7446$ atmosphere.   5,8. $1 \cdot 667$.

5,9. $6 \cdot 60$, $8 \cdot 59$ cal deg^{-1} mole^{-1}.   5,10. $10 \cdot 1$.

5,11. (a) $p_f = 0 \cdot 5$ atm. $T_f = 600°$ K.

(b) The student should show that the work performed equals

$$\frac{p_1 V_1 - p_2 V_2}{n - 1},$$

and so gives the answer 194 cal.

(c) The heat absorbed equals the change in internal energy plus the work performed. The calculation of ΔU requires knowledge of the number of moles concerned, and of C_v. The first can be obtained from the equation $p_1 V_1 = nRT_1$, and the second from the known value of R and γ. The heat absorbed equals 439 cal.

5,12. (a) 5224 joules; (b) 3410 joules.

5,13. Minimum power of engine required equals 649 watts.

The minimum work required to compress a gas isothermally equals the maximum work capable of being performed by the gas in the reverse process. Hence, the minimum quantity of work required per second is

$\dfrac{p_2 V_2}{3600} \log_e \dfrac{V_1}{V_2}$ litre-atmosphere.

5,14. $86 \cdot 4$ cm.

The bullet is accelerated as long as the pressure of air behind it is greater than 1 atmosphere. It should be noted that the expansion process is adiabatic but *not* reversible. The work performed by the air should be equated to its decrease in internal energy. It should be observed that the optimum length of tube is independent of the initial temperature of the compressed air and of that of the atmosphere.

5,15. 11·4 atmospheres.

The student should first consider the throttling process and should show that the substance concerned must be an ideal gas, (i.e. that it obeys the equation $\left(\dfrac{\partial U}{\partial V}\right)_T = 0$).

The values of C_v, C_p and γ may then be determined without difficulty.

5,16. The student should show that

$$U = \tfrac{3}{2}pV + E' \qquad \ldots \ldots \ldots \quad \text{(i)}$$

where the first term represents the kinetic energy of the gas and the term E' all other forms of energy concerned. Expressions for C_v, C_p, γ and E' may then be obtained which on substitution into (i) gives the required result.

5,17. 213 joules.

5,18. All calculations in this problem are necessarily estimates. This is a problem in steady flow requiring the use of equation (4,25). Since no work is done by the gas on the surroundings and since there is no heat exchange, and since it may be assumed that changes in kinetic energy are negligible, equation (4,25) reduces to

$$\Delta H = M(h_1 - h_2)$$

where M is the molecular weight.

i.e. $\qquad\qquad C_p(T_2 - T_1) = -M \times 10^6 \times 981 \text{ erg.}$

C_p proves to be equal to $6R$, so that $T_1 - T_2$ is about 80°, i.e. the temperature of the gas in the subterranean regions is about 180° C.

CHAPTER 6

6,1. $\Delta H_f = 50{,}400$ cal.   6,2. $\Delta H = -373{,}240$ cal.

6,3. $\Delta H = 10\cdot38$ kcal. $\Delta U = 9\cdot81$ kcal.

6,4. $C_7H_6O_2$, $-771{,}500$ cal, $-87{,}500$ cal.

6,5. $\Delta H = 13\cdot36$ kcal.

It may be assumed that NaCl, HCl and NaOH are completely ionised at infinite dilution. It therefore follows that the heat of neutralisation of HCl and NaOH, i.e. ΔH for the reaction

$$\text{HCl, } \infty H_2O + \text{NaOH, } \infty H_2O \longrightarrow \text{NaCl, } \infty H_2O$$

is ΔH for the reaction

$$H^+_{(aq)}, \infty H_2O + OH^-_{(aq)}, \infty H_2O \longrightarrow H_2O_{(liq)}$$

and equals the value of the enthalpy of ionisation of water *with the sign changed*. It follows that the reaction required is obtained by adding reactions (2), (3) and (4), and subtracting reactions (1) and (5).

6,6. $-335\cdot2$ kcal.   6,7. 710 cal.

6,8. 525 cal gm^{-1}.   6,9. $-61{,}772$ cal.

6,10. $\Delta H = 30{,}130 + 3\cdot397T - 1\cdot68 \times 10^{-3}T^2 - 2\cdot2 \times 10^{-8}T^3 + 1\cdot17 \times 10^5T^{-1}$.

6,11. $\Delta U = -21,370$ cal.

6,12. $\Delta H = -1102 \cdot 4$ kcal mole^{-1}.

6,13. $\Delta H = 39,160$ cal, $\Delta U = 37,400$ cal.

CHAPTER 7

7,2. Express q_1 and q_2 in terms of T_c, T_d, T_e and T_b, and use equation (5,14) to express the ratio of these temperatures in terms of V_1 and V_2.

The Carnot efficiency of an engine working between T_d and T_b equals $1 - \dfrac{T_b}{T_d}$ and can be shown to be equal to $1 - \dfrac{1}{r^{\gamma-1} + \dfrac{q_1}{C_v T_b}}$. This value is necessarily greater than $1 - \left(\dfrac{1}{r}\right)^{\gamma-1}$.

7,5. The change in internal energy of the spring for the complete process is zero; i.e.

$$\Delta U = 2 \cdot 00 - w - 5 \cdot 00 = 0$$

where w is the work performed *by* the spring.

Hence the work performed *on* the spring is $3 \cdot 00$ cal.

During the stretching process

$$\Delta S_{\text{spring}} = S_2 - S_1 = \frac{2 \cdot 00}{300} = 6 \cdot 7 \times 10^{-3} \text{ cal deg}^{-1}$$

and $\quad \Delta S_{\text{thermostat}} = -6 \cdot 7 \times 10^{-3}$ cal deg^{-1}.

During the collapse the *decrease* in entropy of the spring must equal $S_2 - S_1$ and is therefore $6 \cdot 7 \times 10^{-3}$ cal deg^{-1}, while the increase in entropy of the thermostat is $\dfrac{5 \cdot 00}{300}$, i.e. $1 \cdot 67 \times 10^{-2}$ cal deg^{-1}. The increase in entropy of the universe is therefore 1×10^{-2} cal deg^{-1}.

7,8. During one cycle of operations q_1 units of heat are absorbed by the working substance from the hot reservoir, w units of work performed and q_2 units of heat rejected to the cold reservoir. If the Clausius statement were not true it would be possible for the q_2 units of heat to pass spontaneously to the hot reservoir to be used again in the second cycle of operations. Repetition of the whole operation an infinite number of times would result in the complete conversion of the energy available as heat into mechanical work.

CHAPTER 8

8,1. $\Delta S = 0 \cdot 941$ cal deg^{-1}.   8,2. $\Delta S = 10 \cdot 32$ cal deg^{-1}.

8,3. $\Delta S = 31 \cdot 55$ cal deg^{-1} mole^{-1}.

8,4. $\Delta S = 0 \cdot 0114$ cal deg^{-1} mole^{-1}.

The process is irreversible, so that an alternative reversible path must be found along which the entropy change may be calculated. It is suggested that the temperature of one mole of supercooled water be raised from $-10°$ to $0°$ C, and that y moles are then permitted to freeze. An expression for y can be obtained in terms of the latent heat of fusion of ice at $0°$ C. The change in entropy for the two stages can then be calculated. It will be found that the value of the latent heat of fusion is not required.

CHAPTER 9

9,2. (a) $\Delta S_0^{298} = (50\cdot339 + 61\cdot24) - (59\cdot40 + 57\cdot47)$

$\qquad\qquad = -5\cdot3$ cal deg^{-1}.

(b) $\Delta H_0^{298} = \Sigma \Delta H_{0f}^{298}$ (reaction products–reactants)

$\qquad\qquad = (21{,}600 - 94{,}450) - (8091 - 70{,}960)$

$\qquad\qquad = -9891$ cal.

Hence the surroundings gain 9981 cal. at 25° C, so that the increase in entropy of the surroundings equals $\dfrac{9981}{298\cdot15}$ cal deg^{-1}, i.e. 33·6 cal deg^{-1}.

(c) It follows from equation (9,28) that the entropy produced by the irreversible chemical reaction at constant temperature and pressure is

$$\Delta S_{\text{irrev}} = -\frac{\Delta G_0}{T}.$$

$$\Delta G_0 = \Sigma \Delta G_{0f}^{298} = -8400 \text{ cal,}$$

so that $\qquad \Delta S_{\text{irrev}} = \dfrac{8400}{298\cdot15}$ cal deg^{-1}, i.e. 28·3 cal deg^{-1}.

The increase in entropy of the universe is 28·3 cal deg^{-1}.

9,3. The system is maintained at constant volume throughout the operation described. The first stage of the operation is to carry out the reaction in a lagged container. Since the reacting system is isolated the spontaneous reaction results in an increase in entropy. The second stage of the operation consists of the removal of the lagging, so that the entropy of the system may be reduced by withdrawing heat. If, for the sake of argument, we suppose that neither stage results in a phase change, that the initial temperature of the reactants is T_1, the temperature at the end of the first stage T_2 and that at the end of the third stage T_3, the value of the entropy of the reactants at T_1 is the same as that of the reaction products at T_3 if

$$\Delta S_{\text{irrev}} = \int_{T_3}^{T_2} \frac{\Sigma n C_v}{T} \, dT$$

where $\Sigma n C_v$ is the sum of the thermal capacities of the reaction products.

We now consider the change in internal energy. Since the first stage of the operation takes place in isolation no change in internal energy can result. The withdrawal of heat in the second stage must, however, result in a decrease in internal energy given by the equation

$$\Delta U = \int_{T_2}^{T_3} \Sigma n C_v dT.$$

9,4. This is a variation on the previous exercise. The overall change is one in which the final entropy and pressure is the same as the initial values. It follows from expression (9,30) that the final enthalpy must be less than the initial, so that if the reaction is endothermic the heat absorbed during the first operation must be less than that rejected in the second, or if the reaction is exothermic the heat rejected during the first operation must be greater than that absorbed during the second.

CHAPTER 10

10,1.
$$TdS = dU - \phi dL. \qquad \cdots \cdots \cdots \quad (1)$$

Since dV is zero in this case it follows that for a constant pressure process

$$dG = -SdT + \phi dL$$

so that
$$\left(\frac{\partial G}{\partial T}\right)_L = -S \quad \text{and} \quad \left(\frac{\partial G}{\partial L}\right)_T = \phi$$

and
$$-\left(\frac{\partial S}{\partial L}\right)_T = \left(\frac{\partial \phi}{\partial T}\right)_L. \qquad \cdots \cdots \cdots \quad (2)$$

From (1)
$$T\left(\frac{\partial S}{\partial L}\right)_T = \left(\frac{\partial U}{\partial L}\right)_T - \phi$$

so that
$$\left(\frac{\partial U}{\partial L}\right)_T = \phi - T\left(\frac{\partial \phi}{\partial T}\right)_L. \qquad \cdots \cdots \cdots \quad (3)$$

It is an experimental fact that over a large temperature range the tension of a piece of rubber maintained at constant length is (approximately) directly proportional to the absolute temperature so that the right-hand side of equation (3) is zero. It follows that $\left(\frac{\partial U}{\partial L}\right)_T = 0$. This equation "defines" a so-called *ideal rubber*, in the same way as the equation $\left(\frac{\partial U}{\partial V}\right)_T = 0$ defines an ideal gas.

It follows from equation (1) that when an ideal rubber is stretched at constant temperature the work performed on the system goes completely to *decrease* the entropy of the system. The physical significance of this will be better appreciated after Chapter 13 has been read.

10,2. $-270°$ C. The result obtained depends on the value estimated for dp/dT, the "best" value being 0·557 cm Hg deg^{-1}. Thereafter, the problem is merely an exercise in units.

10,5. $\Delta G = -\dfrac{2 \times 1·005 \times 96{,}487}{4·184}$ cal.

$$\Delta H = \Delta G - \frac{298·15 \times 2 \times 96{,}487 \times 4 \times 10^{-4}}{4·184} \text{ cal.}$$

$$\Delta S = -\left(\frac{\partial(\Delta G)}{\partial T}\right)_p = 2F\left(\frac{\partial \mathbf{E}}{\partial T}\right)_p$$

$$= -\frac{2 \times 96{,}487 \times 4 \times 10^{-4}}{4·184} \text{ cal deg}^{-1}.$$

Since the cell proceeds reversibly the heat absorbed equals $T\Delta S$.

10.7. $$V = f(p, T)$$

so that $$dV = \left(\frac{\partial V}{\partial p}\right)_T dp + \left(\frac{\partial V}{\partial T}\right)_p dT$$

$$= -\beta V dp + \alpha V dT$$

and $$d \log_e V = -\beta dp + \alpha dT.$$

The answer required follows from Theorem 4, page xv.

CHAPTER 11

11,1. $\Delta S = -50$ cal deg^{-1}.
$\Delta H = -35\cdot4$ kcal.
11,2. $\Delta H = -23{,}790$ cal mole^{-1}.

The equilibrium constant for the reaction

$$Ca(OH)_{2(s)} \longrightarrow CaO_{(s)} + H_2O_{(g)}$$

is the same as the partial pressure of water vapour. Application of these values at the two temperatures concerned gives the mean value of ΔH for the dissociation reaction. This is the same as the value for the hydration of calcium oxide except that the sign is changed.
11,3. $K_p = 8\cdot7 \times 10^{-4}$.
2·9% oxygen.
11,4. $\Delta H = -21{,}180$ cal.
$\Delta S = -11\cdot4$ cal deg^{-1}.
11,6. 794·5° K.

CHAPTER 12

12,1. (i) $\Delta G = \Delta H - T\Delta S$.
Since the reaction results in the disappearance of three gas moles the decrease in entropy of the system is large. Nothing can be deduced, therefore, about the sign of ΔG since ΔH is negative and $-T\Delta S$ positive, and we require evidence as to which quantity is the greater numerically.
The chemical potential of water vapour is the same as that of liquid water in equilibrium with it, hence the standard free energy of water vapour at 100° C and 1 atmosphere pressure is the same as that of liquid water under the same conditions. The value of the free energy change will therefore be the same as that in the first reaction.
(ii) The percentage of CO will increase with rise in temperature.
(iii) ΔS is negative, hence ΔG will increase with rise in temperature, so that $-\Delta G$ will decrease.
12,2. $K_p = 6\cdot6 \times 10^{-3}$ atm.
12,3. Do not forget that two molecules of steam are concerned, so that, for example, $\log_{10} K$ at 298° is 80·094 not 40·047.

12,4. If the reaction is written

$$NH_3 \rightleftharpoons \tfrac{1}{2}N_2 + \tfrac{3}{2}H_2$$
$$K_p = 1 \cdot 05 \times 10^2 \text{ atm.}$$

Under these circumstances the quantity of ammonia remaining is negligible.

12,6. $\Delta G_f = -78$ kcal; $\Delta G = 45 \cdot 2$ kcal.

12,7. Since for the reaction

$$C_{graphite} \longrightarrow C_{diamond}$$
$$\Delta S^{298} = -0 \cdot 78 \text{ cal deg}^{-1} \text{ mole}^{-1}$$

and since
$$\left(\frac{\partial(\Delta G)}{\partial T}\right)_p = -\Delta S,$$

the reaction is even less likely to occur at high temperatures than at low. The fact that the reaction leads to a decrease in volume suggests that the reaction might be possible under very high pressures and at low temperatures. The difficulty which then arises is that at low temperatures the *rate* of reaction will be extremely small. Over the last eighty years there have been many claims that diamonds have been synthesised from graphite, but many of these have been refuted. The student is referred to Bundy *et al*, *Nature*, 1955, **51**, 176 for an account of some of them.

12,9. $\Delta H = 0$ at approximately $650°$ K. It follows from the van't Hoff equation that the equilibrium constant is at a maximum at that temperature. The pressure under which the reaction takes place is without effect, but the maximum yield requires that the initial partial pressures of A and B are the same.

CHAPTER 13

13,1. One mole of ideal gas at 8 atmospheres pressure and at $819°$ K occupies $8 \cdot 4$ litres. Hence the vessel contains $\dfrac{500}{8 \cdot 4}$ moles (i.e. $\dfrac{500}{8 \cdot 4} N$ molecules) of carbon monoxide, and $\dfrac{500}{8 \cdot 4}$ moles (i.e. $\dfrac{500}{8 \cdot 4} N$ molecules) of steam. The chance that one molecule is situated in one particular half of the vessel is $\tfrac{1}{2}$, so that the chance that all the molecules of carbon monoxide occupy one-half, and all the steam molecules the other is

$$(\tfrac{1}{2})^a \times (\tfrac{1}{2})^a, \text{ i.e. } (\tfrac{1}{2})^{2a}$$

where
$$a = \frac{500N}{8 \cdot 4}.$$

The decrease in entropy caused by the separation of the mixture can be calculated in two ways. Let us denote the chance that the gases are found completely mixed by the symbol ω_1, and the chance that the gases are found completely separated by the symbol ω_2. The corresponding W values for the system will be connected by the equation

$$\frac{\omega_1}{\omega_2} = \frac{W_1}{W_2}.$$

P

The value of ω_1 will be *extremely* close to unity, so that

$$\frac{W_2}{W_1} = \left(\frac{1}{2}\right)^{2a}$$

and the corresponding change in entropy when the system changes from W_1 to W_2 equal to $k \log_e (\frac{1}{2})^{2a}$, i.e. $-\dfrac{1000}{8\cdot4} R \log_e 2$.

Precisely the same result may be obtained without reference to statistical theory, because the *decrease* in entropy caused by the separation of the mixture is clearly the same as the *increase* in entropy which results from the mixing of the two gases under the same conditions. It will be remembered that this is given by the equation

$$\Delta S_{mixing} = -n_1 R \log_e y_1 - n_2 R \log_e y_2$$

where n_1 and n_2 are the number of moles of each species, and y_1 and y_2 their corresponding mole fractions. $y_1 = y_2 = 0\cdot5$ and $n_1 = n_2 = \dfrac{500}{8\cdot4}$.

13,2. The solid solution contains

$n_1 N$ molecules of component 1, and

$(1 - n_1)N$ molecules of component 2.

The number of ways in which these may be arranged is

$$\frac{N!}{(n_1 N)![(1 - n_1)N]!},$$

so that the entropy of mixing equals

$$k\{\log_e N! - \log_e (n_1 N)! - \log_e [(1 - n_1)N]!\},$$

which using Stirling's Approximation formula equals

$$k\{N \log_e N - N - n_1 N \log_e n_1 N + n_1 N$$
$$- (1 - n_1)N \log_e (1 - n_1)N + (1 - n_1)N)$$

$$= kN \log_e \frac{N}{(n_1 N)^{n_1}[(1 - n_1)N]^{1-n_1}} = -kN \log_e n_1^{n_1}(1 - n_1)^{1-n_1}.$$

Since in this case $x_1 = n_1$ and $x_2 = 1 - n_1$, and since $kN = R$, the entropy of mixing is $-R\{x_1 \log_e x_1 + x_2 \log_e x_2\}$. It should be observed that since x_1 and x_2 are less than unity, the entropy of mixing must be positive.

It should be noted that this result, i.e. the expression obtained above, is true only for an ideal solid solution, i.e. one in which the process of mixing brings about no changes in the rotational, vibrational and electronic states of the constituent particles. This result would not be true, for example, when the formation of a solid solution results in compound formation as sometimes happens when one metal dissolves in another.

CHAPTER 14

14,1. $1 \cdot 8 \times 10^{-2}\%$, 1%.

It should be noted that at $20,000°$ K the second and some subsequent terms in the expression for f_{elec} can no longer be neglected. In other words, f_{elec} is becoming appreciably greater than 2.

14,2. From (14,13)

$$p = RT \left(\frac{\partial \log_e f}{\partial V} \right)_T.$$

The only part of the partition function which is dependent on volume is the translational partition function, and from (14,22) it follows that

$$\left(\frac{\partial \log_e f_{\text{trans}}}{\partial V} \right)_T = \frac{d \log_e V}{dV} = \frac{1}{V}.$$

14,3. $S_{\text{solid solution}} - \frac{1}{2}(S_A + S_B) = R \log_e 2$.

14,5. (a) $K = 0 \cdot 0185$; (b) $K = 0 \cdot 0174$.

14,7. S_{stat} for CO, H_2 and H_2O; S_{cal} for C_2H_5OH.

14,9. The initial entropy of one mole of graphite and half mole oxygen at $300°$ K and 1 atmosphere pressure is $25 \cdot 9$ cal deg^{-1}. The calculation of $\Delta H_{S=25 \cdot 9,\ p=1\text{ atm}}$ requires therefore knowledge of the temperature at which the molar entropy of carbon monoxide is $25 \cdot 9$ cal deg^{-1}.

In view of the information given equation (14,64) may be put in the form

$$S^T = \frac{7}{2}R \log_e T + y.$$

At $300°$ K

$$47 \cdot 3 = 16 \log_{10} 300 + y, \text{ and } y = 7 \cdot 7,$$

so that the temperature at which $S = 25 \cdot 9$ is given by the equation

$$25 \cdot 9 = 16 \log_{10} T + 7 \cdot 7$$

i.e. $T = 14°$ K. (The fact that $14°$ K and 1 atmosphere pressure is a hypothetical state for carbon monoxide gas is immaterial to the argument.)

The problem reduces therefore to the determination of the difference between the enthalpy of one mole of graphite and half mole of oxygen at $300°$ K and 1 atmosphere pressure and one mole of carbon monoxide at $14°$ K and 1 atmosphere pressure. This may be done in two ways: The first requires the knowledge of $H - E_0^0$ for graphite and oxygen at $300°$ K, the value of $H - E_0^0$ for carbon monoxide gas at $14°$ K and the value of $\Delta H_{T,\ p}$ at any convenient temperature, and the second requires the expression for C_p for carbon monoxide as a function of temperature and the value of $\Delta H_{T,\ p}$ at $300°$ K.

The solution by the first method is as follows:

$H_{\text{CO (14° K)}} - H_{\text{C}+\frac{1}{2}O_2 \text{ (300° K)}}$

$$= (H - E_0^0)_{\text{CO (14° K)}} - (H - E_0^0)_{\text{C}+\frac{1}{2}O_2 \text{ (300° K)}} + \Delta E_0^0,$$

$H - E_0^0{}_{\text{CO (14° K)}} = \frac{7}{2}RT = 98$ cal mole^{-1},

and the values for graphite and oxygen are given.

ΔE_0^0 may be obtained from the equation

$$\Delta E_0^0 = \Delta H_0^{300} - \Delta(H_0 - E_0^0)^{300}$$

and proves to be $-27,000$ cal.

Hence $\Delta H_{S, p} = -28,200$ cal.

The solution by the second method requires the reaction to be carried out at constant pressure in an adiabatic container, when the temperature reached is given by the equation

$$\int_{300}^{T} C_{p_{CO}} \, dT = -\Delta H_{(300° \text{ K, 1 atm})}$$

from which it follows that $T = 3000°$ K.

The value of $\Delta H_{S, p}$ for the reaction then becomes the difference between the molar enthalpy of carbon monoxide at $3000°$ K and 1 atmosphere pressure and that at $14°$ K and 1 atmosphere, i.e.

$$\Delta H_{S, p} = \int_{3000°}^{14°} C_p dT.$$

This gives the answer $-28,100$ cal.

14,10. The value $\frac{1}{2}Nk \log_e 2$ suggests that only one-half the total number of molecules (calculated as NO) have freedom of choice between positions NO, NO, . . . and ON, NO, . . . We therefore suppose that at low temperatures nitric oxide polymerises to the dimer $\frac{NO}{ON}$, which can then "face left or face right".

Each molecule of CH_3D can position itself in four directions with respect to its neighbours, the deuterium atom "facing north, south, east or west".

CHAPTER 15

15,3. The Clausius–Clapeyron equation is written in the form

$$\frac{T d \log_e p}{dT} = \frac{L_e}{RT}$$

and T and p replaced by the products $T_R T_c$ and $p_R p_c$. Since T_c and p are invariable

$$T_R T_c \frac{d \log_e p_R p_c}{d T_R T_c} = T_R \frac{d \log_e p_R}{d T_R}$$

It follows from the van der Waals equation that

$$T_R \frac{d \log_e p_R}{dT_R} = 2 \cdot 3 \frac{k}{T_R}.$$

Hence at the boiling point ($T = T_R = 0 \cdot 6$)

$$\frac{L_e}{T} = 2 \cdot 3 \frac{T}{T_R} \simeq \frac{2 \cdot 3 \times 3R}{\dfrac{T}{T_c}}$$

$$\simeq \frac{2 \cdot 3 \times 3R}{0 \cdot 6} \simeq 23 \text{ cal deg}^{-1}.$$

15,4. At the boiling point the vapour pressure equals 1 atmosphere, so that

$$e^{-\frac{L_e}{RT}} = \frac{1}{2 \cdot 7} \times 10^{-4}.$$

Hence $\qquad \dfrac{L_e}{T} \simeq 20$ cal deg^{-1}.

15,5. $\dfrac{55 \cdot 51}{59 \cdot 51}$. (The sodium ions and chloride ions are separate species.)

15,6. $0 \cdot 0108$ lb.

15,8. Consider a pure solid A in equilibrium with a saturated solution of A. The chemical potential of the solute is the same in each phase, so that, assuming that the solution is ideal, we may write

$$\mu_{A(s)} = \mu_{0_A} + RT \log_e C_{(sat)}$$

where $\mu_{A(s)}$ is the chemical potential of the pure solid, and μ_{0_A} the standard chemical potential of A in solution. Hence

$$-(\mu_{0_A} - \mu_{0(s)}) = RT \log_e C_{(sat)}$$

The left-hand side represents the decrease in free energy which results from the solution of 1 mole of solute to give a solution at unit molality; so that we may write

$$-\Delta G_{0(\text{solution})} = RT \log_e C_{(sat)}$$

We may therefore regard $C_{(sat)}$ as the equilibrium constant for the solution process. It follows that the van't Hoff equation may be used to give the result required.

15,9. $L_e = 23,000$ cal mole^{-1}. $1160°$ K, $1100°$ K.

15,10. $\mathbf{A} = \mu_{\text{pure water}} - \mu_{\text{water in solution}}$.

Since pure water is chosen as the standard state for water, the chemical potential of the water in solution must be expressed in terms of its mole fraction, so that it follows that

$$\mathbf{A} = RT \log_e x_{\text{water}}$$

$$x = \frac{55 \cdot 51}{57 \cdot 51}$$

and $\qquad \mathbf{A} = 9 \cdot 18$ cal.

15,11. $6 \cdot 7$ moles per 1000 gm water.

15,12. The Distribution Law is satisfied either by the condition that benzoic acid is almost completely dissociated in the aqueous layer and exists as the monomer in the benzene layer, or that benzoic acid exists as a monomer in aqueous solution (with very small degree of dissociation) and as the dimer in benzene. Since benzoic acid is a weak acid we assume that the second description is the correct one. It should, however, be noted that the figures would also be satisfied by the condition that the acid exists as the polymer A_2 in water and A_4 in benzene, as the polymer

or in fact by any condition A_n in water, A_m in benzene as long as $\dfrac{m}{n} = 2$.
Some other information such as the molecular weight in one solvent is required in order to choose between the alternatives possible. In this case the molecular weight of benzoic acid in water is known to be 122, so we presume it to be 244 in benzene.

CHAPTER 17

17,1. 0·2225 volt.

17,2. $\mathbf{E} = 0\cdot361 + 0\cdot0296 \log_{10} \dfrac{1\cdot915}{2\cdot98}$.

17,3. The reaction

$$H_2 + Hg_2Cl_2 \longrightarrow 2HCl + 2Hg$$

takes place on the left and the reverse reaction on the right. The overall change which takes place is the transfer of hydrogen from the left-hand electrode to the right; in other words, the isothermal expansion of hydrogen from a pressure of 1 atmosphere to that of 0·0944 atmosphere. The decrease in free energy therefore equals $RT \log_e \dfrac{1}{0\cdot0944}$ mole^{-1}. It follows that the e.m.f. is 0·03033 volt. The very close agreement between this value and the experimental one suggests that the fugacity coefficient of hydrogen in the mixture is unity.

17,4. $1\cdot75 \times 10^{-5}$.

17,5. $\log_{10} \dfrac{a_{Co^{++}}}{a_{Ni^{++}}}$ must be greater than $\dfrac{0\cdot033}{0\cdot0296}$.

17,6. The ratio of chromous to chromic ions is about 2×10^{-7}.

17,7. $\log_{10} K_s = -\dfrac{10{,}800}{2\cdot303RT}$.

17,8. $\mathbf{E}_{o_{Ag/Ag^+}} + \dfrac{RT}{F} \log_e K_s = \mathbf{E}_{o_{Ag/AgN_3,\ N_3^-}}$

hence
$$\log_{10} K_s = -\dfrac{0\cdot507}{0\cdot05916}.$$

17,9. $S_{o_{Zn^{++}}} = -25\cdot9$ cal deg^{-1}.

17,12. $\mathbf{E}_o = 0\cdot0527$ volt.

CHAPTER 18

18,1. $\gamma = 0\cdot935$. The first part of this problem is an exercise in the use of the function j defined by equation (18,3).

18,2. $T^* = 277°$ K.

At 100 atmospheres the reduced pressure is almost exactly 2. Chart (18,3) shows that $\gamma = 0\cdot935$ and $p_R = 2$ when $T_R = 1\cdot8$.

18,3. Construct the following table obtaining the values of γ from the charts:

	$T_C{}^\circ$ K	T° K	T_R	p_c atm	p atm	p_R	γ
H_2	33·2	723	21·8	12·8 $\{$	100 600	7·81 46·9	1·03 1·26
N_2	126·0	723	5·74	33·6 $\{$	100 600	2·98 17·9	1·04 1·32
NH_3	406·0	723	1·78	111·6 $\{$	100 600	0·896 5·38	1·06 0·86

At 100 atmospheres pressure

$$K_p^* = 7·25 \times 10^{-3} \times \frac{1·06}{(1·04)^{\frac{1}{2}}(1·03)^{\frac{3}{2}}}$$

$$= 7·21 \times 10^{-3} \text{ atm}^{-1}.$$

At 600 atmospheres pressure

$$K_p^* = 12·94 \times 10^{-3} \times \frac{0·86}{(1·32)^{\frac{1}{2}}(1·26)^{\frac{3}{2}}}$$

$$= 6·85 \times 10^{-3} \text{ atm}^{-1}.$$

18,4. $\gamma = 0·866$.

18,5. $E_0 = 0·1788$ volt.

m	0·1	0·09	0·08	0·07	0·06
$-\log_{10} \gamma_\pm$	0·1285	0·1252	0·1212	0·1165	0·1117

m	0·05	0·04	0·03	0·02	0·01
$-\log_{10} \gamma_\pm$	0·1046	0·1005	0·0875	0·0752	0·0568

18,6. 0·145 volt.

The pure hydrogen is at a reduced temperature equal to 10 and a reduced pressure equal to 10. The reduced pressure of the hydrogen in the mixture is 5. If the Lewis and Randall rule is assumed, the fugacity coefficient of the pure hydrogen proves to be 1·16 and that of the hydrogen in the mixture 1·06.

The e.m.f. is then given by the equation:

$$E = \frac{RT}{F} \log_e \frac{1·16 \times 128}{1·06 \times 64}.$$

APPENDIX 2

SUGGESTED READING

General

1. M. Planck, *A Scientific Autobiography* (Williams and Norgate, 1950)
   The first essay in this volume is a fascinating account of the way in which the concept of entropy came into being.
2. K. G. Denbigh, *The Principles of Chemical Equilibrium* (Cambridge University Press, 1957)
3. J. D. Fast, *Entropy* (Philips Technical Library, 1962)
4. S. Glasstone, *Thermodynamics for Chemists* (Van Nostrand, 1958)
5. I. Prigogine and R. Defay, *Chemical Thermodynamics* (Longmans Green, 1954) (translated by D. H. Everett)
6. G. J. Janz, *Estimation of Thermodynamic Properties of Organic Compounds* (Academic Press, 1958)

Statistical Thermodynamics

7. F. C. Andrews, *Equilibrium Statistical Mechanics* (John Wiley, 1963)
8. R. H. Fowler and E. A. Guggenheim, *Statistical Thermodynamics* (Cambridge University Press, 1960)

Non-Equilibrium Thermodynamics

9. K. G. Denbigh, *The Thermodynamics of the Steady State* (Methuen, 1958)
10. S. R. de Groot, *Thermodynamics of Irreversible Processes* (North Holland, 1951)
11. H. J. V. Tyrrell, *Diffusion and Heat Flow in Liquids* (Butterworths, 1961)

APPENDIX 3
LOGARITHM TABLES

CHEMICAL THERMODYNAMICS

LOGARITHMS

Proportional Parts

	0	1	2	3	4	5	6	7	8	9	1	2	3	4	5	6	7	8	9
10	0000	0043	0086	0128	0170	0212	0253	0294	0334	0374	4	8	12	17	21	25	29	33	37
11	0414	0453	0492	0531	0569	0607	0645	0682	0719	0755	4	8	11	15	19	23	26	30	34
12	0792	0828	0864	0899	0934	0969	1004	1038	1072	1106	3	7	10	14	17	21	24	28	31
13	1139	1173	1206	1239	1271	1303	1335	1367	1399	1430	3	6	10	13	16	19	23	26	29
14	1461	1492	1523	1553	1584	1614	1644	1673	1703	1732	3	6	9	12	15	18	21	24	27
15	1761	1790	1818	1847	1875	1903	1931	1959	1987	2014	3	6	8	11	14	17	20	22	25
16	2041	2068	2095	2122	2148	2175	2201	2227	2253	2279	3	5	8	11	13	16	18	21	24
17	2304	2330	2355	2380	2405	2430	2455	2480	2504	2529	2	5	7	10	12	15	17	20	22
18	2553	2577	2601	2625	2648	2672	2695	2718	2742	2765	2	5	7	9	12	14	16	19	21
19	2788	2810	2833	2856	2878	2900	2923	2945	2967	2989	2	4	7	9	11	13	16	18	20
20	3010	3032	3054	3075	3096	3118	3139	3160	3181	3201	2	4	6	8	11	13	15	17	19
21	3222	3243	3263	3284	3304	3324	3345	3365	3385	3404	2	4	6	8	10	12	14	16	18
22	3424	3444	3464	3483	3502	3522	3541	3560	3579	3598	2	4	6	8	10	12	14	15	17
23	3617	3636	3655	3674	3692	3711	3729	3747	3766	3784	2	4	6	7	9	11	13	15	17
24	3802	3820	3838	3856	3874	3892	3909	3927	3945	3962	2	4	5	7	9	11	12	14	16
25	3979	3997	4014	4031	4048	4065	4082	4099	4116	4133	2	3	5	7	9	10	12	14	15
26	4150	4166	4183	4200	4216	4232	4249	4265	4281	4298	2	3	5	7	8	10	11	13	15
27	4314	4330	4346	4362	4378	4393	4409	4425	4440	4456	2	3	5	6	8	9	11	13	14
28	4472	4487	4502	4518	4533	4548	4564	4579	4594	4609	2	3	5	6	8	9	11	12	14
29	4624	4639	4654	4669	4683	4698	4713	4728	4742	4757	1	3	4	6	7	9	10	12	13
30	4771	4786	4800	4814	4829	4843	4857	4871	4886	4900	1	3	4	6	7	9	10	11	13
31	4914	4928	4942	4955	4969	4983	4997	5011	5024	5038	1	3	4	5	7	8	10	11	12
32	5051	5065	5079	5092	5105	5119	5132	5145	5159	5172	1	3	4	5	7	8	9	11	12
33	5185	5198	5211	5224	5237	5250	5263	5276	5289	5302	1	3	4	5	6	8	9	10	12
34	5315	5328	5340	5353	5366	5378	5391	5403	5416	5428	1	3	4	5	6	8	9	10	11
35	5441	5453	5465	5478	5490	5502	5514	5527	5539	5551	1	2	4	5	6	7	9	10	11
36	5563	5575	5587	5599	5611	5623	5635	5647	5658	5670	1	2	4	5	6	7	8	10	11
37	5682	5694	5705	5717	5729	5740	5752	5763	5775	5786	1	2	3	5	6	7	8	9	10
38	5798	5809	5821	5832	5843	5855	5866	5877	5888	5899	1	2	3	5	6	7	8	9	10
39	5911	5922	5933	5944	5955	5966	5977	5988	5999	6010	1	2	3	4	5	7	8	9	10
40	6021	6031	6042	6053	6064	6075	6085	6096	6107	6117	1	2	3	4	5	6	7	9	10
41	6128	6138	6149	6160	6170	6180	6191	6201	6212	6222	1	2	3	4	5	6	7	8	9
42	6232	6243	6253	6263	6274	6284	6294	6304	6314	6325	1	2	3	4	5	6	7	8	9
43	6335	6345	6355	6365	6375	6385	6395	6405	6415	6425	1	2	3	4	5	6	7	8	9
44	6435	6444	6454	6464	6474	6484	6493	6503	6513	6522	1	2	3	4	5	6	7	8	9
45	6532	6542	6551	6561	6571	6580	6590	6599	6609	6618	1	2	3	4	5	6	7	8	9
46	6628	6637	6646	6656	6665	6675	6684	6693	6702	6712	1	2	3	4	5	6	7	7	8
47	6721	6730	6739	6749	6758	6767	6776	6785	6794	6803	1	2	3	4	5	5	6	7	8
48	6812	6821	6830	6839	6848	6857	6866	6875	6884	6893	1	2	3	4	4	5	6	7	8
49	6902	6911	6920	6928	6937	6946	6955	6964	6972	6981	1	2	3	4	4	5	6	7	8
50	6990	6998	7007	7016	7024	7033	7042	7050	7059	7067	1	2	3	3	4	5	6	7	8
51	7076	7084	7093	7101	7110	7118	7126	7135	7143	7152	1	2	3	3	4	5	6	7	8
52	7160	7168	7177	7185	7193	7202	7210	7218	7226	7235	1	2	2	3	4	5	6	7	7
53	7243	7251	7259	7267	7275	7284	7292	7300	7308	7316	1	2	2	3	4	5	6	6	7
54	7324	7332	7340	7348	7356	7364	7372	7380	7388	7396	1	2	2	3	4	5	6	6	7
	0	1	2	3	4	5	6	7	8	9	1·	2	3	4	5	6	7	8	9

LOGARITHMS

Proportional Parts

	0	1	2	3	4	5	6	7	8	9	1	2	3	4	5	6	7	8	9
55	7404	7412	7419	7427	7435	7443	7451	7459	7466	7474	1	2	2	3	4	5	5	6	7
56	7482	7490	7497	7505	7513	7520	7528	7536	7543	7551	1	2	2	3	4	5	5	6	7
57	7559	7566	7574	7582	7589	7597	7604	7612	7619	7627	1	2	2	3	4	5	5	6	7
58	7634	7642	7649	7657	7664	7672	7679	7686	7694	7701	1	1	2	3	4	4	5	6	7
59	7709	7716	7723	7731	7738	7745	7752	7760	7767	7774	1	1	2	3	4	4	5	6	7
60	7782	7789	7796	7803	7810	7818	7825	7832	7839	7846	1	1	2	3	4	4	5	6	6
61	7853	7860	7868	7875	7882	7889	7896	7903	7910	7917	1	1	2	3	4	4	5	6	6
62	7924	7931	7938	7945	7952	7959	7966	7973	7980	7987	1	1	2	3	4	4	5	6	6
63	7993	8000	8007	8014	8021	8028	8035	8041	8048	8055	1	1	2	3	3	4	5	6	6
64	8062	8069	8075	8082	8089	8096	8102	8109	8116	8122	1	1	2	3	3	4	5	5	6
65	8129	8136	8142	8149	8156	8162	8169	8176	8182	8189	1	1	2	3	3	4	5	5	6
66	8195	8202	8209	8215	8222	8228	8235	8241	8248	8254	1	1	2	3	3	4	5	5	6
67	8261	8267	8274	8280	8287	8293	8299	8306	8312	8319	1	1	2	3	3	4	4	5	6
68	8325	8331	8338	8344	8351	8357	8363	8370	8376	8382	1	1	2	3	3	4	4	5	6
69	8388	8395	8401	8407	8414	8420	8426	8432	8439	8445	1	1	2	3	3	4	4	5	6
70	8451	8457	8463	8470	8476	8482	8488	8494	8500	8506	1	1	2	2	3	4	4	5	6
71	8513	8519	8525	8531	8537	8543	8549	8555	8561	8567	1	1	2	2	3	4	4	5	5
72	8573	8579	8585	8591	8597	8603	8609	8615	8621	8627	1	1	2	2	3	4	4	5	5
73	8633	8639	8645	8651	8657	8663	8669	8675	8681	8686	1	1	2	2	3	4	4	5	5
74	8692	8698	8704	8710	8716	8722	8727	8733	8739	8745	1	1	2	2	3	4	4	5	5
75	8751	8756	8762	8768	8774	8779	8785	8791	8797	8802	1	1	2	2	3	3	4	5	5
76	8808	8814	8820	8825	8831	8837	8842	8848	8854	8859	1	1	2	2	3	3	4	5	5
77	8865	8871	8876	8882	8887	8893	8899	8904	8910	8915	1	1	2	2	3	3	4	4	5
78	8921	8927	8932	8938	8943	8949	8954	8960	8965	8971	1	1	2	2	3	3	4	4	5
79	8976	8982	8987	8993	8998	9004	9009	9015	9020	9025	1	1	2	2	3	3	4	4	5
80	9031	9036	9042	9047	9053	9058	9063	9069	9074	9079	1	1	2	2	3	3	4	4	5
81	9085	9090	9096	9101	9106	9112	9117	9122	9128	9133	1	1	2	2	3	3	4	4	5
82	9138	9143	9149	9154	9159	9165	9170	9175	9180	9186	1	1	2	2	3	3	4	4	5
83	9191	9196	9201	9206	9212	9217	9222	9227	9232	9238	1	1	2	2	3	3	4	4	5
84	9243	9248	9253	9258	9263	9269	9274	9279	9284	9289	1	1	2	2	3	3	4	4	5
85	9294	9299	9304	9309	9315	9320	9325	9330	9335	9340	1	1	2	2	3	3	4	4	5
86	9345	9350	9355	9360	9365	9370	9375	9380	9385	9390	1	1	2	2	3	3	4	4	5
87	9395	9400	9405	9410	9415	9420	9425	9430	9435	9440	0	1	1	2	2	3	3	4	4
88	9445	9450	9455	9460	9465	9469	9474	9479	9484	9489	0	1	1	2	2	3	3	4	4
89	9494	9499	9504	9509	9513	9518	9523	9528	9533	9538	0	1	1	2	2	3	3	4	4
90	9542	9547	9552	9557	9562	9566	9571	9576	9581	9586	0	1	1	2	2	3	3	4	4
91	9590	9595	9600	9605	9609	9614	9619	9624	9628	9633	0	1	1	2	2	3	3	4	4
92	9638	9643	9647	9652	9657	9661	9666	9671	9675	9680	0	1	1	2	2	3	3	4	4
93	9685	9689	9694	9699	9703	9708	9713	9717	9722	9727	0	1	1	2	2	3	3	4	4
94	9731	9736	9741	9745	9750	9754	9759	9764	9768	9773	0	1	1	2	2	3	3	4	4
95	9777	9782	9786	9791	9795	9800	9805	9809	9814	9818	0	1	1	2	2	3	3	4	4
96	9823	9827	9832	9836	9841	9845	9850	9854	9859	9863	0	1	1	2	2	3	3	4	4
97	9868	9872	9877	9881	9886	9890	9894	9899	9903	9908	0	1	1	2	2	3	3	4	4
98	9912	9917	9921	9926	9930	9934	9939	9943	9948	9952	0	1	1	2	2	3	3	4	4
99	9956	9961	9965	9969	9974	9978	9983	9987	9991	9996	0	1	1	2	2	3	3	4	4
	0	1	2	3	4	5	6	7	8	9	1	2	3	4	5	6	7	8	9

ANTI-LOGARITHMS

Proportional Parts

	0	1	2	3	4	5	6	7	8	9	1	2	3	4	5	6	7	8	9
·00	1000	1002	1005	1007	1009	1012	1014	1016	1019	1021	0	0	1	1	1	1	2	2	2
·01	1023	1026	1028	1030	1033	1035	1038	1040	1042	1045	0	0	1	1	1	1	2	2	2
·02	1047	1050	1052	1054	1057	1059	1062	1064	1067	1069	0	0	1	1	1	1	2	2	2
.03	1072	1074	1076	1079	1081	1084	1086	1089	1091	1094	0	0	1	1	1	1	2	2	2
·04	1096	1099	1102	1104	1107	1109	1112	1114	1117	1119	0	1	1	1	1	2	2	2	2
·05	1122	1125	1127	1130	1132	1135	1138	1140	1143	1146	0	1	1	1	1	2	2	2	2
·06	1148	1151	1153	1156	1159	1161	1164	1167	1169	1172	0	1	1	1	1	2	2	2	2
·07	1175	1178	1180	1183	1186	1189	1191	1194	1197	1199	0	1	1	1	1	2	2	2	2
·08	1202	1205	1208	1211	1213	1216	1219	1222	1225	1227	0	1	1	1	1	2	2	2	3
·09	1230	1233	1236	1239	1242	1245	1247	1250	1253	1256	0	1	1	1	1	2	2	2	3
·10	1259	1262	1265	1268	1271	1274	1276	1279	1282	1285	0	1	1	1	1	2	2	2	3
·11	1288	1291	1294	1297	1300	1303	1306	1309	1312	1315	0	1	1	1	2	2	2	2	3
·12	1318	1321	1324	1327	1330	1334	1337	1340	1343	1346	0	1	1	1	2	2	2	3	3
·13	1349	1352	1355	1358	1361	1365	1368	1371	1374	1377	0	1	1	1	2	2	2	3	3
·14	1380	1384	1387	1390	1393	1396	1400	1403	1406	1409	0	1	1	1	2	2	2	3	3
·15	1413	1416	1419	1422	1426	1429	1432	1435	1439	1442	0	1	1	1	2	2	2	3	3
·16	1445	1449	1452	1455	1459	1462	1466	1469	1472	1476	0	1	1	1	2	2	2	3	3
·17	1479	1483	1486	1489	1493	1496	1500	1503	1507	1510	0	1	1	1	2	2	2	3	3
·18	1514	1517	1521	1524	1528	1531	1535	1538	1542	1545	0	1	1	1	2	2	2	3	3
·19	1549	1552	1556	1560	1563	1567	1570	1574	1578	1581	0	1	1	1	2	2	3	3	3
·20	1585	1589	1592	1596	1600	1603	1607	1611	1614	1618	0	1	1	1	2	2	3	3	3
·21	1622	1626	1629	1633	1637	1641	1644	1648	1652	1656	0	1	1	2	2	2	3	3	3
·22	1660	1663	1667	1671	1675	1679	1683	1687	1690	1694	0	1	1	2	2	2	3	3	3
·23	1698	1702	1706	1710	1714	1718	1722	1726	1730	1734	0	1	1	2	2	2	3	3	4
·24	1738	1742	1746	1750	1754	1758	1762	1766	1770	1774	0	1	1	2	2	2	3	3	4
·25	1778	1782	1786	1791	1795	1799	1803	1807	1811	1816	0	1	1	2	2	3	3	3	4
·26	1820	1824	1828	1832	1837	1841	1845	1849	1854	1858	0	1	1	2	2	3	3	3	4
·27	1862	1866	1871	1875	1879	1884	1888	1892	1897	1901	0	1	1	2	2	3	3	3	4
·28	1905	1910	1914	1919	1923	1928	1932	1936	1941	1945	0	1	1	2	2	3	3	4	4
·29	1950	1954	1959	1963	1968	1972	1977	1982	1986	1991	0	1	1	2	2	3	3	4	4
·30	1995	2000	2004	2009	2014	2018	2023	2028	2032	2037	0	1	1	2	2	3	3	4	4
·31	2042	2046	2051	2056	2061	2065	2070	2075	2080	2084	0	1	1	2	2	3	3	4	4
·32	2089	2094	2099	2104	2109	2113	2118	2123	2128	2133	0	1	1	2	2	3	3	4	4
·33	2138	2143	2148	2153	2158	2163	2168	2173	2178	2183	0	1	1	2	2	3	3	4	4
·34	2188	2193	2198	2203	2208	2213	2218	2223	2228	2234	1	1	2	2	3	3	4	4	5
·35	2239	2244	2249	2254	2259	2265	2270	2275	2280	2286	1	1	2	2	3	3	4	4	5
·36	2291	2296	2301	2307	2312	2317	2323	2328	2333	2339	1	1	2	2	3	3	4	4	5
·37	2344	2350	2355	2360	2366	2371	2377	2382	2388	2393	1	1	2	2	3	3	4	4	5
·38	2399	2404	2410	2415	2421	2427	2432	2438	2443	2449	1	1	2	2	3	3	4	5	5
·39	2455	2460	2466	2472	2477	2483	2489	2495	2500	2506	1	1	2	2	3	3	4	5	5
·40	2512	2518	2523	2529	2535	2541	2547	2553	2559	2564	1	1	2	2	3	3	4	5	5
·41	2570	2576	2582	2588	2594	2600	2606	2612	2618	2624	1	1	2	2	3	4	4	5	5
·42	2630	2636	2642	2648	2655	2661	2667	2673	2679	2685	1	1	2	2	3	4	4	5	6
·43	2692	2698	2704	2710	2716	2723	2729	2735	2742	2748	1	1	2	2	3	4	4	5	6
·44	2754	2761	2767	2773	2780	2786	2793	2799	2805	2812	1	1	2	3	3	4	4	5	6
·45	2818	2825	2831	2838	2844	2851	2858	2864	2871	2877	1	1	2	3	3	4	5	5	6
·46	2884	2891	2897	2904	2911	2917	2924	2931	2938	2944	1	1	2	3	3	4	5	5	6
·47	2951	2958	2965	2972	2979	2985	2992	2999	3006	3013	1	1	2	3	3	4	5	6	6
·48	3020	3027	3034	3041	3048	3055	3062	3069	3076	3083	1	1	2	3	4	4	5	6	6
·49	3090	3097	3105	3112	3119	3126	3133	3141	3148	3155	1	1	2	3	4	4	5	6	7
	0	1	2	3	4	5	6	7	8	9	1	2	3	4	5	6	7	8	9

ANTI-LOGARITHMS

Proportional Parts

	0	1	2	3	4	5	6	7	8	9	1	2	3	4	5	6	7	8	9
·50	3162	3170	3177	3184	3192	3199	3206	3214	3221	3228	1	1	2	3	4	4	5	6	7
·51	3236	3243	3251	3258	3266	3273	3281	3289	3296	3304	1	2	2	3	4	5	5	6	7
·52	3311	3319	3327	3334	3342	3350	3357	3365	3373	3381	1	2	2	3	4	5	5	6	7
·53	3388	3396	3404	3412	3420	3428	3436	3443	3451	3459	1	2	2	3	4	5	6	6	7
·54	3467	3475	3483	3491	3499	3508	3516	3524	3532	3540	1	2	2	3	4	5	6	6	7
·55	3548	3556	3565	3573	3581	3589	3597	3606	3614	3622	1	2	2	3	4	5	6	7	7
·56	3631	3639	3648	3656	3664	3673	3681	3690	3698	3707	1	2	3	3	4	5	6	7	8
·57	3715	3724	3733	3741	3750	3758	3 767	3776	3784	3793	1	2	3	3	4	5	6	7	8
·58	3802	3811	3819	3828	3837	3846	3855	3864	3873	3882	1	2	3	4	4	5	6	7	8
·59	3890	3899	3908	3917	3926	3936	3945	3954	3963	3972	1	2	3	4	5	5	6	7	8
·60	3981	3990	3999	4009	4018	4027	4036	4046	4055	4064	1	2	3	4	5	6	7	7	8
·61	4074	4083	4093	4102	4111	4121	4130	4140	4150	4159	1	2	3	4	5	6	7	8	9
·62	4169	4178	4188	4198	4207	4217	4227	4236	4246	4256	1	2	3	4	5	6	7	8	9
·63	4266	4276	4285	4295	4305	4315	4325	4335	4345	4355	1	2	3	4	5	6	7	8	9
·64	4365	4375	4385	4395	4406	4416	4426	4436	4446	4457	1	2	3	4	5	6	7	8	9
·65	4467	4477	4487	4498	4508	4519	4529	4539	4550	4560	1	2	3	4	5	6	7	8	9
·66	4571	4581	4592	4603	4613	4624	4634	4645	4656	4667	1	2	3	4	5	6	7	8	10
·67	4677	4688	4699	4710	4721	4732	4742	4753	4764	4775	1	2	3	4	5	7	8	9	10
·68	4786	4797	4808	4819	4831	4842	4853	4864	4875	4887	1	2	3	4	6	7	8	9	10
·69	4898	4909	4920	4932	4943	4955	4966	4977	4989	5000	1	2	3	5	6	7	8	9	10
·70	5012	5023	5035	5047	5058	5070	5082	5093	5105	5117	1	2	4	5	6	7	8	9	11
·71	5129	5140	5152	5164	5176	5188	5200	5212	5224	5236	1	2	4	5	6	7	8	10	11
·72	5248	5260	5272	5284	5297	5309	5321	5333	5346	5358	1	2	4	5	6	7	9	10	11
·73	5370	5383	5395	5408	5420	5433	5445	5458	5470	5483	1	3	4	5	6	8	9	10	11
·74	5495	5508	5521	5534	5546	5559	5572	5585	5598	5610	1	3	4	5	6	8	9	10	12
·75	5623	5636	5649	5662	5675	5689	5702	5715	5728	5741	1	3	4	5	7	8	9	10	12
·76	5754	5768	5781	5794	5808	5821	5834	5848	5861	5875	1	3	4	5	7	8	9	11	12
·77	5888	5902	5916	5929	5943	5957	5970	5984	5998	6012	1	3	4	6	7	8	10	11	12
·78	6026	6039	6053	6067	6081	6095	6109	6124	6138	6152	1	3	4	6	7	8	10	11	13
·79	6166	6180	6194	6209	6223	6237	6252	6266	6281	6295	1	3	4	6	7	9	10	12	13
·80	6310	6324	6339	6353	6368	6383	6397	6412	6427	6442	1	3	4	6	7	9	10	12	13
·81	6457	6471	6486	6501	6516	6531	6546	6561	6577	6592	2	3	5	6	8	9	11	12	14
·82	6607	6622	6637	6653	6668	6683	6699	6714	6730	6745	2	3	5	6	8	9	11	12	14
·83	6761	6776	6792	6808	6823	6839	6855	6871	6887	6902	2	3	5	6	8	9	11	13	14
·84	6918	6934	6950	6966	6982	6998	7015	7031	7047	7063	2	3	5	6	8	10	11	13	14
·85	7079	7096	7112	7129	7145	7161	7178	7194	7211	7228	2	3	5	7	8	10	12	13	15
·86	7244	7261	7278	7295	7311	7328	7345	7362	7379	7396	2	3	5	7	8	10	12	14	15
·87	7413	7430	7447	7464	7482	7499	7516	7534	7551	7568	2	3	5	7	9	10	12	14	16
·88	7586	7603	7621	7638	7656	7674	7691	7709	7727	7745	2	4	5	7	9	11	12	14	16
·89	7762	7780	7798	7816	7834	7852	7870	7889	7907	7925	2	4	5	7	9	11	13	14	16
·90	7943	7962	7980	7998	8017	8035	8054	8072	8091	8110	2	4	6	7	9	11	13	15	17
·91	8128	8147	8166	8185	8204	8222	8241	8260	8279	8299	2	4	6	8	10	11	13	15	17
·92	8318	8337	8356	8375	8395	8414	8433	8453	8472	8492	2	4	6	8	10	12	14	15	17
·93	8511	8531	8551	8570	8590	8610	8630	8650	8670	8690	2	4	6	8	10	12	14	16	18
·94	8710	8730	8750	8770	8790	8810	8831	8851	8872	8892	2	4	6	8	10	12	14	16	18
·95	8913	8933	8954	8974	8995	9016	9036	9057	9078	9099	2	4	6	8	10	12	14	17	19
·96	9120	9141	9162	9183	9204	9226	9247	9268	9290	9311	2	4	6	9	11	13	15	17	19
·97	9333	9354	9376	9397	9419	9441	9462	9484	9506	9528	2	4	7	9	11	13	15	17	20
·98	9550	9572	9594	9616	9638	9661	9683	9705	9727	9750	2	4	7	9	11	13	16	18	20
·99	9772	9795	9817	9840	9863	9886	9908	9931	9954	9977	2	5	7	9	11	14	16	18	21
	0	1	2	3	4	5	6	7	8	9	1	2	3	4	5	6	7	8	9

INDEX